AHA Hospital Statistics™

D1358626

2015 Edition

AHA Institutional Members $205
Nonmembers $265
AHA Catalog NUMBER 082015
Telephone ORDERS 1-800-AHA-2626

ISSN 0090-6662
ISBN-13: 978-0-87258-954-4

Contents

Acknowledgments
& Advisements

Acknowledgments

The 2015 edition of *AHA Hospital Statistics* is published by Health Forum, an affiliate of the American Hospital Association, Richard J. Umbdenstock, President and CEO.

Advisements

The data published here should be used with the following advisements: The data are based on replies to an annual survey that seeks a variety of information, not all of which is published in this book. The information gathered by the survey includes specific services, but not all of each hospital's services. Therefore, the data do not reflect an exhaustive list of all services offered by all hospitals. For information on the availability of additional data, please contact Health Forum, (800) 821-2039.

Health Forum does not assume responsibility for the accuracy of information voluntarily reported by the individual institutions surveyed. The purpose of this publication is to provide basic data reflecting the delivery of health care in the United States and associated areas, and is not to serve an official and all-inclusive list of services offered by individual hospitals.

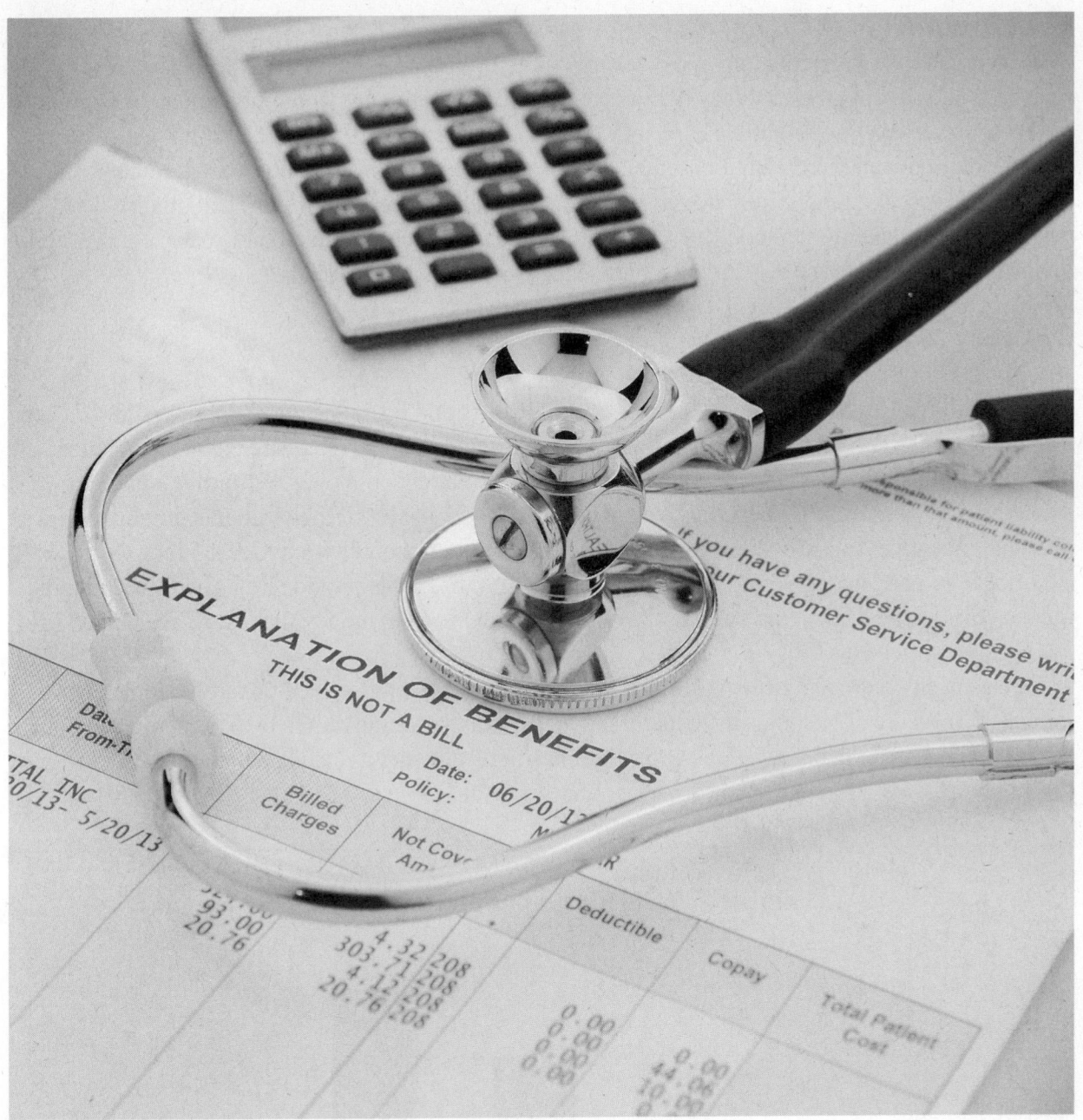

Payment and Care Delivery Models and Physician-Hospital Alignment

by Kevin Kenward, Ph.D.

Background

Health care delivery is in the midst of a seismic transformation. This requires providers to fundamentally rethink the way they deliver care. Increasing pressure from public and commercial payers to lower costs and improve care, as well as increased competition, are driving providers away from long-standing volume-based health care models and toward value-based models. These models seek to more fully align payment and objective measures of clinical quality. The new payment and delivery models described in this chapter include accountable care organizations, medical homes, joint ventures, bundled payments, capitation and shared risk.

Delivery Models

Accountable Care Organizations (ACO)

In the traditional fee-for-service payment system, doctors and hospitals generally are paid for each test and procedure. An ACO is a network of physicians and hospitals that shares financial and medical responsibility for providing coordinated care to patients in hopes of limiting unnecessary spending. ACOs make providers jointly accountable for the health of their patients, giving them financial incentives to cooperate and save money by improving quality outcomes, improving the experience of care, and lowering costs. If physicians and hospitals provide high-quality care and reduce costs to the health care system, they can keep some of the money that they have helped save.

There has been continued growth of ACOs established by hospitals or health care systems. As indicated in Figure 1, hospitals have increased their participation in ACOs by 6 percent in each of the last two years so that almost one-fifth of all hospitals now have established an ACO.

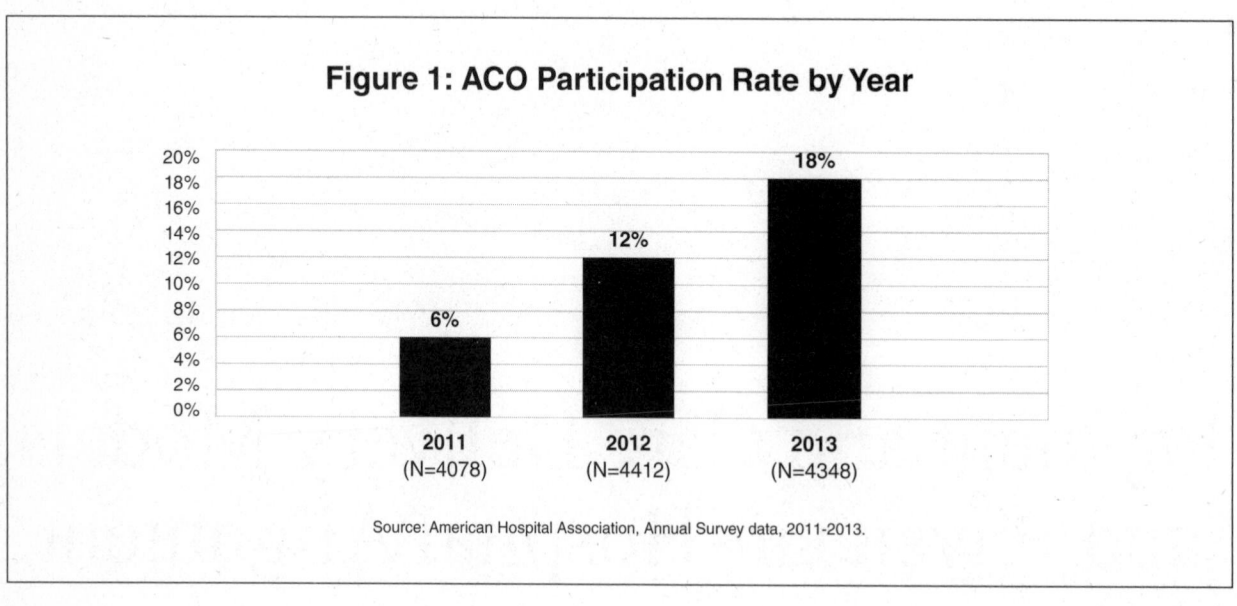

Figure 1: ACO Participation Rate by Year

Year	Participation Rate
2011 (N=4078)	6%
2012 (N=4412)	12%
2013 (N=4348)	18%

Source: American Hospital Association, Annual Survey data, 2011-2013.

ACOs established by hospitals or health care systems have spread to 48 states. The states without an ACO established by hospitals or health care systems are Mississippi and West Virginia, as well as the District of Columbia (Figure 2).

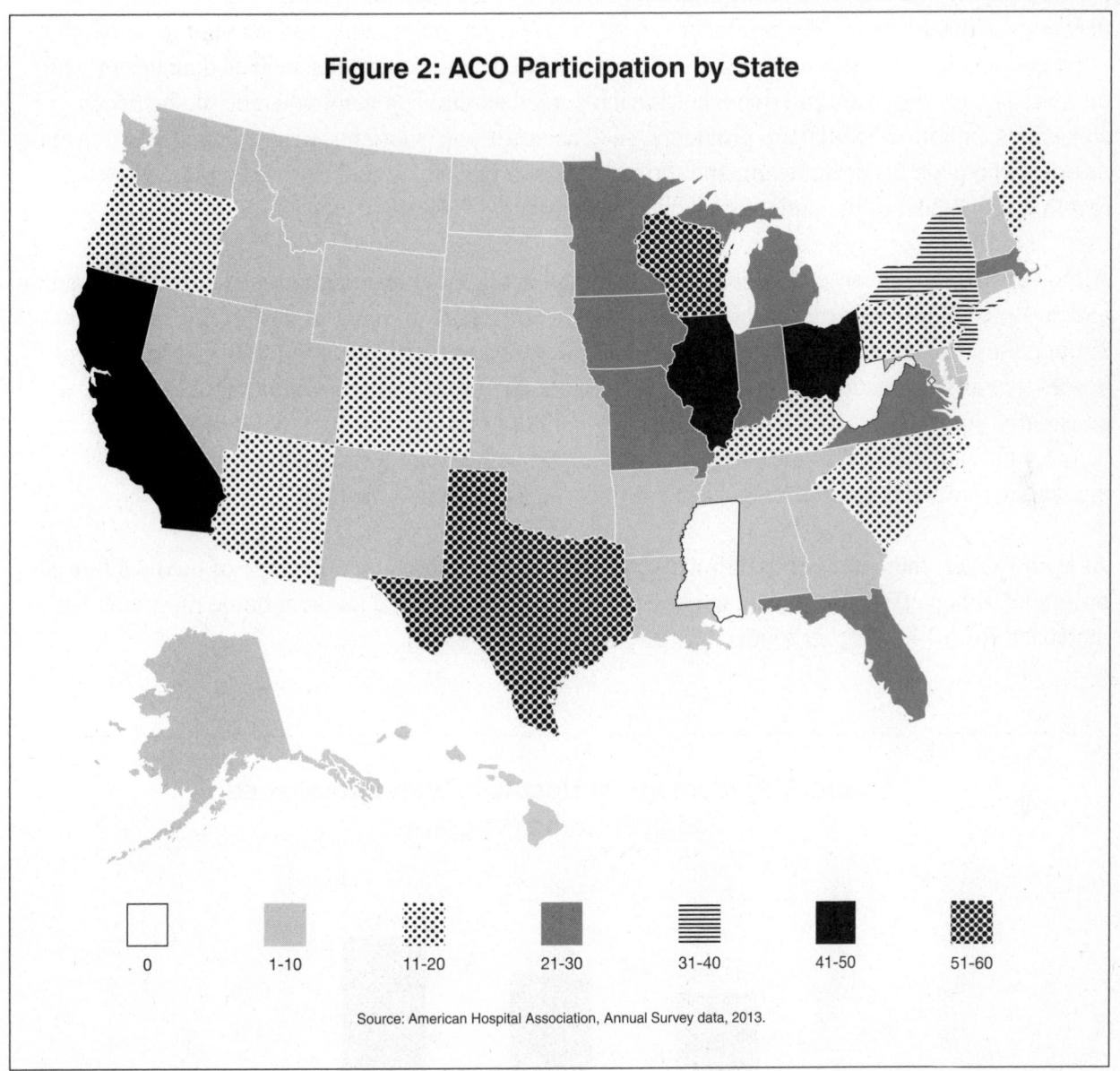

Figure 2: ACO Participation by State

Legend: 0, 1-10, 11-20, 21-30, 31-40, 41-50, 51-60

Source: American Hospital Association, Annual Survey data, 2013.

Medical Homes

A medical home is best described as a model of primary care that is patient-centered, comprehensive, team-based, coordinated, accessible and focused on quality and safety. A patient-centered medical home should have these characteristics: a personal physician, physician-directed medical practice, whole-person orientation, coordinated care, quality and safety focus, enhanced access and adequate payment.

According to this model, the traditional doctor's office is transformed into the central point for Americans to organize and coordinate their health care, based on their needs and priorities.

At its core is an ongoing partnership between each patient and a specially trained primary care physician. This new model provides modern conveniences, like e-mail communication and same-day appointments; quality ratings and pricing information; and secure online tools to help consumers manage their health information, review the latest medical findings and make informed decisions. Consumers receive reminders about necessary appointments and screenings, as well as other support to help them and their families manage chronic conditions such as diabetes or heart disease. The primary care physician helps each person assemble a team when he or she needs specialists and other health care providers, such as nutritionists and physical trainers. The consumer decides who is on his or her team, and the primary care physician makes sure they are working together to meet all of the patient's needs in an integrated, "whole person" fashion.

Although the patient-centered medical home model is all about keeping patients out of the hospital and away from hospital emergency departments, hospitals are an integral part of this movement. Among their business strategies are converting their own hospital-owned practices into medical homes, acquiring practices already certified as medical homes and requiring practices being considered for purchase to convert. And if they cannot build them or buy them, hospitals are connecting with medical homes through information technology infrastructure, staff and management expertise, or serving as an administrator of bundled payment.

As with ACOs , there has been continual growth in the number and percentage of medical home programs. Since 2011, the percentage of hospitals with established medical home programs has increased from 14.5 percent to just over 20 percent (Figure 3).

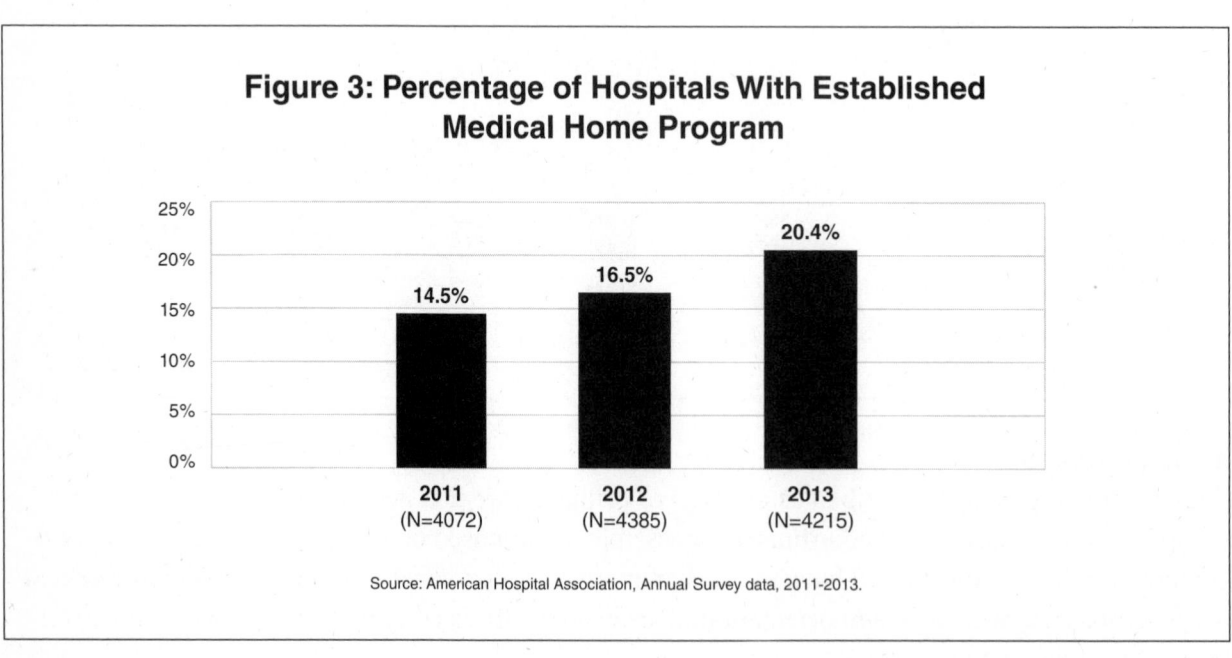

Figure 3: Percentage of Hospitals With Established Medical Home Program

Source: American Hospital Association, Annual Survey data, 2011-2013.

Hospital-Physician Alignment

The shift from volume to value is prompting both hospitals and health systems and physicians to analyze and review existing, and possibly new, relationships. The current "fee-for-service" system is based on the number of procedures or services performed by both hospitals and physicians. Many health care payers are shifting their focus to coordinated care payment models under which there is shared payment risk. These efforts are forcing traditionally separate parts of the health care system into integrated economic models.

One way to integrate clinical services and align financial interests is through legal structures like co-management agreements, in which hospitals contract with physicians to provide a particular clinical service line, such as cardiac services or orthopedics, and pay both base compensation for specific required services and incentive compensation if stated objectives are met. Absent such alliances, it will be increasingly difficult for health care providers to compete.

The mean number of physicians engaged in an arrangement with a hospital that allows for joint contracting with payers or shared responsibility for financial risk or clinical performance between the hospital and physician has increased each year since 2011 (Figure 4).

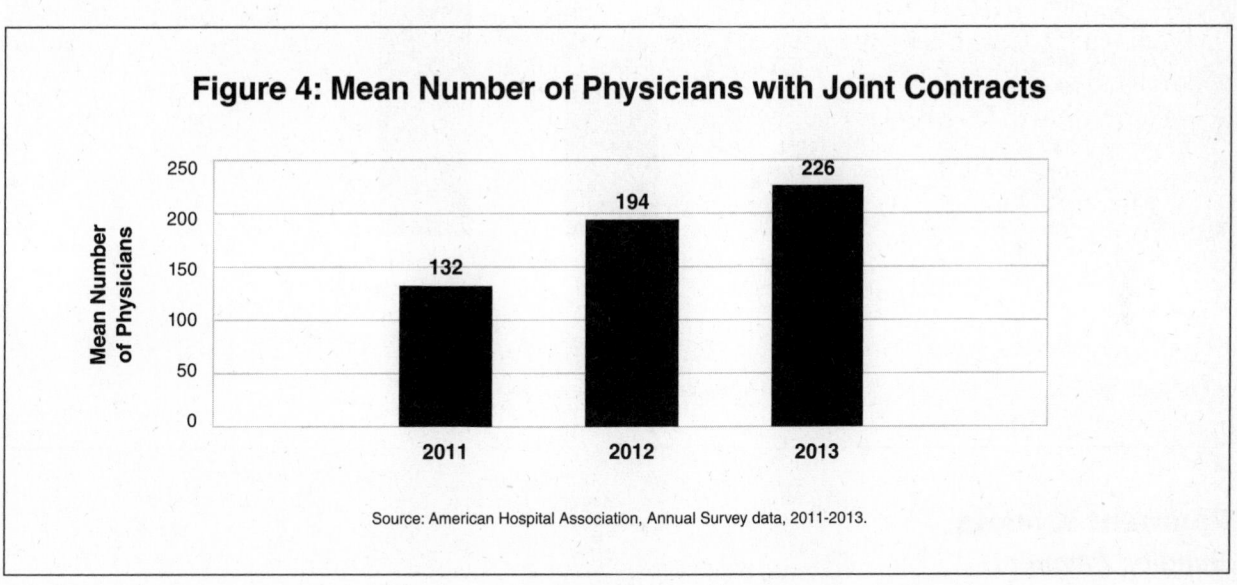

Figure 4: Mean Number of Physicians with Joint Contracts

Source: American Hospital Association, Annual Survey data, 2011-2013.

A different model that can potentially assist in delivering lower-cost care while maintaining focus on patient outcomes is the joint venture. Joint ventures allow hospitals to increase their service capabilities by purchasing new equipment with less financial risk. Physicians benefit from the joint ventures, which provide a means to pool resources to develop and manage diagnostic centers and outpatient centers, which could have been impossible for a single group practice. Joint ventures between hospitals and physicians control costs by increasing operating efficiencies and better utilizing medical resources.

About 26 percent of hospitals participate in a joint venture with physicians or physician groups. The most common type of a physician-hospital joint venture is an imaging center. Of the 26 percent of hospitals that participate with physicians or physician groups in a joint venture, 43 percent participate in imaging centers, 26 percent participate in limited-service hospitals and 12 percent participate in ambulatory surgical centers (Figure 5).

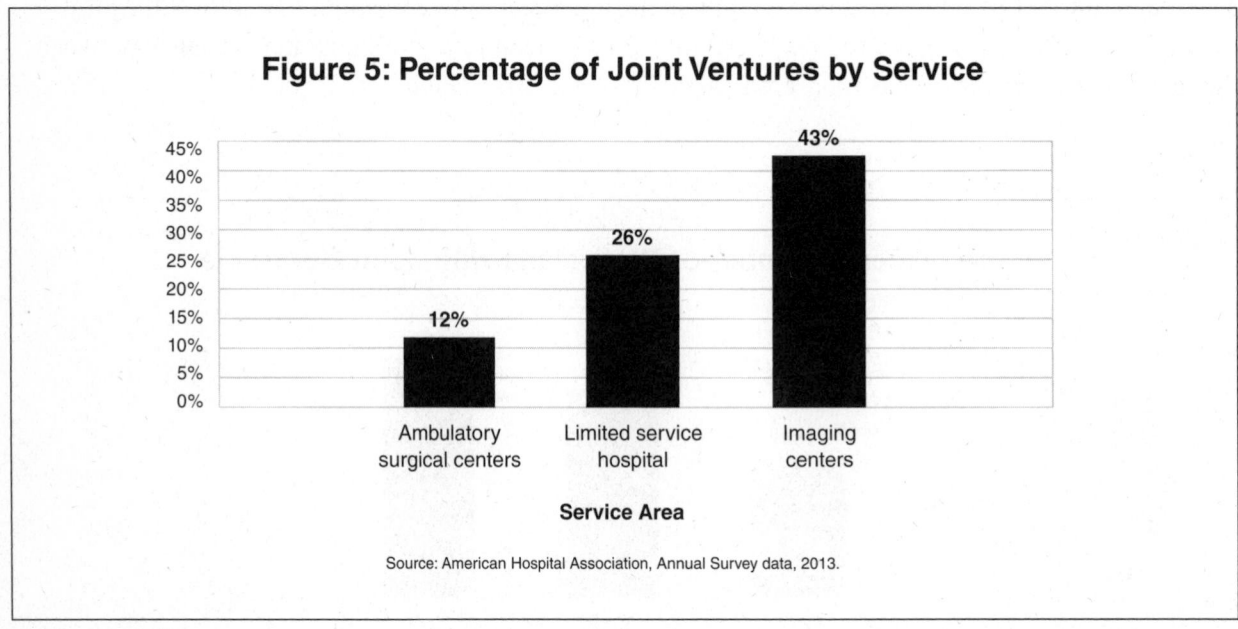

Figure 5: Percentage of Joint Ventures by Service

Source: American Hospital Association, Annual Survey data, 2013.

Payment Models
Bundled Payment
Under bundled payments, doctors, hospitals and other health care providers share a fixed payment that covers the average cost of a "bundle" of services. For example, if a patient has a hip replacement surgery, rather than making one payment to the hospital, a second payment to the surgeon and a third payment to the anesthesiologist, the payer would combine these payments for the entire episode of care. A bundled payment may also include post-acute care services like rehabilitation care in the above example.

Bundled payment arrangements are a type of risk-contracting. If the cost of services is less than the bundled payment amount, participating physicians and other health care providers retain the difference. But if the costs exceed the bundled payment amount, physicians and other providers are not compensated for the difference. Bundled payment models assign a fixed, negotiated fee to cover a set of treatment services, encouraging providers to manage costs, while meeting high-quality care standards.

Just 9 percent of hospitals participate in a bundled payment program. This is an increase of 0.7 percent from 2012. Bundled payment models are largely pursued by mid-sized and larger hospitals and health systems. More than one-quarter of the hospitals that participate in a bundled payment plan are hospitals with more than 500 hospital beds (Figure 6).

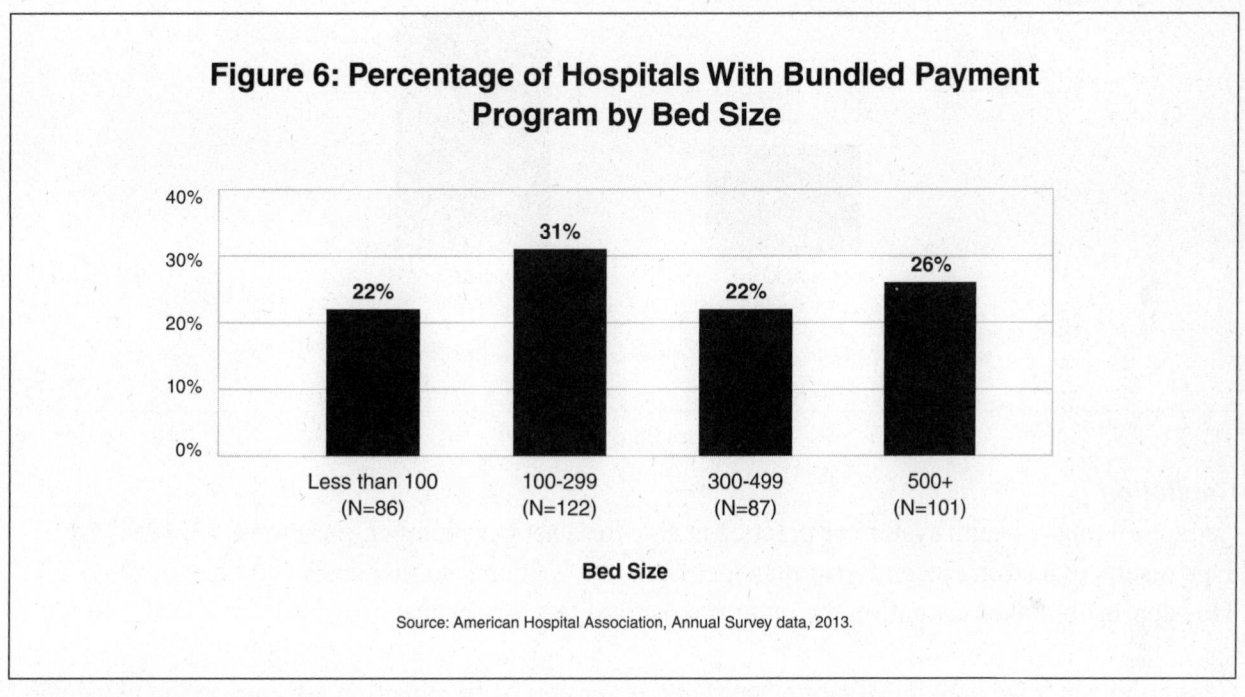

Figure 6: Percentage of Hospitals With Bundled Payment Program by Bed Size

Source: American Hospital Association, Annual Survey data, 2013.

A greater percentage of hospitals with ACOs and medical home programs participate in a bundled payment program. Twenty percent of hospitals with an ACO and 45 percent of hospitals with a medical home program use bundled payments (Figure 7).

Figure 7: Percentage of ACO and Medical Homes with Bundled Payment Programs

Source: American Hospital Association, Annual Survey data, 2013.

Capitation

Capitation puts a health system or practice at risk for a set per member, per month (PMPM) fee. This results in a strong incentive to manage the care of patients so that costs can be controlled. This approach makes capitation the polar opposite of fee-for-service.

Capitation is a fixed amount of money per patient per unit of time paid in advance to the physician for the delivery of health care services. The actual amount of money paid is determined by the range of services that are provided, the number of patients involved, and the period of time during which the services are provided. Providers profit when that sum is more than the expense and absorb the loss if it is not. As incentives go, capitation carries significant risk but also the potential for bigger reward and greater flexibility for providers to pay for whatever care they consider most effective.

Capitation remained a small fraction of net patient revenue for hospitals in 2013. Just over 92 percent of hospitals had no patient revenues based on capitation. Approximately 5 percent of hospitals had between one and ten percent of their net patient revenues from capitated payments and about 2 percent had between 11 and 100 percent (Figure 8). These percentages have changed very little over the past three years.

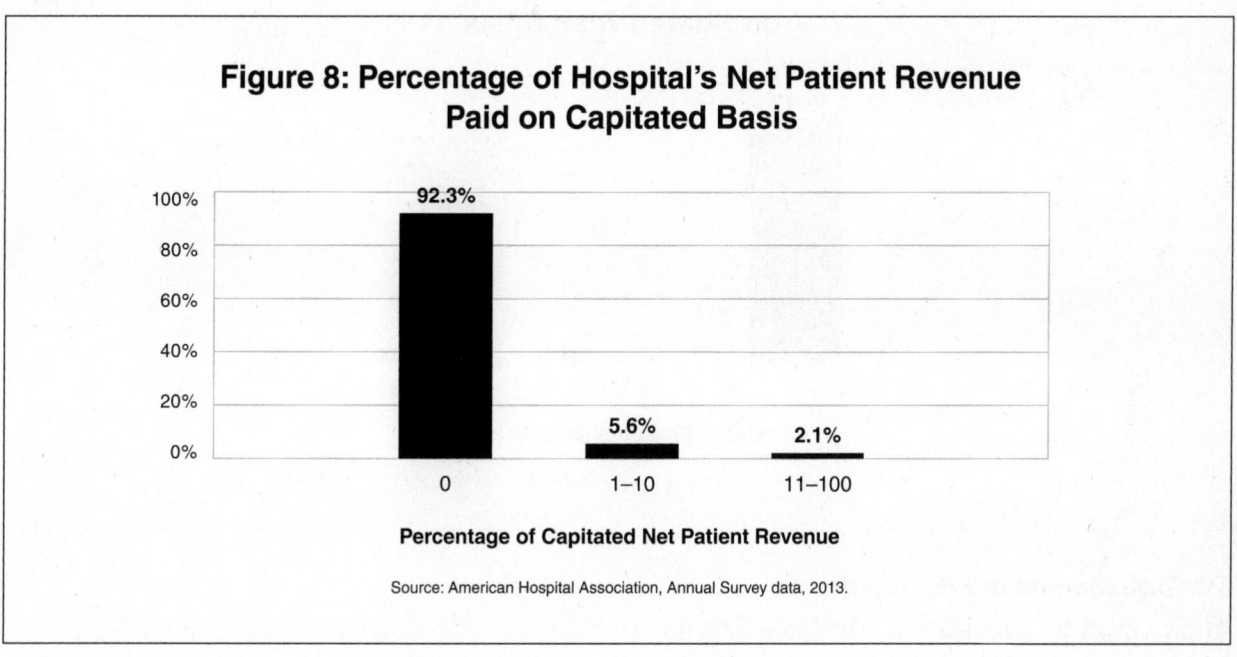

Figure 8: Percentage of Hospital's Net Patient Revenue Paid on Capitated Basis

Percentage of Capitated Net Patient Revenue

Source: American Hospital Association, Annual Survey data, 2013.

Shared Risk

Shared-risk models could be described as the "next-level" of risk arrangements, under which providers receive performance-based incentives to share cost savings but are also at risk for a portion of spending that exceeds an established target. This model is based on an agreed upon budget with a payer, and calls for the provider to cover a portion of costs if savings targets are not achieved; this portion could be a percentage of the premium (e.g., 30 percent of the overall premium flows to provider) or a set amount (e.g., 50/50 sharing of costs above the set amount). As expected, there is a relationship between risk and reward. Because providers take on more risk under this model, most often the opportunity for upside financial gain is larger.

As with capitation, most hospitals are not collecting patient revenues on a shared-risk basis. Over 92 percent have no net patient revenue paid on a shared risk basis. Approximately 5 percent of hospitals had between one and ten percent of their net patient revenues on a shared risk basis and a little over 2 percent had between 11 and 100 percent (Figure 9).

Figure 9: Percentage of Hospital's Net Patient Revenue Paid on Shared Risk Basis

Percentage Paid on Shared Risk Basis

Source: American Hospital Association, Annual Survey data, 2013.

Performance-based Payment

The Centers for Medicare & Medicaid Services (CMS), the federal agency that oversees the Medicare program, is changing the way Medicare pays for hospital care by rewarding hospitals for delivering higher quality and higher value. Commercial payers also are beginning to base payment on hospital performance on selected quality of care measures and performance metrics that meet defined quality, efficiency and other targets. Almost one-third of hospitals have contracts with commercial payers where payment is tied to performance on quality/safety metrics (Figure 10).

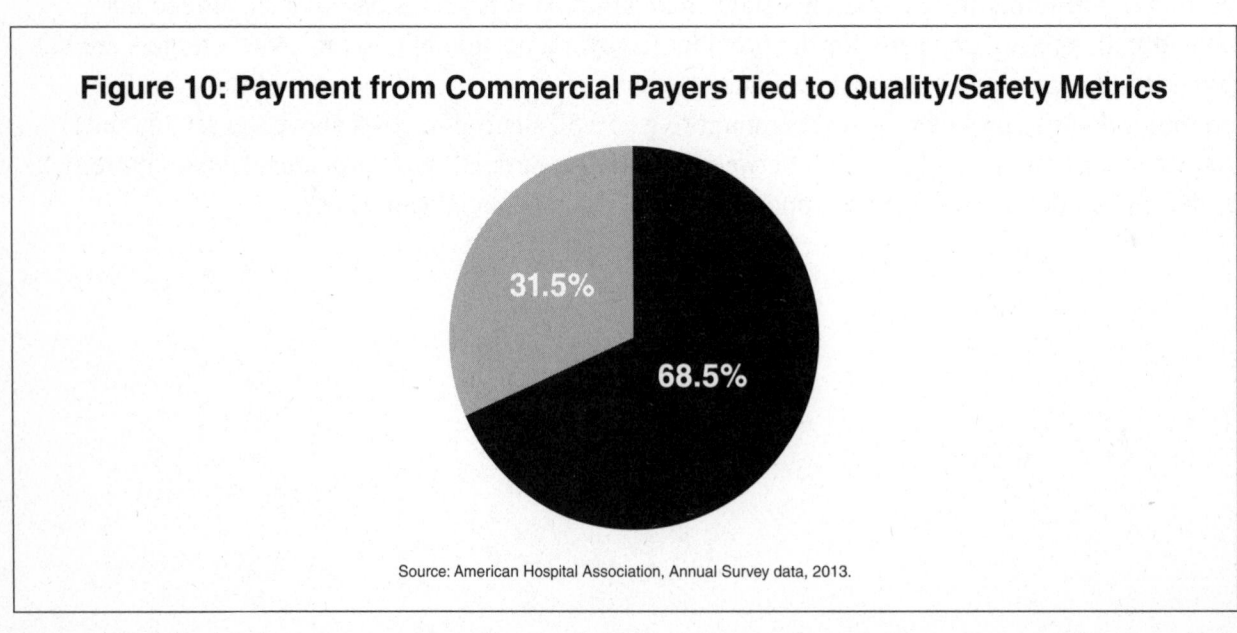

Figure 10: Payment from Commercial Payers Tied to Quality/Safety Metrics

Source: American Hospital Association, Annual Survey data, 2013.

Conclusion

Hospitals and other health care providers today are in the midst of navigating significant changes in how they conduct business and deliver care. The era of fee-for-service medicine is coming to an end. In its place, government and private payers are demanding models that require providers to share the financial risk and deliver both improved outcomes and lower costs. This will require providers to fundamentally rethink the way they deliver care.

Several models have been discussed in this brief paper. In particular, accountable care organizations, medical homes and joint ventures. The lessons learned from the implementation of these models will form the roadmap for future payment and delivery system reforms in health care. While the design of these models varies, a shared objective is the movement away from fee-for-service payment toward financial incentives that reward high-quality, high-value care. To help hospitals, clinicians and policymakers achieve these goals, the AHA will continue to track and report on the progress of these models and delivery systems.

How to Use this Book

For more than seven decades, *AHA Hospital Statistics*™ has reported aggregate hospital data derived from the AHA Annual Survey and is the definitive source when doing trend analysis with data by bed size category, U.S. Census Divisions, States, and Metropolitan Statistical Areas (MSAs). As the health care delivery system changes, so have the data tracked by the survey and presented in this report. Recent additions include:

- **Community health indicators** that offer readers a connection to the community for their analysis and planning: the data are broken down into beds, admissions, inpatient days, ER outpatient visits, and other indicators per 1000 population, as well as expense per capita.

- **Utilization, personnel and finance** by all MSAs in the United States.

- **Five-year trend data** on physician models, insurance products, and managed care contracts enable you to identify changes in relationships between hospitals and other health care systems and providers.

- **Tables 3 through 6 have been organized** to show breakdowns between inpatient and outpatient care to better reflect market shifts toward outpatient-centered care. Additional clarity is gained by the breakdown between total facility data (which includes nursing home type units under the control of the hospital) and hospital units (which exclude the nursing home data).

TABLE 6	Sample State

U.S. Registered Community Hospitals
(Nonfederal, short-term general and other special hospitals)

Overview 2009-2013

	2013	2012	2011	2010	2009
Physician Models					
Independent Practice Association	14	17	17	17	14
Group Practice without Walls	4	5	5	8	4
Open Physician-Hospital Organization	20	21	24	23	18
Closed Physician-Hospital Organization	21	17	18	17	11
Management Service Organization	14	18	20	14	9
Integrated Salary Model	35	29	30	26	24
Equity Model	4	3	4	6	3
Foundation	9	8	23	21	19
Insurance Products					
Health Maintenance Organization	20	22	23	24	19
Preferred Provider Organization	39	47	52	53	37
Indemnity Fee for Service	7	12	14	12	6
Managed Care Contracts					
Health Maintenance Organization	64	67	62	49	42
Preferred Provider Organization	97	93	92	87	72

Example of five-year trend data

- **Facilities and Services information** on more than 100 categories of hospital facilities and services in Table 7. At a glance, you can determine the number and percentage of hospitals offering a specific service such as Oncology, Palliative Care Program, Complementary Medicine, Women's Health Services and Tobacco Cessation.

- **Plus, System and Network involvement along with Group Purchasing Organizations** that demonstrate ways in which organizations are linked.

The survey instrument and the glossary

A good place to begin your analysis is the AHA Annual Survey instrument. Found on page xxx, it includes the instructions, questions, and terms that were used to gather the data for fiscal year 2013. This can be extremely valuable for a clearer understanding of the data we collect and the tables presented in *AHA Hospital Statistics*.

Please also review the glossary in the back of the book. The glossary contains complete definitions for specific terms used in the tables and text of *AHA Hospital Statistics*. These definitions will clarify how terminology is being used.

As mentioned above, it is important to note that the primary focus of the most detailed data contained in *AHA Hospital Statistics* is community hospitals. As defined, community hospitals are all non-federal, short-term general and special hospitals whose facilities and services are available to the public. If the majority of a hospital's patients are admitted to units where the average length of stay is 30 days or less, a hospital may still be classified as short-term even if it includes a nursing- home-type unit. (For a more complete definition of community hospitals, please see the glossary definition, located on page xxx.)

Getting the most out of *AHA Hospital Statistics*
This section of the book provides an introduction for getting the most out of your *AHA Hospital Statistics* 2015 edition. Here, you'll find a guide to the book, with insights into each table.

Equity model: An arrangement that allows established practitioners to become shareholders in a professional corporation in exchange for tangible and intangible assets of their existing practices.

Expenses: Includes all expenses for the reporting period including payroll, non-payroll, and all nonoperating expenses. *Payroll expenses* include all salaries and wages. *Non-payroll expenses* are all professional fees and those salary expenditures excluded from payroll. *Labor related expenses* are defined as payroll expenses plus employee benefits. *Non-labor related expenses* are all other non-payroll expenses. *Bad debt* has been reclassified from a "reduction in revenue" to an expense in accordance with the revised AICPA Audit Guide. However, for purposes of historical consistency, the expense total that appears throughout *AHA Hospital Statistics does not include "bad debt" as an expense item.* Note: Financial data may not add due to rounding.

Extracorporeal shock wave lithotripter (ESWL): A medical device used for treating stones in the kidney or urethra. The device disintegrates kidney stones noninvasively through the transmission of acoustic shock waves directed at the stones.

Fitness center: Provides exercise, testing, or evaluation programs and fitness activities to the community and hospital employees.

Example of Glossary definitions.

| Table 1 | Historical Trends in Utilization, Personnel, and Finances for Selected Years from 1946 through 2013 | | | | | |

CLASSIFICATION	YEAR	HOSPITALS	BEDS (in thousands)	ADMISSIONS (in thousands)	AVERAGE DAILY CENSUS (in thousands)	ADJUSTED AVERAGE DAILY CENSUS (in thousands)
Total United States	1946	6,125	1,436	15,675	1,142	—
	1950	6,788	1,456	18,483	1,253	—
	1955	6,956	1,604	21,073	1,363	—
	1960	6,876	1,658	25,027	1,402	—
	1965	7,123	1,704	28,812	1,403	—
	1970	7,123	1,616	31,759	1,298	—
	1971	7,097	1,556	32,664	1,237	—
	1972	7,061	1,550	33,265	1,209	—
	1973	7,123	1,535	34,352	1,189	—
	1974	7,174	1,513	35,506	1,167	—
	1975	7,156	1,466	36,157	1,125	—
	1976	7,082	1,434	36,776	1,090	—
	1977	7,099	1,407	37,060	1,066	—
	1978	7,015	1,381	37,243	1,042	—
	1979	6,988	1,372	37,802	1,043	—
	1980	6,965	1,365	38,892	1,060	—
	1981	6,933	1,362	39,169	1,061	—
	1982	6,915	1,360	39,095	1,053	—
	1983	6,888	1,350	38,887	1,028	—
	1984	6,872	1,339	37,938	970	—
	1985	6,872	1,318	36,304	910	—
	1986	6,841	1,290	35,219	883	—
	1987	6,821	1,267	34,439	873	—
	1988	6,780	1,248	34,107	863	—
	1989	6,720	1,226	33,742	853	—
	1990	6,649	1,213	33,774	844	—
	1991	6,634	1,202	33,567	827	—
	1992	6,539	1,178	33,536	807	—
	1993	6,467	1,163	33,201	783	—
	1994	6,374	1,128	33,125	745	—
	1995	6,291	1,081	33,282	710	—
	1996	6,201	1,062	33,307	685	—
	1997	6,097	1,035	33,624	673	—
	1998	6,021	1,013	33,766	662	—
	1999	5,890	994	34,181	657	—
	2000	5,810	984	34,891	650	—
	2001	5,801	987	35,644	658	—
	2002	5,794	976	36,326	662	—
	2003	5,764	965	36,611	657	—
	2004	5,759	956	36,942	658	—
	2005	5,756	947	37,006	656	—

Example of Table 1

Table 1 at a Glance

This table is used to evaluate historical data and allows you to examine long-term trends in health care with data dating back more than sixty years. Table 1 reports on all AHA registered hospitals in the United States. One important note: To be considered an AHA-registered hospital, a hospital does not need to be an AHA member. Rather, the hospital must meet particular certification or satisfy a number of requirements. These Registration Requirements immediately follow this section and begin on page (xxviii.)

This table segments the data into various organizational structure categories. Here's a brief look at these different classifications:

- Total United States Hospitals
- Total Non-Federal Short-term and other special hospitals
- Community hospitals
- Non-government not-for-profit community hospitals
- Investor-owned (for-profit) community hospitals
- State and local government community hospitals

Table 1 also provides input on nationwide utilization, personnel and finance trends. You'll find answers to questions such as: *Over the past 25 years, what trends do I see comparing the average length of stay at government and non-government not-for-profit community hospitals and investor-owned for-profit community hospitals?* or *What has been the trend in outpatient visits?*

Table 2 — 2013 U.S. Registered Hospitals: Utilization, Personnel and Finances

Table 2 at a Glance

This table takes a closer look at U.S. Registered Hospitals for 2013. It offers a snapshot of utilization, personnel and finance statistics, and breaks down this information for specialty hospitals. In addition, this is the only table that outlines data on federal hospitals. You'll be able to use this table to better understand the number of beds set-up and staffed, how many personnel and trainees are on the payroll, and what the financial implications of these may be.

TABLE 3

TOTAL UNITED STATES

U.S. Registered Community Hospitals
(Nonfederal, short-term general and other special hospitals)

Utilization, Personnel, Revenue and Expenses, Community Health Indicators 2009-2013

	2013	2012	2011	2010	2009
TOTAL FACILITY (Includes Hospital and Nursing Home Units)					
Utilization - Inpatient					
Beds	839,988	853,287	862,352	872,736	902,061
Admissions	31,811,673	31,576,960	31,098,959	30,945,357	30,718,136
Inpatient Days	191,430,450	192,504,015	193,747,004	199,876,367	207,180,278
Average Length of Stay	6.0	6.1	6.2	6.5	6.7
Inpatient Surgeries	9,735,705	9,509,081	9,545,612	9,700,613	9,833,938
Births	3,726,233	3,742,191	3,723,871	3,764,698	3,809,367
HOSPITAL UNIT (Excludes Separate Nursing Home Units)					
Utilization - Inpatient					
Beds	758,186	769,505	782,504	794,502	824,969
Admissions	31,265,867	31,047,930	30,652,820	30,577,564	30,403,766
Inpatient Days	165,644,176	165,605,620	168,189,130	174,898,504	182,702,882
Average Length of Stay	5.3	5.3	5.5	5.7	6.0
Personnel					
Total Full Time	3,235,153	3,183,730	3,154,603	3,166,729	3,147,922
Total Part Time	1,213,426	1,214,232	1,153,790	1,146,082	1,122,957
Revenue and Expenses - Totals					
(Includes Inpatient and Outpatient)					
Total Net Revenue	$333,054,828,642	$322,459,942,930	$310,513,291,998	$298,519,717,355	$285,858,018,951
Total Expenses	314,709,758,455	301,905,101,393	290,128,641,153	282,372,557,487	272,840,121,437

Example of Table 3. Helps contrast acute and long-term care

Table 3 — Total United States

Table 3 at a Glance

This table provides a look at all U.S. Registered Community Hospitals, in terms of general overview with utilization by inpatient and outpatient, personnel, revenue, expenses and community health indicators. It provides a snapshot of the past five years, allowing you to track emerging trends.

This national information can be compared to local or regional trends, for benchmarking:

- Both inpatient and outpatient information is included, for better evaluation of data.

- Reporting by total facility *Includes hospital and Nursing Home Units* and hospital unit only *Excludes Separate Nursing Home Units* helps contrast acute and long-term care.

- Community health indicators can help uncover trends and help determine future facility needs.

Example of Table 4. Compares facilities with peers.

Table 4 — Bed Size Categories

Table 4 at a Glance
This table provides a look at all U.S. Registered Community Hospitals, broken down by bed size. The table includes general overview, utilization, personnel, and revenue and expense information. These categories of bed sizes were developed by the AHA, and have become an industry standard. By categorizing each facility into a peer group, this table provides a snapshot of the past five years allowing you to compare facilities with their peers.

TABLE 5

U.S. CENSUS DIVISION 2: MIDDLE ATLANTIC

U.S. Registered Community Hospitals
(Nonfederal, short-term general and other special hospitals)

Utilization, Personnel, Revenue and Expenses, Community Health Indicators 2009-2013

	2013	2012	2011	2010	2009
COMMUNITY HEALTH INDICATORS PER 1000 POPULATION					
Total Population (in thousands)...	38,292	38,216	38,184	38,147	38,108
Inpatient					
Beds.........................	3.6	3.8	3.9	4.0	4.1
Admissions....................	135.8	136.7	136.2	138.3	137.4
Inpatient Days.................	963.5	988.8	1,019.0	1,093.8	1,145.0
Inpatient Surgeries.............	42.2	41.4	41.2	42.7	43.6
Births........................	13.0	13.2	13.6	13.7	14.3
Outpatient					
Emergency Outpatient Visits......	367.7	362.0	363.4	379.5	360.1
Other Outpatient Visits..........	1,970.9	1,802.3	1,767.7	1,680.3	1,573.9
Total Outpatient Visits..........	2,338.6	2,164.3	2,131.1	2,059.8	1,934.0
Outpatient Surgeries............	67.8	62.4	59.9	55.4	53.5
Expense per Capita (per person)....	$1,494.9	$1,462.7	$1,428.6	$1,429.8	$1,369.2

Example of Table 5. Uncovers trends to determine future facility needs.

Table 5 — U.S. Census Divisions

Table 5 at a Glance
This table provides a look at all U.S. Registered Community Hospitals, broken down by Census Division. The table includes general overview, utilization, personnel, and expenses, and community health indicator information. It provides a snapshot of the past five years, allowing you to track trends on a regional level. In addition, this allows you to compare this data to other population based health indicators, offering a more comprehensive look than the survey data alone. Community health indicators can help uncover trends and help determine future facility needs.

Table 6 — States

Table 6 at a Glance
This table provides a look at all U.S. Registered Community Hospitals, broken down by State. The table includes general overview, utilization, personnel, revenue and expenses, and community health indicator information. It provides a snapshot of the past five years, allowing you to track trends on a state level.

Note:
You can use the information in tables 3, 4, 5 and 6 to make accurate comparisons across Total U.S., Bed Size Category, Census Division and State.

Table 7 — 2013 Facilities and Services in the U.S. Census Divisions and States

Table 7 at a Glance

This table examines facilities and services by both Census Division and State. A comprehensive alphabetical guide helps make each facility or service easy to find. This table will allow you to better understand what service lines are emerging and how many facilities offer a particular service in a discrete state or region.

This collection of facilities and services information data is unique to *AHA Hospital Statistics* and the list is continually growing. Recent additions include:

- Pediatric Emergency Department
- Psychiatric Residential Treatment
- Magneotoencephalography (MEG)

These new categories reflect the trends as hospitals expand their service lines to mirror the needs of their patients. For example, services such as acupuncture or massage therapy are now accounted for in the Complementary Medicine service item.

Example of Table 7.

This table can answer questions such as: *What percentage of hospitals in the United States offer complementary medicine or wound management?* or *How are these new services distributed by state?*

Table 8 — Utilization, Personnel and Finances in Community Hospitals by MSAs for 2013

Table 8 at a Glance

This table provides a look at all U.S. Registered Community Hospitals, broken down by Metropolitan Statistical Area (MSA). The table includes general overview, utilization, personnel, and finance information. It provides a snapshot of the past year.

Additional Resources

Again, in the back of the book you will find the comprehensive glossary and the 2013 annual survey questionnaire. The survey itself can be a valuable resource to understanding what was asked in order to gather the data in the book. This survey is also used to produce the *AHA Guide®* and AHA Annual Survey Database™.

Registration Requirements for Hospitals

AHA-Registered Hospitals

Any institution that can be classified as a hospital according to the requirements may be registered if it so desires. Membership in the American Hospital Association is not a prerequisite.

The American Hospital Association may, at the sole discretion of the Executive Committee of the Board of Trustees, grant, deny, or withdraw the registration of an institution.

An institution may be registered by the American Hospital Association as a hospital if it is accredited as a hospital by The Joint Commission or is certified as a provider of acute services under Title 18 of the Social Security Act and has provided the Association with documents verifying the accreditation or certification.

In lieu of the preceding accreditation or certification, an institution licensed as a hospital by the appropriate state agency may be registered by AHA as a hospital by meeting the following alternative requirements:

Function: The primary function of the institution is to provide patient services, diagnostic and therapeutic, for particular or general medical conditions.

1. The institution shall maintain at least six inpatient beds, which shall be continuously available for the care of patients who are nonrelated and who stay on the average in excess of 24 hours per admission.

2. The institution shall be constructed, equipped, and maintained to ensure the health and safety of patients and to provide uncrowded, sanitary facilities for the treatment of patients.

3. There shall be an identifiable governing authority legally and morally responsible for the conduct of the hospital.

4. There shall be a chief executive to whom the governing authority delegates the continuous responsibility for the operation of the hospital in accordance with established policy.

5. There shall be an organized medical staff of fully licensed physicians* that may include other licensed individuals permitted by law and by the hospital to provide patient care services independently in the hospital. The medical staff shall be accountable to the governing authority for maintaining proper standards of medical care, and it shall be governed by bylaws adopted by said staff and approved by the governing authority.

6. Each patient shall be admitted on the authority of a member of the medical staff who has been granted the privilege to admit patients to inpatient services in accordance with state law and criteria for standards of medical care established by the individual medical staff. Each patient's general medical condition is the responsibility of a qualified physician member of the medical staff. When nonphysician members of the medical staff are granted privileges to admit patients, provision is made for prompt medical evaluation of these patients by a qualified physician. Any graduate of a foreign medical school who is permitted to assume responsibilities for patient care shall possess a valid license to practice medicine, or shall be certified by the Educational Commission for Foreign Medical Graduates, or shall have qualified for and have successfully completed an academic year of supervised clinical training under the direction of a medical school approved by the Liaison Committee on GAT Medical Education.

7. Registered nurse supervision and other nursing services are continuous.

8. A current and complete‡ medical record shall be maintained by the institution for each patient and shall be available for reference.

9. Pharmacy service shall be maintained in the institution and shall be supervised by a registered pharmacist.

10. The institution shall provide patients with food service that meets their nutritional and therapeutic requirements; special diets shall also be available.

Types of Hospitals
In addition to meeting these 10 general registration requirements, hospitals are registered as one of four types of hospitals: general, special, rehabilitation and chronic disease, or psychiatric. The following type of hospital and special requirements for registration are employed:

General
The primary function of the institution is to provide patient services, diagnostic and therapeutic, for a variety of medical conditions. A general hospital also shall provide:

- diagnostic x-ray services with facilities and staff for a variety of procedures
- clinical laboratory service with facilities and staff for a variety of procedures and with anatomical pathology services regularly and conveniently available
- operating room service with facilities and staff.

Special
The primary function of the institution is to provide diagnostic and treatment services for patients who have specified medical conditions, both surgical and nonsurgical. A special hospital also shall provide:

- such diagnostic and treatment services as may be determined by the Executive Committee of the Board of Trustees of the American Hospital Association to be appropriate for the specified medical conditions for which medical services are provided shall be maintained in the institution with suitable facilities and staff. If such conditions do not normally require diagnostic x-ray service, laboratory service, or operating room service, and if any such services are therefore not maintained in the institution, there shall be written arrangements to make them available to patients requiring them.
- clinical laboratory services capable of providing tissue diagnosis when offering pregnancy termination services.

Rehabilitation and Chronic Disease
The primary function of the institution is to provide diagnostic and treatment services to handicapped or disabled individuals requiring restorative and adjustive services. A rehabilitation and chronic disease hospital also shall provide:

- arrangements for diagnostic x-ray services, as required, on a regular and conveniently available basis
- arrangements for clinical laboratory service, as required on a regular and conveniently available basis
- arrangements for operating room service, as required, on a regular and conveniently available basis
- a physical therapy service with suitable facilities and staff in the institution
- an occupational therapy service with suitable facilities and staff in the institution
- arrangements for psychological and social work services on a regular and conveniently available basis

---

* Physician–Term used to describe an individual with an M.D. or D.O. degree who is fully licensed to practice medicine in all its phases.

‡ The completed records in general shall contain at least the following: the patient's identifying data and consent forms, medical history, record of physical examination, physicians' progress notes, operative notes, nurses' notes, routine x-ray and laboratory reports, doctors' orders, and final diagnosis.

- arrangements for educational and vocational services on a regular and conveniently available basis
- written arrangements with a general hospital for the transfer of patients who require medical, obstetrical, or surgical services not available in the institution.

Psychiatric

The primary function of the institution is to provide diagnostic and treatment services for patients who have psychiatric-related illnesses. A psychiatric hospital also shall provide:

- arrangements for clinical laboratory service, as required, on a regular and conveniently available basis
- arrangements for diagnostic x-ray services, as required on a regular and conveniently available basis
- psychiatric, psychological, and social work service with facilities and staff in the institution
- arrangements for electroencephalograph services, as required, on a regular and conveniently available basis.
- written arrangements with a general hospital for the transfer of patients who require medical, obstetrical, or surgical services not available in the institution.

The American Hospital Association may, at the sole discretion of the Executive Committee of the Board of Trustees, grant, deny, or withdraw the registration of an institution.

Data Comparability

The economic climate, demographic characteristics, personnel issues, and health care financing and payment policies differ by region, state, and city across the country. *Differences in these factors must be taken into account when using the data.* In addition, the profiles of hospitals across comparison groups vary. For example, states will differ in terms of the number and percentage of hospitals by size, ownership, services provided, types of patients treated, and so forth. *Differences in these variables also must be taken into consideration when doing a comparative analysis.*

The 2015 edition of *AHA Hospital Statistics*™ draws its data from the 2013 AHA Annual Survey of Hospitals. It is the statistical complement to the 2015 edition of the *AHA Guide*®, which contains selected data about individual hospitals.

The AHA Survey was mailed to all hospitals, both AHA-registered and nonregistered, in the U.S. and its associated areas: American Samoa, Guam, the Marshall Islands, Puerto Rico, and the Virgin Islands. U.S. government hospitals located outside the U.S. were not included. Overall, the average response rate over the past five years has been approximately 83 percent.

Reporting Period

In completing the survey, hospitals were requested to report data for a full year, in accord with their fiscal year, ending in 2013. The statistical table present data reported or estimated for a 12-month period, except for data on personnel, which represent situations as they existed at the end of the reporting period.

Respondents

Data for Tables 1 and 2 include 5,686 AHA-registered hospitals in the U.S. Data on community hospitals (nonfederal, short-term general and other special hospitals) only are presented in Tables 3-6, and Table 8.

It is important to note that the AHA-registered hospitals included in *AHA Hospital Statistics* are not necessarily identical to those included in *AHA Guide*. The institutions listed in the 2015 edition of *AHA Guide* include all of those institutions CMS certified, Joint Commission accredited, or AHA registered as of June 2014. Tables 1-6 in *AHA Hospital Statistics* present data for AHA-registered hospitals that were in operation during the 12-month reporting period ending 2013.

Estimates

Estimates were made of data for nonreporting hospitals and for reporting hospitals that submitted incomplete AHA Annual Survey questionnaires. Estimates were not made for beds, bassinets and facilities and services. Data for beds and bassinets of nonreporting hospitals were based on the most recent information from those hospitals. (Note that in all statistical tables, whenever bed-size categories are listed, all eight categories appear, whether or not there are hospitals in every category.)

Missing revenue, expenses, admissions, births, inpatient days, surgical operations, outpatient visits, and full-time-equivalent personnel values are estimates from regression models. For all other variables the estimates were based on ratios such as per bed averages derived from data reported by hospitals similar in size, control, major service provided, length of stay, and geographical characteristics to the hospitals that did not report this information.

Tables 1–2

Historical Trends in Utilization, Personnel, and Finances for Selected Years from 1946 through 2013

Data are for all AHA-registered hospitals in the United States. Data are estimated for nonreporting hospitals with the exception of newborn and outpatient data before 1972. Personnel data exclude residents, interns, and students from 1952 on; personnel data include full-time personnel and full-time equivalents for part-time personnel from 1954 on. As a result of the AHA Annual Survey validation process, the New York state expense data from 1976 were revised after the 1977 edition was published. The revised figures are included below. In order to provide trend data on a consistent basis, the 1970 and 1971 psychiatric and long-term data have been slightly modified. The 1982 FTE figures have updated to provide the most accurate data possible.

Table 1

Classification: Total United States

YEAR	HOSPITALS	BEDS (in thousands)	ADMISSIONS (in thousands)	AVERAGE DAILY CENSUS (in thousands)	ADJUSTED AVERAGE DAILY CENSUS (in thousands)	AVERAGE STAY (days)	OUTPATIENT VISITS (in thousands)	NEWBORNS Bassinets	NEWBORNS Births	FTE PERSONNEL Number (in thousands)	FTE PERSONNEL Per 100 Adjusted Census	TOTAL EXPENSES Amount (In Millions of dollars)	TOTAL EXPENSES Adjusted per Inpatient Stay (dollars)	TOTAL EXPENSES Adjusted per Inpatient Day (dollars)
1946	6,125	1,436	15,675	1,142	—	—	—	85,585	2,135,327	830	—	$1,963	—	—
1950	6,788	1,456	18,483	1,253	—	—	—	90,101	2,742,780	1,058	—	$3,651	—	—
1955	6,956	1,604	21,073	1,363	—	—	—	98,823	3,476,753	1,301	—	$5,594	—	—
1960	6,876	1,658	25,027	1,402	—	—	—	102,764	3,835,735	1,598	—	$8,421	—	—
1965	7,123	1,704	28,812	1,403	—	—	125,793	101,287	3,565,344	1,952	—	$12,948	—	—
1970	7,123	1,616	31,759	1,298	—	—	181,370	97,128	3,537,000	2,537	—	$25,556	—	—
1971	7,097	1,556	32,664	1,237	—	—	199,725	94,344	3,464,513	2,589	—	$28,812	—	—
1972	7,061	1,550	33,265	1,209	—	—	219,182	92,960	3,231,875	2,671	—	$32,667	—	—
1973	7,123	1,535	34,352	1,189	—	—	233,555	90,071	3,087,210	2,769	—	$36,290	—	—
1974	7,174	1,513	35,506	1,167	—	—	250,481	88,269	3,043,386	2,919	—	$41,406	—	—
1975	7,156	1,466	36,157	1,125	—	—	254,844	86,875	3,091,629	3,023	—	$48,706	—	—
1976	7,082	1,434	36,776	1,090	—	—	270,951	85,284	3,067,063	3,108	—	$56,005	—	—
1977	7,099	1,407	37,060	1,066	—	—	263,775	83,193	3,223,699	3,213	—	$63,630	—	—
1978	7,015	1,381	37,243	1,042	—	—	263,606	80,650	3,250,373	3,280	—	$70,927	—	—
1979	6,988	1,372	37,802	1,043	—	—	262,009	79,720	3,376,467	3,382	—	$79,796	—	—
1980	6,965	1,365	38,892	1,060	—	—	262,951	79,842	3,500,043	3,492	—	$91,886	—	—
1981	6,933	1,362	39,169	1,061	—	—	265,332	78,823	3,558,274	3,661	—	$107,146	—	—
1982	6,915	1,360	39,095	1,053	—	—	313,667	77,998	3,615,751	3,746	—	$123,219	—	—
1983	6,888	1,350	38,887	1,028	—	—	273,168	77,837	3,596,146	3,707	—	$136,315	—	—
1984	6,872	1,339	37,938	970	—	—	276,566	77,845	3,563,106	3,630	—	$144,114	—	—
1985	6,872	1,318	36,304	910	—	—	282,140	77,202	3,630,961	3,625	—	$153,327	—	—
1986	6,841	1,290	35,219	883	—	—	294,634	76,002	3,680,178	3,647	—	$165,194	—	—
1987	6,821	1,267	34,439	873	—	—	310,707	74,770	3,698,294	3,742	—	$178,662	—	—
1988	6,780	1,248	34,107	863	—	—	336,208	72,568	3,794,369	3,839	—	$196,704	—	—
1989	6,720	1,226	33,742	853	—	—	352,248	71,491	3,920,384	3,937	—	$214,886	—	—
1990	6,649	1,213	33,774	844	—	—	368,184	70,539	4,046,704	4,063	—	$234,870	—	—
1991	6,634	1,202	33,567	827	—	—	387,675	69,464	4,047,504	4,165	—	$258,508	—	—
1992	6,539	1,178	33,536	807	—	—	417,874	69,052	4,007,179	4,236	—	$282,531	—	—
1993	6,467	1,163	33,201	783	—	—	435,619	67,911	3,949,788	4,289	—	$301,538	—	—
1994	6,374	1,128	33,125	745	—	—	453,584	67,311	3,886,667	4,270	—	$310,834	—	—
1995	6,291	1,081	33,282	710	—	—	483,195	66,256	3,833,132	4,273	—	$320,252	—	—
1996	6,201	1,062	33,307	685	—	—	505,455	65,138	3,790,678	4,276	—	$330,531	—	—
1997	6,097	1,035	33,624	673	—	—	520,600	64,649	3,811,522	4,333	—	$342,334	—	—
1998	6,021	1,013	33,766	662	—	—	545,481	63,485	3,795,212	4,407	—	$355,450	—	—
1999	5,890	994	34,181	657	—	—	573,461	62,714	3,829,881	4,369	—	$372,933	—	—
2000	5,810	984	34,891	650	—	—	592,673	61,915	3,940,017	4,454	—	$395,391	—	—
2001	5,801	987	35,644	658	—	—	612,276	61,527	3,929,733	4,535	—	$426,849	—	—
2002	5,794	976	36,326	662	—	—	640,515	62,151	3,934,421	4,610	—	$462,222	—	—
2003	5,764	965	36,611	657	—	—	648,560	60,699	3,976,886	4,651	—	$498,104	—	—
2004	5,759	956	36,942	658	—	—	662,131	59,660	3,965,906	4,696	—	$533,853	—	—
2005	5,756	947	37,006	656	—	—	673,689	59,073	4,048,442	4,791	—	$570,534	—	—
2006	5,747	947	37,189	653	—	—	690,425	58,670	4,126,598	4,907	—	$607,355	—	—
2007	5,708	945	37,120	645	—	—	693,510	58,429	4,128,796	5,024	—	$641,124	—	—
2008	5,815	951	37,529	649	—	—	709,960	58,133	4,109,081	5,116	—	$690,074	—	—
2009	5,795	944	37,480	641	—	—	741,551	58,078	4,001,748	5,178	—	$726,671	—	—
2010	5,754	942	36,915	627	—	—	750,408	57,396	3,871,751	5,184	—	$750,602	—	—
2011	5,724	924	36,565	615	—	—	754,454	57,022	3,767,697	5,196	—	$773,547	—	—
2012	5,723	921	36,156	600	—	—	777,961	56,693	3,754,085	5,258	—	$829,665	—	—
2013	5,686	915	35,416	592	—	—	787,422	57,037	3,749,696	5,342	—	$859,419	—	—

Table

1

Historical Trends in Utilization, Personnel, and Finances for Selected Years from 1946 through 2013

Data are for all AHA-registered hospitals in the United States. Data are estimated for nonreporting hospitals with the exception of newborn and outpatient data before 1972. Personnel data exclude residents, interns, and students from 1952 on; personnel data include full-time personnel and full-time equivalents for part-time personnel from 1954 on. As a result of the AHA Annual Survey validation process, the New York state expense data from 1976 were revised after the 1977 edition was published. The revised figures are included below. In order to provide trend data on a consistent basis, the 1970 and 1971 psychiatric and long-term data have been slightly modified. The 1982 FTE figures have updated to provide the most accurate data possible.

Total nonfederal short-term general and other special

YEAR	HOSPITALS	BEDS (in thousands)	ADMISSIONS (in thousands)	AVERAGE DAILY CENSUS (in thousands)	ADJUSTED AVERAGE DAILY CENSUS (in thousands)	AVERAGE STAY (days)	OUTPATIENT VISITS (in thousands)	NEWBORNS		FTE PERSONNEL		TOTAL EXPENSES		
								Bassinets	Births	Number (in thousands)	Per 100 Adjusted Census	Amount (In Millions of dollars)	Adjusted per Inpatient Stay (dollars)	Adjusted per Inpatient Day (dollars)
1946	4,444	473	13,655	341	—	9.1	—	80,987	2,087,503	505	—	$1,169	—	—
1950	5,031	505	16,663	372	—	8.1	—	86,019	2,660,982	662	—	$2,120	—	—
1955	5,237	568	19,100	407	—	7.8	—	93,868	3,304,451	826	—	$3,434	—	—
1960	5,407	639	22,970	477	—	7.6	—	98,127	3,678,051	1,080	—	$5,617	—	—
1965	5,736	741	26,463	563	620	7.8	92,631	96,782	3,413,370	1,386	224	$9,147	$316.37	$40.56
1970	5,859	848	29,252	662	727	8.2	133,545	93,079	3,403,064	1,929	265	$19,560	$604.59	$73.73
1971	5,865	867	30,142	665	736	8.0	148,423	90,444	3,337,605	1,999	272	$22,400	$667.44	$83.43
1972	5,843	884	30,777	664	739	7.9	166,983	89,315	3,119,446	2,056	278	$25,549	$747.42	$94.61
1973	5,891	903	31,761	681	768	7.8	178,939	86,851	2,987,089	2,149	280	$28,496	$793.88	$101.78
1974	5,977	931	32,943	701	793	7.8	194,838	85,208	2,947,342	2,289	289	$32,751	$883.04	$113.21
1975	5,979	947	33,519	708	806	7.7	196,311	83,834	2,998,590	2,399	298	$39,110	$1,024.72	$133.08
1976	5,956	961	34,068	715	816	7.7	207,725	82,307	2,962,305	2,483	304	$45,402	$1,172.25	$152.24
1977	5,973	974	34,353	717	820	7.6	204,238	80,228	3,117,756	2,581	315	$51,832	$1,316.70	$173.25
1978	5,935	980	34,575	720	841	7.6	204,461	78,090	3,156,570	2,662	323	$58,348	$1,470.13	$193.81
1979	5,923	988	35,160	729	841	7.6	203,873	77,277	3,287,157	2,762	328	$66,184	$1,631.16	$215.75
1980	5,904	992	36,198	748	861	7.6	206,752	77,539	3,408,699	2,879	334	$76,970	$1,844.19	$244.44
1981	5,879	1,007	36,494	764	876	7.6	206,729	76,567	3,465,683	3,039	347	$90,739	$2,167.70	$283.94
1982	5,863	1,015	36,429	763	882	7.6	250,888	75,739	3,514,761	3,110	353	$105,094	$2,493.09	$326.68
1983	5,843	1,021	36,201	750	869	7.6	213,995	75,471	3,490,629	3,102	357	$116,632	$2,775.55	$368.01
1984	5,814	1,020	35,202	703	824	7.3	216,474	75,587	3,456,467	3,023	367	$123,550	$2,984.00	$409.85
1985	5,784	1,003	33,501	650	780	7.1	222,773	74,899	3,521,296	3,003	385	$130,700	$3,238.94	$459.57
1986	5,728	982	32,410	631	774	7.1	234,270	73,688	3,584,530	3,032	392	$140,907	$3,529.60	$499.19
1987	5,659	961	31,633	624	780	7.2	247,704	72,516	3,602,416	3,120	400	$152,909	$3,848.79	$536.96
1988	5,579	949	31,480	622	795	7.2	271,436	70,361	3,706,748	3,209	404	$168,941	$4,194.39	$581.08
1989	5,497	936	31,141	619	805	7.3	287,909	69,436	3,831,051	3,307	411	$185,204	$4,572.23	$630.59
1990	5,420	929	31,203	620	820	7.3	302,691	68,443	3,958,646	3,423	417	$203,927	$4,929.93	$681.52
1991	5,370	926	31,084	612	828	7.2	323,202	67,440	3,965,489	3,539	427	$225,230	$5,345.63	$745.37
1992	5,321	923	31,053	606	832	7.1	349,397	67,095	3,925,024	3,624	436	$248,318	$5,788.52	$815.99
1993	5,289	921	30,770	593	834	7.0	368,358	66,060	3,870,392	3,681	441	$266,382	$6,120.94	$874.98
1994	5,256	904	30,739	569	814	6.8	384,880	65,728	3,809,367	3,697	454	$276,148	$6,230.33	$929.65
1995	5,220	874	30,966	549	811	6.5	415,710	64,742	3,764,756	3,718	458	$286,073	$6,220.54	$966.79
1996	5,160	864	31,116	531	800	6.2	440,845	63,646	3,723,907	3,728	466	$293,920	$6,225.95	$1,005.45
1997	5,082	855	31,595	529	813	6.1	450,907	63,247	3,742,240	3,794	467	$306,088	$6,266.24	$1,031.68
1998	5,039	842	31,830	527	821	6.0	474,366	62,162	3,726,234	3,835	467	$319,035	$6,387.53	$1,064.93
1999	4,977	831	32,377	527	835	5.9	495,850	61,534	3,760,295	3,840	460	$335,405	$6,512.44	$1,101.47
2000	4,934	825	33,102	527	850	5.8	522,970	60,845	3,880,166	3,916	461	$356,757	$6,650.68	$1,147.99
2001	4,927	828	33,834	534	866	5.8	539,316	60,454	3,873,395	3,990	461	$383,911	$6,979.29	$1,216.04
2002	4,949	823	34,501	541	887	5.7	557,336	59,974	3,870,191	4,072	459	$416,791	$7,353.17	$1,288.63
2003	4,918	815	34,800	540	895	5.7	563,804	59,662	3,915,842	4,112	459	$450,403	$7,798.19	$1,378.78
2004	4,942	810	35,098	542	910	5.6	573,126	58,710	3,931,508	4,151	456	$481,517	$8,168.06	$1,449.90
2005	4,956	804	35,265	542	930	5.6	587,296	58,195	3,987,766	4,260	458	$516,172	$8,538.30	$1,521.58
2006	4,947	805	35,403	540	940	5.6	599,597	57,832	4,075,193	4,347	462	$552,276	$8,972.85	$1,610.76
2007	4,915	803	35,370	535	944	5.5	603,411	57,546	4,077,962	4,468	473	$583,550	$9,377.82	$1,694.38
2008	5,026	810	35,776	538	963	5.5	624,185	57,301	4,073,724	4,552	473	$626,823	$9,789.69	$1,780.45
2009	5,023	807	35,603	529	973	5.4	643,420	57,302	3,960,432	4,594	472	$657,242	$10,042.56	$1,851.44
2010	4,995	806	35,160	520	974	5.4	651,617	56,610	3,818,399	4,603	473	$678,254	$10,316.07	$1,908.59
2011	4,983	799	34,852	514	983	5.4	657,071	56,290	3,730,342	4,654	473	$702,822	$10,542.09	$1,959.69
2012	5,010	802	34,438	508	992	5.4	675,223	55,987	3,715,479	4,732	477	$757,213	$11,222.23	$2,089.07
2013	4,986	797	33,625	501	963	5.4	678,203	56,342	3,699,411	4,788	497	$782,360	$11,653.75	$2,155.63

Table 1 (Continued)

CLASSIFICATION	YEAR	HOSPITALS	BEDS (in thousands)	ADMISSIONS (in thousands)	AVERAGE DAILY CENSUS (in thousands)	ADJUSTED AVERAGE DAILY CENSUS (in thousands)	AVERAGE LENGTH OF STAY (days)	OUTPATIENT VISITS (in thousands)	NEWBORNS Bassinets	NEWBORNS Births	FTE PERSONNEL Number (in thousands)	FTE PERSONNEL Per 100 Adjusted Census	EXPENSES Amount (In Millions of dollars)	EXPENSES Adjusted per Inpatient Stay (dollars)	EXPENSES Adjusted per Inpatient Day (dollars)
Total community hospitals	1975	5,875	942	33,435	706	798	7.7	190,672	83,829	2,998,552	2,392	300	$38,962	$1,030.34	$133.81
	1976	5,857	956	33,979	713	810	7.7	201,247	82,296	2,962,216	2,475	306	$45,240	$1,176.25	$152.76
	1979	5,842	984	35,099	727	833	7.6	198,778	77,266	3,287,012	2,756	331	$66,004	$1,641.67	$217.34
	1980	5,830	988	36,143	747	857	7.6	202,310	77,522	3,408,482	2,873	335	$76,851	$1,851.04	$245.12
	1981	5,813	1,003	36,438	763	873	7.6	202,768	76,561	3,465,401	3,033	347	$90,572	$2,171.20	$284.33
	1982	5,801	1,012	36,379	762	878	7.6	248,124	75,733	3,514,457	3,103	353	$104,876	$2,500.52	$327.37
	1983	5,783	1,018	36,152	749	864	7.6	210,044	75,465	3,490,254	3,096	358	$116,438	$2,789.18	$369.49
	1984	5,759	1,017	35,155	702	820	7.3	211,961	75,581	3,456,308	3,017	368	$123,336	$2,995.38	$411.10
	1985	5,732	1,001	33,449	649	777	7.1	218,716	74,893	3,521,135	2,997	386	$130,499	$3,244.74	$460.19
	1986	5,678	978	32,379	629	770	7.1	231,912	73,682	3,584,408	3,025	393	$140,654	$3,532.51	$500.81
	1987	5,611	958	31,601	622	776	7.2	245,524	72,510	3,602,296	3,114	401	$152,585	$3,850.16	$538.96
	1988	5,533	947	31,453	620	787	7.2	269,129	70,325	3,706,402	3,205	407	$168,722	$4,206.73	$586.33
	1989	5,455	933	31,116	618	796	7.2	285,712	69,405	3,830,615	3,303	415	$184,898	$4,587.87	$636.96
	1990	5,384	927	31,181	619	813	7.2	301,329	68,412	3,958,263	3,420	421	$203,693	$4,946.68	$686.83
	1991	5,342	924	31,064	611	820	7.2	322,048	67,434	3,965,396	3,535	431	$225,023	$5,359.56	$752.10
	1992	5,292	921	31,034	604	827	7.1	348,522	67,089	3,924,944	3,620	437	$248,095	$5,794.43	$819.83
	1993	5,261	919	30,748	592	828	7.0	366,885	66,054	3,870,376	3,677	444	$266,089	$6,132.06	$880.52
	1994	5,229	902	30,718	568	812	6.7	382,924	65,722	3,809,367	3,692	455	$275,779	$6,229.83	$930.71
	1995	5,194	873	30,945	548	809	6.5	414,345	64,736	3,764,698	3,714	459	$285,588	$6,215.51	$967.69
	1996	5,134	862	31,099	531	799	6.2	439,863	63,640	3,723,871	3,725	466	$293,755	$6,224.94	$1,006.14
	1997	5,057	853	31,577	528	811	6.1	450,140	63,241	3,742,191	3,790	467	$305,763	$6,261.93	$1,032.70
	1998	5,015	840	31,812	525	819	6.0	474,193	62,156	3,726,233	3,831	468	$318,834	$6,385.99	$1,066.96
	1999	4,956	830	32,359	526	833	5.9	495,346	61,528	3,760,295	3,838	461	$335,246	$6,511.72	$1,102.61
	2000	4,915	824	33,089	526	849	5.8	521,404	60,839	3,880,166	3,911	461	$356,564	$6,648.82	$1,149.40
	2001	4,908	826	33,814	533	865	5.7	538,480	60,448	3,873,395	3,987	461	$383,735	$6,979.53	$1,217.27
	2002	4,927	821	34,478	540	886	5.7	556,404	59,974	3,870,191	4,069	459	$416,591	$7,354.60	$1,289.87
	2003	4,895	813	34,783	539	894	5.7	563,186	59,662	3,915,842	4,109	460	$450,124	$7,796.41	$1,379.48
	2004	4,919	808	35,086	541	909	5.6	571,569	58,710	3,931,508	4,148	456	$481,247	$8,165.55	$1,450.35
	2005	4,936	802	35,239	540	929	5.6	584,429	58,195	3,987,766	4,257	458	$515,740	$8,534.90	$1,522.42
	2006	4,927	803	35,378	538	939	5.6	599,553	57,832	4,075,193	4,343	463	$551,835	$8,970.31	$1,612.23
	2007	4,897	801	35,346	533	943	5.5	603,300	57,546	4,077,962	4,465	474	$583,252	$9,377.17	$1,696.10
	2008	5,010	808	35,761	536	962	5.5	624,098	57,301	4,073,724	4,550	473	$626,577	$9,788.25	$1,782.28
	2009	5,008	806	35,527	528	970	5.4	641,953	57,282	3,959,605	4,585	472	$656,156	$10,045.15	$1,852.59
	2010	4,985	805	35,149	520	973	5.4	651,424	56,610	3,818,399	4,600	473	$677,968	$10,313.44	$1,909.64
	2011	4,973	797	34,843	513	982	5.4	656,079	56,290	3,730,342	4,650	473	$702,091	$10,532.52	$1,959.58
	2012	4,999	801	34,422	507	991	5.4	674,971	55,987	3,715,479	4,731	477	$756,917	$11,220.70	$2,090.01
	2013	4,974	796	33,609	500	962	5.4	677,951	56,342	3,699,411	4,786	497	$782,035	$11,650.90	$2,156.94

Table 1 (Continued)

Nongovernment not-for-profit community hospitals

YEAR	HOSPITALS	BEDS (in thousands)	ADMISSIONS (in thousands)	AVERAGE DAILY CENSUS (in thousands)	ADJUSTED AVERAGE DAILY CENSUS (in thousands)	AVERAGE LENGTH OF STAY (days)	OUTPATIENT VISITS (in thousands)	NEWBORNS Bassinets	NEWBORNS Births	FTE PERSONNEL Number (in thousands)	FTE PERSONNEL Per 100 Adjusted Census	EXPENSES Amount (in Millions of dollars)	EXPENSES Adjusted per Inpatient Stay (dollars)	EXPENSES Adjusted per Inpatient Day (dollars)
1975	3,339	658	23,722	510	574	7.8	131,435	57,496	2,131,057	1,712	298	$27,938	$1,040.21	$133.36
1976	3,345	670	24,082	517	586	7.9	140,914	56,442	2,100,917	1,791	306	$32,764	$1,208.23	$152.94
1979	3,330	690	24,874	528	603	7.7	139,565	52,859	2,308,548	1,999	332	$47,937	$1,684.40	$218.06
1980	3,322	692	25,566	542	621	7.7	142,156	52,659	2,389,478	2,086	336	$55,780	$1,901.64	$245.74
1981	3,340	706	25,945	555	636	7.8	143,380	52,302	2,455,033	2,213	399	$66,267	$2,225.17	$285.64
1982	3,338	712	25,898	553	637	7.8	176,245	51,566	2,483,345	2,265	355	$76,806	$2,572.93	$330.41
1983	3,347	718	25,827	544	629	7.7	150,839	51,649	2,465,604	2,270	362	$85,637	$2,868.80	$373.78
1984	3,351	716	25,236	512	598	7.4	153,281	51,491	2,446,540	2,222	372	$90,814	$3,072.51	$415.04
1985	3,349	707	24,179	476	569	7.2	158,953	51,424	2,507,288	2,216	389	$96,150	$3,307.41	$462.69
1986	3,323	689	23,483	460	563	7.2	167,633	50,885	2,547,170	2,241	398	$103,524	$3,589.64	$503.64
1987	3,274	673	22,937	455	566	7.2	177,413	50,133	2,557,294	2,298	406	$112,325	$3,914.23	$543.67
1988	3,242	668	22,939	456	577	7.3	195,363	48,828	2,653,794	2,373	412	$124,703	$4,272.95	$591.13
1989	3,220	661	22,792	455	584	7.3	209,191	48,305	2,751,426	2,454	420	$136,889	$4,649.22	$642.45
1990	3,191	657	22,878	455	596	7.3	221,073	47,441	2,833,204	2,533	424	$150,673	$5,001.24	$692.36
1991	3,175	656	22,964	451	603	7.2	238,204	47,229	2,845,995	2,624	435	$166,806	$5,393.30	$758.21
1992	3,173	656	23,056	445	606	7.1	257,887	47,185	2,846,386	2,692	443	$183,793	$5,808.80	$828.44
1993	3,154	651	22,749	432	602	6.9	270,138	46,214	2,802,164	2,711	451	$197,187	$6,177.69	$897.70
1994	3,139	637	22,704	413	589	6.6	282,653	46,381	2,792,116	2,719	462	$204,219	$6,256.72	$950.31
1995	3,092	610	22,557	393	578	6.4	303,851	45,198	2,725,641	2,702	468	$209,614	$6,279.17	$994.39
1996	3,045	598	22,542	379	567	6.1	320,746	44,650	2,683,750	2,711	478	$215,950	$6,344.05	$1,042.04
1997	3,000	591	22,905	376	575	6.0	330,215	44,484	2,698,086	2,765	481	$225,287	$6,392.74	$1,074.26
1998	3,026	588	23,282	377	587	5.9	352,114	44,087	2,715,958	2,834	483	$237,978	$6,525.68	$1,110.50
1999	3,012	587	23,871	381	605	5.8	370,784	44,172	2,746,453	2,862	473	$251,534	$6,607.51	$1,139.89
2000	3,003	583	24,452	382	618	5.7	393,168	43,655	2,833,615	2,919	472	$267,051	$6,717.48	$1,182.32
2001	2,998	585	24,983	385	628	5.6	404,901	43,640	2,829,691	2,971	473	$287,250	$7,051.76	$1,255.25
2002	3,025	582	25,425	391	646	5.6	416,910	43,241	2,820,159	3,039	471	$312,726	$7,457.84	$1,328.81
2003	2,984	575	25,668	389	647	5.5	424,215	42,965	2,854,764	3,059	473	$337,696	$7,904.93	$1,429.62
2004	2,967	568	25,757	388	655	5.5	430,262	41,968	2,844,617	3,077	470	$359,414	$8,266.64	$1,501.09
2005	2,958	561	25,881	388	667	5.5	441,653	41,585	2,876,677	3,155	473	$385,993	$8,670.83	$1,585.34
2006	2,919	559	25,798	385	671	5.4	453,501	40,888	2,905,275	3,207	478	$412,868	$9,189.58	$1,685.62
2007	2,913	554	25,752	380	673	5.4	455,825	40,681	2,907,002	3,286	488	$436,319	$9,592.93	$1,776.06
2008	2,923	557	25,899	380	683	5.4	469,804	40,567	2,901,854	3,340	489	$468,080	$10,080.50	$1,875.78
2009	2,918	556	25,783	375	690	5.3	485,935	40,467	2,822,527	3,369	488	$492,853	$10,379.09	$1,956.71
2010	2,904	556	25,532	368	691	5.3	494,178	39,946	2,750,163	3,388	490	$510,744	$10,651.81	$2,025.05
2011	2,903	548	25,185	362	694	5.2	496,643	39,651	2,692,577	3,427	494	$528,303	$10,932.55	$2,088.05
2012	2,894	545	24,751	354	697	5.2	512,237	39,778	2,684,600	3,477	499	$563,960	$11,563.17	$2,214.26
2013	2,904	544	24,319	350	683	5.3	516,162	40,180	2,687,441	3,500	513	$585,470	$12,000.35	$2,288.77

Table 1 (Continued)

Investor-owned (for-profit) community hospitals

CLASSIFICATION / YEAR	HOSPITALS	BEDS (in thousands)	ADMISSIONS (in thousands)	AVERAGE DAILY CENSUS (in thousands)	ADJUSTED AVERAGE DAILY CENSUS (in thousands)	AVERAGE LENGTH OF STAY (days)	OUTPATIENT VISITS (in thousands)	NEWBORNS Bassinets	NEWBORNS Births	FTE PERSONNEL Number (in thousands)	FTE PERSONNEL Per 100 Adjusted Census	EXPENSES Amount (In Millions of dollars)	EXPENSES Adjusted per Inpatient Stay (dollars)	EXPENSES Adjusted per Inpatient Day (dollars)
1975	775	73	2,646	48	53	6.6	7,713	4,062	141,392	139	263	$2,561	$876.48	$132.80
1976	752	76	2,734	50	54	6.6	8,048	4,044	144,751	147	272	$3,085	$1,031.91	$156.35
1979	727	83	2,963	53	59	6.6	9,289	4,110	174,843	174	300	$4,820	$1,476.42	$225.87
1980	730	87	3,165	57	62	6.5	9,696	4,439	199,722	189	304	$5,847	$1,675.85	$257.12
1981	729	88	3,239	58	63	6.5	9,961	4,523	207,405	203	322	$6,856	$1,952.56	$299.02
1982	748	91	3,316	60	66	6.6	13,193	4,736	219,675	212	320	$8,177	$2,224.75	$340.03
1983	757	94	3,299	59	66	6.5	10,389	5,039	228,883	213	323	$9,208	$2,517.53	$385.42
1984	786	100	3,314	57	64	6.3	11,090	5,807	242,088	214	335	$10,251	$2,748.51	$438.30
1985	805	104	3,242	54	63	6.1	12,378	6,117	266,839	221	350	$11,486	$3,033.06	$500.48
1986	834	107	3,231	54	65	6.1	14,896	6,305	291,112	229	354	$12,987	$3,341.79	$552.40
1987	828	106	3,157	54	66	6.2	16,566	6,391	306,492	242	367	$14,067	$3,617.19	$585.01
1988	790	104	3,090	53	66	6.2	17,926	6,254	308,828	249	379	$15,545	$4,022.77	$649.33
1989	769	102	3,071	53	67	6.3	19,341	6,354	325,711	261	390	$17,240	$4,406.20	$707.90
1990	749	101	3,066	54	69	6.4	20,110	6,261	340,555	273	396	$18,822	$4,727.27	$751.55
1991	738	100	3,016	52	69	6.3	21,174	6,358	359,115	281	409	$20,516	$5,133.53	$820.19
1992	723	99	2,969	51	69	6.3	22,900	6,519	357,776	285	412	$22,496	$5,548.24	$888.73
1993	717	99	2,946	51	69	6.2	24,936	6,395	363,358	289	417	$23,077	$5,643.21	$914.39
1994	719	101	3,035	50	70	6.1	26,443	6,329	354,477	302	434	$23,445	$5,528.91	$923.90
1995	752	106	3,428	55	77	5.8	31,940	7,164	408,339	343	443	$26,653	$5,425.20	$946.99
1996	759	109	3,684	56	82	5.6	37,347	7,441	444,697	359	437	$28,385	$5,207.44	$945.49
1997	797	115	3,953	60	89	5.5	40,919	8,026	465,919	385	433	$31,179	$5,218.69	$961.96
1998	771	113	3,971	60	90	5.5	42,072	7,895	466,025	383	425	$31,732	$5,262.44	$968.00
1999	747	107	3,905	58	86	5.5	39,896	7,486	467,585	362	422	$31,179	$5,350.07	$999.03
2000	749	110	4,141	61	90	5.4	43,378	7,792	503,497	378	418	$34,969	$5,642.18	$1,057.32
2001	754	109	4,197	63	92	5.4	44,706	7,413	494,669	379	413	$37,348	$5,971.81	$1,121.31
2002	766	108	4,365	64	93	5.3	45,215	7,467	496,988	380	407	$40,082	$6,161.44	$1,180.83
2003	790	110	4,481	65	95	5.3	44,246	7,491	515,693	391	411	$43,953	$6,589.91	$1,264.50
2004	835	113	4,599	68	100	5.4	44,962	7,763	534,503	406	406	$48,971	$7,139.13	$1,362.42
2005	868	114	4,618	68	101	5.3	46,016	7,714	546,307	421	418	$51,833	$7,351.96	$1,412.74
2006	890	115	4,735	68	103	5.2	44,237	8,012	574,113	423	413	$55,030	$7,422.08	$1,471.53
2007	873	116	4,626	66	101	5.2	43,943	7,760	555,670	432	429	$56,405	$7,823.44	$1,535.98
2008	982	121	4,839	70	109	5.3	44,897	7,791	562,711	450	414	$61,762	$7,984.62	$1,555.55
2009	998	122	4,887	70	112	5.3	47,281	7,965	553,233	464	414	$64,367	$8,037.18	$1,573.64
2010	1,013	125	4,925	71	113	5.3	48,201	7,965	525,427	474	420	$67,168	$8,336.16	$1,628.90
2011	1,025	128	5,060	73	119	5.3	50,013	8,137	508,330	485	409	$70,340	$8,262.74	$1,627.65
2012	1,068	135	5,224	77	124	5.3	53,854	8,192	530,941	515	414	$79,114	$8,860.94	$1,746.85
2013	1,060	135	5,052	77	118	5.5	53,191	8,228	522,864	553	469	$81,552	$9,296.42	$1,791.20

Table 1 (Continued)

CLASSIFICATION: State and local government community hospitals

YEAR	HOSPITALS	BEDS (in thousands)	ADMISSIONS (in thousands)	AVERAGE DAILY CENSUS (in thousands)	ADJUSTED AVERAGE DAILY CENSUS (in thousands)	AVERAGE LENGTH OF STAY (days)	OUTPATIENT VISITS (in thousands)	NEWBORNS Bassinets	NEWBORNS Births	FTE PERSONNEL Number (in thousands)	FTE PERSONNEL Per 100 Adjusted Census	EXPENSES Amount (in Millions of dollars)	EXPENSES Adjusted per Inpatient Stay (dollars)	EXPENSES Adjusted per Inpatient Day (dollars)
1975	1,761	210	7,067	148	171	7.6	51,525	22,271	726,103	540	316	$8,463	$1,030.86	$135.64
1976	1,760	210	7,163	146	170	7.5	52,286	21,810	716,548	537	315	$9,391	$1,132.50	$151.00
1979	1,785	211	7,262	146	171	7.4	49,924	20,297	803,621	583	341	$13,247	$1,561.04	$211.89
1980	1,778	209	7,413	149	174	7.3	50,459	20,424	819,282	598	343	$15,204	$1,750.13	$238.63
1981	1,744	210	7,255	150	174	7.6	49,427	19,736	802,963	618	354	$17,449	$2,071.57	$274.25
1982	1,715	210	7,165	149	175	7.6	58,685	19,431	811,437	627	320	$19,893	$2,364.09	$311.56
1983	1,679	207	7,025	145	170	7.6	48,816	18,777	795,767	613	360	$21,593	$2,621.28	$347.56
1984	1,622	201	6,606	133	158	7.3	47,590	18,283	767,680	581	368	$22,271	$2,823.13	$385.17
1985	1,578	189	6,028	119	145	7.2	47,386	17,352	747,008	561	387	$22,863	$3,106.14	$432.84
1986	1,521	182	5,665	114	142	7.4	49,383	16,492	746,126	555	391	$24,143	$3,404.69	$466.17
1987	1,509	180	5,507	113	144	7.5	51,544	15,986	738,510	573	399	$26,192	$3,717.77	$499.33
1988	1,501	175	5,424	112	145	7.6	55,840	15,243	743,780	583	403	$28,474	$4,033.67	$538.63
1989	1,466	170	5,253	110	145	7.7	57,179	14,746	753,478	589	406	$30,769	$4,430.12	$582.15
1990	1,444	169	5,236	111	148	7.7	60,146	14,710	784,504	614	415	$34,198	$4,837.76	$634.45
1991	1,429	168	5,084	108	148	7.8	62,670	13,847	760,286	630	424	$37,701	$5,339.75	$695.89
1992	1,396	166	5,008	108	152	7.9	67,734	13,385	720,782	643	424	$41,806	$5,870.76	$753.92
1993	1,390	169	5,054	109	157	7.8	71,811	13,445	704,854	676	430	$45,825	$6,205.52	$799.73
1994	1,371	164	4,979	104	154	7.6	73,828	13,012	662,774	672	438	$48,115	$6,513.39	$858.62
1995	1,350	157	4,961	100	154	7.4	78,554	12,374	630,718	670	435	$49,322	$6,445.18	$877.85
1996	1,330	155	4,873	96	150	7.2	81,770	11,549	595,424	654	437	$49,420	$6,418.65	$903.41
1997	1,260	148	4,720	92	148	7.1	79,007	10,731	578,186	640	433	$49,298	$6,475.07	$913.62
1998	1,218	139	4,559	87	142	7.0	80,008	10,174	544,250	614	433	$49,123	$6,612.23	$949.36
1999	1,197	136	4,583	86	143	6.9	84,667	9,870	546,257	614	430	$52,534	$6,923.35	$1,006.91
2000	1,163	131	4,496	83	140	6.7	84,858	9,392	543,054	614	438	$54,544	$7,106.05	$1,063.75
2001	1,156	132	4,634	85	145	6.7	88,873	9,395	549,035	637	438	$59,137	$7,400.01	$1,113.79
2002	1,136	130	4,688	84	147	6.6	94,280	9,266	553,044	651	442	$63,783	$7,772.93	$1,188.12
2003	1,121	129	4,634	84	152	6.6	94,725	9,206	545,385	658	434	$68,475	$8,205.10	$1,237.64
2004	1,117	128	4,730	85	154	6.5	96,345	8,979	552,388	666	431	$72,861	$8,473.18	$1,291.06
2005	1,110	128	4,740	85	161	6.5	96,760	8,896	564,782	681	424	$77,914	$8,793.26	$1,329.64
2006	1,119	128	4,848	86	165	6.5	101,845	8,932	595,805	713	433	$83,974	$9,147.40	$1,400.09
2007	1,111	131	4,967	87	169	6.4	103,532	9,105	615,290	747	443	$90,528	$9,523.22	$1,472.26
2008	1,105	131	5,023	86	170	6.3	109,398	8,943	609,159	760	446	$96,735	$9,826.94	$1,552.32
2009	1,092	127	4,857	83	168	6.2	108,738	8,850	583,845	751	447	$98,937	$10,067.96	$1,611.31
2010	1,068	125	4,693	80	169	6.2	109,045	8,699	542,809	738	437	$100,056	$10,283.35	$1,624.93
2011	1,045	121	4,598	78	170	6.2	109,423	8,502	529,435	738	434	$103,448	$10,531.65	$1,666.96
2012	1,037	120	4,447	77	170	6.3	108,880	8,017	499,938	739	435	$113,843	$11,668.15	$1,831.00
2013	1,010	117	4,238	74	162	6.3	108,599	7,934	489,106	734	453	$115,013	$12,028.02	$1,878.21

Table **2**

2013 U.S. Registered Hospitals: Utilization, Personnel, and Finances

Excludes U.S.-Associated Areas, Puerto Rico, and nonregistered hospitals.

CLASSIFICATION	HOSPITALS	BEDS	ADMISSIONS	INPATIENT DAYS	ADJUSTED PATIENT DAYS	AVERAGE DAILY CENSUS	ADJUSTED AVERAGE DAILY CENSUS	AVERAGE STAY (days)	SURGICAL OPERATIONS	OUTPATIENT VISITS Emergency	OUTPATIENT VISITS Total	NEWBORNS Bassinets	NEWBORNS Births
UNITED STATES	5,686	914,513	35,416,020	215,699,068	—	591,524	—	—	27,270,278	137,474,560	787,422,082	57,037	3,749,696
6-24 Beds	514	8,503	221,431	1,019,968	—	2,801	—	—	339,558	2,181,568	15,977,894	499	18,796
25-49	1,292	41,860	1,178,949	6,881,181	—	18,883	—	—	1,451,278	9,191,224	58,962,022	3,049	130,192
50-99	1,140	81,175	2,346,082	17,042,539	—	46,741	—	—	2,199,427	12,452,536	72,207,661	5,249	231,576
100-199	1,186	170,435	6,310,094	37,800,620	—	103,757	—	—	5,026,111	27,914,333	148,183,324	11,750	666,909
200-299	667	163,722	6,549,735	38,305,773	—	105,017	—	—	4,733,501	25,805,687	136,033,327	10,623	683,788
300-399	372	128,721	5,487,436	31,019,854	—	84,984	—	—	3,807,921	19,142,804	99,917,382	8,437	607,340
400-499	200	88,873	3,820,756	22,061,490	—	60,440	—	—	2,674,182	12,431,127	75,542,684	5,672	417,270
500 or more	315	231,224	9,501,537	61,567,643	—	168,901	—	—	7,038,300	28,355,281	180,597,788	11,758	993,825
Psychiatric	416	70,980	823,168	21,933,200	—	60,064	—	—	7,573	138,210	11,854,047	0	0
Hospitals	410	68,594	823,058	21,068,976	—	57,726	—	—	7,573	138,210	11,854,047	0	0
Inst. for Intellectual Disabilities	6	2,386	110	864,224	—	2,338	—	—	0	0	0	0	0
General	4,653	792,706	33,772,916	181,600,526	—	498,074	—	—	26,747,198	136,899,273	758,562,882	56,276	3,698,235
Hospitals	4,638	790,807	33,754,839	181,061,086	—	496,594	—	—	26,745,676	136,871,676	757,924,893	56,276	3,698,235
Hospital units of institutions	15	1,899	18,077	539,440	—	1,480	—	—	1,522	27,597	637,989	0	0
TB and other respiratory diseases	1	40	69	13,379	—	37	—	193.9	0	0	793	0	0
Obstetrics and gynecology	9	1,565	76,231	342,867	—	939	—	—	58,028	91,528	888,427	612	47,364
Eye, ear, nose and throat	4	137	2,252	7,407	—	20	—	—	75,768	35,815	798,499	0	0
Rehabilitation	202	15,661	274,121	3,965,869	—	10,868	—	—	11,902	11,966	6,756,125	0	0
Orthopedic	24	1,128	49,327	174,602	—	480	—	—	110,858	4,283	904,420	0	0
Chronic Disease	5	588	2,154	147,246	—	402	—	—	32	43,327	72,359	0	0
Surgical	10	382	12,768	64,623	—	178	—	—	22,599	0	199,116	0	0
Cancer	10	2,089	87,514	620,780	—	1,701	—	—	80,702	26,488	4,185,333	0	0
Heart	8	537	25,503	94,869	—	259	—	—	16,000	18,435	129,101	0	0
Acute long-term care hospital	314	24,907	229,854	5,788,878	—	15,916	—	—	90,365	57,840	1,358,595	19	818
All other	30	3,793	60,143	944,822	—	2,586	—	—	49,253	147,395	1,712,385	130	3,279
Federal	213	38,747	949,192	9,125,643	—	25,006	—	—	688,309	3,688,456	98,675,717	693	50,281
Psychiatric	10	2,357	17,038	672,950	—	1,844	—	—	952	403	3,034,205	0	0
General and other special	203	36,390	932,154	8,452,693	—	23,162	—	—	687,357	3,688,053	95,641,512	693	50,281
Nonfederal	5,473	875,766	34,466,828	206,573,425	—	566,518	—	—	26,581,969	133,786,104	688,746,365	56,344	3,699,415
Psychiatric	406	68,623	806,130	21,260,250	—	58,220	—	—	6,621	137,807	8,819,842	0	0
Hospitals	400	66,237	806,020	20,396,026	—	55,882	—	—	6,621	137,807	8,819,842	0	0
Inst. for Intellectual Disabilities	6	2,386	110	864,224	—	2,338	—	—	0	0	0	0	0
TB and other respiratory diseases	1	40	69	13,379	13,379	37	37	193.9	0	0	793	0	0
Long-term general and other special	80	10,121	35,731	2,563,411	2,892,098	7,034	7,868	71.7	9,311	30,627	1,722,925	2	4
Short-term general and other special	4,986	796,982	33,624,898	182,736,385	362,938,083	501,227	963,272	5.4	26,566,037	133,617,670	678,202,805	56,342	3,699,411
Hospital units of institutions	12	1,379	15,815	366,196	371,807	1,005	1,005	23.2	0	0	251,685	0	0
Community Hospitals	4,974	795,603	33,609,083	182,370,189	362,566,276	500,222	962,267	5.4	26,566,037	133,611,670	677,951,120	56,342	3,699,411
6-24 Beds	469	7,763	189,339	862,961	4,155,707	2,370	10,847	4.6	322,743	1,955,889	10,888,116	425	15,322
25-49	1,186	38,039	1,087,215	5,927,960	19,700,278	16,258	51,135	5.5	1,377,846	8,584,767	47,453,135	2,893	118,178
50-99	959	67,892	2,021,449	13,639,948	34,739,459	37,420	90,558	6.7	2,006,309	11,796,586	58,123,057	5,026	224,180
100-199	995	143,760	5,754,158	30,164,685	65,848,762	82,833	174,288	5.2	4,892,270	27,201,787	123,562,108	11,655	654,405
200-299	571	140,113	6,156,487	31,466,013	61,029,205	86,275	159,513	5.1	4,622,449	24,975,730	112,921,427	10,476	668,891
300-399	334	115,511	5,343,652	27,347,329	49,651,400	74,922	132,874	5.1	3,739,006	18,931,461	89,746,969	8,437	607,340
400-499	183	81,148	3,750,238	20,029,447	36,526,485	54,873	97,745	5.3	2,645,695	12,285,620	71,358,951	5,672	417,270
500 or more	277	201,377	9,306,545	52,931,846	90,914,980	145,271	245,307	5.7	6,959,719	27,879,830	163,897,357	11,758	993,825
Nongovernment not-for-profit	2,904	543,929	24,319,095	127,980,128	255,801,349	350,922	682,543	5.3	19,382,530	94,733,087	516,162,065	40,180	2,687,441
Investor-owned (for profit)	1,060	134,643	5,051,975	27,584,960	45,529,338	75,653	117,722	5.5	3,839,478	19,648,695	53,190,548	8,228	522,864
State and Local Government	1,010	117,031	4,238,013	26,805,101	61,235,589	73,647	162,002	6.3	3,344,029	19,229,888	108,598,507	7,934	489,106

Table 2 (Continued)

CLASSIFICATION	FULL-TIME EQUIVALENT PERSONNEL					FULL-TIME EQUIVALENT TRAINEES			EXPENSES — LABOR				EXPENSES	TOTAL	
	Physicians and Dentists	Registered Nurses	Licensed Practical Nurses	Other Salaried Personnel	Total Personnel	Medical and Dental Residents	Other Trainees	Total Trainees	Payroll (in thousands)	Employee Benefits (in thousands)	Total (in thousands)	Percent of Total	Amount (in thousands)	Adjusted per Admission	Adjusted per Inpatient Day
UNITED STATES	154,324	1,470,366	107,128	3,609,972	5,341,790	115,496	13,392	128,888	$340,534,045	$94,494,229	$435,028,273	50.6	$859,419,233	—	—
6-24 Beds	2,172	14,351	3,926	55,500	75,949	40	80	120	$3,908,836	$1,116,710	$5,025,546	52.9	$9,508,781	—	—
25-49	8,357	61,606	10,337	228,153	308,453	812	741	1,553	$15,382,727	$4,155,775	$19,538,502	52.0	$37,564,549	—	—
50-99	10,376	98,986	12,806	298,187	420,355	1,239	541	1,780	$23,205,213	$6,206,516	$29,411,729	52.5	$55,970,396	—	—
100-199	21,251	238,062	19,664	589,775	868,752	7,221	1,832	9,053	$53,739,606	$14,809,870	$68,549,475	50.8	$134,970,309	—	—
200-299	24,267	247,689	23,102	593,652	888,710	11,293	1,863	13,156	$57,403,243	$15,473,579	$72,876,823	50.4	$144,553,862	—	—
300-399	17,799	209,777	11,844	471,956	711,376	13,098	1,187	14,285	$47,426,115	$13,602,913	$61,029,028	50.2	$121,576,581	—	—
400-499	14,561	158,641	7,527	352,547	533,276	14,754	746	15,500	$36,528,338	$10,062,465	$46,590,802	50.4	$92,458,297	—	—
500 or more	55,541	441,254	17,922	1,020,204	1,534,921	67,039	6,402	73,441	$102,939,968	$29,066,401	$132,006,369	50.2	$262,816,458	—	—
Psychiatric	4,254	27,097	6,607	144,986	182,944	355	590	945	$9,565,921	$3,147,054	$12,712,975	71.9	$17,691,933	—	—
Hospitals	4,233	26,906	6,297	139,436	176,872	355	501	856	$9,314,642	$3,027,247	$12,341,889	71.6	$17,248,289	—	—
Inst. for Intellectual Disabilities	21	191	310	5,550	6,072	0	89	89	$251,279	$119,808	$371,086	83.6	$443,643	—	—
General	144,375	1,392,420	93,997	3,262,511	4,893,303	113,595	11,630	125,225	$317,352,843	$87,759,984	$405,112,828	50.1	$809,212,004	—	—
Hospitals	144,166	1,392,076	93,666	3,258,811	4,888,719	113,593	11,625	125,218	$317,103,487	$87,680,673	$404,784,160	50.1	$808,647,702	—	—
TB and other respiratory diseases	209	344	331	3,700	4,584	2	5	7	$249,357	$79,312	$328,668	58.2	$564,302	—	—
Hospital units of institutions	0	23	19	120	162	0	0	0	$6,330	$2,521	$8,850	60.9	$14,539	—	—
Obstetrics and gynecology	157	3,147	43	4,979	8,326	57	0	57	$602,129	$161,907	$764,036	49.9	$1,532,607	—	—
Eye, ear, nose and throat	216	402	16	2,601	3,235	86	61	147	$166,961	$54,707	$221,668	44.9	$493,749	—	—
Rehabilitation	662	11,652	1,826	44,147	58,287	191	39	230	$3,073,991	$732,949	$3,806,939	58.9	$6,464,154	—	—
Orthopedic	491	2,317	130	7,124	10,062	56	8	64	$831,690	$267,429	$1,099,119	52.0	$2,112,615	—	—
Chronic Disease	47	228	32	1,133	1,440	10	12	22	$71,033	$29,281	$100,313	65.4	$153,351	—	—
Surgical	18	554	19	1,160	1,751	0	0	0	$94,517	$21,548	$116,064	34.4	$337,068	—	—
Cancer	2,932	9,264	164	33,942	46,302	751	922	1,673	$3,669,067	$1,074,736	$4,743,803	50.5	$9,387,349	—	—
Heart	17	912	21	1,546	2,496	1	6	7	$159,875	$40,999	$200,874	39.2	$512,263	—	—
Acute long-term care hospital	461	18,262	3,890	92,948	115,561	168	2	170	$3,719,204	$859,051	$4,578,254	52.2	$8,777,903	—	—
All other	694	4,088	364	12,776	17,922	226	122	348	$1,220,486	$342,066	$1,562,551	57.2	$2,729,698	—	—
Federal	27,989	74,163	21,947	234,069	358,168	8,102	3,285	11,387	$26,574,675	$7,554,447	$34,129,121	58.9	$57,905,879	—	—
Psychiatric	531	1,815	747	9,008	12,101	12	95	107	$847,851	$251,074	$1,098,925	68.6	$1,601,937	—	—
General and other special	27,458	72,348	21,200	225,061	346,067	8,090	3,190	11,280	$25,726,824	$7,303,373	$33,030,197	58.7	$56,303,941	—	—
Nonfederal	126,335	1,396,203	85,181	3,375,903	4,983,622	107,394	10,107	117,501	$313,959,370	$86,939,782	$400,899,152	50.0	$801,513,354	—	—
Psychiatric	3,723	25,282	5,860	135,978	170,843	343	495	838	$8,718,070	$2,895,980	$11,614,050	72.2	$16,089,995	—	—
Hospitals	3,702	25,091	5,550	130,428	164,771	343	406	749	$8,466,792	$2,776,173	$11,242,964	71.9	$15,646,352	—	—
Inst. for Intellectual Disabilities	21	191	310	5,550	6,072	0	89	89	$251,279	$119,808	$371,086	83.6	$443,643	—	—
TB and other respiratory diseases	0	23	19	120	162	0	0	0	$6,330	$2,521	$8,850	60.9	$14,539	$210,715.78	$1,086.73
Long-term general and other special	377	4,344	982	19,042	24,745	22	20	42	$1,478,039	$490,515	$1,968,553	64.6	$3,049,313	$73,299.03	$1,054.36
Short-term general and other special	122,235	1,366,554	78,320	3,220,764	4,787,873	107,029	9,592	116,621	$303,756,932	$83,550,766	$387,307,698	49.5	$782,359,507	$11,652.74	$871.84
Hospital units of institutions	116	152	156	1,362	1,786	0	2	2	$121,657	$30,681	$152,338	47.0	$324,157	$18,798.24	—
Community Hospitals	122,119	1,366,402	78,164	3,219,402	4,786,087	107,029	9,592	116,621	$303,635,275	$83,520,086	$387,155,361	49.5	$782,035,350	$11,650.90	$2,156.94
6-24 Beds	1,178	12,492	2,737	41,073	57,480	7	23	30	$2,939,834	$777,711	$3,717,544	48.9	$7,609,007	$7,934.07	$1,830.98
25-49	5,905	56,539	9,576	196,192	268,212	443	709	1,152	$13,381,278	$3,518,974	$16,900,252	51.1	$33,077,262	$8,148.44	$1,679.03
50-99	6,207	83,850	9,536	252,745	352,338	667	272	939	$18,939,307	$4,917,640	$23,856,947	51.5	$46,328,180	$8,711.08	$1,333.59
100-199	14,622	211,486	15,460	502,452	744,020	4,869	716	5,585	$45,608,079	$12,411,557	$58,019,635	49.3	$117,726,796	$9,507.72	$1,787.84
200-299	17,081	225,406	11,878	511,309	765,674	8,632	615	9,247	$49,203,727	$13,368,088	$62,571,815	49.3	$127,003,058	$10,709.48	$2,081.02
300-399	14,206	200,230	8,652	432,303	655,391	12,872	941	13,813	$43,736,182	$12,406,941	$56,143,123	49.1	$114,313,944	$11,755.41	$2,302.33
400-499	12,144	152,592	6,237	332,240	503,213	12,869	600	13,469	$34,159,033	$9,387,434	$43,546,468	49.6	$87,818,901	$12,857.38	$2,404.25
500 or more	50,776	423,807	14,088	951,090	1,439,761	66,670	5,716	72,386	$95,667,836	$26,731,741	$122,399,578	49.3	$248,158,203	$15,519.73	$2,729.56
Nongovernment not-for-profit	100,162	996,495	47,371	2,355,979	3,500,007	75,529	7,525	83,054	$226,818,623	$62,363,474	$289,182,098	49.4	$585,469,912	$12,000.35	$2,288.77
Investor-owned (for profit)	4,523	173,170	13,583	361,240	552,516	5,084	314	5,398	$30,662,666	$6,777,404	$37,440,069	45.9	$81,552,243	$9,296.42	$1,791.20
State and Local Government	17,434	196,737	17,210	502,183	733,564	26,416	1,753	28,169	$46,153,986	$14,379,208	$60,533,194	52.6	$115,013,196	$12,028.02	$1,878.21

Tables 3–6

Total U.S.

TABLE 3

TOTAL UNITED STATES

U.S. Registered Community Hospitals
(Nonfederal, short-term general and other special hospitals)

Overview 2009–2013

	2013	2012	2011	2010	2009
TOTAL U.S. Community Hospitals	4,974	4,999	4,973	4,985	5,008
Bed Size Category					
6-24	469	462	445	424	402
25-49	1,186	1,192	1,177	1,167	1,164
50-99	959	954	955	970	991
100-199	995	1,012	1,005	1,029	1,063
200-299	571	570	582	585	582
300-399	334	348	353	352	348
400-499	183	189	184	185	192
500 + ...	277	272	272	273	266
Location					
Hospitals Urban	3,003	3,019	2,989	2,998	3,011
Hospitals Rural	1,971	1,980	1,984	1,987	1,997
Control					
State and Local Government	1,010	1,037	1,045	1,068	1,092
Not for Profit	2,904	2,894	2,903	2,904	2,918
Investor owned	1,060	1,068	1,025	1,013	998
Physician Models					
Independent Practice Association	473	496	514	563	579
Group Practice without Walls	185	165	161	159	175
Open Physician-Hospital Organization	597	620	622	630	649
Closed Physician-Hospital Organization	230	219	210	203	207
Management Service Organization	423	441	446	454	449
Integrated Salary Model	1,886	1,844	1,795	1,728	1,664
Equity Model	99	84	76	80	92
Foundation	299	269	263	261	237
Insurance Products					
Health Maintenance Organization	698	627	640	614	587
Preferred Provider Organization	676	576	744	740	693
Indemnity Fee for Service	240	210	253	260	235
Managed Care Contracts					
Health Maintenance Organization	2,655	2,697	2,665	2,677	2,702
Preferred Provider Organization	3,012	3,030	3,045	3,074	3,137
Affiliations					
Hospitals in a System*	3,144	3,100	3,007	2,941	2,921
Hospitals in a Network	1,582	1,508	1,535	1,508	1,485
Hospitals in a Group Purchasing Organization . .	3,581	3,519	3,562	3,595	3,674

TABLE 3

TOTAL UNITED STATES

U.S. Registered Community Hospitals
(Nonfederal, short-term general and other special hospitals)

Utilization, Personnel, Revenue and Expenses, Community Health Indicators 2009–2013

	2013	2012	2011	2010	2009
TOTAL FACILITY (Includes Hospital and Nursing Home Units)					
Utilization - Inpatient					
Beds	795,603	800,566	797,403	804,943	805,593
Admissions	33,609,083	34,422,071	34,843,085	35,149,427	35,527,377
Inpatient Days	182,370,189	185,423,035	187,072,013	189,593,349	192,656,804
Average Length of Stay	5.4	5.4	5.4	5.4	5.4
Inpatient Surgeries	9,147,264	9,513,598	9,638,467	9,954,821	10,100,980
Births	3,699,411	3,715,479	3,730,342	3,818,399	3,959,605
Utilization - Outpatient					
Emergency Outpatient Visits	133,611,670	133,221,030	129,461,658	127,249,317	127,298,193
Other Outpatient Visits	544,339,450	541,750,301	526,617,284	524,174,400	514,655,249
Total Outpatient Visits	677,951,120	674,971,331	656,078,942	651,423,717	641,953,442
Outpatient Surgeries	17,418,773	17,297,633	17,269,245	17,357,177	17,357,534
Personnel					
Full Time RNs	1,120,741	1,103,906	1,071,952	1,055,118	1,029,828
Full Time LPNs	66,122	69,318	72,641	76,503	82,159
Part Time RNs	491,401	494,530	483,351	477,739	477,699
Part Time LPNs	24,125	25,892	26,448	29,164	31,647
Total Full Time	4,126,815	4,105,295	4,034,205	3,989,587	3,971,118
Total Part Time	1,453,298	1,471,619	1,446,076	1,427,136	1,434,492
Revenue - Inpatient					
Gross Inpatient Revenue	$1,419,185,900,000	$1,355,940,500,000	$1,275,806,700,000	$1,224,790,500,000	$1,154,085,500,000
Revenue - Outpatient					
Gross Outpatient Revenue	$1,173,050,700,000	$1,075,704,400,000	$968,928,635,990	$887,419,059,972	$802,893,402,009
Revenue and Expenses - Totals **(Includes Inpatient and Outpatient)**					
Total Gross Revenue	$2,592,236,500,000	$2,431,645,000,000	$2,244,735,400,000	$2,112,209,600,000	$1,956,978,900,000
Deductions from Revenue	1,812,842,700,000	1,669,437,800,000	1,545,016,300,000	1,435,826,300,000	1,309,916,100,000
Net Patient Revenue	779,393,886,769	762,207,146,496	699,719,097,711	676,383,280,857	647,062,726,820
Other Operating Revenue	50,139,467,030	47,528,382,573	43,297,884,991	41,269,017,419	38,997,453,520
Other Nonoperating Revenue	19,765,262,658	11,599,107,141	12,267,965,061	13,251,393,842	4,467,480,534
Total Net Revenue	849,298,616,457	821,334,636,210	755,284,947,763	730,903,692,118	690,527,660,874
Total Expenses	782,035,349,979	756,916,756,696	702,091,033,815	677,968,038,012	656,156,258,314
HOSPITAL UNIT (Excludes Separate Nursing Home Units)					
Utilization - Inpatient					
Beds	748,824	751,490	749,181	755,091	755,286
Admissions	33,421,331	34,217,866	34,636,454	34,935,503	35,304,455
Inpatient Days	167,637,410	169,860,722	171,803,076	173,686,925	176,511,062
Average Length of Stay	5.0	5.0	5.0	5.0	5.0
Personnel					
Total Full Time	4,093,683	4,068,209	4,002,112	3,955,083	3,930,304
Total Part Time	1,435,155	1,452,480	1,428,754	1,407,838	1,413,237
Revenue and Expenses - Totals **(Includes Inpatient and Outpatient)**					
Total Net Revenue	$845,194,660,817	$817,155,645,229	$751,284,115,404	$726,685,542,179	$686,454,003,753
Total Expenses	778,422,090,039	753,064,177,148	698,572,269,130	674,188,184,839	652,470,080,058
COMMUNITY HEALTH INDICATORS PER 1000 POPULATION					
Total Population (in thousands)	316,129	313,914	311,592	309,051	307,007
Inpatient					
Beds	2.5	2.6	2.6	2.6	2.6
Admissions	106.3	109.7	111.8	113.7	115.7
Inpatient Days	576.9	590.7	600.4	613.5	627.5
Inpatient Surgeries	28.9	30.3	30.9	32.2	32.9
Births	11.7	11.8	12.0	12.4	12.9
Outpatient					
Emergency Outpatient Visits	422.6	424.4	415.5	411.7	414.6
Other Outpatient Visits	1,721.9	1,725.8	1,690.1	1,696.1	1,676.4
Total Outpatient Visits	2,144.5	2,150.2	2,105.6	2,107.8	2,091.0
Outpatient Surgeries	55.1	55.1	55.4	56.2	56.5
Expense per Capita (per person)	$2,473.8	$2,411.2	$2,253.2	$2,193.7	$2,137.3

TABLE 4

BED SIZE CATEGORY 6-24

U.S. Registered Community Hospitals
(Nonfederal, short-term general and other special hospitals)

Overview 2009–2013

	2013	2012	2011	2010	2009
Total Community Hospitals in					
Bed Size Category 6-24.................	469	462	445	424	402
Location					
Hospitals Urban..........................	122	120	114	113	111
Hospitals Rural	347	342	331	311	291
Control					
State and Local Government................	170	176	178	165	154
Not for Profit.............................	245	235	216	207	194
Investor owned	54	51	51	52	54
Physician Models					
Independent Practice Association	39	46	46	51	57
Group Practice without Walls...............	13	12	12	10	13
Open Physician-Hospital Organization	31	31	32	29	31
Closed Physician-Hospital Organization	7	8	8	5	6
Management Service Organization	14	18	16	17	20
Integrated Salary Model....................	163	163	149	120	116
Equity Model.............................	8	9	5	3	2
Foundation...............................	15	16	14	10	11
Insurance Products					
Health Maintenance Organization	48	42	37	40	36
Preferred Provider Organization..............	49	39	44	44	38
Indemnity Fee for Service	18	13	13	13	11
Managed Care Contracts					
Health Maintenance Organization	180	181	163	156	151
Preferred Provider Organization..............	247	244	231	218	210
Affiliations					
Hospitals in a System......................	205	207	185	172	166
Hospitals in a Network.....................	145	133	138	129	122
Hospitals in a Group Purchasing Organization..	330	317	306	291	286

TABLE 4

BED SIZE CATEGORY 6-24

U.S. Registered Community Hospitals
(Nonfederal, short-term general and other special hospitals)

Utilization, Personnel, Revenue and Expenses, Community Health Indicators 2009–2013

	2013	2012	2011	2010	2009
TOTAL FACILITY (Includes Hospital and Nursing Home Units)					
Utilization - Inpatient					
Beds	7,763	7,791	7,616	7,261	6,894
Admissions	189,339	197,448	197,272	198,692	196,599
Inpatient Days	862,961	879,985	888,064	854,226	846,228
Average Length of Stay	4.6	4.5	4.5	4.3	4.3
Inpatient Surgeries	38,962	41,274	35,479	36,003	33,615
Births	15,322	18,058	14,880	13,839	14,161
Utilization - Outpatient					
Emergency Outpatient Visits	1,955,889	1,929,787	1,702,152	1,658,487	1,558,802
Other Outpatient Visits	8,932,227	8,697,985	8,828,732	8,275,935	7,553,921
Total Outpatient Visits	10,888,116	10,627,772	10,530,884	9,934,422	9,112,723
Outpatient Surgeries	283,781	285,969	271,645	271,260	250,113
Personnel					
Full Time RNs	9,648	9,066	8,052	7,587	6,790
Full Time LPNs	2,258	2,044	2,104	2,113	1,992
Part Time RNs	5,692	5,508	4,752	4,701	4,212
Part Time LPNs	958	903	1,012	886	918
Total Full Time	45,873	42,797	40,408	38,328	34,290
Total Part Time	21,820	20,824	19,087	17,746	16,301
Revenue - Inpatient					
Gross Inpatient Revenue	$3,397,090,171	$3,344,514,225	$2,808,082,491	$2,786,370,995	$2,627,018,044
Revenue - Outpatient					
Gross Outpatient Revenue	$11,459,413,010	$10,460,225,077	$8,967,777,277	$8,039,286,106	$7,310,737,048
Revenue and Expenses - Totals (Includes Inpatient and Outpatient)					
Total Gross Revenue	$14,856,503,181	$13,804,739,302	$11,775,859,768	$10,825,657,101	$9,937,755,092
Deductions from Revenue	7,671,633,328	6,997,808,590	6,019,723,826	5,474,162,402	5,035,910,207
Net Patient Revenue	7,184,869,853	6,806,930,712	5,756,135,942	5,351,494,699	4,901,844,885
Other Operating Revenue	763,864,461	611,148,966	620,276,695	540,121,094	436,638,024
Other Nonoperating Revenue	143,595,341	154,545,670	107,732,522	103,852,868	70,082,709
Total Net Revenue	8,092,329,655	7,572,625,348	6,484,145,159	5,995,468,661	5,408,565,618
Total Expenses	7,609,006,694	6,984,976,928	6,128,099,984	5,644,509,939	5,099,918,468
HOSPITAL UNIT (Excludes Separate Nursing Home Units)					
Utilization - Inpatient					
Beds	7,733	7,738	7,610	7,225	6,852
Admissions	189,316	197,163	197,272	198,651	196,571
Inpatient Days	853,632	854,715	885,028	841,349	829,135
Average Length of Stay	4.5	4.3	4.5	4.2	4.2
Personnel					
Total Full Time	45,498	42,674	40,404	38,313	34,160
Total Part Time	21,381	20,730	19,087	17,743	16,225
Revenue and Expenses - Totals (Includes Inpatient and Outpatient)					
Total Net Revenue	$8,086,815,684	$7,561,431,638	$6,483,007,236	$5,990,190,925	$5,395,279,787
Total Expenses	7,606,122,912	6,979,227,864	6,127,873,361	5,642,553,901	5,092,088,584

TABLE 4

BED SIZE CATEGORY 25-49

U.S. Registered Community Hospitals
(Nonfederal, short-term general and other special hospitals)

Overview 2009–2013

	2013	2012	2011	2010	2009
Total Community Hospitals in					
Bed Size Category 25-49	**1,186**	**1,192**	**1,177**	**1,167**	**1,164**
Location					
Hospitals Urban	414	420	403	408	411
Hospitals Rural	772	772	774	759	753
Control					
State and Local Government	363	367	366	381	391
Not for Profit	576	574	570	547	536
Investor owned	247	251	241	239	237
Physician Models					
Independent Practice Association	87	97	96	102	108
Group Practice without Walls	29	25	30	32	32
Open Physician-Hospital Organization	72	79	80	82	94
Closed Physician-Hospital Organization	33	23	25	23	23
Management Service Organization	50	55	56	54	56
Integrated Salary Model	382	358	353	344	350
Equity Model	10	9	13	17	15
Foundation	47	44	41	39	40
Insurance Products					
Health Maintenance Organization	106	90	93	86	90
Preferred Provider Organization	114	94	142	134	123
Indemnity Fee for Service	40	31	47	44	41
Managed Care Contracts					
Health Maintenance Organization	499	502	477	471	488
Preferred Provider Organization	638	636	631	636	658
Affiliations					
Hospitals in a System	642	639	620	598	593
Hospitals in a Network	326	309	305	302	296
Hospitals in a Group Purchasing Organization . .	799	780	781	791	805

Bed Size Categories

TABLE 4   **BED SIZE CATEGORY 25-49**

U.S. Registered Community Hospitals
(Nonfederal, short-term general and other special hospitals)

Utilization, Personnel, Revenue and Expenses, Community Health Indicators 2009–2013

	2013	2012	2011	2010	2009
TOTAL FACILITY (Includes Hospital and Nursing Home Units)					
Utilization - Inpatient					
Beds	38,039	38,338	37,680	37,446	37,338
Admissions	1,087,215	1,128,446	1,173,246	1,168,665	1,217,233
Inpatient Days	5,927,960	6,029,293	6,091,172	6,116,350	6,265,180
Average Length of Stay	5.5	5.3	5.2	5.2	5.1
Inpatient Surgeries	226,655	235,988	241,364	256,940	266,047
Births	118,178	115,996	112,584	107,380	113,460
Utilization - Outpatient					
Emergency Outpatient Visits	8,584,767	8,566,426	8,170,484	7,923,353	8,004,368
Other Outpatient Visits	38,868,368	38,126,632	36,927,369	35,175,869	34,456,501
Total Outpatient Visits	47,453,135	46,693,058	45,097,853	43,099,222	42,460,869
Outpatient Surgeries	1,151,191	1,147,708	1,084,955	1,092,740	1,067,767
Personnel					
Full Time RNs	43,974	42,864	39,915	37,943	37,289
Full Time LPNs	8,032	8,417	8,460	8,776	8,901
Part Time RNs	25,153	24,910	23,665	22,187	21,865
Part Time LPNs	3,071	3,356	3,365	3,605	3,815
Total Full Time	200,077	201,196	194,434	187,568	184,562
Total Part Time	88,138	88,578	86,421	81,895	80,350
Revenue - Inpatient					
Gross Inpatient Revenue	$26,991,103,197	$26,339,586,346	$23,060,034,924	$21,382,867,485	$20,489,409,044
Revenue - Outpatient					
Gross Outpatient Revenue	$51,160,634,612	$47,719,363,855	$43,836,287,394	$39,164,706,833	$36,064,974,499
Revenue and Expenses - Totals					
(Includes Inpatient and Outpatient)					
Total Gross Revenue	$78,151,737,809	$74,058,950,201	$66,896,322,318	$60,547,574,318	$56,554,383,543
Deductions from Revenue	46,095,620,354	42,336,288,207	38,545,311,880	34,313,307,874	31,432,916,209
Net Patient Revenue	32,056,117,455	31,722,661,994	28,351,010,438	26,234,266,444	25,121,467,334
Other Operating Revenue	2,820,302,433	2,679,807,646	2,558,100,321	2,209,537,503	2,229,830,552
Other Nonoperating Revenue	629,745,342	466,597,263	465,541,424	523,520,663	299,120,900
Total Net Revenue	35,506,165,230	34,869,066,903	31,374,652,183	28,967,324,610	27,650,418,786
Total Expenses	33,077,261,551	32,080,809,215	29,219,811,844	27,075,731,145	26,281,664,624
HOSPITAL UNIT (Excludes Separate Nursing Home Units)					
Utilization - Inpatient					
Beds	36,683	36,965	36,335	35,924	35,726
Admissions	1,085,021	1,126,060	1,171,231	1,166,430	1,213,515
Inpatient Days	5,481,761	5,586,318	5,661,438	5,638,505	5,745,424
Average Length of Stay	5.1	5.0	4.8	4.8	4.7
Personnel					
Total Full Time	199,177	200,121	193,678	186,670	182,894
Total Part Time	87,448	87,785	85,897	81,286	79,370
Revenue and Expenses - Totals					
(Includes Inpatient and Outpatient)					
Total Net Revenue	$35,403,536,439	$34,771,427,302	$31,292,864,199	$28,881,412,934	$27,550,727,504
Total Expenses	32,981,475,196	31,999,027,638	29,151,001,828	27,009,348,946	26,216,346,135

Bed Size Categories

TABLE 4

BED SIZE CATEGORY 50-99

U.S. Registered Community Hospitals
(Nonfederal, short-term general and other special hospitals)

Overview 2009–2013

	2013	2012	2011	2010	2009
Total Community Hospitals in					
Bed Size Category 50-99.................	**959**	**954**	**955**	**970**	**991**
Location					
Hospitals Urban...........................	500	489	484	483	483
Hospitals Rural	459	465	471	487	508
Control					
State and Local Government...............	184	185	190	194	210
Not for Profit	475	470	478	485	501
Investor owned	300	299	287	291	280
Physician Models					
Independent Practice Association	55	61	66	84	86
Group Practice without Walls................	19	21	21	21	20
Open Physician-Hospital Organization	96	98	89	93	94
Closed Physician-Hospital Organization	30	29	32	33	29
Management Service Organization	46	49	48	54	54
Integrated Salary Model....................	299	296	292	288	280
Equity Model	9	9	10	12	13
Foundation...............................	35	34	35	40	35
Insurance Products					
Health Maintenance Organization	100	94	98	89	80
Preferred Provider Organization..............	110	98	129	128	124
Indemnity Fee for Service	37	37	40	49	44
Managed Care Contracts					
Health Maintenance Organization	423	434	426	444	435
Preferred Provider Organization..............	505	512	508	533	548
Affiliations					
Hospitals in a System.....................	621	604	588	584	576
Hospitals in a Network....................	260	254	256	260	257
Hospitals in a Group Purchasing Organization..	637	628	635	649	672

TABLE 4

BED SIZE CATEGORY 50-99

U.S. Registered Community Hospitals
(Nonfederal, short-term general and other special hospitals)

Utilization, Personnel, Revenue and Expenses, Community Health Indicators 2009–2013

	2013	2012	2011	2010	2009
TOTAL FACILITY (Includes Hospital and Nursing Home Units)					
Utilization - Inpatient					
Beds	67,892	67,879	67,844	69,470	71,012
Admissions	2,021,449	2,017,239	2,104,041	2,173,195	2,255,591
Inpatient Days	13,639,948	13,678,515	13,720,587	13,960,874	14,494,367
Average Length of Stay	6.7	6.8	6.5	6.4	6.4
Inpatient Surgeries	464,612	477,962	498,804	543,313	557,900
Births	224,180	222,207	223,326	228,035	245,282
Utilization - Outpatient					
Emergency Outpatient Visits	11,796,586	11,275,005	11,503,565	11,667,902	11,702,839
Other Outpatient Visits	46,326,471	45,524,947	44,622,553	46,033,464	45,633,323
Total Outpatient Visits	58,123,057	56,799,952	56,126,118	57,701,366	57,336,162
Outpatient Surgeries	1,541,697	1,507,344	1,542,936	1,592,532	1,625,749
Personnel					
Full Time RNs	65,776	63,278	61,781	60,774	59,702
Full Time LPNs	7,803	8,560	8,721	9,718	10,384
Part Time RNs	36,146	34,249	33,998	33,585	33,613
Part Time LPNs	3,492	3,584	3,685	4,125	4,537
Total Full Time	268,350	261,529	260,825	260,463	263,865
Total Part Time	124,962	122,577	120,605	118,372	119,501
Revenue - Inpatient					
Gross Inpatient Revenue	$59,688,634,837	$55,035,035,760	$53,109,381,343	$52,180,741,692	$48,434,688,539
Revenue - Outpatient					
Gross Outpatient Revenue	$78,655,991,052	$69,635,311,624	$66,009,645,599	$60,748,431,980	$57,539,780,471
Revenue and Expenses - Totals (Includes Inpatient and Outpatient)					
Total Gross Revenue	$138,344,625,889	$124,670,347,384	$119,119,026,942	$112,929,173,672	$105,974,469,010
Deductions from Revenue	90,642,831,824	79,025,510,314	76,709,358,028	71,250,437,701	65,093,252,794
Net Patient Revenue	47,701,794,065	45,644,837,070	42,409,668,914	41,678,735,971	40,881,216,216
Other Operating Revenue	2,476,450,842	1,974,942,100	1,689,476,095	1,566,850,196	1,628,159,436
Other Nonoperating Revenue	780,849,538	927,504,094	625,595,709	677,949,955	358,788,581
Total Net Revenue	50,959,094,445	48,547,283,264	44,724,740,718	43,923,536,122	42,868,164,233
Total Expenses	46,328,180,009	43,488,785,543	41,141,854,495	40,509,092,623	39,918,181,789
HOSPITAL UNIT (Excludes Separate Nursing Home Units)					
Utilization - Inpatient					
Beds	59,427	59,055	58,517	60,417	60,783
Admissions	2,006,130	1,999,782	2,086,226	2,152,715	2,233,384
Inpatient Days	11,006,139	10,929,906	10,790,706	11,108,738	11,303,044
Average Length of Stay	5.5	5.5	5.2	5.2	5.1
Personnel					
Total Full Time	263,494	256,240	255,669	255,262	257,466
Total Part Time	121,202	118,696	116,620	114,674	115,249
Revenue and Expenses - Totals (Includes Inpatient and Outpatient)					
Total Net Revenue	$50,396,086,960	$47,999,122,812	$44,157,904,896	$43,379,453,757	$42,231,656,619
Total Expenses	45,871,570,407	43,042,562,713	40,660,522,689	40,049,446,577	39,405,302,301

TABLE 4

BED SIZE CATEGORY 100-199

U.S. Registered Community Hospitals
(Nonfederal, short-term general and other special hospitals)

Overview 2009–2013

	2013	2012	2011	2010	2009
Total Community Hospitals in					
Bed Size Category 100-199	995	1,012	1,005	1,029	1,063
Location					
Hospitals Urban.	711	717	707	707	726
Hospitals Rural	284	295	298	322	337
Control					
State and Local Government	123	135	135	149	159
Not for Profit	621	617	623	633	656
Investor owned	251	260	247	247	248
Physician Models					
Independent Practice Association	94	97	107	120	122
Group Practice without Walls.	39	36	35	36	44
Open Physician-Hospital Organization	140	142	144	152	166
Closed Physician-Hospital Organization	45	48	51	47	53
Management Service Organization	91	106	102	103	102
Integrated Salary Model	354	345	343	332	317
Equity Model	26	21	20	17	25
Foundation.	71	62	59	56	49
Insurance Products					
Health Maintenance Organization	139	125	132	124	116
Preferred Provider Organization.	142	122	142	136	134
Indemnity Fee for Service	55	52	58	52	46
Managed Care Contracts					
Health Maintenance Organization	567	566	578	587	621
Preferred Provider Organization.	610	606	624	641	675
Affiliations					
Hospitals in a System.	691	686	667	655	665
Hospitals in a Network	293	281	280	278	298
Hospitals in a Group Purchasing Organization. .	710	688	705	724	779

TABLE 4

BED SIZE CATEGORY 100-199

U.S. Registered Community Hospitals
(Nonfederal, short-term general and other special hospitals)

Utilization, Personnel, Revenue and Expenses, Community Health Indicators 2009–2013

	2013	2012	2011	2010	2009
TOTAL FACILITY (Includes Hospital and Nursing Home Units)					
Utilization - Inpatient					
Beds	143,760	145,556	143,843	148,090	152,655
Admissions	5,754,158	5,920,309	6,022,274	6,124,987	6,337,184
Inpatient Days	30,164,685	30,892,477	31,348,118	32,616,034	34,162,392
Average Length of Stay	5.2	5.2	5.2	5.3	5.4
Inpatient Surgeries	1,472,473	1,546,794	1,520,872	1,602,340	1,687,965
Births	654,405	658,328	677,253	706,284	747,784
Utilization - Outpatient					
Emergency Outpatient Visits	27,201,787	27,668,989	26,551,709	26,433,098	27,527,025
Other Outpatient Visits	96,360,321	96,096,051	94,003,431	94,469,225	99,739,947
Total Outpatient Visits	123,562,108	123,765,040	120,555,140	120,902,323	127,266,972
Outpatient Surgeries	3,419,797	3,421,257	3,466,539	3,551,479	3,694,985
Personnel					
Full Time RNs	168,819	167,593	162,016	163,437	161,715
Full Time LPNs	12,856	13,807	14,534	15,414	16,777
Part Time RNs	85,350	85,380	84,492	87,526	90,352
Part Time LPNs	5,199	5,356	5,653	6,135	6,982
Total Full Time	618,661	622,757	612,257	624,072	634,361
Total Part Time	261,701	265,049	265,264	270,145	275,686
Revenue - Inpatient					
Gross Inpatient Revenue	$206,931,061,736	$196,130,283,474	$181,129,764,497	$177,873,737,781	$172,022,467,282
Revenue - Outpatient					
Gross Outpatient Revenue	$208,345,611,345	$190,830,856,203	$172,268,570,520	$160,748,748,573	$148,908,204,845
Revenue and Expenses - Totals					
(Includes Inpatient and Outpatient)					
Total Gross Revenue	$415,276,658,664	$386,961,139,677	$353,398,335,017	$338,622,486,354	$320,930,672,127
Deductions from Revenue	294,786,238,076	269,772,483,763	245,217,347,870	231,276,346,434	216,014,370,801
Net Patient Revenue	120,490,420,588	117,188,655,914	108,180,987,147	107,346,139,920	104,916,301,326
Other Operating Revenue	5,523,192,766	5,062,039,669	4,265,506,812	4,194,548,704	3,845,471,488
Other Nonoperating Revenue	2,575,090,869	1,638,797,895	1,324,614,718	1,589,574,499	773,148,510
Total Net Revenue	128,588,704,223	123,889,493,478	113,771,108,677	113,130,263,123	109,534,921,324
Total Expenses	117,726,795,452	112,758,082,370	105,195,692,008	104,618,604,747	103,165,948,166
HOSPITAL UNIT (Excludes Separate Nursing Home Units)					
Utilization - Inpatient					
Beds	131,892	132,541	131,102	134,182	138,351
Admissions	5,713,320	5,876,426	5,976,691	6,074,709	6,284,177
Inpatient Days	26,497,775	26,855,548	27,367,543	28,160,867	29,540,921
Average Length of Stay	4.6	4.6	4.6	4.6	4.7
Personnel					
Total Full Time	611,021	613,726	604,314	614,788	624,258
Total Part Time	256,801	259,764	260,194	264,091	269,719
Revenue and Expenses - Totals					
(Includes Inpatient and Outpatient)					
Total Net Revenue	$127,741,585,255	$122,970,772,210	$112,746,343,253	$112,109,514,588	$108,564,165,998
Total Expenses	116,987,799,038	111,908,745,686	104,375,763,548	103,732,105,185	102,320,666,510

Bed Size Categories

TABLE 4

BED SIZE CATEGORY 200-299

U.S. Registered Community Hospitals
(Nonfederal, short-term general and other special hospitals)

Overview 2009–2013

	2013	2012	2011	2010	2009
Total Community Hospitals in					
Bed Size Category 200-299	571	570	582	585	582
Location					
Hospitals Urban..........................	486	487	498	505	503
Hospitals Rural	85	83	84	80	79
Control					
State and Local Government................	57	62	58	63	58
Not for Profit	399	393	410	422	427
Investor owned	115	115	114	100	97
Physician Models					
Independent Practice Association	65	56	60	67	68
Group Practice without Walls...............	28	22	23	18	23
Open Physician-Hospital Organization	91	98	108	111	104
Closed Physician-Hospital Organization	38	30	26	28	26
Management Service Organization	73	69	81	76	74
Integrated Salary Model....................	247	238	225	223	211
Equity Model............................	20	15	13	17	17
Foundation..............................	46	34	38	40	35
Insurance Products					
Health Maintenance Organization	106	90	95	93	89
Preferred Provider Organization.............	91	77	105	105	88
Indemnity Fee for Service	38	32	37	35	36
Managed Care Contracts					
Health Maintenance Organization	358	373	379	380	382
Preferred Provider Organization.............	374	383	399	402	406
Affiliations					
Hospitals in a System.....................	410	390	392	386	381
Hospitals in a Network....................	197	185	194	192	185
Hospitals in a Group Purchasing Organization..	418	424	443	448	452

TABLE 4

BED SIZE CATEGORY 200-299

U.S. Registered Community Hospitals
(Nonfederal, short-term general and other special hospitals)

Utilization, Personnel, Revenue and Expenses, Community Health Indicators 2009–2013

	2013	2012	2011	2010	2009
TOTAL FACILITY (Includes Hospital and Nursing Home Units)					
Utilization - Inpatient					
Beds	140,113	139,212	141,308	142,616	141,920
Admissions	6,156,487	6,297,821	6,463,753	6,569,492	6,684,169
Inpatient Days	31,466,013	32,150,843	32,799,097	33,301,779	33,902,236
Average Length of Stay	5.1	5.1	5.1	5.1	5.1
Inpatient Surgeries	1,623,431	1,728,626	1,749,337	1,896,663	1,871,675
Births	668,891	661,428	660,610	681,848	739,459
Utilization - Outpatient					
Emergency Outpatient Visits	24,975,730	24,468,359	24,513,239	24,171,792	24,181,322
Other Outpatient Visits	87,945,697	87,195,255	85,387,424	86,489,482	83,087,309
Total Outpatient Visits	112,921,427	111,663,614	109,900,663	110,661,274	107,268,631
Outpatient Surgeries	2,999,018	2,963,873	3,017,123	3,001,309	3,015,075
Personnel					
Full Time RNs	181,464	178,938	179,617	178,567	172,868
Full Time LPNs	10,044	10,635	11,593	12,698	13,435
Part Time RNs	87,905	89,327	86,739	84,923	85,762
Part Time LPNs	3,689	4,108	4,315	5,133	5,396
Total Full Time	647,716	654,260	655,559	657,452	650,138
Total Part Time	254,023	257,126	255,998	252,299	256,501
Revenue - Inpatient					
Gross Inpatient Revenue	$243,975,095,899	$240,835,907,576	$222,460,322,498	$216,302,711,528	$203,207,782,786
Revenue - Outpatient					
Gross Outpatient Revenue	$200,229,741,755	$185,911,616,840	$167,530,250,112	$152,845,016,955	$136,999,646,724
Revenue and Expenses - Totals					
(Includes Inpatient and Outpatient)					
Total Gross Revenue	$444,204,837,654	$426,747,524,416	$389,990,572,610	$369,147,728,483	$340,207,429,510
Deductions from Revenue	316,380,880,125	300,061,387,153	272,710,512,076	254,962,232,713	230,420,211,811
Net Patient Revenue	127,823,957,529	126,686,137,263	117,280,060,534	114,185,495,770	109,787,217,699
Other Operating Revenue	6,482,336,012	5,987,888,496	5,683,916,062	5,345,831,411	4,960,901,489
Other Nonoperating Revenue	2,877,258,321	1,814,706,798	2,168,529,841	2,413,672,808	869,665,589
Total Net Revenue	137,183,551,862	134,488,732,557	125,132,506,437	121,944,999,989	115,617,784,777
Total Expenses	127,003,057,863	124,808,644,131	116,575,732,582	113,049,739,427	109,876,595,200
HOSPITAL UNIT (Excludes Separate Nursing Home Units)					
Utilization - Inpatient					
Beds	132,439	130,652	133,352	133,765	133,463
Admissions	6,114,738	6,248,381	6,414,383	6,516,545	6,624,904
Inpatient Days	29,079,526	29,421,703	30,290,801	30,497,421	31,155,392
Average Length of Stay	4.8	4.7	4.7	4.7	4.7
Personnel					
Total Full Time	642,090	647,761	649,600	650,650	642,802
Total Part Time	251,422	254,363	253,312	248,794	252,441
Revenue and Expenses - Totals					
(Includes Inpatient and Outpatient)					
Total Net Revenue	$136,494,821,942	$133,703,328,242	$124,426,000,759	$121,195,426,366	$114,847,552,059
Total Expenses	126,404,652,829	124,088,653,959	115,962,048,197	112,407,841,598	109,171,734,399

TABLE 4

BED SIZE CATEGORY 300-399

U.S. Registered Community Hospitals
(Nonfederal, short-term general and other special hospitals)

Overview 2009–2013

	2013	2012	2011	2010	2009
Total Community Hospitals in Bed Size Category 300-399	**334**	**348**	**353**	**352**	**348**
Location					
Hospitals Urban.	316	331	332	329	327
Hospitals Rural	18	17	21	23	21
Control					
State and Local Government.	37	37	44	41	49
Not for Profit	241	255	258	261	252
Investor owned	56	56	51	50	47
Physician Models					
Independent Practice Association	46	47	49	52	55
Group Practice without Walls.	23	21	15	15	11
Open Physician-Hospital Organization	69	67	71	66	60
Closed Physician-Hospital Organization	25	30	28	28	29
Management Service Organization	48	49	49	57	54
Integrated Salary Model	162	168	165	161	143
Equity Model	6	6	4	5	5
Foundation.	30	30	27	27	20
Insurance Products					
Health Maintenance Organization	64	60	63	61	62
Preferred Provider Organization.	55	47	65	66	65
Indemnity Fee for Service	18	14	19	18	19
Managed Care Contracts					
Health Maintenance Organization	247	254	264	263	251
Preferred Provider Organization.	250	260	273	269	266
Affiliations					
Hospitals in a System.	237	241	237	234	228
Hospitals in a Network.	133	128	146	147	139
Hospitals in a Group Purchasing Organization. .	278	278	291	296	287

TABLE 4

BED SIZE CATEGORY 300-399

U.S. Registered Community Hospitals
(Nonfederal, short-term general and other special hospitals)

Utilization, Personnel, Revenue and Expenses, Community Health Indicators 2009–2013

	2013	2012	2011	2010	2009
TOTAL FACILITY (Includes Hospital and Nursing Home Units)					
Utilization - Inpatient					
Beds	115,511	120,554	122,269	121,749	120,201
Admissions	5,343,652	5,659,683	5,850,631	5,835,325	5,761,848
Inpatient Days	27,347,329	28,628,393	29,754,662	29,931,672	29,771,668
Average Length of Stay	5.1	5.1	5.1	5.1	5.2
Inpatient Surgeries	1,421,836	1,505,394	1,577,523	1,594,088	1,638,540
Births	607,340	635,069	661,840	669,356	669,093
Utilization - Outpatient					
Emergency Outpatient Visits	18,931,461	19,494,322	19,606,197	18,788,786	18,319,154
Other Outpatient Visits	70,815,508	74,292,746	75,676,049	71,726,267	68,364,695
Total Outpatient Visits	89,746,969	93,787,068	95,282,246	90,515,053	86,683,849
Outpatient Surgeries	2,317,170	2,419,594	2,450,334	2,401,308	2,371,683
Personnel					
Full Time RNs	165,887	167,220	166,975	159,878	157,652
Full Time LPNs	7,556	8,157	8,862	8,875	10,238
Part Time RNs	68,700	74,735	75,111	73,727	71,718
Part Time LPNs	2,196	2,519	2,778	3,090	3,461
Total Full Time	573,637	592,655	589,570	572,775	571,380
Total Part Time	190,809	210,937	212,248	211,094	206,711
Revenue - Inpatient					
Gross Inpatient Revenue	$240,832,001,022	$230,446,967,570	$216,619,573,502	$209,508,102,124	$192,767,208,267
Revenue - Outpatient					
Gross Outpatient Revenue	$175,534,042,359	$164,159,129,172	$149,199,860,634	$133,493,602,189	$118,085,940,332
Revenue and Expenses - Totals					
(Includes Inpatient and Outpatient)					
Total Gross Revenue	$416,366,043,381	$394,606,096,742	$365,819,434,136	$343,001,704,313	$310,853,148,599
Deductions from Revenue	300,900,054,698	277,863,090,524	256,798,261,828	239,740,752,936	213,449,294,445
Net Patient Revenue	115,465,988,683	116,743,006,218	109,021,172,308	103,260,951,377	97,403,854,154
Other Operating Revenue	6,912,306,120	6,414,161,778	6,181,177,363	5,624,897,632	5,833,232,696
Other Nonoperating Revenue	3,455,675,896	1,472,292,314	1,684,050,046	2,187,362,723	421,501,249
Total Net Revenue	125,833,970,699	124,629,460,310	116,886,399,717	111,073,211,732	103,658,588,099
Total Expenses	114,313,944,143	114,103,095,511	107,750,738,297	102,319,306,727	97,985,067,095
HOSPITAL UNIT (Excludes Separate Nursing Home Units)					
Utilization - Inpatient					
Beds	110,605	115,302	116,402	115,138	114,177
Admissions	5,311,319	5,626,701	5,812,423	5,794,184	5,722,480
Inpatient Days	25,900,164	27,018,257	27,951,385	27,890,368	27,966,432
Average Length of Stay	4.9	4.8	4.8	4.8	4.9
Personnel					
Total Full Time	569,603	588,298	585,534	567,683	565,928
Total Part Time	189,117	209,136	210,406	208,623	204,570
Revenue and Expenses - Totals					
(Includes Inpatient and Outpatient)					
Total Net Revenue	$125,251,711,673	$124,094,300,216	$116,327,869,334	$110,402,770,436	$102,987,034,415
Total Expenses	113,842,852,106	113,626,750,271	107,307,019,085	101,715,147,145	97,429,327,288

TABLE 4

BED SIZE CATEGORY 400-499

U.S. Registered Community Hospitals
(Nonfederal, short-term general and other special hospitals)

Overview 2009–2013

	2013	2012	2011	2010	2009
Total Community Hospitals in					
Bed Size Category 400-499	183	189	184	185	192
Location					
Hospitals Urban	179	186	181	182	187
Hospitals Rural	4	3	3	3	5
Control					
State and Local Government	30	29	26	28	23
Not for Profit	135	142	141	139	148
Investor owned	18	18	17	18	21
Physician Models					
Independent Practice Association	30	32	31	27	28
Group Practice without Walls	16	14	14	13	16
Open Physician-Hospital Organization	36	44	40	35	41
Closed Physician-Hospital Organization	20	16	12	13	15
Management Service Organization	35	33	35	30	30
Integrated Salary Model	98	96	90	94	86
Equity Model	7	6	4	4	4
Foundation	27	24	24	24	22
Insurance Products					
Health Maintenance Organization	44	38	37	38	33
Preferred Provider Organization	42	37	40	41	37
Indemnity Fee for Service	8	8	13	15	9
Managed Care Contracts					
Health Maintenance Organization	140	151	148	149	147
Preferred Provider Organization	144	152	150	147	149
Affiliations					
Hospitals in a System	135	137	127	128	128
Hospitals in a Network	85	88	86	78	70
Hospitals in a Group Purchasing Organization . .	154	159	160	158	159

TABLE 4

BED SIZE CATEGORY 400-499

U.S. Registered Community Hospitals
(Nonfederal, short-term general and other special hospitals)

Utilization, Personnel, Revenue and Expenses, Community Health Indicators 2009–2013

	2013	2012	2011	2010	2009
TOTAL FACILITY (Includes Hospital and Nursing Home Units)					
Utilization - Inpatient					
Beds	81,148	84,007	81,699	82,071	84,783
Admissions	3,750,238	3,966,019	3,862,877	3,869,124	4,049,002
Inpatient Days	20,029,447	20,755,259	20,364,896	20,521,474	21,675,972
Average Length of Stay	5.3	5.2	5.3	5.3	5.4
Inpatient Surgeries	1,038,085	1,137,327	1,150,202	1,178,350	1,220,457
Births	417,270	427,993	410,117	408,256	431,706
Utilization - Outpatient					
Emergency Outpatient Visits	12,285,620	12,993,712	11,929,789	11,546,221	12,078,252
Other Outpatient Visits	59,073,331	59,418,937	54,498,516	53,996,342	51,649,202
Total Outpatient Visits	71,358,951	72,412,649	66,428,305	65,542,563	63,727,454
Outpatient Surgeries	1,607,610	1,669,549	1,623,929	1,665,216	1,804,693
Personnel					
Full Time RNs	125,451	131,578	123,351	121,762	123,770
Full Time LPNs	5,246	5,571	5,525	6,176	6,578
Part Time RNs	54,284	55,526	53,067	53,293	55,922
Part Time LPNs	1,992	2,269	1,972	2,317	2,330
Total Full Time	440,221	462,528	439,370	441,431	458,527
Total Part Time	152,826	159,252	149,644	146,459	155,793
Revenue - Inpatient					
Gross Inpatient Revenue	$165,377,218,755	$165,404,143,916	$158,709,548,655	$150,837,747,313	$154,483,680,751
Revenue - Outpatient					
Gross Outpatient Revenue	$125,422,311,131	$119,532,259,113	$105,408,223,039	$98,160,076,960	$94,037,031,898
Revenue and Expenses - Totals					
(Includes Inpatient and Outpatient)					
Total Gross Revenue	$290,799,529,886	$284,936,403,029	$264,117,771,694	$248,997,824,273	$248,520,712,649
Deductions from Revenue	204,455,874,952	197,528,264,702	184,087,484,155	172,382,284,117	170,485,791,464
Net Patient Revenue	86,343,654,934	87,408,138,327	80,030,287,539	76,615,540,156	78,034,921,185
Other Operating Revenue	5,485,613,820	5,272,639,678	4,601,079,434	4,922,929,664	4,809,356,943
Other Nonoperating Revenue	2,567,834,662	1,325,875,743	1,374,562,424	1,471,629,299	576,751,753
Total Net Revenue	94,397,103,416	94,006,653,748	86,005,929,397	83,010,099,119	83,421,029,881
Total Expenses	87,818,900,913	87,804,964,580	80,196,968,394	77,854,509,046	79,447,824,942
HOSPITAL UNIT (Excludes Separate Nursing Home Units)					
Utilization - Inpatient					
Beds	77,123	80,458	78,997	79,722	82,330
Admissions	3,734,868	3,947,024	3,848,071	3,854,485	4,034,937
Inpatient Days	18,697,496	19,600,701	19,494,041	19,770,661	20,873,864
Average Length of Stay	5.0	5.0	5.1	5.1	5.2
Personnel					
Total Full Time	436,927	459,192	437,087	439,282	455,941
Total Part Time	151,242	157,372	148,452	145,585	154,827
Revenue and Expenses - Totals					
(Includes Inpatient and Outpatient)					
Total Net Revenue	$93,975,576,086	$93,581,430,291	$85,724,707,161	$82,724,653,206	$83,143,956,566
Total Expenses	87,456,206,840	87,395,944,309	79,940,658,386	77,613,265,522	79,186,633,408

TABLE 4

BED SIZE CATEGORY 500 +

U.S. Registered Community Hospitals
(Nonfederal, short-term general and other special hospitals)

Overview 2009–2013

	2013	2012	2011	2010	2009
Total Community Hospitals in					
Bed Size Category 500 +..................	277	272	272	273	266
Location					
Hospitals Urban..........................	275	269	270	271	263
Hospitals Rural	2	3	2	2	3
Control					
State and Local Government................	46	46	48	47	48
Not for Profit	212	208	207	210	204
Investor owned	19	18	17	16	14
Physician Models					
Independent Practice Association	57	60	59	60	55
Group Practice without Walls...............	18	14	11	14	16
Open Physician-Hospital Organization	62	61	58	62	59
Closed Physician-Hospital Organization	32	35	28	26	26
Management Service Organization	66	62	59	63	59
Integrated Salary Model...................	181	180	178	166	161
Equity Model............................	13	9	7	5	11
Foundation..............................	28	25	25	25	25
Insurance Products					
Health Maintenance Organization	91	88	85	83	81
Preferred Provider Organization..............	73	62	77	86	84
Indemnity Fee for Service	26	23	26	34	29
Managed Care Contracts					
Health Maintenance Organization	241	236	230	227	227
Preferred Provider Organization..............	244	237	229	228	225
Affiliations					
Hospitals in a System.....................	203	196	191	184	184
Hospitals in a Network....................	143	130	130	122	118
Hospitals in a Group Purchasing Organization..	255	245	241	238	234

TABLE **4**

BED SIZE CATEGORY 500 +

U.S. Registered Community Hospitals
(Nonfederal, short-term general and other special hospitals)

Utilization, Personnel, Revenue and Expenses, Community Health Indicators 2009–2013

	2013	2012	2011	2010	2009
TOTAL FACILITY (Includes Hospital and Nursing Home Units)					
Utilization - Inpatient					
Beds	201,377	197,229	195,144	196,240	190,790
Admissions	9,306,545	9,235,106	9,168,991	9,209,947	9,025,751
Inpatient Days	52,931,846	52,408,270	52,105,417	52,290,940	51,538,761
Average Length of Stay.	5.7	5.7	5.7	5.7	5.7
Inpatient Surgeries.	2,861,210	2,840,233	2,864,886	2,847,124	2,824,781
Births.	993,825	976,400	969,732	1,003,401	998,660
Utilization - Outpatient					
Emergency Outpatient Visits	27,879,830	26,824,430	25,484,523	25,059,678	23,926,431
Other Outpatient Visits.	136,017,527	132,397,748	126,673,210	128,007,816	124,170,351
Total Outpatient Visits	163,897,357	159,222,178	152,157,733	153,067,494	148,096,782
Outpatient Surgeries	4,098,509	3,882,339	3,811,784	3,781,333	3,527,469
Personnel					
Full Time RNs	359,722	343,369	330,245	325,170	310,042
Full Time LPNs	12,327	12,127	12,842	12,733	13,854
Part Time RNs.	128,171	124,895	121,527	117,797	114,255
Part Time LPNs	3,528	3,797	3,668	3,873	4,208
Total Full Time	1,332,280	1,267,573	1,241,782	1,207,498	1,173,995
Total Part Time	359,019	347,276	336,809	329,126	323,649
Revenue - Inpatient					
Gross Inpatient Revenue.	$471,993,651,262	$438,404,095,774	$417,910,035,060	$393,918,219,709	$360,053,211,932
Revenue - Outpatient					
Gross Outpatient Revenue	$322,242,954,475	$287,455,681,774	$255,708,021,415	$234,219,190,376	$203,947,086,192
Revenue and Expenses - Totals					
(Includes Inpatient and Outpatient)					
Total Gross Revenue.	$794,236,605,737	$725,859,777,548	$673,618,056,475	$628,137,410,085	$564,000,298,124
Deductions from Revenue.	551,909,522,075	495,852,998,550	464,928,281,586	426,426,753,565	377,984,394,103
Net Patient Revenue	242,327,083,662	230,006,778,998	208,689,774,889	201,710,656,520	186,015,904,021
Other Operating Revenue	19,675,400,576	19,525,754,240	17,698,352,209	16,864,301,215	15,253,862,892
Other Nonoperating Revenue	6,735,212,689	3,798,787,364	4,517,338,377	4,283,831,027	1,098,421,243
Total Net Revenue.	268,737,696,927	253,331,320,602	230,905,465,475	222,858,788,762	202,368,188,156
Total Expenses.	248,158,203,354	234,887,398,418	215,882,136,211	206,896,544,358	194,381,058,030
HOSPITAL UNIT (Excludes Separate Nursing Home Units)					
Utilization - Inpatient					
Beds	192,922	188,779	186,866	188,718	183,604
Admissions	9,266,619	9,196,329	9,130,157	9,177,784	8,994,487
Inpatient Days	50,120,917	49,593,574	49,362,134	49,779,016	49,096,850
Average Length of Stay.	5.4	5.4	5.4	5.4	5.5
Personnel					
Total Full Time.	1,325,873	1,260,197	1,235,826	1,202,435	1,166,855
Total Part Time	356,542	344,634	334,786	327,042	320,836
Revenue and Expenses - Totals					
(Includes Inpatient and Outpatient)					
Total Net Revenue.	$267,844,526,778	$252,473,832,518	$230,125,418,566	$222,002,119,967	$201,733,630,805
Total Expenses.	247,271,410,711	234,023,264,708	215,047,382,036	206,018,475,965	193,647,981,433

Bed Size Categories

Census Divisions

Census Division 1

New England
Connecticut, Maine, Massachusetts, New Hampshire, Rhode Island, Vermont

Census Division 2

Middle Atlantic
New Jersey, New York, Pennsylvania

Census Division 3

South Atlantic
Delaware, District of Columbia, Florida, Georgia, Maryland, North Carolina, South Carolina, Virginia, West Virginia

Census Division 4

East North Central
Illinois, Indiana, Michigan, Ohio, Wisconsin

Census Division 5

East South Central
Alabama, Kentucky, Mississippi, Tennessee

Census Division 6

West North Central
Iowa, Kansas, Minnesota, Missouri, Nebraska, North Dakota, South Dakota

Census Division 7

West South Central
Arkansas, Louisiana, Oklahoma, Texas

Census Division 8

Mountain
Arizona, Colorado, Idaho, Montana, Nevada, New Mexico, Utah, Wyoming

Census Division 9

Pacific
Alaska, California, Hawaii, Oregon, Washington

U.S. Census Divisions

TABLE 5

U.S. CENSUS DIVISION 1: NEW ENGLAND

U.S. Registered Community Hospitals
(Nonfederal, short-term general and other special hospitals)

Overview 2009–2013

	2013	2012	2011	2010	2009
Total Community Hospitals					
in Census Division 1, New England	203	207	204	203	203
Bed Size Category					
6-24	7	10	10	10	10
25-49	44	43	42	39	40
50-99	45	47	40	40	41
100-199	55	51	56	59	57
200-299	23	26	27	25	22
300-399	13	15	15	14	17
400-499	5	4	3	4	4
500 + ...	11	11	11	12	12
Location					
Hospitals Urban..........................	146	149	146	145	145
Hospitals Rural	57	58	58	58	58
Control					
State and Local Government................	6	6	4	4	5
Not for Profit	170	176	181	182	184
Investor owned	27	25	19	17	14
Physician Models					
Independent Practice Association	34	32	36	44	40
Group Practice without Walls...............	8	7	9	11	8
Open Physician-Hospital Organization	41	43	47	52	51
Closed Physician-Hospital Organization	10	12	12	14	12
Management Service Organization	17	20	21	24	21
Integrated Salary Model....................	93	101	105	107	98
Equity Model	5	6	4	4	6
Foundation..............................	12	14	16	13	10
Insurance Products					
Health Maintenance Organization	13	15	18	19	17
Preferred Provider Organization..............	9	9	14	9	8
Indemnity Fee for Service	3	4	8	6	4
Managed Care Contracts					
Health Maintenance Organization	116	119	137	141	133
Preferred Provider Organization..............	116	119	133	136	132
Affiliations					
Hospitals in a System.....................	105	102	93	89	77
Hospitals in a Network....................	77	75	80	75	69
Hospitals in a Group Purchasing Organization..	147	148	157	166	159

TABLE 5

U.S. CENSUS DIVISION 1: NEW ENGLAND

U.S. Registered Community Hospitals
(Nonfederal, short-term general and other special hospitals)

Utilization, Personnel, Revenue and Expenses, Community Health Indicators 2009–2013

	2013	2012	2011	2010	2009
TOTAL FACILITY (Includes Hospital and Nursing Home Units)					
Utilization - Inpatient					
Beds	34,028	34,399	33,693	33,974	33,672
Admissions	1,597,809	1,608,353	1,677,325	1,668,378	1,678,176
Inpatient Days	8,611,159	8,482,806	8,650,119	8,813,799	8,987,254
Average Length of Stay	5.4	5.3	5.2	5.3	5.4
Inpatient Surgeries	409,361	418,336	429,342	439,721	454,138
Births	146,765	146,147	159,359	152,389	156,346
Utilization - Outpatient					
Emergency Outpatient Visits	7,168,129	7,131,256	7,018,233	7,120,183	7,004,583
Other Outpatient Visits	41,529,159	40,756,179	40,285,469	39,615,363	38,999,668
Total Outpatient Visits	48,697,288	47,887,435	47,303,702	46,735,546	46,004,251
Outpatient Surgeries	949,198	960,370	954,123	1,018,591	980,423
Personnel					
Full Time RNs	47,004	46,323	46,138	44,258	44,777
Full Time LPNs	1,800	1,816	1,794	1,811	1,898
Part Time RNs	40,843	41,454	41,003	39,689	38,236
Part Time LPNs	1,203	1,370	1,361	1,359	1,508
Total Full Time	230,028	226,202	227,567	223,298	223,553
Total Part Time	122,493	126,716	128,182	123,799	118,235
Revenue - Inpatient					
Gross Inpatient Revenue	$55,981,458,810	$52,549,975,311	$49,993,866,945	$47,986,647,777	$46,367,979,779
Revenue - Outpatient					
Gross Outpatient Revenue	$64,787,872,297	$60,296,411,970	$55,511,810,142	$52,517,753,883	$49,137,348,602
Revenue and Expenses - Totals					
(Includes Inpatient and Outpatient)					
Total Gross Revenue	$120,769,331,107	$112,846,387,281	$105,505,677,087	$100,504,401,660	$95,505,328,381
Deductions from Revenue	75,150,281,353	68,108,106,958	62,731,335,770	59,098,902,583	55,719,745,134
Net Patient Revenue	45,619,049,754	44,738,280,323	42,774,341,317	41,405,499,077	39,785,583,247
Other Operating Revenue	5,170,226,128	4,894,336,432	4,641,150,617	4,151,761,895	3,962,230,864
Other Nonoperating Revenue	1,095,149,728	464,999,614	187,237,842	426,472,039	-167,328,782
Total Net Revenue	51,884,425,610	50,097,616,369	47,602,729,776	45,983,733,011	43,580,485,329
Total Expenses	48,855,355,041	47,321,636,263	45,537,927,696	44,366,268,718	42,351,771,503
HOSPITAL UNIT (Excludes Separate Nursing Home Units)					
Utilization - Inpatient					
Beds	33,135	33,332	32,627	32,710	32,524
Admissions	1,594,828	1,605,312	1,674,145	1,662,431	1,673,090
Inpatient Days	8,301,445	8,161,998	8,384,172	8,377,660	8,601,239
Average Length of Stay	5.2	5.1	5.0	5.0	5.1
Personnel					
Total Full Time	229,182	224,884	226,972	222,354	222,494
Total Part Time	121,946	125,777	127,672	123,029	117,563
Revenue and Expenses - Totals					
(Includes Inpatient and Outpatient)					
Total Net Revenue	$51,788,888,807	$49,974,043,473	$47,525,027,006	$45,855,486,664	$43,455,515,086
Total Expenses	48,773,242,820	47,206,585,210	45,467,953,143	44,254,639,824	42,232,006,786
COMMUNITY HEALTH INDICATORS PER 1000 POPULATION					
Total Population (in thousands)	14,619	14,563	14,492	14,474	14,430
Inpatient					
Beds	2.3	2.4	2.3	2.3	2.3
Admissions	109.3	110.4	115.7	115.3	116.3
Inpatient Days	589.0	582.5	596.9	608.9	622.8
Inpatient Surgeries	28.0	28.7	29.6	30.4	31.5
Births	10.0	10.0	11.0	10.5	10.8
Outpatient					
Emergency Outpatient Visits	490.3	489.7	484.3	491.9	485.4
Other Outpatient Visits	2,840.8	2,798.7	2,779.8	2,737.0	2,702.7
Total Outpatient Visits	3,331.1	3,288.4	3,264.0	3,228.9	3,188.2
Outpatient Surgeries	64.9	65.9	65.8	70.4	67.9
Expense per Capita (per person)	$3,342.0	$3,249.5	$3,142.2	$3,065.2	$2,935.0

U.S. Census Divisions

TABLE 5

U.S. CENSUS DIVISION 2: MIDDLE ATLANTIC

U.S. Registered Community Hospitals
(Nonfederal, short-term general and other special hospitals)

Overview 2009–2013

	2013	2012	2011	2010	2009
Total Community Hospitals					
in Census Division 2, Middle Atlantic.......	444	447	449	454	457
Bed Size Category					
6-24..................................	10	11	9	8	7
25-49.................................	37	36	36	38	39
50-99.................................	63	63	66	66	64
100-199...............................	106	107	106	102	111
200-299...............................	90	91	91	98	93
300-399...............................	53	52	54	53	53
400-499...............................	27	30	33	33	36
500 +.................................	58	57	54	56	54
Location					
Hospitals Urban........................	359	362	364	367	369
Hospitals Rural........................	85	85	85	87	88
Control					
State and Local Government..............	31	31	30	30	30
Not for Profit.........................	353	354	362	373	381
Investor owned........................	60	62	57	51	46
Physician Models					
Independent Practice Association...........	62	61	53	54	54
Group Practice without Walls..............	16	17	12	17	20
Open Physician-Hospital Organization.......	40	42	39	40	41
Closed Physician-Hospital Organization......	15	19	15	15	18
Management Service Organization...........	49	52	47	51	54
Integrated Salary Model...................	195	182	175	172	158
Equity Model...........................	8	7	3	2	5
Foundation.............................	17	15	18	14	12
Insurance Products					
Health Maintenance Organization...........	97	91	90	80	66
Preferred Provider Organization............	74	65	69	79	66
Indemnity Fee for Service.................	40	37	31	42	28
Managed Care Contracts					
Health Maintenance Organization...........	281	295	284	286	279
Preferred Provider Organization............	277	285	274	277	264
Affiliations					
Hospitals in a System....................	277	261	254	242	235
Hospitals in a Network...................	166	157	163	157	151
Hospitals in a Group Purchasing Organization..	335	323	321	321	305

U.S. Census Divisions

TABLE 5   **U.S. CENSUS DIVISION 2: MIDDLE ATLANTIC**

U.S. Registered Community Hospitals
(Nonfederal, short-term general and other special hospitals)

Utilization, Personnel, Revenue and Expenses, Community Health Indicators 2009–2013

	2013	2012	2011	2010	2009
TOTAL FACILITY (Includes Hospital and Nursing Home Units)					
Utilization - Inpatient					
Beds	116,588	117,624	118,152	120,495	120,666
Admissions	4,974,821	5,183,982	5,308,422	5,387,182	5,469,937
Inpatient Days	30,254,395	31,440,731	31,927,960	32,429,928	32,905,796
Average Length of Stay	6.1	6.1	6.0	6.0	6.0
Inpatient Surgeries	1,327,290	1,404,460	1,385,212	1,472,258	1,444,280
Births	460,691	468,787	473,951	473,143	481,966
Utilization - Outpatient					
Emergency Outpatient Visits	18,464,278	18,321,971	18,128,050	17,544,922	18,036,427
Other Outpatient Visits	91,471,231	92,940,002	89,610,828	90,638,433	92,532,690
Total Outpatient Visits	109,935,509	111,261,973	107,738,878	108,183,355	110,569,117
Outpatient Surgeries	2,644,536	2,604,246	2,612,230	2,662,613	2,672,246
Personnel					
Full Time RNs	166,205	164,025	163,685	159,336	157,599
Full Time LPNs	8,442	8,908	9,399	9,477	10,498
Part Time RNs	61,534	61,911	62,925	61,970	58,758
Part Time LPNs	2,676	2,910	3,059	3,392	3,492
Total Full Time	665,974	667,785	663,442	641,848	649,700
Total Part Time	197,905	200,851	201,876	193,048	188,250
Revenue - Inpatient					
Gross Inpatient Revenue	$237,733,249,795	$232,928,664,012	$224,663,669,372	$214,875,701,636	$207,428,274,807
Revenue - Outpatient					
Gross Outpatient Revenue	$169,822,609,385	$159,129,515,739	$142,077,957,104	$131,067,665,392	$119,608,818,446
Revenue and Expenses - Totals					
(Includes Inpatient and Outpatient)					
Total Gross Revenue	$407,555,859,180	$392,058,179,751	$366,741,626,476	$345,943,367,028	$327,037,093,253
Deductions from Revenue	290,276,723,196	276,630,776,133	258,245,571,725	241,791,805,319	226,954,454,439
Net Patient Revenue	117,279,135,984	115,427,403,618	108,496,054,751	104,151,561,709	100,082,638,814
Other Operating Revenue	8,770,801,527	7,842,143,044	7,014,856,042	6,773,917,247	6,240,458,318
Other Nonoperating Revenue	2,945,630,852	1,401,364,085	1,370,628,711	1,636,895,627	1,079,935,145
Total Net Revenue	128,995,568,363	124,670,910,747	116,881,539,504	112,562,374,583	107,403,032,277
Total Expenses	123,273,293,065	119,193,201,375	112,027,433,487	107,964,477,816	104,601,314,499
HOSPITAL UNIT (Excludes Separate Nursing Home Units)					
Utilization - Inpatient					
Beds	108,138	108,572	108,920	112,240	112,737
Admissions	4,936,296	5,143,373	5,266,742	5,349,564	5,432,647
Inpatient Days	27,418,799	28,351,497	28,745,893	29,691,180	30,267,570
Average Length of Stay	5.6	5.5	5.5	5.6	5.6
Personnel					
Total Full Time	659,374	660,600	657,123	636,513	642,529
Total Part Time	194,622	197,298	198,919	189,998	184,726
Revenue and Expenses - Totals					
(Includes Inpatient and Outpatient)					
Total Net Revenue	$128,084,425,548	$123,724,968,154	$116,030,325,922	$111,642,685,649	$106,605,542,714
Total Expenses	122,409,617,966	118,279,090,752	111,216,627,510	107,117,179,018	103,815,232,446
COMMUNITY HEALTH INDICATORS PER 1000 POPULATION					
Total Population (in thousands)	41,324	41,198	41,029	40,943	40,854
Inpatient					
Beds	2.8	2.9	2.9	2.9	3.0
Admissions	120.4	125.8	129.4	131.6	133.9
Inpatient Days	732.1	763.2	778.2	792.1	805.4
Inpatient Surgeries	32.1	34.1	33.8	36.0	35.4
Births	11.1	11.4	11.6	11.6	11.8
Outpatient					
Emergency Outpatient Visits	446.8	444.7	441.8	428.5	441.5
Other Outpatient Visits	2,213.5	2,255.9	2,184.1	2,213.8	2,265.0
Total Outpatient Visits	2,660.3	2,700.6	2,625.9	2,642.3	2,706.4
Outpatient Surgeries	64.0	63.2	63.7	65.0	65.4
Expense per Capita (per person)	$2,983.1	$2,893.2	$2,730.4	$2,636.9	$2,560.4

U.S. Census Divisions

TABLE 5

U.S. CENSUS DIVISION 3: SOUTH ATLANTIC

U.S. Registered Community Hospitals
(Nonfederal, short-term general and other special hospitals)

Overview 2009–2013

	2013	2012	2011	2010	2009
Total Community Hospitals					
in Census Division 3, South Atlantic	758	766	759	758	759
Bed Size Category					
6-24	23	22	22	21	20
25-49	142	139	130	129	127
50-99	141	138	138	133	133
100-199	175	192	193	196	202
200-299	110	109	110	115	115
300-399	64	66	66	65	62
400-499	36	37	33	34	37
500 + ...	67	63	67	65	63
Location					
Hospitals Urban.	521	526	515	514	516
Hospitals Rural	237	240	244	244	243
Control					
State and Local Government.	129	135	137	141	144
Not for Profit	407	403	404	398	402
Investor owned	222	228	218	219	213
Physician Models					
Independent Practice Association	48	52	49	52	51
Group Practice without Walls.	30	30	23	23	26
Open Physician-Hospital Organization	69	77	78	79	77
Closed Physician-Hospital Organization	45	42	37	38	36
Management Service Organization	70	72	66	67	56
Integrated Salary Model.	292	291	287	287	256
Equity Model	17	19	20	21	20
Foundation.	15	17	19	20	16
Insurance Products					
Health Maintenance Organization	88	70	78	74	72
Preferred Provider Organization.	96	73	95	94	85
Indemnity Fee for Service	37	26	32	29	27
Managed Care Contracts					
Health Maintenance Organization	414	410	428	417	412
Preferred Provider Organization.	443	432	455	448	452
Affiliations					
Hospitals in a System.	564	554	527	504	493
Hospitals in a Network	229	220	218	215	205
Hospitals in a Group Purchasing Organization. .	525	516	522	538	535

TABLE 5

U.S. CENSUS DIVISION 3: SOUTH ATLANTIC

U.S. Registered Community Hospitals
(Nonfederal, short-term general and other special hospitals)

Utilization, Personnel, Revenue and Expenses, Community Health Indicators 2009–2013

	2013	2012	2011	2010	2009
TOTAL FACILITY (Includes Hospital and Nursing Home Units)					
Utilization - Inpatient					
Beds	156,366	156,937	156,421	156,678	156,435
Admissions	6,775,396	6,928,298	6,995,044	6,970,769	7,001,234
Inpatient Days	37,330,440	37,724,388	37,874,666	37,775,346	37,871,460
Average Length of Stay.	5.5	5.4	5.4	5.4	5.4
Inpatient Surgeries.	1,885,705	1,904,557	1,922,638	1,978,051	2,014,276
Births.	688,383	690,305	691,803	718,161	736,030
Utilization - Outpatient					
Emergency Outpatient Visits	27,180,478	26,665,515	25,719,396	25,132,194	25,680,948
Other Outpatient Visits.	76,008,760	74,855,137	72,465,338	70,980,844	71,516,908
Total Outpatient Visits	103,189,238	101,520,652	98,184,734	96,113,038	97,197,856
Outpatient Surgeries	3,402,928	3,293,896	3,285,368	3,275,089	3,347,083
Personnel					
Full Time RNs	229,245	226,678	218,388	214,222	209,172
Full Time LPNs	11,445	12,717	13,119	14,299	15,153
Part Time RNs	73,838	72,103	71,740	73,321	75,692
Part Time LPNs	3,227	3,438	3,608	4,092	4,515
Total Full Time.	777,852	782,368	764,221	753,621	746,119
Total Part Time	211,042	209,662	206,195	204,742	211,449
Revenue - Inpatient					
Gross Inpatient Revenue	$262,531,564,774	$247,143,243,581	$230,857,582,404	$221,881,724,341	$206,158,157,529
Revenue - Outpatient					
Gross Outpatient Revenue	$211,522,275,589	$191,354,643,518	$171,171,466,560	$156,997,699,889	$141,704,232,345
Revenue and Expenses - Totals					
(Includes Inpatient and Outpatient)					
Total Gross Revenue.	$474,053,840,363	$438,497,887,099	$402,029,048,964	$378,879,424,230	$347,862,389,874
Deductions from Revenue	334,573,003,794	301,779,297,485	278,266,927,544	257,534,395,622	231,360,708,001
Net Patient Revenue	139,480,836,569	136,718,589,614	123,762,121,420	121,345,028,608	116,501,681,873
Other Operating Revenue	6,380,425,184	6,785,768,283	6,233,574,974	5,739,614,294	5,340,444,911
Other Nonoperating Revenue	3,307,649,993	2,215,518,159	1,983,730,368	2,153,138,363	702,305,382
Total Net Revenue.	149,168,911,746	145,719,876,056	131,979,426,762	129,237,781,265	122,544,432,166
Total Expenses.	135,926,142,419	132,934,775,278	122,100,282,752	118,053,521,062	115,183,239,713
HOSPITAL UNIT (Excludes Separate Nursing Home Units)					
Utilization - Inpatient					
Beds	146,568	146,488	145,614	145,304	146,162
Admissions	6,734,481	6,885,814	6,952,755	6,925,183	6,957,697
Inpatient Days	34,230,779	34,334,087	34,472,561	34,041,050	34,447,166
Average Length of Stay.	5.1	5.0	5.0	4.9	5.0
Personnel					
Total Full Time.	770,841	774,599	756,853	745,348	737,233
Total Part Time	208,582	207,045	203,449	201,603	208,120
Revenue and Expenses - Totals					
(Includes Inpatient and Outpatient)					
Total Net Revenue.	$148,368,495,581	$144,879,731,362	$131,160,884,248	$128,322,166,959	$121,761,391,092
Total Expenses.	135,196,659,731	132,134,543,784	121,286,710,334	117,214,899,415	114,453,158,594
COMMUNITY HEALTH INDICATORS PER 1000 POPULATION					
Total Population (in thousands)	61,784	61,189	60,514	59,659	59,196
Inpatient					
Beds	2.5	2.6	2.6	2.6	2.6
Admissions	109.7	113.2	115.6	116.8	118.3
Inpatient Days	604.2	616.5	625.9	633.2	639.8
Inpatient Surgeries.	30.5	31.1	31.8	33.2	34.0
Births.	11.1	11.3	11.4	12.0	12.4
Outpatient					
Emergency Outpatient Visits	439.9	435.8	425.0	421.3	433.8
Other Outpatient Visits.	1,230.2	1,223.4	1,197.5	1,189.8	1,208.1
Total Outpatient Visits	1,670.2	1,659.1	1,622.5	1,611.0	1,642.0
Outpatient Surgeries	55.1	53.8	54.3	54.9	56.5
Expense per Capita (per person).	$2,200.0	$2,172.5	$2,017.7	$1,978.8	$1,945.8

TABLE 5

U.S. CENSUS DIVISION 4: EAST NORTH CENTRAL

U.S. Registered Community Hospitals
(Nonfederal, short-term general and other special hospitals)

Overview 2009–2013

	2013	2012	2011	2010	2009
Total Community Hospitals					
in Census Division 4, East North Central....	**775**	**776**	**774**	**777**	**779**
Bed Size Category					
6-24	59	57	45	43	40
25-49	203	204	204	198	196
50-99	148	146	155	163	166
100-199	162	161	155	151	161
200-299	90	84	93	100	96
300-399	42	55	56	56	52
400-499	30	29	27	26	29
500 + ...	41	40	39	40	39
Location					
Hospitals Urban.........................	502	503	501	503	504
Hospitals Rural	273	273	273	274	275
Control					
State and Local Government...............	87	90	89	96	99
Not for Profit..........................	587	588	592	590	593
Investor owned	101	98	93	91	87
Physician Models					
Independent Practice Association	67	71	69	73	86
Group Practice without Walls...............	43	27	30	25	23
Open Physician-Hospital Organization	173	162	163	164	163
Closed Physician-Hospital Organization	57	46	52	51	45
Management Service Organization	74	65	82	87	93
Integrated Salary Model....................	353	346	321	312	303
Equity Model............................	39	22	21	22	26
Foundation..............................	53	40	49	59	52
Insurance Products					
Health Maintenance Organization	163	152	151	145	143
Preferred Provider Organization..............	161	141	161	165	167
Indemnity Fee for Service	54	52	54	57	59
Managed Care Contracts					
Health Maintenance Organization	519	527	514	531	552
Preferred Provider Organization..............	556	555	547	568	597
Affiliations					
Hospitals in a System.....................	503	492	486	475	467
Hospitals in a Network....................	282	277	272	277	276
Hospitals in a Group Purchasing Organization..	613	618	608	632	645

U.S. Census Divisions

TABLE 5

U.S. CENSUS DIVISION 4: EAST NORTH CENTRAL

U.S. Registered Community Hospitals
(Nonfederal, short-term general and other special hospitals)

Utilization, Personnel, Revenue and Expenses, Community Health Indicators 2009–2013

	2013	2012	2011	2010	2009
TOTAL FACILITY (Includes Hospital and Nursing Home Units)					
Utilization - Inpatient					
Beds	120,050	121,997	122,555	124,528	124,648
Admissions	5,309,578	5,477,164	5,518,124	5,573,945	5,631,570
Inpatient Days	26,367,306	27,190,027	27,603,703	28,088,741	28,659,008
Average Length of Stay	5.0	5.0	5.0	5.0	5.1
Inpatient Surgeries	1,415,474	1,499,944	1,537,005	1,598,684	1,629,031
Births	520,879	524,244	531,487	549,668	569,683
Utilization - Outpatient					
Emergency Outpatient Visits	21,840,082	22,161,580	21,873,056	21,645,563	21,143,963
Other Outpatient Visits	115,696,131	114,778,170	110,723,087	110,255,848	106,866,440
Total Outpatient Visits	137,536,213	136,939,750	132,596,143	131,901,411	128,010,403
Outpatient Surgeries	3,116,354	3,185,907	3,152,571	3,207,896	3,184,812
Personnel					
Full Time RNs	178,559	176,706	171,026	166,190	159,198
Full Time LPNs	7,894	7,987	9,094	8,792	9,506
Part Time RNs	95,846	99,210	97,012	97,309	97,165
Part Time LPNs	4,236	4,590	4,841	5,200	5,538
Total Full Time	670,958	672,905	661,130	656,411	652,503
Total Part Time	295,422	302,574	301,819	305,777	309,198
Revenue - Inpatient					
Gross Inpatient Revenue	$193,599,807,491	$187,228,187,292	$176,586,489,578	$169,254,285,621	$159,626,875,101
Revenue - Outpatient					
Gross Outpatient Revenue	$200,738,677,953	$185,825,760,037	$167,198,588,978	$153,605,458,204	$139,937,321,698
Revenue and Expenses - Totals					
(Includes Inpatient and Outpatient)					
Total Gross Revenue	$394,338,485,444	$373,053,947,329	$343,785,078,556	$322,859,743,825	$299,564,196,799
Deductions from Revenue	263,377,222,866	243,148,787,597	224,785,581,163	206,741,773,300	188,295,725,972
Net Patient Revenue	130,961,262,578	129,905,159,732	118,999,497,393	116,117,970,525	111,268,470,827
Other Operating Revenue	8,342,665,932	7,734,468,170	7,235,875,567	6,838,675,527	6,706,843,261
Other Nonoperating Revenue	3,963,965,511	2,372,671,286	2,481,023,683	2,812,190,226	360,822,911
Total Net Revenue	143,267,894,021	140,012,299,188	128,716,396,643	125,768,836,278	118,336,136,999
Total Expenses	130,380,820,276	128,508,223,081	118,844,737,908	116,021,099,796	112,388,231,445
HOSPITAL UNIT (Excludes Separate Nursing Home Units)					
Utilization - Inpatient					
Beds	115,570	116,777	117,051	118,315	118,136
Admissions	5,281,193	5,443,973	5,480,695	5,532,131	5,587,798
Inpatient Days	25,031,404	25,617,733	25,917,067	26,193,965	26,630,592
Average Length of Stay	4.7	4.7	4.7	4.7	4.8
Personnel					
Total Full Time	668,467	669,734	657,862	652,317	647,481
Total Part Time	293,112	299,781	298,789	302,371	305,428
Revenue and Expenses - Totals					
(Includes Inpatient and Outpatient)					
Total Net Revenue	$142,884,583,269	$139,565,247,628	$128,223,217,900	$125,272,982,180	$117,798,388,335
Total Expenses	130,048,404,828	128,116,255,360	118,428,199,417	115,557,672,594	111,947,643,021
COMMUNITY HEALTH INDICATORS PER 1000 POPULATION					
Total Population (in thousands)	46,662	46,567	46,519	46,522	46,501
Inpatient					
Beds	2.6	2.6	2.6	2.7	2.7
Admissions	113.8	117.6	118.6	119.8	121.1
Inpatient Days	565.1	583.9	593.4	603.8	616.3
Inpatient Surgeries	30.3	32.2	33.0	34.4	35.0
Births	11.2	11.3	11.4	11.8	12.3
Outpatient					
Emergency Outpatient Visits	468.0	475.9	470.2	465.3	454.7
Other Outpatient Visits	2,479.4	2,464.8	2,380.2	2,370.0	2,298.2
Total Outpatient Visits	2,947.5	2,940.7	2,850.4	2,835.3	2,752.9
Outpatient Surgeries	66.8	68.4	67.8	69.0	68.5
Expense per Capita (per person)	$2,794.1	$2,759.7	$2,554.8	$2,493.9	$2,416.9

TABLE 5

U.S. CENSUS DIVISION 5: EAST SOUTH CENTRAL

U.S. Registered Community Hospitals
(Nonfederal, short-term general and other special hospitals)

Overview 2009–2013

	2013	2012	2011	2010	2009
Total Community Hospitals					
in Census Division 5, East South Central ...	432	433	440	441	446
Bed Size Category					
6-24	19	21	22	16	16
25-49	123	125	125	128	128
50-99	98	95	98	100	104
100-199	97	97	99	104	104
200-299	42	41	40	35	35
300-399	24	24	25	25	26
400-499	9	8	10	14	15
500 + ...	20	22	21	19	18
Location					
Hospitals Urban.........................	200	200	207	208	211
Hospitals Rural	232	233	233	233	235
Control					
State and Local Government................	113	111	112	112	115
Not for Profit	177	176	177	182	186
Investor owned	142	146	151	147	145
Physician Models					
Independent Practice Association	24	30	31	36	36
Group Practice without Walls...............	7	7	7	7	10
Open Physician-Hospital Organization	43	45	43	43	41
Closed Physician-Hospital Organization	8	12	10	8	11
Management Service Organization	32	44	46	39	34
Integrated Salary Model....................	112	113	111	114	102
Equity Model	4	2	1	1	3
Foundation.............................	20	15	21	22	23
Insurance Products					
Health Maintenance Organization	30	26	25	32	26
Preferred Provider Organization..............	78	65	80	75	70
Indemnity Fee for Service	23	19	18	21	15
Managed Care Contracts					
Health Maintenance Organization	152	159	165	165	164
Preferred Provider Organization..............	184	194	204	215	211
Affiliations					
Hospitals in a System.....................	300	295	294	289	289
Hospitals in a Network....................	97	89	91	101	105
Hospitals in a Group Purchasing Organization..	175	192	194	205	224

TABLE 5

U.S. CENSUS DIVISION 5: EAST SOUTH CENTRAL

U.S. Registered Community Hospitals
(Nonfederal, short-term general and other special hospitals)

Utilization, Personnel, Revenue and Expenses, Community Health Indicators 2009–2013

	2013	2012	2011	2010	2009
TOTAL FACILITY (Includes Hospital and Nursing Home Units)					
Utilization - Inpatient					
Beds	62,235	62,199	62,478	63,079	63,252
Admissions	2,419,265	2,430,269	2,424,397	2,486,454	2,535,115
Inpatient Days	13,421,013	13,150,314	13,300,397	13,614,893	13,973,205
Average Length of Stay	5.5	5.4	5.5	5.5	5.5
Inpatient Surgeries	676,161	728,421	732,580	728,125	746,929
Births	215,234	209,932	207,943	221,646	233,974
Utilization - Outpatient					
Emergency Outpatient Visits	9,732,264	9,782,661	9,526,218	9,527,974	9,630,514
Other Outpatient Visits	25,969,056	25,794,437	25,425,473	25,726,751	25,948,613
Total Outpatient Visits	35,701,320	35,577,098	34,951,691	35,254,725	35,579,127
Outpatient Surgeries	1,351,037	1,405,286	1,386,491	1,344,976	1,337,590
Personnel					
Full Time RNs	77,713	75,991	75,308	73,350	73,191
Full Time LPNs	6,016	6,263	6,748	7,457	8,025
Part Time RNs	24,713	25,437	24,560	25,319	24,568
Part Time LPNs	1,534	1,640	1,692	2,052	2,168
Total Full Time	267,164	266,388	265,560	262,113	265,884
Total Part Time	68,124	71,714	68,968	72,591	71,457
Revenue - Inpatient					
Gross Inpatient Revenue	$85,886,311,001	$80,646,954,304	$75,686,751,272	$73,345,815,567	$70,177,022,070
Revenue - Outpatient					
Gross Outpatient Revenue	$76,616,972,839	$71,015,770,262	$61,846,614,466	$56,798,252,271	$52,231,598,393
Revenue and Expenses - Totals					
(Includes Inpatient and Outpatient)					
Total Gross Revenue	$162,503,283,840	$151,662,724,566	$137,533,365,738	$130,144,067,838	$122,408,620,463
Deductions from Revenue	118,611,464,301	109,016,339,180	99,633,059,934	92,627,817,898	85,830,854,030
Net Patient Revenue	43,891,819,539	42,646,385,386	37,900,305,804	37,516,249,940	36,577,766,433
Other Operating Revenue	1,929,535,883	1,820,681,077	1,532,546,010	1,479,335,426	1,540,908,813
Other Nonoperating Revenue	758,473,581	407,005,231	481,348,514	696,071,058	193,864,288
Total Net Revenue	46,579,829,003	44,874,071,694	39,914,200,328	39,691,656,424	38,312,539,534
Total Expenses	42,687,366,112	41,101,364,805	36,909,370,915	36,471,494,399	36,466,730,541
HOSPITAL UNIT (Excludes Separate Nursing Home Units)					
Utilization - Inpatient					
Beds	58,109	58,411	58,770	58,946	58,982
Admissions	2,403,639	2,413,202	2,407,693	2,471,184	2,518,083
Inpatient Days	12,117,469	11,963,248	12,159,845	12,327,182	12,606,657
Average Length of Stay	5.0	5.0	5.1	5.0	5.0
Personnel					
Total Full Time	263,499	263,124	262,518	258,805	262,043
Total Part Time	66,771	70,861	68,301	71,637	70,556
Revenue and Expenses - Totals					
(Includes Inpatient and Outpatient)					
Total Net Revenue	$46,303,139,122	$44,641,587,474	$39,631,141,073	$39,425,199,072	$38,036,670,123
Total Expenses	42,457,268,955	40,885,625,657	36,701,651,997	36,231,662,045	36,228,704,518
COMMUNITY HEALTH INDICATORS PER 1000 POPULATION					
Total Population (in thousands)	18,716	18,644	18,554	18,368	18,271
Inpatient					
Beds	3.3	3.3	3.4	3.4	3.5
Admissions	129.3	130.4	130.7	135.4	138.8
Inpatient Days	717.1	705.4	716.8	741.2	764.8
Inpatient Surgeries	36.1	39.1	39.5	39.6	40.9
Births	11.5	11.3	11.2	12.1	12.8
Outpatient					
Emergency Outpatient Visits	520.0	524.7	513.4	518.7	527.1
Other Outpatient Visits	1,387.5	1,383.6	1,370.4	1,400.7	1,420.2
Total Outpatient Visits	1,907.5	1,908.3	1,883.8	1,919.4	1,947.3
Outpatient Surgeries	72.2	75.4	74.7	73.2	73.2
Expense per Capita (per person)	$2,280.8	$2,204.6	$1,989.3	$1,985.6	$1,995.9

U.S. Census Divisions

TABLE 5

U.S. CENSUS DIVISION 6: WEST NORTH CENTRAL

U.S. Registered Community Hospitals
(Nonfederal, short-term general and other special hospitals)

Overview 2009–2013

	2013	2012	2011	2010	2009
Total Community Hospitals					
in Census Division 6, West North Central . . .	**683**	**692**	**682**	**685**	**689**
Bed Size Category					
6-24	134	128	126	113	108
25-49	212	217	218	220	217
50-99	156	160	154	164	167
100-199	90	97	91	97	104
200-299	37	35	38	35	38
300-399	24	25	25	28	25
400-499	14	14	14	12	14
500 + ...	16	16	16	16	16
Location					
Hospitals Urban	224	226	220	223	224
Hospitals Rural	459	466	462	462	465
Control					
State and Local Government	228	233	236	235	237
Not for Profit	401	405	396	398	399
Investor owned	54	54	50	52	53
Physician Models					
Independent Practice Association	55	63	62	70	77
Group Practice without Walls	12	16	12	11	14
Open Physician-Hospital Organization	68	70	68	70	84
Closed Physician-Hospital Organization	23	26	26	23	27
Management Service Organization	12	16	20	17	19
Integrated Salary Model	341	336	330	317	339
Equity Model	6	7	6	2	5
Foundation	18	17	22	17	14
Insurance Products					
Health Maintenance Organization	68	59	56	59	56
Preferred Provider Organization	67	69	89	88	84
Indemnity Fee for Service	19	20	29	27	29
Managed Care Contracts					
Health Maintenance Organization	312	318	311	310	320
Preferred Provider Organization	433	445	442	446	469
Affiliations					
Hospitals in a System	367	372	352	348	347
Hospitals in a Network	291	288	287	277	282
Hospitals in a Group Purchasing Organization . .	551	562	557	552	573

TABLE 5

U.S. CENSUS DIVISION 6: WEST NORTH CENTRAL

U.S. Registered Community Hospitals
(Nonfederal, short-term general and other special hospitals)

Utilization, Personnel, Revenue and Expenses, Community Health Indicators 2009–2013

	2013	2012	2011	2010	2009
TOTAL FACILITY (Includes Hospital and Nursing Home Units)					
Utilization - Inpatient					
Beds	67,386	68,455	67,559	68,830	70,039
Admissions	2,355,948	2,421,698	2,453,988	2,464,267	2,523,626
Inpatient Days	14,286,092	14,638,214	14,718,938	14,928,227	15,492,237
Average Length of Stay	6.1	6.0	6.0	6.1	6.1
Inpatient Surgeries	649,575	667,171	674,685	683,170	705,862
Births	267,407	268,618	264,259	264,621	274,101
Utilization - Outpatient					
Emergency Outpatient Visits	8,653,473	8,725,139	8,573,615	8,260,672	8,272,930
Other Outpatient Visits	51,914,260	52,156,664	49,766,340	50,003,264	48,365,884
Total Outpatient Visits	60,567,733	60,881,803	58,339,955	58,263,936	56,638,814
Outpatient Surgeries	1,356,009	1,381,534	1,352,232	1,322,974	1,367,598
Personnel					
Full Time RNs	81,791	78,654	75,384	73,425	70,664
Full Time LPNs	7,140	7,145	7,158	7,282	7,481
Part Time RNs	53,163	54,342	51,864	52,648	54,581
Part Time LPNs	3,944	4,109	4,132	4,485	4,775
Total Full Time	336,351	311,613	301,105	297,067	289,975
Total Part Time	161,075	164,991	160,171	164,985	169,233
Revenue - Inpatient					
Gross Inpatient Revenue	$80,759,847,710	$77,970,550,986	$74,583,373,377	$71,077,555,297	$68,351,872,323
Revenue - Outpatient					
Gross Outpatient Revenue	$81,195,833,655	$76,310,450,463	$68,953,101,651	$62,710,234,207	$58,193,971,919
Revenue and Expenses - Totals					
(Includes Inpatient and Outpatient)					
Total Gross Revenue	$161,955,681,365	$154,281,001,449	$143,536,475,028	$133,787,789,504	$126,545,844,242
Deductions from Revenue	102,735,424,002	96,278,090,518	89,596,077,363	82,115,750,561	76,480,891,243
Net Patient Revenue	59,220,257,363	58,002,910,931	53,940,397,665	51,672,038,943	50,064,952,999
Other Operating Revenue	3,513,084,143	3,444,366,586	2,870,841,462	2,830,841,723	2,646,149,834
Other Nonoperating Revenue	1,693,175,535	1,330,357,727	1,096,847,381	1,318,194,215	557,107,759
Total Net Revenue	64,426,517,041	62,777,635,244	57,908,086,508	55,821,074,881	53,268,210,592
Total Expenses	59,579,626,804	56,450,154,448	54,026,689,854	51,771,367,599	50,238,229,445
HOSPITAL UNIT (Excludes Separate Nursing Home Units)					
Utilization - Inpatient					
Beds	58,424	59,408	58,568	59,661	59,833
Admissions	2,336,928	2,400,701	2,432,961	2,443,671	2,498,928
Inpatient Days	11,484,252	11,768,543	11,849,105	12,018,243	12,233,218
Average Length of Stay	4.9	4.9	4.9	4.9	4.9
Personnel					
Total Full Time	330,962	305,819	295,954	291,819	283,837
Total Part Time	156,709	160,210	155,670	160,316	164,037
Revenue and Expenses - Totals					
(Includes Inpatient and Outpatient)					
Total Net Revenue	$63,856,543,055	$62,194,053,711	$57,296,078,737	$55,268,629,929	$52,624,057,167
Total Expenses	59,040,011,689	55,903,031,384	53,536,656,669	51,251,683,260	49,653,268,189
COMMUNITY HEALTH INDICATORS PER 1000 POPULATION					
Total Population (in thousands)	20,886	20,750	20,640	20,451	20,336
Inpatient					
Beds	3.2	3.3	3.3	3.4	3.4
Admissions	112.8	116.7	118.9	120.5	124.1
Inpatient Days	684.0	705.5	713.1	729.9	761.8
Inpatient Surgeries	31.1	32.2	32.7	33.4	34.7
Births	12.8	12.9	12.8	12.9	13.5
Outpatient					
Emergency Outpatient Visits	414.3	420.5	415.4	403.9	406.8
Other Outpatient Visits	2,485.6	2,513.6	2,411.2	2,445.0	2,378.3
Total Outpatient Visits	2,900.0	2,934.1	2,826.6	2,848.9	2,785.1
Outpatient Surgeries	64.9	66.6	65.5	64.7	67.2
Expense per Capita (per person)	$2,852.7	$2,720.5	$2,617.6	$2,531.4	$2,470.4

TABLE 5

U.S. CENSUS DIVISION 7: WEST SOUTH CENTRAL

U.S. Registered Community Hospitals
(Nonfederal, short-term general and other special hospitals)

Overview 2009–2013

	2013	2012	2011	2010	2009
Total Community Hospitals					
in Census Division 7, West South Central...	746	749	746	750	758
Bed Size Category					
6-24	118	117	114	119	112
25-49	223	224	226	220	223
50-99	149	149	144	146	147
100-199	101	104	109	115	124
200-299	62	62	62	61	61
300-399	39	40	37	35	35
400-499	19	19	20	20	22
500 + ...	35	34	34	34	34
Location					
Hospitals Urban..........................	438	439	431	436	440
Hospitals Rural	308	310	315	314	318
Control					
State and Local Government...............	195	206	210	221	230
Not for Profit	282	275	276	267	263
Investor owned	269	268	260	262	265
Physician Models					
Independent Practice Association	80	82	94	109	109
Group Practice without Walls...............	34	28	31	33	41
Open Physician-Hospital Organization	117	128	126	128	137
Closed Physician-Hospital Organization	40	38	32	30	31
Management Service Organization	83	88	93	94	99
Integrated Salary Model....................	228	215	211	181	168
Equity Model.............................	10	11	10	16	17
Foundation...............................	52	48	47	43	44
Insurance Products					
Health Maintenance Organization	104	93	101	96	90
Preferred Provider Organization..............	88	76	116	118	105
Indemnity Fee for Service	25	22	34	36	30
Managed Care Contracts					
Health Maintenance Organization	481	468	457	449	458
Preferred Provider Organization..............	559	542	554	540	544
Affiliations					
Hospitals in a System.....................	452	451	436	434	457
Hospitals in a Network....................	204	193	193	184	175
Hospitals in a Group Purchasing Organization..	637	625	629	623	624

TABLE 5

U.S. CENSUS DIVISION 7: WEST SOUTH CENTRAL

U.S. Registered Community Hospitals
(Nonfederal, short-term general and other special hospitals)

Utilization, Personnel, Revenue and Expenses, Community Health Indicators 2009–2013

	2013	2012	2011	2010	2009
TOTAL FACILITY (Includes Hospital and Nursing Home Units)					
Utilization - Inpatient					
Beds	97,967	97,260	96,825	97,399	98,807
Admissions	3,852,821	3,908,065	3,929,807	4,005,387	4,083,758
Inpatient Days	20,284,467	20,396,936	20,460,393	20,922,699	21,466,556
Average Length of Stay	5.3	5.2	5.2	5.2	5.3
Inpatient Surgeries	1,055,227	1,080,738	1,118,349	1,150,547	1,181,045
Births	530,165	516,124	503,256	528,045	561,702
Utilization - Outpatient					
Emergency Outpatient Visits	16,301,738	16,269,062	15,575,261	15,392,542	14,987,499
Other Outpatient Visits	45,227,309	45,892,246	44,066,578	45,924,148	44,027,580
Total Outpatient Visits	61,529,047	62,161,308	59,641,839	61,316,690	59,015,079
Outpatient Surgeries	1,719,039	1,675,034	1,683,472	1,707,264	1,671,570
Personnel					
Full Time RNs	131,052	126,908	121,426	123,112	120,752
Full Time LPNs	13,147	13,783	14,606	15,573	16,584
Part Time RNs	37,846	36,330	35,553	33,058	33,815
Part Time LPNs	3,153	3,352	3,347	3,961	4,411
Total Full Time	440,358	435,758	428,649	434,296	436,301
Total Part Time	110,628	106,477	103,538	99,628	101,491
Revenue - Inpatient					
Gross Inpatient Revenue	$165,441,811,098	$157,197,100,160	$146,271,380,775	$139,926,153,510	$132,565,357,014
Revenue - Outpatient					
Gross Outpatient Revenue	$129,896,699,181	$118,343,524,306	$104,883,587,404	$95,633,086,065	$84,978,216,080
Revenue and Expenses - Totals					
(Includes Inpatient and Outpatient)					
Total Gross Revenue	$295,338,510,279	$275,540,624,466	$251,154,968,179	$235,559,239,575	$217,543,573,094
Deductions from Revenue	218,013,431,324	199,811,182,037	184,194,250,743	169,768,881,745	154,142,249,102
Net Patient Revenue	77,325,078,955	75,729,442,429	66,960,717,436	65,790,357,830	63,401,323,992
Other Operating Revenue	6,605,401,355	6,473,296,689	5,893,843,564	5,622,273,906	5,328,857,978
Other Nonoperating Revenue	1,436,996,905	1,074,127,947	1,909,520,980	1,791,442,768	267,367,879
Total Net Revenue	85,367,477,215	83,276,867,065	74,764,081,980	73,204,074,504	68,997,549,849
Total Expenses	77,562,496,193	74,523,034,451	67,280,680,393	65,549,933,822	64,399,048,894
HOSPITAL UNIT (Excludes Separate Nursing Home Units)					
Utilization - Inpatient					
Beds	95,923	95,188	94,783	95,427	96,504
Admissions	3,841,094	3,894,508	3,916,503	3,991,294	4,068,586
Inpatient Days	19,723,627	19,839,649	19,861,338	20,336,517	20,737,974
Average Length of Stay	5.1	5.1	5.1	5.1	5.1
Personnel					
Total Full Time	438,804	433,602	427,100	432,842	433,900
Total Part Time	110,195	106,091	103,146	99,156	100,856
Revenue and Expenses - Totals					
(Includes Inpatient and Outpatient)					
Total Net Revenue	$85,208,123,466	$83,105,764,389	$74,607,353,353	$73,043,779,992	$68,839,731,724
Total Expenses	77,432,447,297	74,387,874,023	67,137,888,126	65,399,265,396	64,241,260,529
COMMUNITY HEALTH INDICATORS PER 1000 POPULATION					
Total Population (in thousands)	37,884	37,425	36,979	36,378	35,851
Inpatient					
Beds	2.6	2.6	2.6	2.7	2.8
Admissions	101.7	104.4	106.3	110.1	113.9
Inpatient Days	535.4	545.0	553.3	575.2	598.8
Inpatient Surgeries	27.9	28.9	30.2	31.6	32.9
Births	14.0	13.8	13.6	14.5	15.7
Outpatient					
Emergency Outpatient Visits	430.3	434.7	421.2	423.1	418.1
Other Outpatient Visits	1,193.8	1,226.2	1,191.7	1,262.4	1,228.1
Total Outpatient Visits	1,624.2	1,661.0	1,612.9	1,685.6	1,646.1
Outpatient Surgeries	45.4	44.8	45.5	46.9	46.6
Expense per Capita (per person)	$2,047.4	$1,991.3	$1,819.4	$1,801.9	$1,796.3

TABLE 5

U.S. CENSUS DIVISION 8: MOUNTAIN

U.S. Registered Community Hospitals
(Nonfederal, short-term general and other special hospitals)

Overview 2009–2013

	2013	2012	2011	2010	2009
Total Community Hospitals					
in Census Division 8, Mountain............	390	388	384	382	382
Bed Size Category					
6-24..................................	57	57	55	53	50
25-49.................................	103	102	99	98	96
50-99.................................	87	84	87	88	96
100-199...............................	65	65	63	66	61
200-299...............................	33	34	35	32	35
300-399...............................	20	20	20	21	21
400-499...............................	13	14	13	11	8
500 +.................................	12	12	12	13	15
Location					
Hospitals Urban..........................	193	193	191	189	189
Hospitals Rural	197	195	193	193	193
Control					
State and Local Government...............	90	93	94	94	97
Not for Profit...........................	202	196	197	195	191
Investor owned	98	99	93	93	94
Physician Models					
Independent Practice Association	32	40	41	42	48
Group Practice without Walls...............	13	12	13	8	9
Open Physician-Hospital Organization	34	37	36	34	36
Closed Physician-Hospital Organization	14	13	15	14	16
Management Service Organization	22	21	24	27	26
Integrated Salary Model....................	150	148	140	125	130
Equity Model............................	4	4	5	5	5
Foundation..............................	13	12	12	13	11
Insurance Products					
Health Maintenance Organization	57	55	57	54	53
Preferred Provider Organization.............	53	40	58	56	54
Indemnity Fee for Service	24	20	26	27	29
Managed Care Contracts					
Health Maintenance Organization	142	143	141	147	153
Preferred Provider Organization.............	193	190	184	185	198
Affiliations					
Hospitals in a System.....................	234	234	229	230	232
Hospitals in a Network....................	107	99	110	112	111
Hospitals in a Group Purchasing Organization..	268	240	259	248	257

TABLE 5

U.S. CENSUS DIVISION 8: MOUNTAIN

U.S. Registered Community Hospitals
(Nonfederal, short-term general and other special hospitals)

Utilization, Personnel, Revenue and Expenses, Community Health Indicators 2009–2013

	2013	2012	2011	2010	2009
TOTAL FACILITY (Includes Hospital and Nursing Home Units)					
Utilization - Inpatient					
Beds	47,322	47,501	47,119	46,872	47,028
Admissions	1,962,391	2,060,596	2,064,195	2,091,454	2,089,087
Inpatient Days	9,977,101	10,231,226	10,303,057	10,379,491	10,509,716
Average Length of Stay	5.1	5.0	5.0	5.0	5.0
Inpatient Surgeries	559,564	614,124	646,125	662,412	673,176
Births	266,237	269,841	268,969	278,694	300,722
Utilization - Outpatient					
Emergency Outpatient Visits	7,787,157	7,821,770	7,567,323	7,497,043	7,485,406
Other Outpatient Visits	32,829,124	32,436,477	31,476,244	29,432,803	28,867,801
Total Outpatient Visits	40,616,281	40,258,247	39,043,567	36,929,846	36,353,207
Outpatient Surgeries	1,024,797	982,976	996,441	982,327	962,734
Personnel					
Full Time RNs	69,945	66,845	64,271	66,717	64,343
Full Time LPNs	3,039	3,085	3,129	3,511	4,372
Part Time RNs	26,487	26,537	25,828	23,141	24,303
Part Time LPNs	1,109	1,204	1,197	1,170	1,401
Total Full Time	241,359	234,035	228,851	233,880	229,182
Total Part Time	80,434	78,088	76,297	68,863	73,288
Revenue - Inpatient					
Gross Inpatient Revenue	$87,638,841,277	$83,441,071,276	$77,570,487,787	$74,568,371,912	$69,773,749,237
Revenue - Outpatient					
Gross Outpatient Revenue	$73,378,356,271	$65,655,835,782	$59,010,644,319	$53,530,101,037	$47,901,898,628
Revenue and Expenses - Totals					
(Includes Inpatient and Outpatient)					
Total Gross Revenue	$161,017,197,548	$149,096,907,058	$136,581,132,106	$128,098,472,949	$117,675,647,865
Deductions from Revenue	113,683,233,185	102,954,441,992	94,240,727,395	86,894,343,376	78,561,440,721
Net Patient Revenue	47,333,964,363	46,142,465,066	42,340,404,711	41,204,129,573	39,114,207,144
Other Operating Revenue	2,195,077,380	1,890,523,158	1,885,009,958	1,804,886,179	1,641,533,021
Other Nonoperating Revenue	686,369,507	353,858,460	497,930,676	550,761,263	383,043,417
Total Net Revenue	50,215,411,250	48,386,846,684	44,723,345,345	43,559,777,015	41,138,783,582
Total Expenses	45,094,874,475	43,346,401,522	40,362,478,873	38,771,182,258	37,489,628,683
HOSPITAL UNIT (Excludes Separate Nursing Home Units)					
Utilization - Inpatient					
Beds	44,166	44,388	43,922	43,563	43,572
Admissions	1,954,560	2,052,402	2,054,557	2,081,194	2,078,283
Inpatient Days	9,030,424	9,282,591	9,320,023	9,356,938	9,453,606
Average Length of Stay	4.6	4.5	4.5	4.5	4.5
Personnel					
Total Full Time	239,029	232,008	226,920	231,537	226,895
Total Part Time	78,848	76,862	75,224	67,617	72,075
Revenue and Expenses - Totals					
(Includes Inpatient and Outpatient)					
Total Net Revenue	$49,982,879,096	$48,172,247,901	$44,490,329,013	$43,323,260,876	$40,917,090,747
Total Expenses	44,908,887,608	43,160,567,568	40,156,890,139	38,565,221,584	37,287,396,355
COMMUNITY HEALTH INDICATORS PER 1000 POPULATION					
Total Population (in thousands)	22,881	22,618	22,373	22,379	22,123
Inpatient					
Beds	2.1	2.1	2.1	2.1	2.1
Admissions	85.8	91.1	92.3	93.5	94.4
Inpatient Days	436.0	452.4	460.5	463.8	475.1
Inpatient Surgeries	24.5	27.2	28.9	29.6	30.4
Births	11.6	11.9	12.0	12.5	13.6
Outpatient					
Emergency Outpatient Visits	340.3	345.8	338.2	335.0	338.4
Other Outpatient Visits	1,434.8	1,434.1	1,406.9	1,315.2	1,304.9
Total Outpatient Visits	1,775.1	1,779.9	1,745.1	1,650.2	1,643.2
Outpatient Surgeries	44.8	43.5	44.5	43.9	43.5
Expense per Capita (per person)	$1,970.8	$1,916.5	$1,804.0	$1,732.5	$1,694.6

U.S. Census Divisions

TABLE 5

U.S. CENSUS DIVISION 9: PACIFIC

U.S. Registered Community Hospitals
(Nonfederal, short-term general and other special hospitals)

Overview 2009–2013

	2013	2012	2011	2010	2009
Total Community Hospitals					
in Census Division 9, Pacific	543	541	535	535	535
Bed Size Category					
6-24	42	39	42	41	39
25-49	99	102	97	97	98
50-99	72	72	73	70	73
100-199	144	138	133	139	139
200-299	84	88	86	84	87
300-399	55	51	55	55	57
400-499	30	34	31	31	27
500 + ...	17	17	18	18	15
Location					
Hospitals Urban..........................	420	421	414	413	413
Hospitals Rural	123	120	121	122	122
Control					
State and Local Government...............	131	132	133	135	135
Not for Profit	325	321	318	319	319
Investor owned	87	88	84	81	81
Physician Models					
Independent Practice Association	71	65	79	83	78
Group Practice without Walls...............	22	21	24	24	24
Open Physician-Hospital Organization	12	16	22	20	19
Closed Physician-Hospital Organization	18	11	11	10	11
Management Service Organization	64	63	47	48	47
Integrated Salary Model....................	122	112	115	113	110
Equity Model	6	6	6	7	5
Foundation...............................	99	91	59	60	55
Insurance Products					
Health Maintenance Organization	78	66	64	55	64
Preferred Provider Organization..............	50	38	62	56	54
Indemnity Fee for Service	15	10	21	15	14
Managed Care Contracts					
Health Maintenance Organization	238	258	228	231	231
Preferred Provider Organization..............	251	268	252	259	270
Affiliations					
Hospitals in a System......................	342	339	336	330	324
Hospitals in a Network.....................	129	110	121	110	111
Hospitals in a Group Purchasing Organization..	330	295	315	310	352

TABLE **5**

U.S. Registered Community Hospitals
(Nonfederal, short-term general and other special hospitals)

Utilization, Personnel, Revenue and Expenses, Community Health Indicators 2009–2013

	2013	2012	2011	2010	2009
TOTAL FACILITY (Includes Hospital and Nursing Home Units)					
Utilization - Inpatient					
Beds	93,661	94,194	92,601	93,088	91,046
Admissions	4,361,054	4,403,646	4,471,783	4,501,591	4,514,874
Inpatient Days	21,838,216	22,168,393	22,232,780	22,640,225	22,791,572
Average Length of Stay	5.0	5.0	5.0	5.0	5.0
Inpatient Surgeries	1,168,907	1,195,847	1,192,531	1,241,853	1,252,243
Births	603,650	621,481	629,315	632,032	645,081
Utilization - Outpatient					
Emergency Outpatient Visits	16,484,071	16,342,076	15,480,506	15,128,224	15,055,923
Other Outpatient Visits	63,694,420	62,140,989	62,797,927	61,596,946	57,529,665
Total Outpatient Visits	80,178,491	78,483,065	78,278,433	76,725,170	72,585,588
Outpatient Surgeries	1,854,875	1,808,384	1,846,317	1,835,447	1,833,478
Personnel					
Full Time RNs	139,227	141,776	136,326	134,508	130,132
Full Time LPNs	7,199	7,614	7,594	8,301	8,642
Part Time RNs	77,131	77,206	72,866	71,284	70,581
Part Time LPNs	3,043	3,279	3,211	3,453	3,839
Total Full Time	496,771	508,241	493,680	487,053	477,901
Total Part Time	206,175	210,546	199,030	193,703	191,891
Revenue - Inpatient					
Gross Inpatient Revenue	$249,612,964,923	$236,834,787,719	$219,593,141,460	$211,874,242,966	$193,636,178,785
Revenue - Outpatient					
Gross Outpatient Revenue	$165,091,402,569	$147,772,531,581	$138,274,865,366	$124,558,809,024	$109,199,995,898
Revenue and Expenses - Totals **(Includes Inpatient and Outpatient)**					
Total Gross Revenue	$414,704,353,075	$384,607,319,300	$357,868,006,826	$336,433,051,990	$302,836,174,683
Deductions from Revenue	296,421,871,411	271,710,809,903	253,322,749,612	239,252,607,338	212,570,073,192
Net Patient Revenue	118,282,481,664	112,896,509,397	104,545,257,214	97,180,444,652	90,266,101,491
Other Operating Revenue	7,232,249,498	6,642,799,134	5,990,186,797	6,027,711,222	5,590,026,520
Other Nonoperating Revenue	3,877,851,046	1,979,204,632	2,259,696,906	1,866,228,283	1,090,362,535
Total Net Revenue	129,392,582,208	121,518,513,163	112,795,140,917	105,074,384,157	96,946,490,546
Total Expenses	118,675,375,594	113,537,965,473	105,001,431,937	98,998,692,542	93,038,063,591
HOSPITAL UNIT (Excludes Separate Nursing Home Units)					
Utilization - Inpatient					
Beds	88,791	88,926	88,926	88,925	86,836
Admissions	4,338,312	4,378,581	4,450,403	4,478,851	4,489,343
Inpatient Days	20,299,211	20,541,376	21,093,072	21,344,190	21,533,040
Average Length of Stay	4.7	4.7	4.7	4.8	4.8
Personnel					
Total Full Time	493,525	503,839	490,810	483,548	473,892
Total Part Time	204,370	208,555	197,584	192,111	189,876
Revenue and Expenses - Totals **(Includes Inpatient and Outpatient)**					
Total Net Revenue	$128,717,582,873	$120,898,001,137	$112,319,758,152	$104,531,350,858	$96,415,616,765
Total Expenses	118,155,549,145	112,990,603,410	104,639,691,795	98,595,961,703	92,611,409,620
COMMUNITY HEALTH INDICATORS PER 1000 POPULATION					
Total Population (in thousands)	51,373	50,962	50,491	49,877	49,445
Inpatient					
Beds	1.8	1.8	1.8	1.9	1.8
Admissions	84.9	86.4	88.6	90.3	91.3
Inpatient Days	425.1	435.0	440.3	453.9	460.9
Inpatient Surgeries	22.8	23.5	23.6	24.9	25.3
Births	11.8	12.2	12.5	12.7	13.0
Outpatient					
Emergency Outpatient Visits	320.9	320.7	306.6	303.3	304.5
Other Outpatient Visits	1,239.8	1,219.4	1,243.7	1,235.0	1,163.5
Total Outpatient Visits	1,560.7	1,540.0	1,550.3	1,538.3	1,468.0
Outpatient Surgeries	36.1	35.5	36.6	36.8	37.1
Expense per Capita (per person)	$2,310.1	$2,227.9	$2,079.6	$1,984.8	$1,881.6

TABLE 6

ALABAMA

U.S. Registered Community Hospitals
(Nonfederal, short-term general and other special hospitals)

Overview 2009–2013

	2013	2012	2011	2010	2009
Total Community Hospitals in Alabama	97	97	102	105	108
Bed Size Category					
6-24	5	7	9	7	7
25-49	24	23	23	27	27
50-99	21	21	21	22	24
100-199	25	23	24	28	28
200-299	9	10	12	9	9
300-399	6	6	6	6	7
400-499	2	2	3	3	3
500 + ...	5	5	4	3	3
Location					
Hospitals Urban...........................	53	52	57	58	60
Hospitals Rural	44	45	45	47	48
Control					
State and Local Government................	39	38	39	40	42
Not for Profit	24	24	24	24	26
Investor owned	34	35	39	41	40
Physician Models					
Independent Practice Association	2	3	4	7	8
Group Practice without Walls...............	0	0	0	1	2
Open Physician-Hospital Organization	6	6	7	7	3
Closed Physician-Hospital Organization	0	4	4	0	1
Management Service Organization	3	11	10	7	5
Integrated Salary Model....................	9	13	13	18	16
Equity Model	0	0	0	0	0
Foundation...............................	4	4	5	7	5
Insurance Products					
Health Maintenance Organization	4	2	3	7	10
Preferred Provider Organization..............	7	9	12	8	9
Indemnity Fee for Service	1	0	1	1	1
Managed Care Contracts					
Health Maintenance Organization	29	34	35	37	36
Preferred Provider Organization..............	33	43	44	51	49
Affiliations					
Hospitals in a System......................	62	61	61	64	67
Hospitals in a Network.....................	6	8	8	9	11
Hospitals in a Group Purchasing Organization..	37	50	53	56	70

TABLE 6

ALABAMA

U.S. Registered Community Hospitals
(Nonfederal, short-term general and other special hospitals)

Utilization, Personnel, Revenue and Expenses, Community Health Indicators 2009–2013

	2013	2012	2011	2010	2009
TOTAL FACILITY (Includes Hospital and Nursing Home Units)					
Utilization - Inpatient					
Beds	15,129	14,983	15,387	15,086	15,290
Admissions	641,249	650,116	625,425	642,309	665,788
Inpatient Days	3,369,852	3,235,410	3,259,740	3,336,285	3,459,946
Average Length of Stay	5.3	5.0	5.2	5.2	5.2
Inpatient Surgeries	188,370	216,437	225,340	197,605	203,945
Births	57,811	54,169	56,038	58,287	62,819
Utilization - Outpatient					
Emergency Outpatient Visits	2,279,572	2,349,349	2,301,480	2,304,682	2,286,343
Other Outpatient Visits	6,032,550	5,787,211	6,428,214	6,496,039	6,905,010
Total Outpatient Visits	8,312,122	8,136,560	8,729,694	8,800,721	9,191,353
Outpatient Surgeries	377,910	416,822	410,937	372,359	380,226
Personnel					
Full Time RNs	20,357	18,971	19,179	19,033	18,906
Full Time LPNs	1,207	1,284	1,334	1,533	1,587
Part Time RNs	6,329	6,450	6,030	6,521	6,495
Part Time LPNs	376	423	407	544	584
Total Full Time	67,282	63,711	63,640	63,565	64,706
Total Part Time	16,854	17,393	16,258	17,485	17,181
Revenue - Inpatient					
Gross Inpatient Revenue	$22,037,388,309	$21,905,302,437	$20,721,285,712	$20,382,077,101	$19,226,829,885
Revenue - Outpatient					
Gross Outpatient Revenue	$19,204,120,871	$18,451,159,730	$16,116,899,016	$15,107,168,189	$13,746,107,465
Revenue and Expenses - Totals					
(Includes Inpatient and Outpatient)					
Total Gross Revenue	$41,241,509,180	$40,356,462,167	$36,838,184,728	$35,489,245,290	$32,972,937,350
Deductions from Revenue	31,119,196,377	30,849,527,537	28,275,034,462	26,885,327,851	24,887,051,667
Net Patient Revenue	10,122,312,803	9,506,934,630	8,563,150,266	8,603,917,439	8,085,885,683
Other Operating Revenue	574,099,002	530,660,281	419,270,245	398,593,891	476,168,844
Other Nonoperating Revenue	239,417,197	117,222,122	124,960,404	180,032,402	209,998,612
Total Net Revenue	10,935,829,002	10,154,817,033	9,107,380,915	9,182,543,732	8,772,053,139
Total Expenses	9,699,338,172	9,009,790,217	8,285,877,588	8,334,444,846	8,276,604,492
HOSPITAL UNIT (Excludes Separate Nursing Home Units)					
Utilization - Inpatient					
Beds	14,695	14,684	14,953	14,569	14,861
Admissions	640,039	649,138	624,134	641,118	664,534
Inpatient Days	3,231,272	3,135,159	3,142,919	3,188,617	3,314,802
Average Length of Stay	5.0	4.8	5.0	5.0	5.0
Personnel					
Total Full Time	66,636	63,419	63,302	63,159	64,371
Total Part Time	16,433	17,324	16,224	17,373	17,120
Revenue and Expenses - Totals					
(Includes Inpatient and Outpatient)					
Total Net Revenue	$10,910,655,198	$10,139,471,861	$9,085,772,314	$9,160,325,136	$8,749,089,004
Total Expenses	9,676,090,169	8,994,674,312	8,272,890,643	8,308,793,595	8,249,699,883
COMMUNITY HEALTH INDICATORS PER 1000 POPULATION					
Total Population (in thousands)	4,834	4,822	4,803	4,730	4,709
Inpatient					
Beds	3.1	3.1	3.2	3.2	3.2
Admissions	132.7	134.8	130.2	135.8	141.4
Inpatient Days	697.2	671.0	678.7	705.4	734.8
Inpatient Surgeries	39.0	44.9	46.9	41.8	43.3
Births	12.0	11.2	11.7	12.3	13.3
Outpatient					
Emergency Outpatient Visits	471.6	487.2	479.2	487.3	485.6
Other Outpatient Visits	1,248.0	1,200.2	1,338.4	1,373.5	1,466.4
Total Outpatient Visits	1,719.6	1,687.4	1,817.6	1,860.8	1,952.0
Outpatient Surgeries	78.2	86.4	85.6	78.7	80.7
Expense per Capita (per person)	$2,006.6	$1,868.5	$1,725.2	$1,762.2	$1,757.7

States

TABLE 6

ALASKA

U.S. Registered Community Hospitals
(Nonfederal, short-term general and other special hospitals)

Overview 2009–2013

	2013	2012	2011	2010	2009
Total Community Hospitals in Alaska.........	22	23	23	22	22
Bed Size Category					
6-24	5	7	7	6	6
25-49	9	8	7	7	8
50-99	3	3	4	4	3
100-199	3	3	3	3	3
200-299	1	1	1	1	1
300-399	1	1	1	1	1
400-499	0	0	0	0	0
500 + ...	0	0	0	0	0
Location					
Hospitals Urban...........................	6	6	6	5	5
Hospitals Rural	16	17	17	17	17
Control					
State and Local Government................	7	7	7	7	6
Not for Profit	13	14	14	13	14
Investor owned	2	2	2	2	2
Physician Models					
Independent Practice Association	1	1	1	1	0
Group Practice without Walls................	0	0	0	0	0
Open Physician-Hospital Organization	1	2	2	2	2
Closed Physician-Hospital Organization	1	1	1	1	1
Management Service Organization	0	0	0	0	1
Integrated Salary Model....................	4	3	4	4	3
Equity Model.............................	0	0	0	0	0
Foundation..............................	1	0	0	0	0
Insurance Products					
Health Maintenance Organization	0	0	0	0	0
Preferred Provider Organization..............	2	1	4	1	2
Indemnity Fee for Service	0	0	1	0	0
Managed Care Contracts					
Health Maintenance Organization	0	0	1	0	0
Preferred Provider Organization..............	4	5	7	5	7
Affiliations					
Hospitals in a System.....................	8	8	9	9	8
Hospitals in a Network....................	1	2	1	3	5
Hospitals in a Group Purchasing Organization..	9	6	8	8	12

TABLE 6

ALASKA

U.S. Registered Community Hospitals
(Nonfederal, short-term general and other special hospitals)

Utilization, Personnel, Revenue and Expenses, Community Health Indicators 2009–2013

	2013	2012	2011	2010	2009
TOTAL FACILITY (Includes Hospital and Nursing Home Units)					
Utilization - Inpatient					
Beds	1,560	1,549	1,556	1,543	1,532
Admissions	57,621	56,131	54,715	57,005	57,227
Inpatient Days	376,393	341,987	340,060	342,960	338,547
Average Length of Stay.	6.5	6.1	6.2	6.0	5.9
Inpatient Surgeries.	13,001	15,613	16,420	17,999	20,294
Births.	7,372	8,522	9,196	8,919	9,358
Utilization - Outpatient					
Emergency Outpatient Visits	257,285	290,711	315,181	296,573	296,524
Other Outpatient Visits.	1,110,025	1,161,515	1,450,455	1,486,369	1,470,894
Total Outpatient Visits	1,367,310	1,452,226	1,765,636	1,782,942	1,767,418
Outpatient Surgeries	39,216	40,892	43,714	47,417	50,469
Personnel					
Full Time RNs	2,095	2,209	2,456	2,238	2,348
Full Time LPNs	150	145	177	178	163
Part Time RNs	823	893	820	906	816
Part Time LPNs	45	37	35	28	27
Total Full Time.	8,364	8,723	10,064	9,608	9,421
Total Part Time	2,726	2,467	2,177	2,584	2,125
Revenue - Inpatient					
Gross Inpatient Revenue.	$2,857,156,569	$2,628,751,616	$2,510,713,374	$2,340,223,028	$1,920,419,380
Revenue - Outpatient					
Gross Outpatient Revenue	$2,965,846,524	$2,524,384,455	$2,540,116,099	$2,263,620,240	$1,956,296,065
Revenue and Expenses - Totals					
(Includes Inpatient and Outpatient)					
Total Gross Revenue.	$5,823,003,093	$5,153,136,071	$5,050,829,473	$4,603,843,268	$3,876,715,445
Deductions from Revenue	3,746,662,160	3,134,854,935	3,205,558,785	2,836,623,088	2,198,399,661
Net Patient Revenue	2,076,340,933	2,018,281,136	1,845,270,688	1,767,220,180	1,678,315,784
Other Operating Revenue	100,248,551	100,656,142	216,227,533	146,570,128	65,784,620
Other Nonoperating Revenue	42,606,280	33,745,177	19,647,439	21,027,327	18,948,295
Total Net Revenue.	2,219,195,764	2,152,682,455	2,081,145,660	1,934,817,635	1,763,048,699
Total Expenses.	1,824,096,637	1,765,708,752	1,747,385,857	1,590,214,704	1,753,736,940
HOSPITAL UNIT (Excludes Separate Nursing Home Units)					
Utilization - Inpatient					
Beds	1,273	1,293	1,346	1,334	1,300
Admissions	57,215	55,667	54,498	56,797	56,918
Inpatient Days	282,965	257,797	270,835	275,518	263,515
Average Length of Stay.	4.9	4.6	5.0	4.9	4.6
Personnel					
Total Full Time	8,116	8,486	9,855	9,428	9,174
Total Part Time	2,596	2,371	2,080	2,443	1,990
Revenue and Expenses - Totals					
(Includes Inpatient and Outpatient)					
Total Net Revenue.	$2,171,602,536	$2,105,900,495	$2,048,187,683	$1,900,578,038	$1,724,497,539
Total Expenses.	1,783,712,793	1,730,733,295	1,720,343,546	1,564,596,210	1,726,965,040
COMMUNITY HEALTH INDICATORS PER 1000 POPULATION					
Total Population (in thousands)	735	731	723	709	698
Inpatient					
Beds	2.1	2.1	2.2	2.2	2.2
Admissions	78.4	76.7	75.7	80.4	81.9
Inpatient Days	512.0	467.5	470.5	483.8	484.7
Inpatient Surgeries.	17.7	21.3	22.7	25.4	29.1
Births.	10.0	11.7	12.7	12.6	13.4
Outpatient					
Emergency Outpatient Visits	350.0	397.4	436.1	418.4	424.5
Other Outpatient Visits.	1,510.0	1,588.0	2,006.9	2,096.8	2,105.9
Total Outpatient Visits	1,860.0	1,985.4	2,443.0	2,515.2	2,530.4
Outpatient Surgeries	53.3	55.9	60.5	66.9	72.3
Expense per Capita (per person).	$2,481.3	$2,414.0	$2,417.8	$2,243.3	$2,510.8

States

TABLE 6

ARIZONA

U.S. Registered Community Hospitals
(Nonfederal, short-term general and other special hospitals)

Overview 2009–2013

	2013	2012	2011	2010	2009
Total Community Hospitals in Arizona	72	72	70	73	72
Bed Size Category					
6-24	5	5	5	5	4
25-49	13	12	12	10	10
50-99	14	15	14	18	18
100-199	13	13	12	13	11
200-299	11	10	11	11	12
300-399	5	6	4	5	8
400-499	6	5	7	6	4
500 + ...	5	6	5	5	5
Location					
Hospitals Urban..........................	58	58	56	58	58
Hospitals Rural	14	14	14	15	14
Control					
State and Local Government...............	4	4	4	5	7
Not for Profit	47	46	47	46	43
Investor owned	21	22	19	22	22
Physician Models					
Independent Practice Association	6	9	7	8	9
Group Practice without Walls...............	2	3	3	1	1
Open Physician-Hospital Organization	4	5	5	6	6
Closed Physician-Hospital Organization	4	3	2	3	4
Management Service Organization	5	7	9	8	4
Integrated Salary Model....................	16	16	19	15	16
Equity Model	0	0	0	0	0
Foundation...............................	1	1	2	2	2
Insurance Products					
Health Maintenance Organization	14	12	10	9	8
Preferred Provider Organization..............	8	4	8	7	5
Indemnity Fee for Service	2	0	5	5	4
Managed Care Contracts					
Health Maintenance Organization	23	26	30	32	32
Preferred Provider Organization..............	24	27	31	31	33
Affiliations					
Hospitals in a System.....................	49	49	46	48	49
Hospitals in a Network....................	19	17	17	19	14
Hospitals in a Group Purchasing Organization..	42	37	40	45	41

TABLE 6

ARIZONA

U.S. Registered Community Hospitals
(Nonfederal, short-term general and other special hospitals)

Utilization, Personnel, Revenue and Expenses, Community Health Indicators 2009–2013

	2013	2012	2011	2010	2009
TOTAL FACILITY (Includes Hospital and Nursing Home Units)					
Utilization - Inpatient					
Beds	13,347	13,527	13,352	13,385	13,455
Admissions	639,279	674,808	700,855	711,901	705,371
Inpatient Days	2,890,733	2,977,605	3,106,331	3,160,244	3,203,551
Average Length of Stay	4.5	4.4	4.4	4.4	4.5
Inpatient Surgeries	187,369	216,991	239,277	247,886	249,404
Births	75,166	73,033	74,547	80,960	88,943
Utilization - Outpatient					
Emergency Outpatient Visits	2,066,382	2,309,621	2,189,955	2,240,946	2,137,007
Other Outpatient Visits	6,673,210	6,427,396	6,362,148	5,886,520	4,965,037
Total Outpatient Visits	8,739,592	8,737,017	8,552,103	8,127,466	7,102,044
Outpatient Surgeries	279,931	245,168	250,415	257,530	264,098
Personnel					
Full Time RNs	22,027	20,977	20,524	22,440	21,733
Full Time LPNs	577	590	649	807	1,428
Part Time RNs	5,825	6,167	5,929	5,419	6,207
Part Time LPNs	114	150	152	135	217
Total Full Time	67,017	66,940	67,996	71,092	68,218
Total Part Time	14,793	16,020	15,965	14,521	16,938
Revenue - Inpatient					
Gross Inpatient Revenue	$28,048,084,817	$27,609,357,979	$26,796,619,071	$26,745,329,251	$25,403,304,711
Revenue - Outpatient					
Gross Outpatient Revenue	$21,244,955,845	$18,858,344,930	$16,955,905,216	$15,678,580,294	$14,088,508,773
Revenue and Expenses - Totals					
(Includes Inpatient and Outpatient)					
Total Gross Revenue	$49,293,040,662	$46,467,702,909	$43,752,524,287	$42,423,909,545	$39,491,813,484
Deductions from Revenue	36,737,029,960	34,058,007,365	32,157,030,582	30,579,491,050	28,395,520,445
Net Patient Revenue	12,556,010,702	12,409,695,544	11,595,493,705	11,844,418,495	11,096,293,039
Other Operating Revenue	603,598,689	475,139,314	515,033,121	504,651,779	405,351,865
Other Nonoperating Revenue	139,238,418	86,412,468	82,344,006	65,552,870	146,545,191
Total Net Revenue	13,298,847,809	12,971,247,326	12,192,870,832	12,414,623,144	11,648,190,095
Total Expenses	12,377,784,591	12,112,683,858	11,520,903,768	11,271,574,937	10,838,466,876
HOSPITAL UNIT (Excludes Separate Nursing Home Units)					
Utilization - Inpatient					
Beds	13,252	13,401	13,226	13,265	13,311
Admissions	637,557	672,834	698,689	709,606	703,074
Inpatient Days	2,863,151	2,944,802	3,063,786	3,120,611	3,154,344
Average Length of Stay	4.5	4.4	4.4	4.4	4.5
Personnel					
Total Full Time	66,942	66,850	67,911	70,791	68,133
Total Part Time	14,777	16,010	15,936	14,477	16,909
Revenue and Expenses - Totals					
(Includes Inpatient and Outpatient)					
Total Net Revenue	$13,268,304,844	$12,943,620,235	$12,154,799,416	$12,377,572,952	$11,622,780,339
Total Expenses	12,365,050,443	12,098,532,372	11,504,061,948	11,256,388,031	10,821,151,582
COMMUNITY HEALTH INDICATORS PER 1000 POPULATION					
Total Population (in thousands)	6,627	6,553	6,483	6,677	6,596
Inpatient					
Beds	2.0	2.1	2.1	2.0	2.0
Admissions	96.5	103.0	108.1	106.6	106.9
Inpatient Days	436.2	454.4	479.2	473.3	485.7
Inpatient Surgeries	28.3	33.1	36.9	37.1	37.8
Births	11.3	11.1	11.5	12.1	13.5
Outpatient					
Emergency Outpatient Visits	311.8	352.4	337.8	335.6	324.0
Other Outpatient Visits	1,007.0	980.8	981.4	881.7	752.8
Total Outpatient Visits	1,318.9	1,333.2	1,319.3	1,217.3	1,076.8
Outpatient Surgeries	42.2	37.4	38.6	38.6	40.0
Expense per Capita (per person)	$1,867.9	$1,848.3	$1,777.2	$1,688.2	$1,643.2

TABLE 6

ARKANSAS

U.S. Registered Community Hospitals
(Nonfederal, short-term general and other special hospitals)

Overview 2009–2013

	2013	2012	2011	2010	2009
Total Community Hospitals in Arkansas.......	84	83	84	85	86
Bed Size Category					
6-24	6	5	5	6	7
25-49	31	32	33	32	31
50-99	16	14	14	16	18
100-199	15	16	18	18	17
200-299	7	7	5	6	5
300-399	6	6	6	4	5
400-499	2	2	2	2	2
500 + ...	1	1	1	1	1
Location					
Hospitals Urban..........................	36	35	36	37	37
Hospitals Rural	48	48	48	48	49
Control					
State and Local Government...............	10	11	11	14	15
Not for Profit	50	49	50	45	45
Investor owned	24	23	23	26	26
Physician Models					
Independent Practice Association	6	6	9	16	16
Group Practice without Walls...............	5	5	5	6	6
Open Physician-Hospital Organization	24	23	24	25	28
Closed Physician-Hospital Organization	6	4	5	6	6
Management Service Organization	12	9	10	10	10
Integrated Salary Model....................	29	20	18	21	20
Equity Model	1	1	0	1	2
Foundation...............................	6	5	6	7	8
Insurance Products					
Health Maintenance Organization	15	14	14	14	14
Preferred Provider Organization..............	6	7	10	14	14
Indemnity Fee for Service	0	1	2	4	3
Managed Care Contracts					
Health Maintenance Organization	47	40	46	46	50
Preferred Provider Organization..............	64	53	64	62	66
Affiliations					
Hospitals in a System......................	47	46	44	46	47
Hospitals in a Network.....................	28	22	26	26	28
Hospitals in a Group Purchasing Organization..	77	61	73	67	78

TABLE 6

ARKANSAS

U.S. Registered Community Hospitals
(Nonfederal, short-term general and other special hospitals)

Utilization, Personnel, Revenue and Expenses, Community Health Indicators 2009–2013

	2013	2012	2011	2010	2009
TOTAL FACILITY (Includes Hospital and Nursing Home Units)					
Utilization - Inpatient					
Beds	9,452	9,417	9,425	9,451	9,565
Admissions	352,362	352,752	363,516	370,401	380,478
Inpatient Days	1,817,099	1,845,443	1,882,912	1,908,843	1,957,556
Average Length of Stay	5.2	5.2	5.2	5.2	5.1
Inpatient Surgeries	95,834	101,156	102,964	104,912	101,681
Births	36,313	35,421	36,809	36,913	38,556
Utilization - Outpatient					
Emergency Outpatient Visits	1,438,617	1,382,183	1,391,537	1,376,649	1,355,032
Other Outpatient Visits	3,674,902	3,743,252	3,419,087	3,645,562	3,692,949
Total Outpatient Visits	5,113,519	5,125,435	4,810,624	5,022,211	5,047,981
Outpatient Surgeries	174,981	174,095	160,223	155,784	143,094
Personnel					
Full Time RNs	11,915	11,964	11,429	11,059	10,620
Full Time LPNs	1,579	1,587	1,897	1,890	2,080
Part Time RNs	3,353	3,576	3,700	4,068	4,030
Part Time LPNs	384	455	606	663	809
Total Full Time	39,095	40,286	39,108	38,553	38,571
Total Part Time	9,459	10,397	10,746	11,921	11,981
Revenue - Inpatient					
Gross Inpatient Revenue	$10,391,798,234	$9,975,710,168	$9,587,181,461	$9,211,448,957	$8,800,185,973
Revenue - Outpatient					
Gross Outpatient Revenue	$9,513,953,822	$8,663,764,850	$7,800,635,792	$7,084,460,315	$6,421,124,915
Revenue and Expenses - Totals					
(Includes Inpatient and Outpatient)					
Total Gross Revenue	$19,905,752,056	$18,639,475,018	$17,387,817,253	$16,295,909,272	$15,221,310,888
Deductions from Revenue	14,135,092,803	12,820,230,814	12,106,848,283	11,007,346,255	10,164,398,525
Net Patient Revenue	5,770,659,253	5,819,244,204	5,280,968,970	5,288,563,017	5,056,912,363
Other Operating Revenue	269,134,329	256,162,838	220,871,438	221,189,649	193,955,665
Other Nonoperating Revenue	87,213,991	85,908,563	52,395,249	69,605,801	73,678,302
Total Net Revenue	6,127,007,573	6,161,315,605	5,554,235,657	5,579,358,467	5,324,546,330
Total Expenses	5,917,263,241	5,759,240,612	5,236,539,234	5,246,234,974	5,161,176,256
HOSPITAL UNIT (Excludes Separate Nursing Home Units)					
Utilization - Inpatient					
Beds	9,176	9,200	9,041	9,228	9,132
Admissions	351,947	351,712	362,005	368,895	378,746
Inpatient Days	1,738,385	1,774,671	1,757,602	1,830,615	1,824,645
Average Length of Stay	4.9	5.0	4.9	5.0	4.8
Personnel					
Total Full Time	38,944	40,123	38,835	38,362	38,050
Total Part Time	9,429	10,347	10,639	11,881	11,767
Revenue and Expenses - Totals					
(Includes Inpatient and Outpatient)					
Total Net Revenue	$6,113,021,586	$6,148,169,295	$5,526,988,517	$5,558,657,844	$5,301,946,109
Total Expenses	5,907,194,626	5,749,516,565	5,219,018,613	5,234,362,445	5,141,870,990
COMMUNITY HEALTH INDICATORS PER 1000 POPULATION					
Total Population (in thousands)	2,959	2,949	2,938	2,910	2,889
Inpatient					
Beds	3.2	3.2	3.2	3.2	3.3
Admissions	119.1	119.6	123.7	127.3	131.7
Inpatient Days	614.0	625.8	640.9	655.9	677.5
Inpatient Surgeries	32.4	34.3	35.0	36.0	35.2
Births	12.3	12.0	12.5	12.7	13.3
Outpatient					
Emergency Outpatient Visits	486.1	468.7	473.6	473.0	469.0
Other Outpatient Visits	1,241.8	1,269.3	1,163.8	1,252.7	1,278.1
Total Outpatient Visits	1,727.9	1,737.9	1,637.4	1,725.7	1,747.0
Outpatient Surgeries	59.1	59.0	54.5	53.5	49.5
Expense per Capita (per person)	$1,999.5	$1,952.9	$1,782.4	$1,802.7	$1,786.2

TABLE 6

CALIFORNIA

U.S. Registered Community Hospitals
(Nonfederal, short-term general and other special hospitals)

Overview 2009–2013

	2013	2012	2011	2010	2009
Total Community Hospitals in California	**347**	**349**	**345**	**343**	**343**
Bed Size Category					
6-24	13	11	13	13	13
25-49	40	44	39	38	37
50-99	39	40	43	42	42
100-199	109	105	101	104	106
200-299	64	67	65	61	64
300-399	47	44	47	47	50
400-499	22	25	23	24	20
500 + ...	13	13	14	14	11
Location					
Hospitals Urban...........................	316	318	314	312	313
Hospitals Rural	31	31	31	31	30
Control					
State and Local Government...............	63	66	69	69	69
Not for Profit	207	206	202	202	202
Investor owned	77	77	74	72	72
Physician Models					
Independent Practice Association	58	51	64	66	62
Group Practice without Walls...............	13	10	11	11	12
Open Physician-Hospital Organization	5	4	6	5	5
Closed Physician-Hospital Organization	9	4	5	6	7
Management Service Organization	52	46	30	28	26
Integrated Salary Model....................	22	20	24	24	25
Equity Model	3	2	3	3	0
Foundation...............................	91	83	51	50	40
Insurance Products					
Health Maintenance Organization	54	47	40	35	42
Preferred Provider Organization..............	20	18	24	22	22
Indemnity Fee for Service	9	8	16	11	9
Managed Care Contracts					
Health Maintenance Organization	156	168	147	156	157
Preferred Provider Organization..............	149	161	146	157	159
Affiliations					
Hospitals in a System......................	231	231	230	226	225
Hospitals in a Network	70	60	70	59	59
Hospitals in a Group Purchasing Organization..	199	174	185	182	210

TABLE 6

CALIFORNIA

U.S. Registered Community Hospitals
(Nonfederal, short-term general and other special hospitals)

Utilization, Personnel, Revenue and Expenses, Community Health Indicators 2009–2013

	2013	2012	2011	2010	2009
TOTAL FACILITY (Includes Hospital and Nursing Home Units)					
Utilization - Inpatient					
Beds	70,326	71,004	70,008	70,440	68,745
Admissions	3,255,312	3,304,230	3,393,166	3,423,820	3,433,319
Inpatient Days	16,482,984	16,919,921	17,090,593	17,443,427	17,582,055
Average Length of Stay	5.1	5.1	5.0	5.1	5.1
Inpatient Surgeries	835,298	867,839	858,118	907,650	899,439
Births	465,752	482,313	488,863	493,712	500,085
Utilization - Outpatient					
Emergency Outpatient Visits	12,088,159	11,859,123	11,073,272	10,945,256	10,554,310
Other Outpatient Visits	41,724,982	40,365,732	41,601,911	40,784,007	37,700,623
Total Outpatient Visits	53,813,141	52,224,855	52,675,183	51,729,263	48,254,933
Outpatient Surgeries	1,276,491	1,249,704	1,273,633	1,261,889	1,248,053
Personnel					
Full Time RNs	103,849	106,195	103,753	103,010	98,905
Full Time LPNs	5,860	6,108	6,227	6,817	7,145
Part Time RNs	54,052	55,861	50,209	48,553	48,356
Part Time LPNs	2,328	2,574	2,420	2,625	2,900
Total Full Time	359,887	370,238	365,577	358,559	353,440
Total Part Time	140,888	147,910	134,162	129,897	130,048
Revenue - Inpatient					
Gross Inpatient Revenue	$205,071,437,854	$194,710,241,465	$183,080,834,445	$176,241,777,468	$160,482,118,425
Revenue - Outpatient					
Gross Outpatient Revenue	$123,867,181,756	$110,355,399,582	$105,412,786,768	$93,211,672,697	$81,537,158,136
Revenue and Expenses - Totals					
(Includes Inpatient and Outpatient)					
Total Gross Revenue	$328,938,605,193	$305,065,641,047	$288,493,621,213	$269,453,450,165	$242,019,276,561
Deductions from Revenue	242,255,300,320	222,641,523,180	211,224,646,235	198,665,132,469	176,891,970,909
Net Patient Revenue	86,683,304,873	82,424,117,867	77,268,974,978	70,788,317,696	65,127,305,652
Other Operating Revenue	5,417,248,967	4,935,487,999	4,404,016,212	4,549,376,153	4,239,820,033
Other Nonoperating Revenue	3,336,499,298	1,579,522,303	1,779,948,031	1,405,680,400	900,886,474
Total Net Revenue	95,437,053,138	88,939,128,169	83,452,939,221	76,743,374,249	70,268,012,159
Total Expenses	86,710,652,989	83,074,054,310	77,265,358,490	72,279,546,582	67,532,620,386
HOSPITAL UNIT (Excludes Separate Nursing Home Units)					
Utilization - Inpatient					
Beds	66,388	66,826	67,306	67,288	65,699
Admissions	3,235,117	3,281,803	3,374,467	3,404,159	3,411,915
Inpatient Days	15,256,633	15,596,063	16,266,645	16,480,612	16,688,765
Average Length of Stay	4.7	4.8	4.8	4.8	4.9
Personnel					
Total Full Time	357,289	366,919	363,402	355,707	350,441
Total Part Time	139,433	146,283	133,098	128,661	128,548
Revenue and Expenses - Totals					
(Includes Inpatient and Outpatient)					
Total Net Revenue	$94,867,298,781	$88,462,119,698	$83,072,725,098	$76,308,938,222	$69,852,937,155
Total Expenses	86,290,640,782	82,671,685,266	77,001,174,879	71,979,685,381	67,204,581,934
COMMUNITY HEALTH INDICATORS PER 1000 POPULATION					
Total Population (in thousands)	38,333	38,041	37,692	37,267	36,962
Inpatient					
Beds	1.8	1.9	1.9	1.9	1.9
Admissions	84.9	86.9	90.0	91.9	92.9
Inpatient Days	430.0	444.8	453.4	468.1	475.7
Inpatient Surgeries	21.8	22.8	22.8	24.4	24.3
Births	12.2	12.7	13.0	13.2	13.5
Outpatient					
Emergency Outpatient Visits	315.3	311.7	293.8	293.7	285.5
Other Outpatient Visits	1,088.5	1,061.1	1,103.7	1,094.4	1,020.0
Total Outpatient Visits	1,403.9	1,372.8	1,397.5	1,388.1	1,305.5
Outpatient Surgeries	33.3	32.9	33.8	33.9	33.8
Expense per Capita (per person)	$2,262.1	$2,183.8	$2,049.9	$1,939.5	$1,827.1

States

TABLE 6

COLORADO

U.S. Registered Community Hospitals
(Nonfederal, short-term general and other special hospitals)

Overview 2009–2013

	2013	2012	2011	2010	2009
Total Community Hospitals in Colorado.......	82	82	82	80	81
Bed Size Category					
6-24	12	12	11	11	13
25-49	20	22	23	21	19
50-99	19	17	17	16	18
100-199	13	12	12	14	11
200-299	6	7	7	6	10
300-399	7	6	8	8	5
400-499	4	6	3	2	3
500 + ...	1	0	1	2	2
Location					
Hospitals Urban..........................	44	44	44	43	43
Hospitals Rural	38	38	38	37	38
Control					
State and Local Government................	25	26	27	27	28
Not for Profit	40	39	38	37	37
Investor owned	17	17	17	16	16
Physician Models					
Independent Practice Association	10	10	11	10	9
Group Practice without Walls...............	3	3	3	2	1
Open Physician-Hospital Organization	11	11	13	13	12
Closed Physician-Hospital Organization	3	3	4	3	3
Management Service Organization	4	4	4	4	3
Integrated Salary Model....................	40	40	37	34	33
Equity Model	1	1	2	2	1
Foundation...............................	3	3	2	4	1
Insurance Products					
Health Maintenance Organization	7	9	9	10	11
Preferred Provider Organization.............	4	3	9	10	10
Indemnity Fee for Service	0	1	1	2	3
Managed Care Contracts					
Health Maintenance Organization	46	44	40	46	47
Preferred Provider Organization.............	55	51	45	52	53
Affiliations					
Hospitals in a System.....................	48	47	46	46	46
Hospitals in a Network....................	20	19	27	27	24
Hospitals in a Group Purchasing Organization..	61	54	63	60	58

TABLE 6

COLORADO

U.S. Registered Community Hospitals
(Nonfederal, short-term general and other special hospitals)

Utilization, Personnel, Revenue and Expenses, Community Health Indicators 2009–2013

	2013	2012	2011	2010	2009
TOTAL FACILITY (Includes Hospital and Nursing Home Units)					
Utilization - Inpatient					
Beds	10,301	10,244	10,167	10,208	10,364
Admissions	407,432	444,430	432,887	449,369	445,291
Inpatient Days	2,147,937	2,253,793	2,170,349	2,234,925	2,237,893
Average Length of Stay	5.3	5.1	5.0	5.0	5.0
Inpatient Surgeries	122,685	134,849	137,218	141,751	143,822
Births	56,439	58,253	62,264	63,653	65,130
Utilization - Outpatient					
Emergency Outpatient Visits	1,875,842	1,818,858	1,730,788	1,677,353	1,725,417
Other Outpatient Visits	6,904,552	7,139,929	6,934,427	6,572,791	7,134,664
Total Outpatient Visits	8,780,394	8,958,787	8,665,215	8,250,144	8,860,081
Outpatient Surgeries	237,551	232,063	219,321	211,730	206,315
Personnel					
Full Time RNs	15,466	15,678	15,239	15,787	15,411
Full Time LPNs	479	479	472	551	684
Part Time RNs	6,711	6,456	6,449	5,235	5,377
Part Time LPNs	184	191	190	179	215
Total Full Time	54,760	54,125	53,370	55,072	54,311
Total Part Time	20,369	17,930	18,322	15,268	15,782
Revenue - Inpatient					
Gross Inpatient Revenue	$23,145,163,295	$22,263,097,740	$19,860,096,681	$19,013,208,766	$17,525,068,092
Revenue - Outpatient					
Gross Outpatient Revenue	$20,071,791,832	$18,360,253,142	$16,603,620,063	$14,766,810,304	$13,322,614,754
Revenue and Expenses - Totals					
(Includes Inpatient and Outpatient)					
Total Gross Revenue	$43,216,955,127	$40,623,350,882	$36,463,716,744	$33,780,019,070	$30,847,682,846
Deductions from Revenue	31,041,601,067	28,720,794,917	25,752,881,907	23,450,147,224	21,100,773,225
Net Patient Revenue	12,175,354,060	11,902,555,965	10,710,834,837	10,329,871,846	9,746,909,621
Other Operating Revenue	601,507,479	559,939,985	513,568,821	501,184,086	489,463,546
Other Nonoperating Revenue	289,329,393	156,458,722	143,185,607	196,854,806	146,646,198
Total Net Revenue	13,066,190,932	12,618,954,672	11,367,589,265	11,027,910,738	10,383,019,365
Total Expenses	11,468,752,081	10,941,848,898	10,054,322,089	9,590,946,802	9,244,357,277
HOSPITAL UNIT (Excludes Separate Nursing Home Units)					
Utilization - Inpatient					
Beds	9,561	9,663	9,599	9,537	9,777
Admissions	405,640	442,623	430,676	447,782	443,718
Inpatient Days	1,924,396	2,067,062	1,995,737	2,026,168	2,056,115
Average Length of Stay	4.7	4.7	4.6	4.5	4.6
Personnel					
Total Full Time	54,115	53,774	52,935	54,554	53,795
Total Part Time	19,867	17,727	18,169	14,960	15,572
Revenue and Expenses - Totals					
(Includes Inpatient and Outpatient)					
Total Net Revenue	$13,018,522,807	$12,577,500,290	$11,330,471,189	$10,984,832,365	$10,343,931,411
Total Expenses	11,416,084,053	10,898,966,203	10,014,190,366	9,546,862,102	9,207,018,816
COMMUNITY HEALTH INDICATORS PER 1000 POPULATION					
Total Population (in thousands)	5,268	5,188	5,117	5,095	5,025
Inpatient					
Beds	2.0	2.0	2.0	2.0	2.1
Admissions	77.3	85.7	84.6	88.2	88.6
Inpatient Days	407.7	434.5	424.2	438.6	445.4
Inpatient Surgeries	23.3	26.0	26.8	27.8	28.6
Births	10.7	11.2	12.2	12.5	13.0
Outpatient					
Emergency Outpatient Visits	356.1	350.6	338.3	329.2	343.4
Other Outpatient Visits	1,310.6	1,376.4	1,355.2	1,290.0	1,419.9
Total Outpatient Visits	1,666.6	1,727.0	1,693.5	1,619.2	1,763.3
Outpatient Surgeries	45.1	44.7	42.9	41.6	41.1
Expense per Capita (per person)	$2,176.9	$2,109.2	$1,965.0	$1,882.3	$1,839.8

States

TABLE 6

CONNECTICUT

U.S. Registered Community Hospitals
(Nonfederal, short-term general and other special hospitals)

Overview 2009–2013

	2013	2012	2011	2010	2009
Total Community Hospitals in Connecticut	33	34	35	34	35
Bed Size Category					
6-24	0	0	0	0	0
25-49	3	2	2	1	1
50-99	8	9	8	8	8
100-199	12	10	12	10	12
200-299	2	4	4	5	3
300-399	4	5	5	5	6
400-499	1	1	1	2	2
500 + ...	3	3	3	3	3
Location					
Hospitals Urban............................	28	29	30	29	30
Hospitals Rural	5	5	5	5	5
Control					
State and Local Government................	1	1	1	1	1
Not for Profit	31	32	33	32	33
Investor owned	1	1	1	1	1
Physician Models					
Independent Practice Association	8	7	6	7	8
Group Practice without Walls................	2	0	0	2	0
Open Physician-Hospital Organization	6	5	4	5	6
Closed Physician-Hospital Organization	3	4	3	2	2
Management Service Organization	3	6	4	5	4
Integrated Salary Model.....................	16	17	17	17	15
Equity Model	4	4	1	1	1
Foundation................................	8	8	9	5	1
Insurance Products					
Health Maintenance Organization	0	0	0	2	2
Preferred Provider Organization..............	0	1	0	0	0
Indemnity Fee for Service	0	0	0	0	0
Managed Care Contracts					
Health Maintenance Organization	20	24	25	23	22
Preferred Provider Organization..............	20	24	25	22	23
Affiliations					
Hospitals in a System......................	17	18	15	14	12
Hospitals in a Network.....................	16	12	12	11	12
Hospitals in a Group Purchasing Organization..	26	25	27	28	28

TABLE 6

CONNECTICUT

U.S. Registered Community Hospitals
(Nonfederal, short-term general and other special hospitals)

Utilization, Personnel, Revenue and Expenses, Community Health Indicators 2009–2013

	2013	2012	2011	2010	2009
TOTAL FACILITY (Includes Hospital and Nursing Home Units)					
Utilization - Inpatient					
Beds	7,811	8,120	7,745	8,091	7,935
Admissions	391,394	378,130	402,838	406,718	407,710
Inpatient Days	2,144,945	2,053,559	2,110,564	2,290,323	2,345,878
Average Length of Stay	5.5	5.4	5.2	5.6	5.8
Inpatient Surgeries	105,579	99,309	103,828	108,070	109,334
Births	36,851	35,891	37,565	37,483	38,932
Utilization - Outpatient					
Emergency Outpatient Visits	1,626,044	1,643,476	1,643,282	1,661,088	1,607,670
Other Outpatient Visits	7,648,981	7,342,754	6,884,506	6,605,714	6,567,848
Total Outpatient Visits	9,275,025	8,986,230	8,527,788	8,266,802	8,175,518
Outpatient Surgeries	217,602	216,262	204,949	201,480	198,390
Personnel					
Full Time RNs	10,664	10,989	11,075	10,483	10,831
Full Time LPNs	240	261	258	264	311
Part Time RNs	6,924	7,221	7,107	6,609	6,512
Part Time LPNs	190	221	229	194	229
Total Full Time	44,827	44,994	44,784	43,689	44,091
Total Part Time	20,843	22,084	22,538	21,507	20,842
Revenue - Inpatient					
Gross Inpatient Revenue	$15,912,651,412	$14,329,380,117	$14,148,582,803	$13,295,787,334	$12,736,578,199
Revenue - Outpatient					
Gross Outpatient Revenue	$15,494,331,680	$13,501,775,551	$11,773,260,720	$10,537,030,956	$9,767,664,004
Revenue and Expenses - Totals					
(Includes Inpatient and Outpatient)					
Total Gross Revenue	$31,406,983,092	$27,831,155,668	$25,921,843,523	$23,832,818,290	$22,504,242,203
Deductions from Revenue	21,131,372,170	18,019,019,740	16,507,379,096	15,121,712,588	14,125,599,354
Net Patient Revenue	10,275,610,922	9,812,135,928	9,414,464,427	8,711,105,702	8,378,642,849
Other Operating Revenue	567,209,554	562,656,610	462,365,876	455,355,109	420,171,188
Other Nonoperating Revenue	234,905,027	123,095,744	57,595,778	115,215,987	-1,279,820
Total Net Revenue	11,077,725,503	10,497,888,282	9,934,426,081	9,281,676,798	8,797,534,217
Total Expenses	10,399,557,016	9,795,239,002	9,561,576,935	8,928,296,028	8,565,211,235
HOSPITAL UNIT (Excludes Separate Nursing Home Units)					
Utilization - Inpatient					
Beds	7,599	7,777	7,468	7,676	7,648
Admissions	390,412	377,468	402,394	405,842	407,207
Inpatient Days	2,069,739	1,973,687	2,109,561	2,146,637	2,245,293
Average Length of Stay	5.3	5.2	5.2	5.3	5.5
Personnel					
Total Full Time	44,665	44,726	44,768	43,306	44,052
Total Part Time	20,672	21,876	22,521	21,256	20,826
Revenue and Expenses - Totals					
(Includes Inpatient and Outpatient)					
Total Net Revenue	$11,043,626,112	$10,439,662,013	$9,928,376,462	$9,235,623,435	$8,759,788,307
Total Expenses	10,376,600,813	9,741,183,887	9,556,797,059	8,888,242,578	8,530,306,215
COMMUNITY HEALTH INDICATORS PER 1000 POPULATION					
Total Population (in thousands)	3,596	3,590	3,581	3,527	3,518
Inpatient					
Beds	2.2	2.3	2.2	2.3	2.3
Admissions	108.8	105.3	112.5	115.3	115.9
Inpatient Days	596.5	572.0	589.4	649.4	666.8
Inpatient Surgeries	29.4	27.7	29.0	30.6	31.1
Births	10.2	10.0	10.5	10.6	11.1
Outpatient					
Emergency Outpatient Visits	452.2	457.7	458.9	471.0	456.9
Other Outpatient Visits	2,127.0	2,045.1	1,922.7	1,872.9	1,866.8
Total Outpatient Visits	2,579.2	2,502.9	2,381.6	2,343.9	2,323.7
Outpatient Surgeries	60.5	60.2	57.2	57.1	56.4
Expense per Capita (per person)	$2,891.9	$2,728.2	$2,670.3	$2,531.5	$2,434.5

TABLE 6

DELAWARE

U.S. Registered Community Hospitals
(Nonfederal, short-term general and other special hospitals)

Overview 2009–2013

	2013	2012	2011	2010	2009
Total Community Hospitals in Delaware.......	7	7	7	7	7
Bed Size Category					
6-24	0	0	0	0	0
25-49	1	1	1	1	1
50-99	1	1	0	0	0
100-199	2	2	2	2	2
200-299	1	1	2	2	2
300-399	1	1	1	1	1
400-499	0	0	0	0	0
500 + ...	1	1	1	1	1
Location					
Hospitals Urban.........................	5	5	5	5	5
Hospitals Rural	2	2	2	2	2
Control					
State and Local Government...............	0	0	0	0	0
Not for Profit	6	6	6	6	6
Investor owned	1	1	1	1	1
Physician Models					
Independent Practice Association	0	0	0	0	0
Group Practice without Walls...............	1	0	0	0	0
Open Physician-Hospital Organization	0	0	0	0	0
Closed Physician-Hospital Organization	0	0	0	0	0
Management Service Organization	0	0	0	0	0
Integrated Salary Model.....................	1	1	2	3	3
Equity Model	0	0	0	0	0
Foundation...............................	1	1	1	1	1
Insurance Products					
Health Maintenance Organization	0	0	0	1	1
Preferred Provider Organization..............	0	0	0	1	1
Indemnity Fee for Service	0	0	0	1	1
Managed Care Contracts					
Health Maintenance Organization	3	3	3	4	5
Preferred Provider Organization..............	3	3	3	4	5
Affiliations					
Hospitals in a System......................	4	4	3	3	3
Hospitals in a Network	0	0	0	0	0
Hospitals in a Group Purchasing Organization..	5	5	5	6	6

States

TABLE 6

DELAWARE

U.S. Registered Community Hospitals
(Nonfederal, short-term general and other special hospitals)

Utilization, Personnel, Revenue and Expenses, Community Health Indicators 2009–2013

	2013	2012	2011	2010	2009
TOTAL FACILITY (Includes Hospital and Nursing Home Units)					
Utilization - Inpatient					
Beds	2,034	1,998	2,143	2,155	2,125
Admissions	104,769	104,803	100,288	101,735	102,153
Inpatient Days	538,590	526,678	578,466	580,261	597,993
Average Length of Stay	5.1	5.0	5.8	5.7	5.9
Inpatient Surgeries	31,227	32,163	31,852	28,828	29,930
Births	11,037	11,358	11,496	11,486	12,158
Utilization - Outpatient					
Emergency Outpatient Visits	441,756	437,706	417,689	406,652	392,660
Other Outpatient Visits	1,648,654	1,653,598	1,432,957	1,380,658	1,351,824
Total Outpatient Visits	2,090,410	2,091,304	1,850,646	1,787,310	1,744,484
Outpatient Surgeries	63,281	64,243	62,618	67,852	70,362
Personnel					
Full Time RNs	4,156	3,997	3,990	3,689	3,485
Full Time LPNs	134	142	171	126	135
Part Time RNs	2,082	2,166	1,927	2,195	2,486
Part Time LPNs	123	118	136	125	133
Total Full Time	15,155	15,421	14,456	13,885	13,707
Total Part Time	5,682	5,918	5,598	5,846	6,406
Revenue - Inpatient					
Gross Inpatient Revenue	$3,299,554,275	$3,097,560,492	$2,830,331,928	$2,671,560,601	$2,528,530,549
Revenue - Outpatient					
Gross Outpatient Revenue	$2,900,967,707	$2,677,941,719	$2,262,497,249	$2,026,156,087	$1,797,902,276
Revenue and Expenses - Totals					
(Includes Inpatient and Outpatient)					
Total Gross Revenue	$6,200,521,982	$5,775,502,211	$5,092,829,177	$4,697,716,688	$4,326,432,825
Deductions from Revenue	3,349,882,012	3,063,219,162	2,640,575,715	2,394,621,807	2,111,070,905
Net Patient Revenue	2,850,639,970	2,712,283,049	2,452,253,462	2,303,094,881	2,215,361,920
Other Operating Revenue	110,674,336	118,067,679	178,700,023	165,608,644	159,598,810
Other Nonoperating Revenue	136,656,471	17,706,306	171,781,254	77,555,669	-156,561,766
Total Net Revenue	3,097,970,777	2,848,057,034	2,802,734,739	2,546,259,194	2,218,398,964
Total Expenses	2,744,800,158	2,662,272,646	2,408,075,977	2,344,087,243	2,264,467,218
HOSPITAL UNIT (Excludes Separate Nursing Home Units)					
Utilization - Inpatient					
Beds	2,034	1,998	2,033	1,941	1,911
Admissions	104,769	104,803	99,921	101,130	101,502
Inpatient Days	538,590	526,678	540,146	509,077	525,133
Average Length of Stay	5.1	5.0	5.4	5.0	5.2
Personnel					
Total Full Time	15,155	15,421	14,301	13,670	13,553
Total Part Time	5,682	5,918	5,582	5,705	6,246
Revenue and Expenses - Totals					
(Includes Inpatient and Outpatient)					
Total Net Revenue	$3,097,970,777	$2,848,057,034	$2,791,771,225	$2,525,583,028	$2,197,822,141
Total Expenses	2,744,800,158	2,662,272,646	2,396,081,133	2,323,082,005	2,243,045,075
COMMUNITY HEALTH INDICATORS PER 1000 POPULATION					
Total Population (in thousands)	926	917	907	891	885
Inpatient					
Beds	2.2	2.2	2.4	2.4	2.4
Admissions	113.2	114.3	110.6	114.1	115.4
Inpatient Days	581.8	574.3	637.7	650.9	675.6
Inpatient Surgeries	33.7	35.1	35.1	32.3	33.8
Births	11.9	12.4	12.7	12.9	13.7
Outpatient					
Emergency Outpatient Visits	477.2	477.3	460.4	456.2	443.6
Other Outpatient Visits	1,780.9	1,803.1	1,579.7	1,548.8	1,527.3
Total Outpatient Visits	2,258.1	2,280.4	2,040.1	2,004.9	1,970.9
Outpatient Surgeries	68.4	70.1	69.0	76.1	79.5
Expense per Capita (per person)	$2,965.0	$2,903.0	$2,654.6	$2,629.5	$2,558.4

States

TABLE **6**

DISTRICT OF COLUMBIA

U.S. Registered Community Hospitals
(Nonfederal, short-term general and other special hospitals)

Overview 2009–2013

	2013	2012	2011	2010	2009
Total Community Hospitals in District of Columbia	11	11	11	11	10
Bed Size Category					
6-24	0	0	0	0	0
25-49	0	0	0	0	0
50-99	1	1	1	1	1
100-199	2	2	2	2	1
200-299	2	2	3	4	3
300-399	4	4	2	1	2
400-499	0	0	1	1	1
500 +	2	2	2	2	2
Location					
Hospitals Urban	11	11	11	11	10
Hospitals Rural	0	0	0	0	0
Control					
State and Local Government	1	1	1	1	0
Not for Profit	7	7	7	7	7
Investor owned	3	3	3	3	3
Physician Models					
Independent Practice Association	1	3	0	1	0
Group Practice without Walls	2	4	1	0	1
Open Physician-Hospital Organization	0	0	0	0	0
Closed Physician-Hospital Organization	2	3	1	1	1
Management Service Organization	1	3	1	1	1
Integrated Salary Model	4	5	4	5	5
Equity Model	0	0	0	0	0
Foundation	1	1	1	1	1
Insurance Products					
Health Maintenance Organization	4	5	4	2	3
Preferred Provider Organization	1	4	1	0	0
Indemnity Fee for Service	1	0	1	0	0
Managed Care Contracts					
Health Maintenance Organization	7	8	6	7	7
Preferred Provider Organization	7	7	6	6	7
Affiliations					
Hospitals in a System	8	8	8	9	7
Hospitals in a Network	2	1	4	5	4
Hospitals in a Group Purchasing Organization	9	9	7	8	8

States

TABLE 6

DISTRICT OF COLUMBIA

U.S. Registered Community Hospitals
(Nonfederal, short-term general and other special hospitals)

Utilization, Personnel, Revenue and Expenses, Community Health Indicators 2009–2013

	2013	2012	2011	2010	2009
TOTAL FACILITY (Includes Hospital and Nursing Home Units)					
Utilization - Inpatient					
Beds	3,609	3,617	3,635	3,458	3,452
Admissions	132,633	132,539	131,577	131,976	138,456
Inpatient Days	946,679	933,177	954,752	926,254	927,419
Average Length of Stay	7.1	7.0	7.3	7.0	6.7
Inpatient Surgeries	43,045	39,163	40,477	41,736	42,667
Births	13,718	13,783	13,792	13,814	14,507
Utilization - Outpatient					
Emergency Outpatient Visits	482,319	499,154	455,553	430,637	457,292
Other Outpatient Visits	2,095,979	1,961,067	1,994,547	1,888,245	1,954,514
Total Outpatient Visits	2,578,298	2,460,221	2,450,100	2,318,882	2,411,806
Outpatient Surgeries	72,560	66,622	62,767	58,907	62,497
Personnel					
Full Time RNs	5,930	5,647	5,435	5,458	5,222
Full Time LPNs	190	249	216	267	304
Part Time RNs	1,544	1,318	1,643	1,966	1,845
Part Time LPNs	27	38	32	46	35
Total Full Time	23,125	22,972	22,815	22,654	22,371
Total Part Time	3,984	3,313	4,525	5,259	4,666
Revenue - Inpatient					
Gross Inpatient Revenue	$7,091,366,429	$6,515,832,670	$6,334,158,623	$6,016,677,081	$5,895,449,855
Revenue - Outpatient					
Gross Outpatient Revenue	$4,311,322,460	$3,968,228,093	$3,932,470,181	$3,476,432,807	$3,108,162,999
Revenue and Expenses - Totals **(Includes Inpatient and Outpatient)**					
Total Gross Revenue	$11,402,688,889	$10,484,060,763	$10,266,628,804	$9,493,109,888	$9,003,612,854
Deductions from Revenue	7,509,944,561	6,640,686,593	6,617,584,769	5,971,324,649	5,592,219,614
Net Patient Revenue	3,892,744,328	3,843,374,170	3,649,044,035	3,521,785,239	3,411,393,240
Other Operating Revenue	300,528,852	299,523,683	277,637,308	205,891,415	214,814,678
Other Nonoperating Revenue	118,719,257	-15,527,022	95,995,539	33,913,566	32,415,954
Total Net Revenue	4,311,992,437	4,127,370,831	4,022,676,882	3,761,590,220	3,658,623,872
Total Expenses	3,946,217,682	3,937,620,808	3,766,313,652	3,582,285,072	3,585,829,997
HOSPITAL UNIT (Excludes Separate Nursing Home Units)					
Utilization - Inpatient					
Beds	3,192	3,200	3,470	3,161	3,157
Admissions	130,885	130,696	130,232	130,125	136,578
Inpatient Days	802,846	791,242	909,564	822,314	822,965
Average Length of Stay	6.1	6.1	7.0	6.3	6.0
Personnel					
Total Full Time	23,026	22,602	22,710	22,327	22,067
Total Part Time	3,968	3,241	4,500	5,181	4,595
Revenue and Expenses - Totals **(Includes Inpatient and Outpatient)**					
Total Net Revenue	$4,286,006,742	$4,074,614,436	$4,007,011,323	$3,726,836,744	$3,624,105,283
Total Expenses	3,922,587,203	3,890,891,777	3,750,371,864	3,552,676,361	3,556,839,618
COMMUNITY HEALTH INDICATORS PER 1000 POPULATION					
Total Population (in thousands)	646	632	618	611	600
Inpatient					
Beds	5.6	5.7	5.9	5.7	5.8
Admissions	205.2	209.6	212.9	216.1	230.9
Inpatient Days	1,464.4	1,475.8	1,544.9	1,517.0	1,546.6
Inpatient Surgeries	66.6	61.9	65.5	68.4	71.2
Births	21.2	21.8	22.3	22.6	24.2
Outpatient					
Emergency Outpatient Visits	746.1	789.4	737.1	705.3	762.6
Other Outpatient Visits	3,242.3	3,101.4	3,227.4	3,092.5	3,259.4
Total Outpatient Visits	3,988.4	3,890.8	3,964.6	3,797.8	4,022.0
Outpatient Surgeries	112.2	105.4	101.6	96.5	104.2
Expense per Capita (per person)	$6,104.5	$6,227.2	$6,094.4	$5,866.9	$5,979.8

TABLE 6

FLORIDA

U.S. Registered Community Hospitals
(Nonfederal, short-term general and other special hospitals)

Overview 2009–2013

	2013	2012	2011	2010	2009
Total Community Hospitals in Florida.........	212	216	213	210	210
Bed Size Category					
6-24	3	4	3	2	2
25-49	24	23	21	21	21
50-99	40	39	38	39	39
100-199	50	55	55	50	51
200-299	37	37	37	38	37
300-399	24	25	27	27	25
400-499	11	10	9	9	12
500 + ...	23	23	23	24	23
Location					
Hospitals Urban..........................	182	186	184	181	181
Hospitals Rural	30	30	29	29	29
Control					
State and Local Government...............	24	24	26	27	25
Not for Profit	79	80	81	79	82
Investor owned	109	112	106	104	103
Physician Models					
Independent Practice Association	3	3	5	5	4
Group Practice without Walls................	7	6	9	7	9
Open Physician-Hospital Organization	15	19	24	19	19
Closed Physician-Hospital Organization	4	2	5	7	6
Management Service Organization	22	15	14	14	8
Integrated Salary Model	71	66	64	59	52
Equity Model	0	0	1	1	0
Foundation..............................	1	2	3	4	4
Insurance Products					
Health Maintenance Organization	19	14	15	11	13
Preferred Provider Organization.............	15	7	18	16	17
Indemnity Fee for Service	8	4	7	5	6
Managed Care Contracts					
Health Maintenance Organization	107	100	111	98	88
Preferred Provider Organization.............	104	100	113	101	91
Affiliations					
Hospitals in a System.....................	175	176	167	160	160
Hospitals in a Network....................	51	48	37	35	35
Hospitals in a Group Purchasing Organization..	112	113	101	106	116

TABLE 6

FLORIDA

U.S. Registered Community Hospitals
(Nonfederal, short-term general and other special hospitals)

Utilization, Personnel, Revenue and Expenses, Community Health Indicators 2009–2013

	2013	2012	2011	2010	2009
TOTAL FACILITY (Includes Hospital and Nursing Home Units)					
Utilization - Inpatient					
Beds	53,198	53,785	52,923	53,318	53,293
Admissions	2,407,117	2,472,181	2,508,311	2,452,089	2,452,546
Inpatient Days	12,063,283	12,372,261	12,365,513	12,191,209	12,261,161
Average Length of Stay	5.0	5.0	4.9	5.0	5.0
Inpatient Surgeries	602,806	610,533	614,726	650,557	655,203
Births	198,157	196,681	186,919	202,862	206,284
Utilization - Outpatient					
Emergency Outpatient Visits	8,436,473	8,126,914	7,580,718	7,559,853	7,477,209
Other Outpatient Visits	15,558,477	15,367,371	16,827,980	16,683,248	17,396,409
Total Outpatient Visits	23,994,950	23,494,285	24,408,698	24,243,101	24,873,618
Outpatient Surgeries	837,962	800,782	782,871	798,189	822,841
Personnel					
Full Time RNs	72,327	74,829	72,090	69,840	68,581
Full Time LPNs	3,041	3,495	3,595	4,111	4,470
Part Time RNs	20,562	18,183	16,461	16,844	17,495
Part Time LPNs	836	885	789	901	1,092
Total Full Time	229,333	239,356	234,893	232,349	229,515
Total Part Time	58,340	55,168	49,243	47,580	49,670
Revenue - Inpatient					
Gross Inpatient Revenue	$113,515,265,844	$106,765,072,734	$100,263,145,301	$98,439,589,940	$90,412,617,613
Revenue - Outpatient					
Gross Outpatient Revenue	$77,113,649,369	$70,527,318,626	$63,221,928,643	$58,858,434,042	$52,572,001,561
Revenue and Expenses - Totals (Includes Inpatient and Outpatient)					
Total Gross Revenue	$190,628,915,213	$177,292,391,360	$163,485,073,944	$157,298,023,982	$142,984,619,174
Deductions from Revenue	148,060,768,748	135,271,195,802	126,350,152,571	119,355,324,858	107,498,135,646
Net Patient Revenue	42,568,146,465	42,021,195,558	37,134,921,373	37,942,699,124	35,486,483,528
Other Operating Revenue	2,224,603,404	2,402,722,300	2,293,290,171	2,190,285,623	1,811,268,561
Other Nonoperating Revenue	681,074,241	498,972,173	613,632,452	562,284,781	483,113,737
Total Net Revenue	45,473,824,110	44,922,890,031	40,041,843,996	40,695,269,528	37,780,865,826
Total Expenses	41,035,030,196	40,816,430,398	36,908,772,722	36,318,160,204	34,922,141,446
HOSPITAL UNIT (Excludes Separate Nursing Home Units)					
Utilization - Inpatient					
Beds	52,204	52,723	52,055	52,415	52,361
Admissions	2,401,783	2,465,633	2,504,407	2,448,276	2,448,331
Inpatient Days	11,737,932	12,021,523	12,096,907	11,888,876	11,942,896
Average Length of Stay	4.9	4.9	4.8	4.9	4.9
Personnel					
Total Full Time	228,398	238,286	234,104	231,450	228,263
Total Part Time	58,061	54,951	49,111	47,423	49,227
Revenue and Expenses - Totals (Includes Inpatient and Outpatient)					
Total Net Revenue	$45,368,763,076	$44,817,002,142	$39,961,735,021	$40,594,960,399	$37,709,543,480
Total Expenses	40,928,021,253	40,697,886,032	36,803,286,544	36,197,864,998	34,839,959,163
COMMUNITY HEALTH INDICATORS PER 1000 POPULATION					
Total Population (in thousands)	19,553	19,318	19,058	18,678	18,538
Inpatient					
Beds	2.7	2.8	2.8	2.9	2.9
Admissions	123.1	128.0	131.6	131.3	132.3
Inpatient Days	617.0	640.5	648.9	652.7	661.4
Inpatient Surgeries	30.8	31.6	32.3	34.8	35.3
Births	10.1	10.2	9.8	10.9	11.1
Outpatient					
Emergency Outpatient Visits	431.5	420.7	397.8	404.7	403.3
Other Outpatient Visits	795.7	795.5	883.0	893.2	938.4
Total Outpatient Visits	1,227.2	1,216.2	1,280.8	1,297.9	1,341.8
Outpatient Surgeries	42.9	41.5	41.1	42.7	44.4
Expense per Capita (per person)	$2,098.7	$2,112.9	$1,936.7	$1,944.4	$1,883.8

States

TABLE 6

GEORGIA

U.S. Registered Community Hospitals
(Nonfederal, short-term general and other special hospitals)

Overview 2009–2013

	2013	2012	2011	2010	2009
Total Community Hospitals in Georgia........	144	148	153	154	152
Bed Size Category					
6-24.....................................	4	4	6	6	6
25-49....................................	40	38	38	39	38
50-99....................................	25	25	26	24	24
100-199..................................	33	39	41	42	42
200-299..................................	15	18	17	17	16
300-399..................................	8	6	6	7	8
400-499..................................	9	10	8	10	10
500 +....................................	10	8	11	9	8
Location					
Hospitals Urban............................	84	86	88	89	87
Hospitals Rural	60	62	65	65	65
Control					
State and Local Government................	46	49	49	52	53
Not for Profit	67	66	68	66	63
Investor owned	31	33	36	36	36
Physician Models					
Independent Practice Association	8	5	6	8	10
Group Practice without Walls................	0	0	0	0	1
Open Physician-Hospital Organization	12	12	14	18	15
Closed Physician-Hospital Organization	18	18	16	17	16
Management Service Organization	5	7	9	8	7
Integrated Salary Model....................	34	35	39	41	37
Equity Model.............................	2	2	4	5	5
Foundation...............................	5	3	4	4	3
Insurance Products					
Health Maintenance Organization	7	6	8	9	12
Preferred Provider Organization.............	10	8	15	20	21
Indemnity Fee for Service	2	2	4	5	7
Managed Care Contracts					
Health Maintenance Organization	67	67	77	81	83
Preferred Provider Organization.............	74	72	83	94	95
Affiliations					
Hospitals in a System.....................	81	78	80	81	79
Hospitals in a Network	38	36	41	40	39
Hospitals in a Group Purchasing Organization..	83	76	95	104	105

TABLE 6

GEORGIA

U.S. Registered Community Hospitals
(Nonfederal, short-term general and other special hospitals)

Utilization, Personnel, Revenue and Expenses, Community Health Indicators 2009–2013

	2013	2012	2011	2010	2009
TOTAL FACILITY (Includes Hospital and Nursing Home Units)					
Utilization - Inpatient					
Beds	24,729	24,657	25,282	25,513	25,419
Admissions	947,299	953,817	956,503	961,391	956,870
Inpatient Days	6,034,948	5,970,497	6,094,960	6,138,828	6,059,475
Average Length of Stay	6.4	6.3	6.4	6.4	6.3
Inpatient Surgeries	259,747	257,747	265,074	265,789	267,788
Births	119,564	119,564	123,546	128,531	135,505
Utilization - Outpatient					
Emergency Outpatient Visits	4,221,105	4,153,101	4,035,426	4,095,951	4,081,812
Other Outpatient Visits	11,801,504	10,881,116	10,740,295	10,195,629	10,308,523
Total Outpatient Visits	16,022,609	15,034,217	14,775,721	14,291,580	14,390,335
Outpatient Surgeries	467,792	474,453	494,889	497,929	511,272
Personnel					
Full Time RNs	32,648	31,786	30,458	30,393	29,719
Full Time LPNs	2,359	2,866	3,119	3,276	3,506
Part Time RNs	9,376	9,066	10,000	10,469	11,965
Part Time LPNs	628	591	740	857	977
Total Full Time	114,844	111,769	110,421	112,040	111,451
Total Part Time	27,612	26,565	29,260	29,110	32,522
Revenue - Inpatient					
Gross Inpatient Revenue	$36,086,097,252	$32,638,245,514	$30,470,684,745	$28,768,523,466	$26,548,862,459
Revenue - Outpatient					
Gross Outpatient Revenue	$31,192,879,578	$26,952,133,432	$24,110,026,415	$22,700,713,568	$20,738,855,918
Revenue and Expenses - Totals					
(Includes Inpatient and Outpatient)					
Total Gross Revenue	$67,278,976,830	$59,590,378,946	$54,580,711,160	$51,469,237,034	$47,287,718,377
Deductions from Revenue	47,570,657,745	41,286,051,494	38,089,080,759	35,169,736,402	31,401,538,356
Net Patient Revenue	19,708,319,085	18,304,327,452	16,491,630,401	16,299,500,632	15,886,180,021
Other Operating Revenue	938,355,641	896,928,314	811,702,301	773,260,104	755,206,277
Other Nonoperating Revenue	591,589,397	313,593,866	228,081,442	324,122,628	128,720,872
Total Net Revenue	21,238,264,123	19,514,849,632	17,531,414,144	17,396,883,364	16,770,107,170
Total Expenses	19,519,696,158	17,663,914,623	16,450,926,776	16,079,597,038	15,616,820,380
HOSPITAL UNIT (Excludes Separate Nursing Home Units)					
Utilization - Inpatient					
Beds	21,808	21,695	21,581	21,605	21,868
Admissions	939,876	947,058	949,217	953,677	949,070
Inpatient Days	5,145,091	4,988,750	4,924,671	4,826,637	4,890,754
Average Length of Stay	5.5	5.3	5.2	5.1	5.2
Personnel					
Total Full Time	113,000	109,799	107,993	109,514	108,900
Total Part Time	27,296	26,140	28,663	28,416	31,885
Revenue and Expenses - Totals					
(Includes Inpatient and Outpatient)					
Total Net Revenue	$21,061,224,646	$19,343,288,346	$17,334,774,424	$17,166,588,760	$16,591,803,789
Total Expenses	19,365,889,564	17,517,267,271	16,266,797,779	15,896,591,116	15,452,332,194
COMMUNITY HEALTH INDICATORS PER 1000 POPULATION					
Total Population (in thousands)	9,992	9,920	9,815	9,908	9,829
Inpatient					
Beds	2.5	2.5	2.6	2.6	2.6
Admissions	94.8	96.2	97.5	97.0	97.3
Inpatient Days	604.0	601.9	621.0	619.6	616.5
Inpatient Surgeries	26.0	26.0	27.0	26.8	27.2
Births	12.0	12.1	12.6	13.0	13.8
Outpatient					
Emergency Outpatient Visits	422.4	418.7	411.1	413.4	415.3
Other Outpatient Visits	1,181.1	1,096.9	1,094.3	1,029.0	1,048.8
Total Outpatient Visits	1,603.5	1,515.6	1,505.4	1,442.4	1,464.0
Outpatient Surgeries	46.8	47.8	50.4	50.3	52.0
Expense per Capita (per person)	$1,953.5	$1,780.6	$1,676.1	$1,622.8	$1,588.8

TABLE 6

HAWAII

U.S. Registered Community Hospitals
(Nonfederal, short-term general and other special hospitals)

Overview 2009–2013

	2013	2012	2011	2010	2009
Total Community Hospitals in Hawaii	25	24	23	26	25
Bed Size Category					
6-24	6	5	5	6	5
25-49	3	3	4	3	4
50-99	6	6	5	4	5
100-199	5	5	4	7	5
200-299	4	4	4	5	5
300-399	0	0	0	0	0
400-499	1	1	1	1	1
500 + ...	0	0	0	0	0
Location					
Hospitals Urban..........................	12	12	11	14	13
Hospitals Rural	13	12	12	12	12
Control					
State and Local Government...............	9	10	7	8	7
Not for Profit	16	14	16	18	18
Investor owned	0	0	0	0	0
Physician Models					
Independent Practice Association	2	2	2	2	1
Group Practice without Walls...............	0	0	0	0	0
Open Physician-Hospital Organization	2	2	2	2	2
Closed Physician-Hospital Organization	2	3	2	1	1
Management Service Organization	0	0	0	0	0
Integrated Salary Model....................	6	9	7	7	5
Equity Model	0	0	0	0	0
Foundation..............................	0	0	0	0	2
Insurance Products					
Health Maintenance Organization	1	1	1	1	2
Preferred Provider Organization..............	0	0	3	3	3
Indemnity Fee for Service	0	0	0	1	1
Managed Care Contracts					
Health Maintenance Organization	12	14	10	7	9
Preferred Provider Organization..............	12	14	10	8	9
Affiliations					
Hospitals in a System.....................	20	19	18	21	20
Hospitals in a Network....................	4	3	2	2	3
Hospitals in a Group Purchasing Organization..	13	15	13	15	14

TABLE 6

HAWAII

U.S. Registered Community Hospitals
(Nonfederal, short-term general and other special hospitals)

Utilization, Personnel, Revenue and Expenses, Community Health Indicators 2009–2013

	2013	2012	2011	2010	2009
TOTAL FACILITY (Includes Hospital and Nursing Home Units)					
Utilization - Inpatient					
Beds	2,817	2,803	2,562	3,148	2,966
Admissions	110,374	109,270	105,039	110,577	111,706
Inpatient Days	760,960	745,956	720,633	827,977	772,508
Average Length of Stay	6.9	6.8	6.9	7.5	6.9
Inpatient Surgeries	26,137	27,141	27,447	30,626	32,340
Births	10,229	11,085	10,756	9,271	11,031
Utilization - Outpatient					
Emergency Outpatient Visits	401,191	399,437	366,276	365,903	383,778
Other Outpatient Visits	1,752,696	1,635,223	1,639,876	1,828,179	1,773,550
Total Outpatient Visits	2,153,887	2,034,660	2,006,152	2,194,082	2,157,328
Outpatient Surgeries	47,416	48,246	55,968	58,602	61,508
Personnel					
Full Time RNs	4,045	3,863	3,637	3,858	3,860
Full Time LPNs	221	253	231	292	252
Part Time RNs	963	867	722	974	1,136
Part Time LPNs	37	46	42	53	82
Total Full Time	14,561	15,008	13,674	14,755	14,505
Total Part Time	2,660	3,143	2,369	3,083	3,514
Revenue - Inpatient					
Gross Inpatient Revenue	$4,009,282,994	$4,003,578,286	$3,138,945,148	$3,433,349,265	$3,279,585,271
Revenue - Outpatient					
Gross Outpatient Revenue	$3,536,452,224	$3,523,042,969	$2,692,147,508	$2,820,300,482	$2,476,907,535
Revenue and Expenses - Totals					
(Includes Inpatient and Outpatient)					
Total Gross Revenue	$7,545,735,218	$7,526,621,255	$5,831,092,656	$6,253,649,747	$5,756,492,806
Deductions from Revenue	4,709,531,039	4,871,561,656	3,693,272,779	3,827,427,740	3,433,368,063
Net Patient Revenue	2,836,204,179	2,655,059,599	2,137,819,877	2,426,222,007	2,323,124,743
Other Operating Revenue	208,314,941	202,568,356	170,282,864	171,665,631	174,637,723
Other Nonoperating Revenue	132,431,586	35,719,144	43,411,366	48,234,523	40,300,553
Total Net Revenue	3,176,950,706	2,893,347,099	2,351,514,107	2,646,122,161	2,538,063,019
Total Expenses	2,917,345,070	2,855,849,784	2,391,952,134	2,611,062,195	2,576,059,889
HOSPITAL UNIT (Excludes Separate Nursing Home Units)					
Utilization - Inpatient					
Beds	2,523	2,355	2,203	2,688	2,635
Admissions	108,687	107,534	103,143	108,956	109,467
Inpatient Days	660,686	644,358	598,213	660,450	657,887
Average Length of Stay	6.1	6.0	5.8	6.1	6.0
Personnel					
Total Full Time	14,355	14,408	13,399	14,428	14,178
Total Part Time	2,623	3,077	2,318	3,047	3,446
Revenue and Expenses - Totals					
(Includes Inpatient and Outpatient)					
Total Net Revenue	$3,149,956,310	$2,828,961,559	$2,318,674,997	$2,601,754,091	$2,512,905,897
Total Expenses	2,886,933,350	2,775,697,478	2,347,459,882	2,561,364,433	2,550,665,438
COMMUNITY HEALTH INDICATORS PER 1000 POPULATION					
Total Population (in thousands)	1,404	1,392	1,375	1,300	1,295
Inpatient					
Beds	2.0	2.0	1.9	2.4	2.3
Admissions	78.6	78.5	76.4	85.1	86.2
Inpatient Days	542.0	535.8	524.2	636.9	596.4
Inpatient Surgeries	18.6	19.5	20.0	23.6	25.0
Births	7.3	8.0	7.8	7.1	8.5
Outpatient					
Emergency Outpatient Visits	285.7	286.9	266.4	281.4	296.3
Other Outpatient Visits	1,248.3	1,174.5	1,192.8	1,406.2	1,369.3
Total Outpatient Visits	1,534.0	1,461.4	1,459.2	1,687.6	1,665.7
Outpatient Surgeries	33.8	34.7	40.7	45.1	47.5
Expense per Capita (per person)	$2,077.8	$2,051.2	$1,739.8	$2,008.4	$1,989.0

States

TABLE **6**

IDAHO

U.S. Registered Community Hospitals
(Nonfederal, short-term general and other special hospitals)

Overview 2009–2013

	2013	2012	2011	2010	2009
Total Community Hospitals in Idaho	40	40	40	41	41
Bed Size Category					
6-24	12	11	12	11	11
25-49	10	13	11	12	11
50-99	9	7	8	9	10
100-199	4	5	4	5	5
200-299	2	1	2	1	1
300-399	2	2	2	2	2
400-499	0	0	0	0	0
500 + ...	1	1	1	1	1
Location					
Hospitals Urban.	14	14	14	15	15
Hospitals Rural	26	26	26	26	26
Control					
State and Local Government	18	19	19	20	20
Not for Profit	17	16	17	16	16
Investor owned	5	5	4	5	5
Physician Models					
Independent Practice Association	1	4	5	5	5
Group Practice without Walls.	0	0	1	1	2
Open Physician-Hospital Organization	6	10	7	4	4
Closed Physician-Hospital Organization	1	1	2	2	3
Management Service Organization	0	0	1	3	4
Integrated Salary Model	14	15	12	13	13
Equity Model	1	1	0	0	0
Foundation.	1	1	1	1	1
Insurance Products					
Health Maintenance Organization	1	0	1	2	2
Preferred Provider Organization.	2	2	2	2	4
Indemnity Fee for Service	1	1	1	0	1
Managed Care Contracts					
Health Maintenance Organization	12	14	13	14	15
Preferred Provider Organization.	17	17	17	19	22
Affiliations					
Hospitals in a System.	20	21	20	23	23
Hospitals in a Network	9	10	11	13	15
Hospitals in a Group Purchasing Organization. .	24	26	25	25	28

TABLE 6

IDAHO

U.S. Registered Community Hospitals
(Nonfederal, short-term general and other special hospitals)

Utilization, Personnel, Revenue and Expenses, Community Health Indicators 2009–2013

	2013	2012	2011	2010	2009
TOTAL FACILITY (Includes Hospital and Nursing Home Units)					
Utilization - Inpatient					
Beds.........................	3,355	3,305	3,306	3,376	3,382
Admissions.....................	126,164	123,794	128,742	131,375	129,645
Inpatient Days	609,999	611,785	605,718	628,840	627,077
Average Length of Stay............	4.8	4.9	4.7	4.8	4.8
Inpatient Surgeries...............	36,416	40,313	39,858	39,614	40,358
Births.........................	19,285	20,117	19,487	18,941	20,126
Utilization - Outpatient					
Emergency Outpatient Visits........	590,382	543,272	517,995	489,718	514,299
Other Outpatient Visits............	4,187,775	3,807,298	3,516,106	2,672,240	2,558,653
Total Outpatient Visits	4,778,157	4,350,570	4,034,101	3,161,958	3,072,952
Outpatient Surgeries	76,661	81,915	84,221	73,409	68,339
Personnel					
Full Time RNs	4,878	4,651	4,334	4,103	3,898
Full Time LPNs	448	443	458	403	399
Part Time RNs	2,688	2,418	2,341	2,245	2,119
Part Time LPNs	201	193	209	166	169
Total Full Time..................	22,143	20,340	19,181	18,010	16,594
Total Part Time	8,840	8,192	8,019	7,175	6,408
Revenue - Inpatient					
Gross Inpatient Revenue...........	$4,216,564,570	$3,543,382,140	$3,108,970,857	$2,899,758,710	$2,707,480,791
Revenue - Outpatient					
Gross Outpatient Revenue	$4,739,814,434	$4,029,848,296	$3,623,818,467	$3,113,164,805	$2,775,500,660
Revenue and Expenses - Totals					
(Includes Inpatient and Outpatient)					
Total Gross Revenue..............	$8,956,379,004	$7,573,230,436	$6,732,789,324	$6,012,923,515	$5,482,981,451
Deductions from Revenue.........	5,257,575,535	4,057,678,208	3,621,413,551	3,190,452,073	2,796,704,816
Net Patient Revenue	3,698,803,469	3,515,552,228	3,111,375,773	2,822,471,442	2,686,276,635
Other Operating Revenue	149,063,415	116,996,412	103,709,342	96,182,670	83,202,052
Other Nonoperating Revenue	38,229,484	17,730,950	49,967,037	47,366,046	-11,931,355
Total Net Revenue...............	3,886,096,368	3,650,279,590	3,265,052,152	2,966,020,158	2,757,547,332
Total Expenses..................	3,549,202,960	3,127,967,915	2,791,035,799	2,546,624,205	2,563,109,938
HOSPITAL UNIT (Excludes Separate Nursing Home Units)					
Utilization - Inpatient					
Beds.........................	3,087	3,041	2,950	3,027	3,013
Admissions.....................	125,217	122,840	127,750	129,900	127,927
Inpatient Days	536,798	536,537	503,243	525,428	518,291
Average Length of Stay............	4.3	4.4	3.9	4.0	4.1
Personnel					
Total Full Time..................	21,912	20,159	18,937	17,803	16,327
Total Part Time	8,716	8,074	7,878	7,040	6,227
Revenue and Expenses - Totals					
(Includes Inpatient and Outpatient)					
Total Net Revenue...............	$3,858,606,336	$3,630,538,385	$3,240,672,233	$2,934,932,796	$2,730,768,774
Total Expenses..................	3,530,094,122	3,117,054,550	2,775,730,301	2,524,919,767	2,541,756,270
COMMUNITY HEALTH INDICATORS PER 1000 POPULATION					
Total Population (in thousands)	1,612	1,596	1,585	1,560	1,546
Inpatient					
Beds.........................	2.1	2.1	2.1	2.2	2.2
Admissions.....................	78.3	77.6	81.2	84.2	83.9
Inpatient Days	378.4	383.4	382.2	403.2	405.7
Inpatient Surgeries...............	22.6	25.3	25.1	25.4	26.1
Births.........................	12.0	12.6	12.3	12.1	13.0
Outpatient					
Emergency Outpatient Visits.......	366.2	340.5	326.8	314.0	332.7
Other Outpatient Visits............	2,597.7	2,385.9	2,218.4	1,713.2	1,655.2
Total Outpatient Visits	2,963.9	2,726.4	2,545.2	2,027.2	1,987.9
Outpatient Surgeries	47.6	51.3	53.1	47.1	44.2
Expense per Capita (per person).....	$2,201.6	$1,960.2	$1,760.9	$1,632.7	$1,658.1

TABLE 6

ILLINOIS

U.S. Registered Community Hospitals
(Nonfederal, short-term general and other special hospitals)

Overview 2009–2013

	2013	2012	2011	2010	2009
Total Community Hospitals in Illinois	189	188	188	189	189
Bed Size Category					
6-24	13	12	11	10	8
25-49	37	38	36	32	31
50-99	29	27	31	36	37
100-199	54	53	51	50	49
200-299	25	22	24	25	29
300-399	17	20	18	19	17
400-499	6	9	9	9	10
500 + ...	8	7	8	8	8
Location					
Hospitals Urban.........................	125	124	124	125	125
Hospitals Rural	64	64	64	64	64
Control					
State and Local Government................	23	24	24	26	26
Not for Profit	146	144	145	143	147
Investor owned	20	20	19	20	16
Physician Models					
Independent Practice Association	24	26	22	28	30
Group Practice without Walls..............	12	8	8	4	5
Open Physician-Hospital Organization	56	46	43	43	47
Closed Physician-Hospital Organization	11	9	11	13	11
Management Service Organization	19	21	21	22	27
Integrated Salary Model....................	71	63	59	62	64
Equity Model	5	3	3	2	4
Foundation..............................	10	8	8	13	6
Insurance Products					
Health Maintenance Organization	25	21	16	19	18
Preferred Provider Organization.............	17	13	17	17	16
Indemnity Fee for Service	6	4	7	7	7
Managed Care Contracts					
Health Maintenance Organization	120	122	114	123	127
Preferred Provider Organization.............	136	137	127	134	142
Affiliations					
Hospitals in a System.....................	118	114	113	108	104
Hospitals in a Network....................	58	52	43	47	47
Hospitals in a Group Purchasing Organization..	149	145	142	157	158

TABLE 6

ILLINOIS

U.S. Registered Community Hospitals
(Nonfederal, short-term general and other special hospitals)

Utilization, Personnel, Revenue and Expenses, Community Health Indicators 2009–2013

	2013	2012	2011	2010	2009
TOTAL FACILITY (Includes Hospital and Nursing Home Units)					
Utilization - Inpatient					
Beds	31,745	32,662	32,775	33,310	33,856
Admissions	1,426,848	1,484,155	1,511,770	1,542,958	1,557,816
Inpatient Days	6,865,573	7,190,230	7,398,797	7,552,956	7,769,059
Average Length of Stay	4.8	4.8	4.9	4.9	5.0
Inpatient Surgeries	368,428	376,684	386,166	403,226	399,042
Births	146,392	150,234	152,929	159,563	166,005
Utilization - Outpatient					
Emergency Outpatient Visits	5,252,340	5,422,193	5,414,964	5,366,010	5,312,763
Other Outpatient Visits	27,556,186	27,694,668	26,277,834	27,192,086	26,780,252
Total Outpatient Visits	32,808,526	33,116,861	31,692,798	32,558,096	32,093,015
Outpatient Surgeries	743,687	728,808	731,909	738,783	723,461
Personnel					
Full Time RNs	46,160	44,894	42,707	41,948	39,989
Full Time LPNs	1,679	1,684	1,730	1,769	1,882
Part Time RNs	21,818	23,656	23,563	23,493	24,237
Part Time LPNs	633	690	769	808	827
Total Full Time	168,524	168,745	163,470	163,519	162,002
Total Part Time	70,370	72,684	74,154	74,448	76,241
Revenue - Inpatient					
Gross Inpatient Revenue	$55,496,665,893	$54,040,034,827	$51,831,662,656	$50,630,716,983	$48,011,580,288
Revenue - Outpatient					
Gross Outpatient Revenue	$55,220,592,255	$51,085,072,799	$45,237,976,561	$41,884,636,238	$38,198,138,940
Revenue and Expenses - Totals					
(Includes Inpatient and Outpatient)					
Total Gross Revenue	$110,717,258,148	$105,125,107,626	$97,069,639,217	$92,515,353,221	$86,209,719,228
Deductions from Revenue	78,196,471,517	73,249,630,932	67,477,849,736	63,248,692,053	58,012,296,593
Net Patient Revenue	32,520,786,631	31,875,476,694	29,591,789,481	29,266,661,168	28,197,422,635
Other Operating Revenue	2,131,938,656	1,930,010,171	1,900,816,882	1,918,358,653	1,923,701,500
Other Nonoperating Revenue	1,098,662,582	597,357,110	1,093,755,704	712,723,108	-244,005,396
Total Net Revenue	35,751,387,869	34,402,843,975	32,586,362,067	31,897,742,929	29,877,118,739
Total Expenses	32,752,851,815	31,914,764,033	29,831,858,047	29,193,599,201	28,870,203,691
HOSPITAL UNIT (Excludes Separate Nursing Home Units)					
Utilization - Inpatient					
Beds	30,716	31,431	31,305	31,615	32,096
Admissions	1,417,171	1,471,741	1,497,436	1,526,371	1,540,936
Inpatient Days	6,623,180	6,891,159	7,012,553	7,117,426	7,294,792
Average Length of Stay	4.7	4.7	4.7	4.7	4.7
Personnel					
Total Full Time	167,903	168,056	162,704	162,567	160,793
Total Part Time	69,892	72,171	73,555	73,868	75,623
Revenue and Expenses - Totals					
(Includes Inpatient and Outpatient)					
Total Net Revenue	$35,673,229,824	$34,307,140,177	$32,474,980,131	$31,785,482,525	$29,750,884,315
Total Expenses	32,686,336,226	31,835,376,910	29,734,524,075	29,102,876,687	28,774,155,633
COMMUNITY HEALTH INDICATORS PER 1000 POPULATION					
Total Population (in thousands)	12,882	12,875	12,869	12,944	12,910
Inpatient					
Beds	2.5	2.5	2.5	2.6	2.6
Admissions	110.8	115.3	117.5	119.2	120.7
Inpatient Days	533.0	558.5	574.9	583.5	601.8
Inpatient Surgeries	28.6	29.3	30.0	31.2	30.9
Births	11.4	11.7	11.9	12.3	12.9
Outpatient					
Emergency Outpatient Visits	407.7	421.1	420.8	414.5	411.5
Other Outpatient Visits	2,139.1	2,151.0	2,041.9	2,100.7	2,074.3
Total Outpatient Visits	2,546.8	2,572.1	2,462.7	2,515.2	2,485.8
Outpatient Surgeries	57.7	56.6	56.9	57.1	56.0
Expense per Capita (per person)	$2,542.5	$2,478.8	$2,318.1	$2,255.3	$2,236.2

States

TABLE 6

INDIANA

U.S. Registered Community Hospitals
(Nonfederal, short-term general and other special hospitals)

Overview 2009–2013

	2013	2012	2011	2010	2009
Total Community Hospitals in Indiana	123	124	125	125	123
Bed Size Category					
6-24	6	6	5	5	5
25-49	42	40	40	41	41
50-99	26	28	30	28	27
100-199	23	24	23	21	23
200-299	12	11	13	16	14
300-399	3	5	5	5	4
400-499	6	4	3	3	2
500 + ...	5	6	6	6	7
Location					
Hospitals Urban..........................	83	84	85	85	83
Hospitals Rural	40	40	40	40	40
Control					
State and Local Government................	30	30	30	33	34
Not for Profit	68	69	71	67	64
Investor owned	25	25	24	25	25
Physician Models					
Independent Practice Association	5	7	3	6	9
Group Practice without Walls...............	4	5	4	2	2
Open Physician-Hospital Organization	23	21	21	26	26
Closed Physician-Hospital Organization	5	8	7	8	9
Management Service Organization	9	7	8	9	9
Integrated Salary Model....................	61	58	53	55	53
Equity Model	4	3	3	2	3
Foundation..............................	6	4	2	5	7
Insurance Products					
Health Maintenance Organization	31	28	27	29	26
Preferred Provider Organization..............	35	29	30	33	27
Indemnity Fee for Service	9	9	4	6	4
Managed Care Contracts					
Health Maintenance Organization	64	64	62	65	69
Preferred Provider Organization..............	78	76	71	77	84
Affiliations					
Hospitals in a System.....................	86	85	87	85	82
Hospitals in a Network....................	45	42	45	46	44
Hospitals in a Group Purchasing Organization..	96	92	87	97	98

TABLE 6

INDIANA

U.S. Registered Community Hospitals
(Nonfederal, short-term general and other special hospitals)

Utilization, Personnel, Revenue and Expenses, Community Health Indicators 2009–2013

	2013	2012	2011	2010	2009
TOTAL FACILITY (Includes Hospital and Nursing Home Units)					
Utilization - Inpatient					
Beds	17,264	17,556	17,467	17,759	17,298
Admissions	701,743	731,046	737,438	718,348	713,456
Inpatient Days	3,653,922	3,739,056	3,724,041	3,756,021	3,687,549
Average Length of Stay	5.2	5.1	5.0	5.2	5.2
Inpatient Surgeries	186,776	200,708	200,907	206,124	206,101
Births	71,984	73,460	76,049	77,124	78,371
Utilization - Outpatient					
Emergency Outpatient Visits	3,129,456	3,207,214	3,144,973	3,185,166	3,004,721
Other Outpatient Visits	15,270,100	14,711,090	15,367,982	15,543,606	14,446,277
Total Outpatient Visits	18,399,556	17,918,304	18,512,955	18,728,772	17,450,998
Outpatient Surgeries	420,844	441,917	429,164	423,827	430,435
Personnel					
Full Time RNs	23,370	23,611	23,243	22,345	21,653
Full Time LPNs	1,468	1,536	1,697	1,664	1,742
Part Time RNs	14,311	14,379	13,697	14,136	13,502
Part Time LPNs	711	722	768	874	995
Total Full Time	87,286	88,265	87,241	86,266	86,530
Total Part Time	41,032	41,617	39,619	41,019	40,675
Revenue - Inpatient					
Gross Inpatient Revenue	$26,593,801,942	$26,099,729,709	$23,724,867,721	$21,889,172,836	$19,297,952,821
Revenue - Outpatient					
Gross Outpatient Revenue	$28,186,114,204	$26,487,465,316	$23,279,155,929	$20,791,179,952	$18,451,255,529
Revenue and Expenses - Totals **(Includes Inpatient and Outpatient)**					
Total Gross Revenue	$54,779,916,146	$52,587,195,025	$47,004,023,650	$42,680,352,788	$37,749,208,350
Deductions from Revenue	36,132,735,438	33,296,640,742	30,555,814,094	26,936,969,969	22,765,297,520
Net Patient Revenue	18,647,180,708	19,290,554,283	16,448,209,556	15,743,382,819	14,983,910,830
Other Operating Revenue	1,042,257,524	1,104,200,980	1,117,137,691	881,745,072	769,461,090
Other Nonoperating Revenue	607,370,565	439,930,085	405,284,123	434,805,381	282,345,047
Total Net Revenue	20,296,808,797	20,834,685,348	17,970,631,370	17,059,933,272	16,035,716,967
Total Expenses	17,893,508,316	17,926,526,564	16,082,098,784	15,349,922,777	14,724,925,283
HOSPITAL UNIT (Excludes Separate Nursing Home Units)					
Utilization - Inpatient					
Beds	16,552	16,911	16,942	17,208	16,879
Admissions	698,347	726,693	732,496	713,224	707,886
Inpatient Days	3,442,577	3,569,377	3,562,156	3,584,106	3,567,515
Average Length of Stay	4.9	4.9	4.9	5.0	5.0
Personnel					
Total Full Time	86,819	87,873	86,943	85,948	85,900
Total Part Time	40,642	41,296	39,255	40,630	40,280
Revenue and Expenses - Totals **(Includes Inpatient and Outpatient)**					
Total Net Revenue	$20,233,420,523	$20,781,574,841	$17,906,999,370	$17,017,380,655	$15,997,778,555
Total Expenses	17,841,711,211	17,894,880,475	16,032,853,104	15,311,258,669	14,696,533,580
COMMUNITY HEALTH INDICATORS PER 1000 POPULATION					
Total Population (in thousands)	6,571	6,537	6,517	6,445	6,423
Inpatient					
Beds	2.6	2.7	2.7	2.8	2.7
Admissions	106.8	111.8	113.2	111.5	111.1
Inpatient Days	556.1	572.0	571.4	582.8	574.1
Inpatient Surgeries	28.4	30.7	30.8	32.0	32.1
Births	11.0	11.2	11.7	12.0	12.2
Outpatient					
Emergency Outpatient Visits	476.3	490.6	482.6	494.2	467.8
Other Outpatient Visits	2,323.9	2,250.3	2,358.2	2,411.6	2,249.1
Total Outpatient Visits	2,800.2	2,740.9	2,840.8	2,905.8	2,716.9
Outpatient Surgeries	64.0	67.6	65.9	65.8	67.0
Expense per Capita (per person)	$2,723.1	$2,742.2	$2,467.7	$2,381.6	$2,292.5

States

TABLE 6

IOWA

U.S. Registered Community Hospitals
(Nonfederal, short-term general and other special hospitals)

Overview 2009–2013

	2013	2012	2011	2010	2009
Total Community Hospitals in Iowa..........	118	118	118	118	118
Bed Size Category					
6-24	20	19	19	18	15
25-49	49	48	48	49	51
50-99	26	26	27	27	26
100-199	9	11	10	10	12
200-299	6	6	6	6	6
300-399	5	5	5	5	5
400-499	1	1	1	1	1
500 + ...	2	2	2	2	2
Location					
Hospitals Urban...........................	34	34	34	34	34
Hospitals Rural	84	84	84	84	84
Control					
State and Local Government................	59	59	59	59	59
Not for Profit	57	57	57	57	58
Investor owned	2	2	2	2	1
Physician Models					
Independent Practice Association	13	14	12	13	13
Group Practice without Walls...............	5	5	5	4	3
Open Physician-Hospital Organization	20	19	18	20	24
Closed Physician-Hospital Organization	11	11	11	10	10
Management Service Organization	8	8	9	8	9
Integrated Salary Model....................	77	76	74	72	70
Equity Model	1	1	1	0	0
Foundation...............................	4	3	5	4	4
Insurance Products					
Health Maintenance Organization	14	10	8	8	9
Preferred Provider Organization.............	15	12	20	23	22
Indemnity Fee for Service	3	4	5	5	6
Managed Care Contracts					
Health Maintenance Organization	75	75	74	73	71
Preferred Provider Organization.............	95	95	94	99	98
Affiliations					
Hospitals in a System.....................	70	69	64	66	64
Hospitals in a Network....................	79	79	77	73	72
Hospitals in a Group Purchasing Organization..	117	116	115	115	112

TABLE 6

IOWA

U.S. Registered Community Hospitals
(Nonfederal, short-term general and other special hospitals)

Utilization, Personnel, Revenue and Expenses, Community Health Indicators 2009–2013

	2013	2012	2011	2010	2009
TOTAL FACILITY (Includes Hospital and Nursing Home Units)					
Utilization - Inpatient					
Beds	9,839	9,962	9,981	10,075	10,276
Admissions	326,593	336,765	340,412	341,744	354,534
Inpatient Days	2,001,590	2,022,552	2,058,730	2,058,304	2,185,446
Average Length of Stay	6.1	6.0	6.0	6.0	6.2
Inpatient Surgeries	80,936	84,008	83,333	87,343	92,154
Births	38,344	37,967	37,284	38,193	39,522
Utilization - Outpatient					
Emergency Outpatient Visits	1,292,810	1,297,129	1,273,985	1,223,271	1,230,737
Other Outpatient Visits	9,316,036	9,318,536	9,053,438	9,805,308	9,724,268
Total Outpatient Visits	10,608,846	10,615,665	10,327,423	11,028,579	10,955,005
Outpatient Surgeries	247,077	253,460	256,117	253,148	265,368
Personnel					
Full Time RNs	11,653	11,208	11,084	10,516	10,657
Full Time LPNs	702	761	788	775	814
Part Time RNs	6,734	6,913	6,843	6,988	7,147
Part Time LPNs	497	563	412	548	587
Total Full Time	45,507	44,797	44,535	43,589	43,659
Total Part Time	22,560	23,460	23,019	23,392	24,045
Revenue - Inpatient					
Gross Inpatient Revenue	$8,806,484,946	$8,408,565,148	$7,955,026,036	$7,478,207,382	$7,402,854,971
Revenue - Outpatient					
Gross Outpatient Revenue	$10,917,710,660	$10,161,337,605	$9,276,348,064	$8,615,345,555	$7,932,610,080
Revenue and Expenses - Totals					
(Includes Inpatient and Outpatient)					
Total Gross Revenue	$19,724,195,606	$18,569,902,753	$17,231,374,100	$16,093,552,937	$15,335,465,051
Deductions from Revenue	12,194,888,808	11,074,628,171	10,246,167,955	9,374,915,563	8,788,605,112
Net Patient Revenue	7,529,306,798	7,495,274,582	6,985,206,145	6,718,637,374	6,546,859,939
Other Operating Revenue	620,140,454	591,931,420	502,660,629	483,246,348	490,608,985
Other Nonoperating Revenue	292,293,006	149,767,795	223,831,009	236,093,511	9,177,812
Total Net Revenue	8,441,740,258	8,236,973,797	7,711,697,783	7,437,977,233	7,046,646,736
Total Expenses	7,832,928,280	7,709,621,525	7,174,090,504	6,934,527,799	6,824,533,485
HOSPITAL UNIT (Excludes Separate Nursing Home Units)					
Utilization - Inpatient					
Beds	8,153	8,275	8,287	8,341	8,385
Admissions	323,713	332,949	336,335	337,483	348,765
Inpatient Days	1,482,642	1,501,406	1,533,884	1,521,829	1,602,497
Average Length of Stay	4.6	4.5	4.6	4.5	4.6
Personnel					
Total Full Time	44,714	44,073	43,792	42,836	42,865
Total Part Time	21,781	22,722	22,278	22,670	23,241
Revenue and Expenses - Totals					
(Includes Inpatient and Outpatient)					
Total Net Revenue	$8,349,001,790	$8,147,277,912	$7,624,566,231	$7,354,382,506	$6,945,244,251
Total Expenses	7,756,011,550	7,631,417,462	7,096,506,924	6,860,708,589	6,739,111,985
COMMUNITY HEALTH INDICATORS PER 1000 POPULATION					
Total Population (in thousands)	3,090	3,074	3,062	3,023	3,008
Inpatient					
Beds	3.2	3.2	3.3	3.3	3.4
Admissions	105.7	109.5	111.2	113.0	117.9
Inpatient Days	647.7	657.9	672.3	680.9	726.6
Inpatient Surgeries	26.2	27.3	27.2	28.9	30.6
Births	12.4	12.4	12.2	12.6	13.1
Outpatient					
Emergency Outpatient Visits	418.3	421.9	416.0	404.6	409.2
Other Outpatient Visits	3,014.5	3,031.2	2,956.4	3,243.5	3,233.0
Total Outpatient Visits	3,432.8	3,453.2	3,372.4	3,648.1	3,642.1
Outpatient Surgeries	79.9	82.4	83.6	83.7	88.2
Expense per Capita (per person)	$2,534.6	$2,507.9	$2,342.7	$2,293.9	$2,268.9

States

TABLE **6**

KANSAS

U.S. Registered Community Hospitals
(Nonfederal, short-term general and other special hospitals)

Overview 2009–2013

	2013	2012	2011	2010	2009
Total Community Hospitals in Kansas	130	131	132	130	133
Bed Size Category					
6-24	21	20	20	19	18
25-49	49	49	50	49	50
50-99	35	37	38	37	40
100-199	16	16	14	16	15
200-299	4	4	5	4	5
300-399	2	2	2	2	2
400-499	0	0	0	0	0
500 + ...	3	3	3	3	3
Location					
Hospitals Urban...........................	34	34	33	33	33
Hospitals Rural	96	97	99	97	100
Control					
State and Local Government................	61	61	63	62	62
Not for Profit	51	53	53	51	54
Investor owned	18	17	16	17	17
Physician Models					
Independent Practice Association	10	13	15	13	14
Group Practice without Walls...............	3	4	3	2	2
Open Physician-Hospital Organization	11	12	12	11	14
Closed Physician-Hospital Organization	1	2	1	0	2
Management Service Organization	1	2	5	3	4
Integrated Salary Model....................	79	79	77	69	71
Equity Model	1	2	1	0	0
Foundation...............................	4	5	8	5	3
Insurance Products					
Health Maintenance Organization	2	2	1	1	2
Preferred Provider Organization..............	5	7	9	9	8
Indemnity Fee for Service	1	3	0	1	2
Managed Care Contracts					
Health Maintenance Organization	57	56	55	56	52
Preferred Provider Organization..............	109	112	110	109	111
Affiliations					
Hospitals in a System.....................	53	56	55	53	54
Hospitals in a Network....................	80	79	82	83	83
Hospitals in a Group Purchasing Organization..	129	128	129	128	126

States

TABLE 6

KANSAS

U.S. Registered Community Hospitals
(Nonfederal, short-term general and other special hospitals)

Utilization, Personnel, Revenue and Expenses, Community Health Indicators 2009–2013

	2013	2012	2011	2010	2009
TOTAL FACILITY (Includes Hospital and Nursing Home Units)					
Utilization - Inpatient					
Beds	9,998	10,127	10,023	9,965	10,127
Admissions	289,696	296,267	302,351	304,769	315,820
Inpatient Days	1,899,716	1,915,826	1,923,661	1,960,261	2,014,165
Average Length of Stay	6.6	6.5	6.4	6.4	6.4
Inpatient Surgeries	71,156	73,240	76,828	79,305	79,857
Births	37,311	38,623	38,707	39,777	41,092
Utilization - Outpatient					
Emergency Outpatient Visits	1,127,551	1,114,026	1,041,234	1,019,521	1,042,407
Other Outpatient Visits	5,962,793	6,179,011	5,955,302	5,660,293	5,687,308
Total Outpatient Visits	7,090,344	7,293,037	6,996,536	6,679,814	6,729,715
Outpatient Surgeries	156,088	166,253	161,889	157,746	160,653
Personnel					
Full Time RNs	12,146	11,619	10,968	10,852	10,517
Full Time LPNs	1,036	1,009	1,014	1,056	1,132
Part Time RNs	4,861	4,917	4,533	4,535	4,550
Part Time LPNs	389	405	409	441	495
Total Full Time	40,892	40,129	39,286	38,881	38,833
Total Part Time	14,722	14,838	14,111	14,183	14,585
Revenue - Inpatient					
Gross Inpatient Revenue	$10,790,044,124	$10,396,751,854	$9,707,362,014	$9,158,840,266	$8,857,616,660
Revenue - Outpatient					
Gross Outpatient Revenue	$10,497,568,428	$10,046,165,626	$8,606,191,704	$7,804,133,580	$7,296,946,111
Revenue and Expenses - Totals					
(Includes Inpatient and Outpatient)					
Total Gross Revenue	$21,287,612,552	$20,442,917,480	$18,313,553,718	$16,962,973,846	$16,154,562,771
Deductions from Revenue	14,616,689,279	13,766,315,018	12,295,093,634	11,147,817,611	10,508,920,047
Net Patient Revenue	6,670,923,273	6,676,602,462	6,018,460,084	5,815,156,235	5,645,642,724
Other Operating Revenue	288,774,222	284,943,541	215,888,633	203,257,460	212,360,609
Other Nonoperating Revenue	171,234,302	160,005,906	66,106,732	128,773,371	25,755,861
Total Net Revenue	7,130,931,797	7,121,551,909	6,300,455,449	6,147,187,066	5,883,759,194
Total Expenses	6,616,602,126	6,513,729,367	5,963,380,431	5,759,373,331	5,603,169,760
HOSPITAL UNIT (Excludes Separate Nursing Home Units)					
Utilization - Inpatient					
Beds	8,440	8,568	8,495	8,338	8,418
Admissions	287,249	293,835	299,829	302,003	313,046
Inpatient Days	1,426,105	1,440,628	1,449,789	1,447,040	1,507,027
Average Length of Stay	5.0	4.9	4.8	4.8	4.8
Personnel					
Total Full Time	39,877	39,007	38,237	37,806	37,721
Total Part Time	14,237	14,268	13,543	13,660	13,972
Revenue and Expenses - Totals					
(Includes Inpatient and Outpatient)					
Total Net Revenue	$7,047,938,513	$7,040,162,578	$6,224,061,786	$6,068,771,082	$5,807,209,303
Total Expenses	6,548,127,097	6,440,417,821	5,897,756,162	5,694,269,627	5,536,264,786
COMMUNITY HEALTH INDICATORS PER 1000 POPULATION					
Total Population (in thousands)	2,894	2,886	2,871	2,841	2,819
Inpatient					
Beds	3.5	3.5	3.5	3.5	3.6
Admissions	100.1	102.7	105.3	107.3	112.0
Inpatient Days	656.4	663.9	670.0	690.0	714.6
Inpatient Surgeries	24.6	25.4	26.8	27.9	28.3
Births	12.9	13.4	13.5	14.0	14.6
Outpatient					
Emergency Outpatient Visits	389.6	386.0	362.6	358.8	369.8
Other Outpatient Visits	2,060.4	2,141.1	2,074.1	1,992.3	2,017.7
Total Outpatient Visits	2,450.1	2,527.1	2,436.8	2,351.1	2,387.5
Outpatient Surgeries	53.9	57.6	56.4	55.5	57.0
Expense per Capita (per person)	$2,286.4	$2,257.1	$2,076.9	$2,027.1	$1,987.8

TABLE 6

KENTUCKY

U.S. Registered Community Hospitals
(Nonfederal, short-term general and other special hospitals)

Overview 2009–2013

	2013	2012	2011	2010	2009
Total Community Hospitals in Kentucky	106	106	106	106	104
Bed Size Category					
6-24	3	3	3	1	1
25-49	35	36	34	34	33
50-99	19	19	22	24	24
100-199	26	25	25	24	23
200-299	10	10	7	8	8
300-399	9	9	10	10	9
400-499	2	0	1	3	3
500 +	2	4	4	2	3
Location					
Hospitals Urban	43	43	43	43	42
Hospitals Rural	63	63	63	63	62
Control					
State and Local Government	11	12	12	11	11
Not for Profit	75	74	74	75	73
Investor owned	20	20	20	20	20
Physician Models					
Independent Practice Association	3	6	5	5	6
Group Practice without Walls	1	1	0	0	2
Open Physician-Hospital Organization	5	6	7	9	12
Closed Physician-Hospital Organization	1	1	2	3	4
Management Service Organization	9	10	8	8	3
Integrated Salary Model	40	44	42	43	38
Equity Model	0	0	0	0	1
Foundation	2	2	3	4	3
Insurance Products					
Health Maintenance Organization	6	7	7	10	5
Preferred Provider Organization	10	7	14	15	9
Indemnity Fee for Service	4	3	5	8	2
Managed Care Contracts					
Health Maintenance Organization	41	43	44	48	46
Preferred Provider Organization	42	44	53	59	57
Affiliations					
Hospitals in a System	80	80	80	79	76
Hospitals in a Network	28	24	17	22	23
Hospitals in a Group Purchasing Organization	70	74	71	80	77

TABLE 6   KENTUCKY

U.S. Registered Community Hospitals
(Nonfederal, short-term general and other special hospitals)

Utilization, Personnel, Revenue and Expenses, Community Health Indicators 2009–2013

	2013	2012	2011	2010	2009
TOTAL FACILITY (Includes Hospital and Nursing Home Units)					
Utilization - Inpatient					
Beds	14,021	14,180	14,182	14,238	14,124
Admissions	578,841	572,294	599,601	608,644	597,224
Inpatient Days	3,026,582	2,908,461	3,061,415	3,141,502	3,113,326
Average Length of Stay..........	5.2	5.1	5.1	5.2	5.2
Inpatient Surgeries...........	159,628	166,885	170,702	173,656	173,196
Births........	54,263	53,538	49,657	53,630	50,085
Utilization - Outpatient					
Emergency Outpatient Visits........	2,279,740	2,404,826	2,350,367	2,386,673	2,321,519
Other Outpatient Visits...........	8,241,623	8,166,103	8,182,293	8,050,866	7,798,087
Total Outpatient Visits	10,521,363	10,570,929	10,532,660	10,437,539	10,119,606
Outpatient Surgeries	368,971	371,089	400,593	385,960	372,057
Personnel					
Full Time RNs	18,551	18,672	17,989	17,666	16,592
Full Time LPNs	1,243	1,290	1,436	1,648	1,849
Part Time RNs...........	6,624	6,093	6,060	6,087	6,016
Part Time LPNs	261	268	343	397	419
Total Full Time...........	62,625	64,131	64,035	63,493	61,699
Total Part Time	19,000	17,391	18,453	18,309	18,144
Revenue - Inpatient					
Gross Inpatient Revenue..........	$18,199,474,364	$16,779,961,324	$16,313,648,119	$15,503,184,961	$14,536,872,535
Revenue - Outpatient					
Gross Outpatient Revenue	$18,314,577,975	$16,724,256,215	$15,995,475,627	$14,305,855,765	$12,460,315,729
Revenue and Expenses - Totals					
(Includes Inpatient and Outpatient)					
Total Gross Revenue.............	$36,514,052,339	$33,504,217,539	$32,309,123,746	$29,809,040,726	$26,997,188,264
Deductions from Revenue..........	25,507,901,441	22,702,995,327	22,051,533,008	19,784,508,926	17,477,244,235
Net Patient Revenue	11,006,150,898	10,801,222,212	10,257,590,738	10,024,531,800	9,519,944,029
Other Operating Revenue	407,398,136	406,456,390	383,110,150	338,831,936	353,366,856
Other Nonoperating Revenue	237,296,737	56,938,657	135,433,381	145,526,221	-11,001,226
Total Net Revenue.............	11,650,845,771	11,264,617,259	10,776,134,269	10,508,889,957	9,862,309,659
Total Expenses.................	10,884,059,289	10,400,750,170	10,049,280,333	9,801,870,954	9,424,000,735
HOSPITAL UNIT (Excludes Separate Nursing Home Units)					
Utilization - Inpatient					
Beds	13,319	13,573	13,595	13,367	13,243
Admissions	572,724	564,937	592,962	602,635	591,112
Inpatient Days	2,818,046	2,743,755	2,886,190	2,889,658	2,843,189
Average Length of Stay...........	4.9	4.9	4.9	4.8	4.8
Personnel					
Total Full Time.............	61,903	63,588	63,514	62,730	60,717
Total Part Time	18,769	17,221	18,315	17,998	17,826
Revenue and Expenses - Totals					
(Includes Inpatient and Outpatient)					
Total Net Revenue...............	$11,593,715,843	$11,207,210,342	$10,690,507,752	$10,416,730,891	$9,778,913,020
Total Expenses..................	10,817,318,399	10,337,675,256	9,975,988,671	9,715,872,866	9,348,520,481
COMMUNITY HEALTH INDICATORS PER 1000 POPULATION					
Total Population (in thousands)	4,395	4,380	4,369	4,339	4,314
Inpatient					
Beds	3.2	3.2	3.2	3.3	3.3
Admissions	131.7	130.6	137.2	140.3	138.4
Inpatient Days	688.6	664.0	700.7	723.9	721.7
Inpatient Surgeries...........	36.3	38.1	39.1	40.0	40.1
Births........	12.3	12.2	11.4	12.4	11.6
Outpatient					
Emergency Outpatient Visits........	518.7	549.0	537.9	550.0	538.1
Other Outpatient Visits...........	1,875.1	1,864.2	1,872.7	1,855.3	1,807.6
Total Outpatient Visits	2,393.8	2,413.2	2,410.6	2,405.3	2,345.7
Outpatient Surgeries	83.9	84.7	91.7	88.9	86.2
Expense per Capita (per person).....	$2,476.3	$2,374.4	$2,299.9	$2,258.8	$2,184.5

States

TABLE 6

LOUISIANA

U.S. Registered Community Hospitals
(Nonfederal, short-term general and other special hospitals)

Overview 2009–2013

	2013	2012	2011	2010	2009
Total Community Hospitals in Louisiana	**122**	**124**	**127**	**126**	**128**
Bed Size Category					
6-24	17	17	18	18	16
25-49	38	38	40	40	39
50-99	24	25	24	22	24
100-199	19	20	19	21	26
200-299	10	10	12	12	10
300-399	7	7	8	6	5
400-499	4	4	2	3	3
500 + ...	3	3	4	4	5
Location					
Hospitals Urban..........................	74	77	77	76	77
Hospitals Rural	48	47	50	50	51
Control					
State and Local Government...............	44	49	48	50	54
Not for Profit	41	38	39	38	35
Investor owned	37	37	40	38	39
Physician Models					
Independent Practice Association	6	5	7	7	9
Group Practice without Walls...............	4	3	7	6	5
Open Physician-Hospital Organization	8	10	12	12	14
Closed Physician-Hospital Organization	5	5	6	5	7
Management Service Organization	7	8	5	4	4
Integrated Salary Model....................	25	28	30	29	27
Equity Model.............................	1	1	0	2	2
Foundation...............................	5	4	3	1	2
Insurance Products					
Health Maintenance Organization	8	6	9	8	7
Preferred Provider Organization..............	7	7	11	10	8
Indemnity Fee for Service	2	3	2	2	1
Managed Care Contracts					
Health Maintenance Organization	44	45	45	47	47
Preferred Provider Organization..............	48	51	57	57	55
Affiliations					
Hospitals in a System.....................	59	57	60	57	64
Hospitals in a Network....................	20	22	22	22	22
Hospitals in a Group Purchasing Organization..	59	62	66	71	71

TABLE 6

LOUISIANA

U.S. Registered Community Hospitals
(Nonfederal, short-term general and other special hospitals)

Utilization, Personnel, Revenue and Expenses, Community Health Indicators 2009–2013

	2013	2012	2011	2010	2009
TOTAL FACILITY (Includes Hospital and Nursing Home Units)					
Utilization - Inpatient					
Beds	15,550	15,204	15,342	15,421	15,857
Admissions	565,779	582,425	607,413	625,489	639,450
Inpatient Days	3,073,041	3,138,473	3,257,484	3,341,419	3,517,185
Average Length of Stay	5.4	5.4	5.4	5.3	5.5
Inpatient Surgeries	138,430	142,744	171,534	174,853	180,909
Births	64,083	60,736	54,963	61,525	71,711
Utilization - Outpatient					
Emergency Outpatient Visits	2,587,672	2,539,449	2,446,704	2,514,006	2,450,514
Other Outpatient Visits	7,076,596	7,011,868	7,096,563	9,840,934	9,922,624
Total Outpatient Visits	9,664,268	9,551,317	9,543,267	12,354,940	12,373,138
Outpatient Surgeries	263,440	253,503	277,370	283,987	279,065
Personnel					
Full Time RNs	18,917	18,885	18,529	18,458	18,666
Full Time LPNs	2,668	2,829	2,819	2,884	2,803
Part Time RNs	6,792	5,624	5,250	4,899	5,230
Part Time LPNs	905	728	594	628	686
Total Full Time	71,050	70,723	70,360	71,458	73,220
Total Part Time	21,073	17,577	15,769	15,447	16,165
Revenue - Inpatient					
Gross Inpatient Revenue	$19,263,175,093	$18,651,353,386	$17,640,121,981	$17,480,238,475	$16,516,892,572
Revenue - Outpatient					
Gross Outpatient Revenue	$17,447,605,153	$15,579,961,189	$14,296,885,978	$13,195,535,770	$11,720,385,666
Revenue and Expenses - Totals					
(Includes Inpatient and Outpatient)					
Total Gross Revenue	$36,710,780,246	$34,231,314,575	$31,937,007,959	$30,675,774,245	$28,237,278,238
Deductions from Revenue	26,304,382,131	24,308,385,152	22,487,315,530	21,158,064,386	19,280,756,846
Net Patient Revenue	10,406,398,115	9,922,929,423	9,449,692,429	9,517,709,859	8,956,521,392
Other Operating Revenue	683,792,470	650,768,859	727,155,809	672,891,456	549,360,404
Other Nonoperating Revenue	167,277,594	118,810,348	297,471,661	498,721,170	-74,290,469
Total Net Revenue	11,257,468,179	10,692,508,630	10,474,319,899	10,689,322,485	9,431,591,327
Total Expenses	10,689,977,269	10,146,975,702	9,705,109,556	9,593,366,678	9,451,348,220
HOSPITAL UNIT (Excludes Separate Nursing Home Units)					
Utilization - Inpatient					
Beds	14,850	14,552	14,874	14,721	15,199
Admissions	563,829	580,792	606,108	623,661	638,013
Inpatient Days	2,895,780	3,001,522	3,126,298	3,134,514	3,306,229
Average Length of Stay	5.1	5.2	5.2	5.0	5.2
Personnel					
Total Full Time	70,604	69,836	69,994	70,950	72,664
Total Part Time	20,881	17,416	15,644	15,241	15,946
Revenue and Expenses - Totals					
(Includes Inpatient and Outpatient)					
Total Net Revenue	$11,211,808,807	$10,660,949,288	$10,452,759,116	$10,655,165,063	$9,395,699,394
Total Expenses	10,646,734,797	10,112,917,995	9,680,765,455	9,556,204,131	9,410,102,839
COMMUNITY HEALTH INDICATORS PER 1000 POPULATION					
Total Population (in thousands)	4,625	4,602	4,575	4,529	4,492
Inpatient					
Beds	3.4	3.3	3.4	3.4	3.5
Admissions	122.3	126.6	132.8	138.1	142.4
Inpatient Days	664.4	682.0	712.0	737.7	783.0
Inpatient Surgeries	29.9	31.0	37.5	38.6	40.3
Births	13.9	13.2	12.0	13.6	16.0
Outpatient					
Emergency Outpatient Visits	559.4	551.8	534.8	555.0	545.5
Other Outpatient Visits	1,529.9	1,523.7	1,551.2	2,172.7	2,208.9
Total Outpatient Visits	2,089.4	2,075.5	2,086.0	2,727.7	2,754.4
Outpatient Surgeries	57.0	55.1	60.6	62.7	62.1
Expense per Capita (per person)	$2,311.1	$2,205.0	$2,121.4	$2,118.0	$2,104.0

States

TABLE 6

MAINE

U.S. Registered Community Hospitals
(Nonfederal, short-term general and other special hospitals)

Overview 2009–2013

	2013	2012	2011	2010	2009
Total Community Hospitals in Maine.........	35	37	37	37	37
Bed Size Category					
6-24	1	2	2	2	2
25-49	17	17	16	15	16
50-99	7	8	9	10	9
100-199	6	7	7	7	7
200-299	2	1	1	1	1
300-399	1	1	1	1	1
400-499	0	0	0	0	0
500 + ...	1	1	1	1	1
Location					
Hospitals Urban..........................	14	15	15	15	15
Hospitals Rural	21	22	22	22	22
Control					
State and Local Government...............	2	2	2	2	2
Not for Profit	32	34	34	34	34
Investor owned	1	1	1	1	1
Physician Models					
Independent Practice Association	0	2	3	4	4
Group Practice without Walls...............	1	2	4	4	4
Open Physician-Hospital Organization	8	9	10	10	10
Closed Physician-Hospital Organization	2	3	3	4	1
Management Service Organization	2	3	4	5	5
Integrated Salary Model...................	17	22	24	24	23
Equity Model	0	1	1	1	1
Foundation..............................	0	1	1	1	1
Insurance Products					
Health Maintenance Organization	4	3	4	5	3
Preferred Provider Organization.............	4	3	4	4	3
Indemnity Fee for Service	1	0	2	3	2
Managed Care Contracts					
Health Maintenance Organization	19	21	25	23	20
Preferred Provider Organization.............	21	23	26	26	22
Affiliations					
Hospitals in a System.....................	18	20	20	20	12
Hospitals in a Network....................	17	18	19	18	18
Hospitals in a Group Purchasing Organization..	28	32	33	33	32

TABLE 6

MAINE

U.S. Registered Community Hospitals
(Nonfederal, short-term general and other special hospitals)

Utilization, Personnel, Revenue and Expenses, Community Health Indicators 2009–2013

	2013	2012	2011	2010	2009
TOTAL FACILITY (Includes Hospital and Nursing Home Units)					
Utilization - Inpatient					
Beds	3,474	3,523	3,557	3,571	3,583
Admissions	139,976	142,159	144,718	145,806	150,199
Inpatient Days	782,150	783,992	814,216	808,166	822,849
Average Length of Stay	5.6	5.5	5.6	5.5	5.5
Inpatient Surgeries	40,786	42,816	39,585	42,190	43,395
Births	11,687	11,224	12,434	12,874	13,146
Utilization - Outpatient					
Emergency Outpatient Visits	795,374	790,258	765,481	790,243	792,592
Other Outpatient Visits	6,358,880	5,387,237	5,388,213	5,174,906	4,967,837
Total Outpatient Visits	7,154,254	6,177,495	6,153,694	5,965,149	5,760,429
Outpatient Surgeries	103,239	117,491	123,494	137,762	115,503
Personnel					
Full Time RNs	5,509	5,229	4,999	4,813	4,909
Full Time LPNs	242	190	204	248	262
Part Time RNs	3,503	3,884	3,429	3,658	3,232
Part Time LPNs	118	149	132	116	153
Total Full Time	24,591	23,343	23,480	22,775	23,628
Total Part Time	11,034	12,446	12,998	12,597	10,590
Revenue - Inpatient					
Gross Inpatient Revenue	$3,801,387,888	$3,743,957,102	$3,332,670,956	$3,184,130,431	$3,177,081,239
Revenue - Outpatient					
Gross Outpatient Revenue	$5,272,970,618	$5,068,158,029	$4,713,427,286	$4,265,543,968	$3,904,796,010
Revenue and Expenses - Totals					
(Includes Inpatient and Outpatient)					
Total Gross Revenue	$9,074,358,506	$8,812,115,131	$8,046,098,242	$7,449,674,399	$7,081,877,249
Deductions from Revenue	4,805,408,453	4,477,604,537	3,940,954,482	3,559,422,414	3,352,561,094
Net Patient Revenue	4,268,950,053	4,334,510,594	4,105,143,760	3,890,251,985	3,729,316,155
Other Operating Revenue	307,982,903	257,362,641	195,118,835	106,225,360	98,806,755
Other Nonoperating Revenue	85,107,098	52,339,735	40,642,341	36,578,921	24,828,817
Total Net Revenue	4,662,040,054	4,644,212,970	4,340,904,936	4,033,056,266	3,852,951,727
Total Expenses	4,501,336,652	4,421,717,517	4,160,648,639	4,238,756,324	3,725,426,220
HOSPITAL UNIT (Excludes Separate Nursing Home Units)					
Utilization - Inpatient					
Beds	3,078	3,109	3,135	3,185	3,189
Admissions	139,093	141,049	143,500	144,564	148,985
Inpatient Days	646,155	645,365	669,361	673,425	685,582
Average Length of Stay	4.6	4.6	4.7	4.7	4.6
Personnel					
Total Full Time	24,087	22,538	23,121	22,465	23,103
Total Part Time	10,755	11,898	12,682	12,310	10,299
Revenue and Expenses - Totals					
(Includes Inpatient and Outpatient)					
Total Net Revenue	$4,629,095,790	$4,608,434,715	$4,305,024,694	$4,000,528,653	$3,820,585,488
Total Expenses	4,470,359,564	4,389,756,790	4,127,705,413	4,208,922,953	3,694,875,984
COMMUNITY HEALTH INDICATORS PER 1000 POPULATION					
Total Population (in thousands)	1,328	1,329	1,328	1,313	1,318
Inpatient					
Beds	2.6	2.7	2.7	2.7	2.7
Admissions	105.4	107.0	109.0	111.1	113.9
Inpatient Days	588.8	589.8	613.0	615.5	624.2
Inpatient Surgeries	30.7	32.2	29.8	32.1	32.9
Births	8.8	8.4	9.4	9.8	10.0
Outpatient					
Emergency Outpatient Visits	598.8	594.5	576.3	601.9	601.2
Other Outpatient Visits	4,787.2	4,053.0	4,056.8	3,941.5	3,768.4
Total Outpatient Visits	5,386.0	4,647.6	4,633.1	4,543.4	4,369.6
Outpatient Surgeries	77.7	88.4	93.0	104.9	87.6
Expense per Capita (per person)	$3,388.8	$3,326.6	$3,132.6	$3,228.4	$2,825.9

States

TABLE 6

MARYLAND

U.S. Registered Community Hospitals
(Nonfederal, short-term general and other special hospitals)

Overview 2009–2013

	2013	2012	2011	2010	2009
Total Community Hospitals in Maryland.......	50	50	48	47	49
Bed Size Category					
6-24	0	0	0	0	0
25-49	3	3	3	2	2
50-99	9	8	6	6	6
100-199	9	11	14	13	13
200-299	14	11	9	11	15
300-399	8	9	8	9	6
400-499	4	6	5	4	5
500 + ...	3	2	3	2	2
Location					
Hospitals Urban..........................	44	44	42	41	43
Hospitals Rural	6	6	6	6	6
Control					
State and Local Government...............	0	0	0	0	0
Not for Profit	49	48	46	45	47
Investor owned	1	2	2	2	2
Physician Models					
Independent Practice Association	9	12	8	7	5
Group Practice without Walls...............	6	8	2	3	3
Open Physician-Hospital Organization	5	6	5	6	4
Closed Physician-Hospital Organization	9	9	4	1	2
Management Service Organization	10	14	11	10	7
Integrated Salary Model....................	31	32	29	30	29
Equity Model	3	4	4	3	3
Foundation..............................	5	6	6	6	4
Insurance Products					
Health Maintenance Organization	18	16	16	16	14
Preferred Provider Organization..............	10	13	6	5	5
Indemnity Fee for Service	5	5	2	2	2
Managed Care Contracts					
Health Maintenance Organization	29	31	30	32	34
Preferred Provider Organization..............	29	30	29	29	32
Affiliations					
Hospitals in a System......................	35	35	32	30	33
Hospitals in a Network	16	16	16	17	17
Hospitals in a Group Purchasing Organization..	41	42	43	42	42

TABLE **6**

MARYLAND

U.S. Registered Community Hospitals
(Nonfederal, short-term general and other special hospitals)

Utilization, Personnel, Revenue and Expenses, Community Health Indicators 2009–2013

	2013	2012	2011	2010	2009
TOTAL FACILITY (Includes Hospital and Nursing Home Units)					
Utilization - Inpatient					
Beds	12,392	12,271	11,887	11,682	11,887
Admissions	628,485	659,128	683,678	707,549	715,496
Inpatient Days	3,165,089	3,230,567	3,147,613	3,160,045	3,252,959
Average Length of Stay	5.0	4.9	4.6	4.5	4.5
Inpatient Surgeries	182,075	193,816	195,892	195,577	201,144
Births	66,699	67,554	68,727	69,042	70,210
Utilization - Outpatient					
Emergency Outpatient Visits	2,542,407	2,552,154	2,469,637	2,460,678	2,429,724
Other Outpatient Visits	6,879,374	7,244,174	6,301,934	5,912,927	5,864,175
Total Outpatient Visits	9,421,781	9,796,328	8,771,571	8,373,605	8,293,899
Outpatient Surgeries	355,688	348,264	363,469	352,770	354,443
Personnel					
Full Time RNs	19,966	19,382	18,228	17,338	16,670
Full Time LPNs	434	502	453	429	472
Part Time RNs	8,383	8,776	8,618	8,448	9,291
Part Time LPNs	212	241	188	185	236
Total Full Time	75,810	75,558	72,370	68,011	66,942
Total Part Time	25,681	28,069	27,470	26,604	28,595
Revenue - Inpatient					
Gross Inpatient Revenue	$10,661,965,230	$11,340,693,112	$10,026,767,506	$9,444,745,728	$9,330,184,751
Revenue - Outpatient					
Gross Outpatient Revenue	$8,799,199,791	$8,221,461,005	$6,952,785,584	$5,942,458,212	$5,482,610,364
Revenue and Expenses - Totals					
(Includes Inpatient and Outpatient)					
Total Gross Revenue	$19,461,165,021	$19,562,154,117	$16,979,553,090	$15,387,203,940	$14,812,795,115
Deductions from Revenue	5,848,369,205	5,814,859,991	4,223,063,054	3,358,927,214	3,011,679,371
Net Patient Revenue	13,612,795,816	13,747,294,126	12,756,490,036	12,028,276,726	11,801,115,744
Other Operating Revenue	720,549,006	587,505,820	520,917,847	481,101,758	477,892,272
Other Nonoperating Revenue	258,822,436	16,735,289	289,518,580	134,850,598	-253,477,709
Total Net Revenue	14,592,167,258	14,351,535,235	13,566,926,463	12,644,229,082	12,025,530,307
Total Expenses	13,836,110,822	13,808,394,036	12,730,746,066	12,132,497,694	11,898,147,143
HOSPITAL UNIT (Excludes Separate Nursing Home Units)					
Utilization - Inpatient					
Beds	11,614	11,503	11,310	11,113	11,318
Admissions	621,936	653,062	677,236	700,707	708,844
Inpatient Days	2,926,235	3,003,853	2,995,832	2,998,068	3,079,527
Average Length of Stay	4.7	4.6	4.4	4.3	4.3
Personnel					
Total Full Time	75,010	74,873	71,903	67,425	66,271
Total Part Time	25,282	27,724	27,194	26,242	28,247
Revenue and Expenses - Totals					
(Includes Inpatient and Outpatient)					
Total Net Revenue	$14,477,831,557	$14,246,938,190	$13,476,477,632	$12,543,530,248	$11,912,050,531
Total Expenses	13,728,619,619	13,710,327,354	12,629,434,037	12,026,632,893	11,787,009,932
COMMUNITY HEALTH INDICATORS PER 1000 POPULATION					
Total Population (in thousands)	5,929	5,885	5,828	5,737	5,699
Inpatient					
Beds	2.1	2.1	2.0	2.0	2.1
Admissions	106.0	112.0	117.3	123.3	125.5
Inpatient Days	533.8	549.0	540.1	550.8	570.7
Inpatient Surgeries	30.7	32.9	33.6	34.1	35.3
Births	11.2	11.5	11.8	12.0	12.3
Outpatient					
Emergency Outpatient Visits	428.8	433.7	423.7	428.9	426.3
Other Outpatient Visits	1,160.3	1,231.0	1,081.3	1,030.6	1,028.9
Total Outpatient Visits	1,589.2	1,664.8	1,505.0	1,459.5	1,455.2
Outpatient Surgeries	60.0	59.2	62.4	61.5	62.2
Expense per Capita (per person)	$2,333.7	$2,346.5	$2,184.3	$2,114.7	$2,087.6

States

TABLE 6

MASSACHUSETTS

U.S. Registered Community Hospitals
(Nonfederal, short-term general and other special hospitals)

Overview 2009–2013

	2013	2012	2011	2010	2009
Total Community Hospitals in Massachusetts..	82	83	79	79	78
Bed Size Category					
6-24	4	5	5	6	6
25-49	7	8	8	8	8
50-99	18	19	13	10	12
100-199	25	22	24	29	25
200-299	13	14	15	12	11
300-399	6	7	7	6	8
400-499	3	2	1	1	1
500 +	6	6	6	7	7
Location					
Hospitals Urban	80	81	77	77	76
Hospitals Rural	2	2	2	2	2
Control					
State and Local Government	3	3	1	1	2
Not for Profit	59	61	65	67	68
Investor owned	20	19	13	11	8
Physician Models					
Independent Practice Association	19	17	20	26	22
Group Practice without Walls	1	2	2	3	2
Open Physician-Hospital Organization	17	18	20	19	17
Closed Physician-Hospital Organization	5	5	5	7	7
Management Service Organization	9	9	11	12	9
Integrated Salary Model	30	31	32	35	32
Equity Model	1	1	2	2	4
Foundation	2	3	4	5	6
Insurance Products					
Health Maintenance Organization	7	9	11	9	8
Preferred Provider Organization	4	4	8	5	5
Indemnity Fee for Service	1	2	5	3	2
Managed Care Contracts					
Health Maintenance Organization	48	47	56	59	52
Preferred Provider Organization	47	45	51	55	51
Affiliations					
Hospitals in a System	52	51	46	43	41
Hospitals in a Network	24	24	27	25	20
Hospitals in a Group Purchasing Organization..	50	50	55	62	55

States

TABLE 6

MASSACHUSETTS

U.S. Registered Community Hospitals
(Nonfederal, short-term general and other special hospitals)

Utilization, Personnel, Revenue and Expenses, Community Health Indicators 2009–2013

	2013	2012	2011	2010	2009
TOTAL FACILITY (Includes Hospital and Nursing Home Units)					
Utilization - Inpatient					
Beds	16,483	16,233	15,865	15,694	15,483
Admissions	787,003	802,312	838,080	823,246	819,625
Inpatient Days	4,181,114	4,130,110	4,168,038	4,164,008	4,187,076
Average Length of Stay	5.3	5.1	5.0	5.1	5.1
Inpatient Surgeries	188,191	197,450	205,653	209,277	213,059
Births	68,965	70,702	72,707	72,306	73,363
Utilization - Outpatient					
Emergency Outpatient Visits	3,221,445	3,164,871	3,092,821	3,153,290	3,116,535
Other Outpatient Visits	18,876,709	19,349,547	19,206,984	18,597,755	18,237,800
Total Outpatient Visits	22,098,154	22,514,418	22,299,805	21,751,045	21,354,335
Outpatient Surgeries	426,553	421,694	418,519	471,811	446,779
Personnel					
Full Time RNs	21,855	21,137	21,636	20,665	20,920
Full Time LPNs	835	868	827	797	825
Part Time RNs	23,005	22,948	23,007	22,332	21,508
Part Time LPNs	641	708	686	707	745
Total Full Time	115,714	113,291	114,923	112,453	112,122
Total Part Time	67,465	69,520	69,916	67,465	64,882
Revenue - Inpatient					
Gross Inpatient Revenue	$26,147,419,070	$25,212,735,967	$23,543,488,752	$22,838,917,130	$22,083,175,335
Revenue - Outpatient					
Gross Outpatient Revenue	$29,745,996,654	$28,198,949,623	$26,601,731,821	$26,120,785,816	$24,897,792,185
Revenue and Expenses - Totals					
(Includes Inpatient and Outpatient)					
Total Gross Revenue	$55,893,415,724	$53,411,685,590	$50,145,220,573	$48,959,702,946	$46,980,967,520
Deductions from Revenue	34,008,609,464	31,738,657,662	29,585,822,724	28,469,292,992	27,289,257,271
Net Patient Revenue	21,884,806,260	21,673,027,928	20,559,397,849	20,490,409,954	19,691,710,249
Other Operating Revenue	3,772,351,494	3,570,796,587	3,539,011,217	3,161,300,000	3,056,380,254
Other Nonoperating Revenue	600,472,377	158,781,349	59,227,576	180,218,312	-134,832,543
Total Net Revenue	26,257,630,131	25,402,605,864	24,157,636,642	23,831,928,266	22,613,257,960
Total Expenses	24,670,533,446	24,080,576,139	23,068,835,920	22,819,002,547	22,049,297,978
HOSPITAL UNIT (Excludes Separate Nursing Home Units)					
Utilization - Inpatient					
Beds	16,454	16,204	15,836	15,569	15,374
Admissions	786,315	801,583	837,325	820,368	817,254
Inpatient Days	4,172,412	4,121,270	4,158,948	4,125,806	4,153,746
Average Length of Stay	5.3	5.1	5.0	5.0	5.1
Personnel					
Total Full Time	115,708	113,273	114,916	112,401	112,051
Total Part Time	67,446	69,452	69,898	67,389	64,777
Revenue and Expenses - Totals					
(Includes Inpatient and Outpatient)					
Total Net Revenue	$26,252,955,720	$25,397,992,218	$24,152,583,333	$23,814,188,986	$22,595,437,262
Total Expenses	24,665,183,716	24,075,430,900	23,064,002,066	22,805,667,399	22,031,539,336
COMMUNITY HEALTH INDICATORS PER 1000 POPULATION					
Total Population (in thousands)	6,693	6,646	6,588	6,631	6,594
Inpatient					
Beds	2.5	2.4	2.4	2.4	2.3
Admissions	117.6	120.7	127.2	124.1	124.3
Inpatient Days	624.7	621.4	632.7	627.9	635.0
Inpatient Surgeries	28.1	29.7	31.2	31.6	32.3
Births	10.3	10.6	11.0	10.9	11.1
Outpatient					
Emergency Outpatient Visits	481.3	476.2	469.5	475.5	472.7
Other Outpatient Visits	2,820.4	2,911.4	2,915.7	2,804.5	2,766.0
Total Outpatient Visits	3,301.8	3,387.6	3,385.2	3,280.1	3,238.7
Outpatient Surgeries	63.7	63.4	63.5	71.1	67.8
Expense per Capita (per person)	$3,686.1	$3,623.2	$3,501.9	$3,441.1	$3,344.1

TABLE 6

MICHIGAN

U.S. Registered Community Hospitals
(Nonfederal, short-term general and other special hospitals)

Overview 2009–2013

	2013	2012	2011	2010	2009
Total Community Hospitals in Michigan	151	151	153	156	158
Bed Size Category					
6-24	13	12	12	12	11
25-49	44	46	45	44	42
50-99	32	29	30	35	38
100-199	19	20	19	18	21
200-299	15	15	18	18	17
300-399	10	11	14	15	14
400-499	6	7	5	3	4
500 + ...	12	11	10	11	11
Location					
Hospitals Urban............................	93	93	95	97	99
Hospitals Rural	58	58	58	59	59
Control					
State and Local Government................	14	15	14	14	15
Not for Profit	114	114	119	125	126
Investor owned	23	22	20	17	17
Physician Models					
Independent Practice Association	12	14	18	15	15
Group Practice without Walls................	8	8	9	9	5
Open Physician-Hospital Organization	40	45	45	39	41
Closed Physician-Hospital Organization	16	11	15	17	13
Management Service Organization	13	16	18	19	15
Integrated Salary Model.....................	88	85	83	86	88
Equity Model	1	1	1	0	0
Foundation................................	6	6	8	8	9
Insurance Products					
Health Maintenance Organization	40	38	39	41	44
Preferred Provider Organization..............	28	27	39	41	45
Indemnity Fee for Service	8	10	14	13	17
Managed Care Contracts					
Health Maintenance Organization	100	102	106	114	120
Preferred Provider Organization..............	102	104	110	119	124
Affiliations					
Hospitals in a System......................	100	96	96	96	96
Hospitals in a Network	58	62	65	70	72
Hospitals in a Group Purchasing Organization..	116	119	121	127	130

TABLE 6

MICHIGAN

U.S. Registered Community Hospitals
(Nonfederal, short-term general and other special hospitals)

Utilization, Personnel, Revenue and Expenses, Community Health Indicators 2009–2013

	2013	2012	2011	2010	2009
TOTAL FACILITY (Includes Hospital and Nursing Home Units)					
Utilization - Inpatient					
Beds	25,059	25,100	25,351	25,623	25,863
Admissions	1,158,802	1,182,541	1,191,236	1,207,546	1,219,893
Inpatient Days	5,912,166	6,037,474	6,173,528	6,214,588	6,332,816
Average Length of Stay	5.1	5.1	5.2	5.1	5.2
Inpatient Surgeries	315,259	325,219	342,090	355,358	359,169
Births	107,429	106,525	107,031	111,192	113,883
Utilization - Outpatient					
Emergency Outpatient Visits	4,875,899	4,781,685	4,675,863	4,550,617	4,538,588
Other Outpatient Visits	27,692,597	28,037,761	26,307,833	25,699,720	24,759,189
Total Outpatient Visits	32,568,496	32,819,446	30,983,696	30,250,337	29,297,777
Outpatient Surgeries	674,583	678,329	656,318	704,866	694,079
Personnel					
Full Time RNs	38,800	38,759	37,356	36,166	34,530
Full Time LPNs	1,341	1,270	1,255	1,377	1,591
Part Time RNs	18,723	19,313	18,736	18,803	18,878
Part Time LPNs	796	748	810	916	949
Total Full Time	144,269	146,597	143,186	144,577	141,897
Total Part Time	61,716	63,422	63,510	64,909	65,113
Revenue - Inpatient					
Gross Inpatient Revenue	$35,163,188,185	$34,248,317,962	$33,127,653,060	$32,307,141,469	$31,376,243,717
Revenue - Outpatient					
Gross Outpatient Revenue	$36,798,222,853	$34,632,987,398	$31,983,063,304	$30,177,541,390	$28,205,271,055
Revenue and Expenses - Totals					
(Includes Inpatient and Outpatient)					
Total Gross Revenue	$71,961,411,038	$68,881,305,360	$65,110,716,364	$62,484,682,859	$59,581,514,772
Deductions from Revenue	45,245,940,980	41,938,126,634	40,060,740,730	38,000,334,594	35,829,939,127
Net Patient Revenue	26,715,470,058	26,943,178,726	25,049,975,634	24,484,348,265	23,751,575,645
Other Operating Revenue	1,525,618,772	1,306,714,292	1,133,933,341	1,105,518,315	1,092,750,061
Other Nonoperating Revenue	551,058,172	242,121,301	626,908,309	555,064,648	-550,883,455
Total Net Revenue	28,792,147,002	28,492,014,319	26,810,817,284	26,144,931,228	24,293,442,251
Total Expenses	27,272,388,730	27,293,081,777	25,328,136,970	24,872,817,460	24,366,675,781
HOSPITAL UNIT (Excludes Separate Nursing Home Units)					
Utilization - Inpatient					
Beds	24,121	23,759	24,256	24,243	24,499
Admissions	1,154,598	1,177,789	1,187,933	1,203,343	1,215,211
Inpatient Days	5,605,462	5,600,603	5,802,388	5,761,918	5,877,775
Average Length of Stay	4.9	4.8	4.9	4.8	4.8
Personnel					
Total Full Time	143,689	145,517	142,322	143,514	140,743
Total Part Time	61,162	62,504	62,695	64,019	64,048
Revenue and Expenses - Totals					
(Includes Inpatient and Outpatient)					
Total Net Revenue	$28,697,947,450	$28,374,005,103	$26,702,789,590	$26,022,486,264	$24,172,162,834
Total Expenses	27,200,999,172	27,190,001,432	25,261,120,163	24,753,757,439	24,287,466,409
COMMUNITY HEALTH INDICATORS PER 1000 POPULATION					
Total Population (in thousands)	9,896	9,883	9,876	9,931	9,970
Inpatient					
Beds	2.5	2.5	2.6	2.6	2.6
Admissions	117.1	119.6	120.6	121.6	122.4
Inpatient Days	597.5	610.9	625.1	625.8	635.2
Inpatient Surgeries	31.9	32.9	34.6	35.8	36.0
Births	10.9	10.8	10.8	11.2	11.4
Outpatient					
Emergency Outpatient Visits	492.7	483.8	473.4	458.2	455.2
Other Outpatient Visits	2,798.5	2,836.9	2,663.8	2,587.8	2,483.4
Total Outpatient Visits	3,291.2	3,320.7	3,137.2	3,046.0	2,938.7
Outpatient Surgeries	68.2	68.6	66.5	71.0	69.6
Expense per Capita (per person)	$2,756.0	$2,761.5	$2,564.6	$2,504.5	$2,444.1

TABLE 6

MINNESOTA

U.S. Registered Community Hospitals
(Nonfederal, short-term general and other special hospitals)

Overview 2009–2013

	2013	2012	2011	2010	2009
Total Community Hospitals in Minnesota......	131	133	132	133	132
Bed Size Category					
6-24	21	21	23	19	19
25-49	34	32	29	29	26
50-99	35	37	34	38	37
100-199	25	26	29	30	34
200-299	4	4	4	5	4
300-399	6	7	6	5	4
400-499	3	3	4	4	5
500 + ...	3	3	3	3	3
Location					
Hospitals Urban...........................	49	51	51	51	50
Hospitals Rural	82	82	81	82	82
Control					
State and Local Government...............	36	37	38	36	38
Not for Profit	95	95	93	96	93
Investor owned	0	1	1	1	1
Physician Models					
Independent Practice Association	11	10	10	18	20
Group Practice without Walls..............	2	2	2	3	4
Open Physician-Hospital Organization	9	8	8	9	10
Closed Physician-Hospital Organization	2	2	3	3	3
Management Service Organization	1	2	1	1	1
Integrated Salary Model....................	61	56	52	49	52
Equity Model	1	0	1	0	1
Foundation...............................	1	1	2	1	1
Insurance Products					
Health Maintenance Organization	19	19	15	14	11
Preferred Provider Organization..............	19	19	16	15	13
Indemnity Fee for Service	6	5	6	6	3
Managed Care Contracts					
Health Maintenance Organization	47	44	47	46	54
Preferred Provider Organization..............	55	49	53	52	57
Affiliations					
Hospitals in a System......................	81	82	78	77	73
Hospitals in a Network....................	31	30	29	27	22
Hospitals in a Group Purchasing Organization..	92	90	90	90	93

TABLE 6

MINNESOTA

U.S. Registered Community Hospitals
(Nonfederal, short-term general and other special hospitals)

Utilization, Personnel, Revenue and Expenses, Community Health Indicators 2009–2013

	2013	2012	2011	2010	2009
TOTAL FACILITY (Includes Hospital and Nursing Home Units)					
Utilization - Inpatient					
Beds	14,781	14,895	14,985	15,346	15,589
Admissions	562,035	583,142	596,199	591,919	623,504
Inpatient Days	3,395,406	3,479,304	3,592,914	3,596,879	3,726,573
Average Length of Stay	6.0	6.0	6.0	6.1	6.0
Inpatient Surgeries	181,758	166,285	178,802	177,600	186,593
Births	67,898	64,001	64,004	62,885	67,064
Utilization - Outpatient					
Emergency Outpatient Visits	1,933,651	1,898,093	1,928,364	1,832,257	1,873,419
Other Outpatient Visits	9,732,473	9,532,070	8,863,642	9,232,626	8,906,635
Total Outpatient Visits	11,666,124	11,430,163	10,792,006	11,064,883	10,780,054
Outpatient Surgeries	322,895	302,985	315,819	303,839	311,336
Personnel					
Full Time RNs	12,220	11,693	11,275	11,163	9,976
Full Time LPNs	1,559	1,538	1,491	1,467	1,361
Part Time RNs	22,010	20,586	20,434	21,198	22,208
Part Time LPNs	1,666	1,524	1,716	1,767	1,862
Total Full Time	83,940	62,967	58,426	56,863	51,952
Total Part Time	61,875	57,938	58,167	62,186	64,411
Revenue - Inpatient					
Gross Inpatient Revenue	$20,263,141,343	$19,494,970,283	$19,485,000,173	$18,410,175,974	$17,936,453,916
Revenue - Outpatient					
Gross Outpatient Revenue	$18,010,747,799	$17,426,213,830	$16,843,850,432	$15,401,043,442	$13,869,730,845
Revenue and Expenses - Totals					
(Includes Inpatient and Outpatient)					
Total Gross Revenue	$38,273,889,142	$36,921,184,113	$36,328,850,605	$33,811,219,416	$31,806,184,761
Deductions from Revenue	22,240,528,284	21,566,323,331	21,780,756,415	20,208,906,364	18,729,750,687
Net Patient Revenue	16,033,360,858	15,354,860,782	14,548,094,190	13,602,313,052	13,076,434,074
Other Operating Revenue	797,395,199	736,968,011	673,017,078	627,863,165	654,722,103
Other Nonoperating Revenue	285,377,987	105,178,701	265,096,109	222,331,201	35,427,093
Total Net Revenue	17,116,134,044	16,197,007,494	15,486,207,377	14,452,507,418	13,766,583,270
Total Expenses	15,886,275,897	15,069,347,845	14,474,689,902	13,507,569,053	12,894,812,345
HOSPITAL UNIT (Excludes Separate Nursing Home Units)					
Utilization - Inpatient					
Beds	12,773	12,798	12,651	13,128	13,443
Admissions	558,324	579,267	592,372	588,566	620,484
Inpatient Days	2,749,985	2,790,444	2,813,323	2,835,161	2,987,272
Average Length of Stay	4.9	4.8	4.7	4.8	4.8
Personnel					
Total Full Time	82,892	61,780	57,414	55,794	51,026
Total Part Time	60,139	56,197	56,546	60,461	62,837
Revenue and Expenses - Totals					
(Includes Inpatient and Outpatient)					
Total Net Revenue	$16,969,593,334	$16,055,142,778	$15,260,507,840	$14,309,968,863	$13,627,368,247
Total Expenses	15,749,642,682	14,927,729,599	14,318,110,391	13,362,374,519	12,751,881,151
COMMUNITY HEALTH INDICATORS PER 1000 POPULATION					
Total Population (in thousands)	5,420	5,379	5,345	5,290	5,266
Inpatient					
Beds	2.7	2.8	2.8	2.9	3.0
Admissions	103.7	108.4	111.5	111.9	118.4
Inpatient Days	626.4	646.8	672.2	679.9	707.6
Inpatient Surgeries	33.5	30.9	33.5	33.6	35.4
Births	12.5	11.9	12.0	11.9	12.7
Outpatient					
Emergency Outpatient Visits	356.7	352.9	360.8	346.3	355.7
Other Outpatient Visits	1,795.5	1,772.0	1,658.3	1,745.2	1,691.3
Total Outpatient Visits	2,152.3	2,124.9	2,019.1	2,091.5	2,047.0
Outpatient Surgeries	59.6	56.3	59.1	57.4	59.1
Expense per Capita (per person)	$2,930.8	$2,801.4	$2,708.2	$2,553.2	$2,448.6

States

TABLE 6

MISSISSIPPI

U.S. Registered Community Hospitals
(Nonfederal, short-term general and other special hospitals)

Overview 2009–2013

	2013	2012	2011	2010	2009
Total Community Hospitals in Mississippi	99	98	99	96	97
Bed Size Category					
6-24	2	2	3	2	2
25-49	32	32	32	32	32
50-99	25	24	23	22	24
100-199	22	23	24	23	23
200-299	10	8	8	6	5
300-399	1	2	2	3	3
400-499	3	3	3	3	3
500 + ...	4	4	4	5	5
Location					
Hospitals Urban	28	28	29	29	28
Hospitals Rural	71	70	70	67	69
Control					
State and Local Government	41	40	40	41	40
Not for Profit	29	29	29	27	28
Investor owned	29	29	30	28	29
Physician Models					
Independent Practice Association	5	5	5	5	5
Group Practice without Walls	2	2	2	2	3
Open Physician-Hospital Organization	15	16	18	16	15
Closed Physician-Hospital Organization	4	3	1	2	3
Management Service Organization	8	9	11	8	8
Integrated Salary Model	29	26	27	22	22
Equity Model	1	2	1	1	2
Foundation	8	7	10	7	8
Insurance Products					
Health Maintenance Organization	8	8	7	7	6
Preferred Provider Organization	37	36	37	35	36
Indemnity Fee for Service	8	9	9	9	10
Managed Care Contracts					
Health Maintenance Organization	26	26	18	14	15
Preferred Provider Organization	46	45	38	33	30
Affiliations					
Hospitals in a System	51	47	48	45	43
Hospitals in a Network	26	26	28	29	30
Hospitals in a Group Purchasing Organization . .	2	0	0	0	0

States

TABLE 6

MISSISSIPPI

U.S. Registered Community Hospitals
(Nonfederal, short-term general and other special hospitals)

Utilization, Personnel, Revenue and Expenses, Community Health Indicators 2009–2013

	2013	2012	2011	2010	2009
TOTAL FACILITY (Includes Hospital and Nursing Home Units)					
Utilization - Inpatient					
Beds	12,826	12,882	12,867	12,925	12,879
Admissions	380,059	384,078	393,566	402,947	412,912
Inpatient Days	2,499,123	2,505,846	2,513,957	2,557,704	2,600,075
Average Length of Stay	6.6	6.5	6.4	6.3	6.3
Inpatient Surgeries	100,878	104,043	102,170	107,497	114,231
Births	36,911	37,565	38,046	39,044	41,266
Utilization - Outpatient					
Emergency Outpatient Visits	1,794,793	1,767,684	1,761,207	1,705,959	1,720,780
Other Outpatient Visits	3,160,783	3,321,143	3,015,093	2,880,177	2,964,042
Total Outpatient Visits	4,955,576	5,088,827	4,776,300	4,586,136	4,684,822
Outpatient Surgeries	173,872	169,096	169,856	174,969	172,105
Personnel					
Full Time RNs	12,265	12,179	12,842	12,176	11,847
Full Time LPNs	1,427	1,437	1,475	1,570	1,651
Part Time RNs	4,134	3,784	3,346	3,489	3,543
Part Time LPNs	379	339	290	344	423
Total Full Time	46,669	46,695	48,461	46,910	46,451
Total Part Time	11,989	11,755	10,875	11,258	11,656
Revenue - Inpatient					
Gross Inpatient Revenue	$13,886,931,276	$12,982,460,621	$10,947,704,087	$10,614,195,531	$11,045,652,557
Revenue - Outpatient					
Gross Outpatient Revenue	$12,199,680,887	$11,618,451,746	$9,159,843,292	$8,108,639,171	$8,571,533,053
Revenue and Expenses - Totals **(Includes Inpatient and Outpatient)**					
Total Gross Revenue	$26,086,612,163	$24,600,912,367	$20,107,547,379	$18,722,834,702	$19,617,185,610
Deductions from Revenue	18,961,333,700	17,485,118,401	14,441,074,648	13,026,769,588	13,518,559,893
Net Patient Revenue	7,125,278,463	7,115,793,966	5,666,472,731	5,696,065,114	6,098,625,717
Other Operating Revenue	316,465,170	336,578,667	284,527,695	332,166,296	279,046,585
Other Nonoperating Revenue	122,250,060	124,396,684	62,903,487	101,837,598	76,839,630
Total Net Revenue	7,563,993,693	7,576,769,317	6,013,903,913	6,130,069,008	6,454,511,932
Total Expenses	7,101,439,812	6,982,689,683	5,804,948,349	5,635,912,981	6,071,620,664
HOSPITAL UNIT (Excludes Separate Nursing Home Units)					
Utilization - Inpatient					
Beds	11,037	11,102	11,142	11,260	11,196
Admissions	378,968	383,020	392,650	402,148	412,159
Inpatient Days	1,896,950	1,906,203	1,948,010	2,004,002	2,048,068
Average Length of Stay	5.0	5.0	5.0	5.0	5.0
Personnel					
Total Full Time	45,233	45,222	47,168	45,658	45,069
Total Part Time	11,496	11,330	10,502	10,899	11,336
Revenue and Expenses - Totals **(Includes Inpatient and Outpatient)**					
Total Net Revenue	$7,460,470,583	$7,501,877,310	$5,924,570,004	$6,056,564,286	$6,377,178,448
Total Expenses	7,040,309,114	6,920,499,818	5,744,275,169	5,576,805,214	6,011,102,605
COMMUNITY HEALTH INDICATORS PER 1000 POPULATION					
Total Population (in thousands)	2,991	2,985	2,979	2,960	2,952
Inpatient					
Beds	4.3	4.3	4.3	4.4	4.4
Admissions	127.1	128.7	132.1	136.1	139.9
Inpatient Days	835.5	839.5	844.0	864.0	880.8
Inpatient Surgeries	33.7	34.9	34.3	36.3	38.7
Births	12.3	12.6	12.8	13.2	14.0
Outpatient					
Emergency Outpatient Visits	600.0	592.2	591.3	576.2	582.9
Other Outpatient Visits	1,056.7	1,112.6	1,012.3	972.9	1,004.1
Total Outpatient Visits	1,656.7	1,704.8	1,603.6	1,549.1	1,587.0
Outpatient Surgeries	58.1	56.6	57.0	59.1	58.3
Expense per Capita (per person)	$2,374.1	$2,339.3	$1,948.9	$1,903.7	$2,056.8

States

TABLE 6

MISSOURI

U.S. Registered Community Hospitals
(Nonfederal, short-term general and other special hospitals)

Overview 2009–2013

	2013	2012	2011	2010	2009
Total Community Hospitals in Missouri	123	123	120	122	125
Bed Size Category					
6-24	11	9	8	7	8
25-49	38	39	40	41	39
50-99	19	20	19	21	22
100-199	25	25	21	22	24
200-299	11	11	12	11	12
300-399	7	7	9	11	9
400-499	6	6	5	3	5
500 + ...	6	6	6	6	6
Location					
Hospitals Urban...........................	70	70	67	69	72
Hospitals Rural	53	53	53	53	53
Control					
State and Local Government................	32	34	35	35	35
Not for Profit	65	64	63	64	64
Investor owned	26	25	22	23	26
Physician Models					
Independent Practice Association	8	8	6	8	8
Group Practice without Walls...............	0	0	0	0	0
Open Physician-Hospital Organization	15	15	15	14	15
Closed Physician-Hospital Organization	6	6	7	8	8
Management Service Organization	0	0	0	1	1
Integrated Salary Model....................	70	66	66	67	69
Equity Model	1	1	1	1	1
Foundation................................	4	2	2	4	2
Insurance Products					
Health Maintenance Organization	11	11	16	16	15
Preferred Provider Organization..............	10	10	14	14	13
Indemnity Fee for Service	3	2	5	4	4
Managed Care Contracts					
Health Maintenance Organization	97	99	93	95	99
Preferred Provider Organization..............	107	105	101	103	107
Affiliations					
Hospitals in a System......................	77	77	70	72	73
Hospitals in a Network.....................	39	38	36	37	38
Hospitals in a Group Purchasing Organization..	122	121	116	114	115

TABLE 6

MISSOURI

U.S. Registered Community Hospitals
(Nonfederal, short-term general and other special hospitals)

Utilization, Personnel, Revenue and Expenses, Community Health Indicators 2009–2013

	2013	2012	2011	2010	2009
TOTAL FACILITY (Includes Hospital and Nursing Home Units)					
Utilization - Inpatient					
Beds	18,899	19,032	18,749	18,745	19,101
Admissions	781,070	799,256	815,640	821,322	825,090
Inpatient Days	4,060,151	4,120,318	4,172,415	4,196,865	4,256,929
Average Length of Stay	5.2	5.2	5.1	5.1	5.2
Inpatient Surgeries	199,770	206,215	210,625	213,685	219,835
Births	74,688	75,301	73,779	74,903	77,799
Utilization - Outpatient					
Emergency Outpatient Visits	2,987,268	3,042,008	2,952,675	2,871,884	2,894,040
Other Outpatient Visits	18,856,989	18,024,433	17,251,450	16,929,041	16,319,944
Total Outpatient Visits	21,844,257	21,066,441	20,204,125	19,800,925	19,213,984
Outpatient Surgeries	385,614	382,699	370,574	374,120	382,232
Personnel					
Full Time RNs	28,943	27,597	27,023	26,334	25,768
Full Time LPNs	2,377	2,375	2,407	2,398	2,508
Part Time RNs	11,212	12,913	11,436	11,453	12,399
Part Time LPNs	555	664	654	719	826
Total Full Time	104,194	102,089	101,030	100,265	98,635
Total Part Time	33,507	38,730	35,841	36,219	37,004
Revenue - Inpatient					
Gross Inpatient Revenue	$27,966,288,581	$27,122,625,962	$25,816,258,642	$24,578,843,364	$23,360,022,165
Revenue - Outpatient					
Gross Outpatient Revenue	$27,913,913,149	$26,031,861,914	$23,228,488,113	$20,597,557,308	$19,480,819,585
Revenue and Expenses - Totals					
(Includes Inpatient and Outpatient)					
Total Gross Revenue	$55,880,201,730	$53,154,487,876	$49,044,746,755	$45,176,400,672	$42,840,841,750
Deductions from Revenue	37,726,886,672	35,362,416,605	32,241,337,674	28,944,744,487	27,014,970,190
Net Patient Revenue	18,153,315,058	17,792,071,271	16,803,409,081	16,231,656,185	15,825,871,560
Other Operating Revenue	1,154,601,122	1,281,736,177	999,246,088	1,085,534,981	875,169,162
Other Nonoperating Revenue	665,919,682	794,602,472	214,485,919	529,984,875	522,159,166
Total Net Revenue	19,973,835,862	19,868,409,920	18,017,141,088	17,847,176,041	17,223,199,888
Total Expenses	18,734,464,777	17,024,103,374	17,172,219,045	16,521,828,978	16,235,293,324
HOSPITAL UNIT (Excludes Separate Nursing Home Units)					
Utilization - Inpatient					
Beds	17,904	18,035	17,772	17,754	18,188
Admissions	775,368	793,155	809,450	816,764	818,739
Inpatient Days	3,767,287	3,822,166	3,892,314	3,946,461	3,999,089
Average Length of Stay	4.9	4.8	4.8	4.8	4.9
Personnel					
Total Full Time	103,345	101,135	100,248	99,631	97,598
Total Part Time	33,091	38,172	35,394	35,866	36,601
Revenue and Expenses - Totals					
(Includes Inpatient and Outpatient)					
Total Net Revenue	$19,902,552,926	$19,777,379,107	$17,938,622,213	$17,771,368,041	$17,122,754,301
Total Expenses	18,659,708,181	16,948,096,420	17,109,487,583	16,444,776,729	16,149,196,359
COMMUNITY HEALTH INDICATORS PER 1000 POPULATION					
Total Population (in thousands)	6,044	6,022	6,011	6,012	5,988
Inpatient					
Beds	3.1	3.2	3.1	3.1	3.2
Admissions	129.2	132.7	135.7	136.6	137.8
Inpatient Days	671.7	684.2	694.2	698.1	711.0
Inpatient Surgeries	33.1	34.2	35.0	35.5	36.7
Births	12.4	12.5	12.3	12.5	13.0
Outpatient					
Emergency Outpatient Visits	494.2	505.2	491.2	477.7	483.3
Other Outpatient Visits	3,119.9	2,993.1	2,870.1	2,816.0	2,725.6
Total Outpatient Visits	3,614.1	3,498.3	3,361.4	3,293.7	3,209.0
Outpatient Surgeries	63.8	63.6	61.7	62.2	63.8
Expense per Capita (per person)	$3,099.6	$2,827.0	$2,856.9	$2,748.3	$2,711.5

States

TABLE 6

MONTANA

U.S. Registered Community Hospitals
(Nonfederal, short-term general and other special hospitals)

Overview 2009–2013

	2013	2012	2011	2010	2009
Total Community Hospitals in Montana	50	48	48	48	48
Bed Size Category					
6-24	9	10	11	10	8
25-49	16	13	12	15	16
50-99	16	15	14	12	13
100-199	6	7	8	8	8
200-299	1	1	1	1	1
300-399	1	1	1	1	1
400-499	1	1	1	1	0
500 + ...	0	0	0	0	1
Location					
Hospitals Urban..........................	6	6	6	6	6
Hospitals Rural	44	42	42	42	42
Control					
State and Local Government...............	9	10	10	8	7
Not for Profit	40	37	37	39	40
Investor owned	1	1	1	1	1
Physician Models					
Independent Practice Association	5	4	5	7	9
Group Practice without Walls...............	5	4	4	3	3
Open Physician-Hospital Organization	4	4	4	5	5
Closed Physician-Hospital Organization	1	1	1	1	1
Management Service Organization	6	5	5	6	7
Integrated Salary Model....................	30	28	29	27	28
Equity Model	1	1	1	2	2
Foundation..............................	6	6	6	4	3
Insurance Products					
Health Maintenance Organization	2	2	4	4	4
Preferred Provider Organization.............	9	9	7	8	8
Indemnity Fee for Service	3	4	5	6	6
Managed Care Contracts					
Health Maintenance Organization	7	8	9	11	11
Preferred Provider Organization.............	26	27	25	22	25
Affiliations					
Hospitals in a System.....................	11	11	12	12	12
Hospitals in a Network	23	23	23	22	22
Hospitals in a Group Purchasing Organization..	45	40	41	39	44

TABLE 6

MONTANA

U.S. Registered Community Hospitals
(Nonfederal, short-term general and other special hospitals)

Utilization, Personnel, Revenue and Expenses, Community Health Indicators 2009–2013

	2013	2012	2011	2010	2009
TOTAL FACILITY (Includes Hospital and Nursing Home Units)					
Utilization - Inpatient					
Beds	3,722	3,710	3,626	3,692	3,820
Admissions	95,321	93,423	94,966	97,453	101,327
Inpatient Days	820,251	809,199	828,778	848,356	869,897
Average Length of Stay	8.6	8.7	8.7	8.7	8.6
Inpatient Surgeries	28,116	27,627	28,395	29,136	30,167
Births	10,245	10,191	10,254	10,217	10,432
Utilization - Outpatient					
Emergency Outpatient Visits	376,845	366,756	369,610	357,543	357,066
Other Outpatient Visits	3,386,696	3,218,282	3,173,110	3,146,841	2,973,218
Total Outpatient Visits	3,763,541	3,585,038	3,542,720	3,504,384	3,330,284
Outpatient Surgeries	52,787	48,788	47,582	48,043	45,364
Personnel					
Full Time RNs	3,304	3,191	2,860	2,946	2,843
Full Time LPNs	491	486	454	478	508
Part Time RNs	2,052	2,047	2,088	1,930	2,067
Part Time LPNs	238	280	256	257	283
Total Full Time	15,919	15,720	14,304	14,816	14,621
Total Part Time	8,209	7,743	7,502	7,138	7,470
Revenue - Inpatient					
Gross Inpatient Revenue	$2,454,369,080	$2,279,133,191	$2,102,143,134	$2,049,917,318	$2,001,422,796
Revenue - Outpatient					
Gross Outpatient Revenue	$3,397,775,194	$2,990,024,968	$2,622,907,633	$2,452,151,901	$2,187,645,447
Revenue and Expenses - Totals					
(Includes Inpatient and Outpatient)					
Total Gross Revenue	$5,852,144,274	$5,269,158,159	$4,725,050,767	$4,502,069,219	$4,189,068,243
Deductions from Revenue	3,015,777,016	2,595,587,712	2,261,961,105	2,145,913,313	1,939,387,748
Net Patient Revenue	2,836,367,258	2,673,570,447	2,463,089,662	2,356,155,906	2,249,680,495
Other Operating Revenue	155,924,250	110,280,462	98,796,127	93,578,995	90,423,031
Other Nonoperating Revenue	71,944,698	22,151,981	56,310,483	64,235,515	-5,428,277
Total Net Revenue	3,064,236,206	2,806,002,890	2,618,196,272	2,513,970,416	2,334,675,249
Total Expenses	2,874,246,551	2,660,995,740	2,485,931,042	2,379,151,295	2,263,313,965
HOSPITAL UNIT (Excludes Separate Nursing Home Units)					
Utilization - Inpatient					
Beds	2,424	2,403	2,347	2,398	2,421
Admissions	93,268	91,325	92,852	95,238	99,163
Inpatient Days	426,085	410,312	430,418	442,106	435,087
Average Length of Stay	4.6	4.5	4.6	4.6	4.4
Personnel					
Total Full Time	15,182	14,970	13,628	14,038	13,813
Total Part Time	7,616	7,213	7,007	6,602	6,946
Revenue and Expenses - Totals					
(Includes Inpatient and Outpatient)					
Total Net Revenue	$2,986,335,907	$2,733,592,548	$2,538,770,978	$2,441,209,709	$2,259,366,824
Total Expenses	2,812,268,630	2,591,928,424	2,403,184,670	2,306,425,879	2,191,842,514
COMMUNITY HEALTH INDICATORS PER 1000 POPULATION					
Total Population (in thousands)	1,015	1,005	998	980	975
Inpatient					
Beds	3.7	3.7	3.6	3.8	3.9
Admissions	93.9	92.9	95.1	99.4	103.9
Inpatient Days	808.0	805.1	830.3	865.5	892.2
Inpatient Surgeries	27.7	27.5	28.4	29.7	30.9
Births	10.1	10.1	10.3	10.4	10.7
Outpatient					
Emergency Outpatient Visits	371.2	364.9	370.3	364.8	366.2
Other Outpatient Visits	3,336.1	3,201.8	3,178.8	3,210.6	3,049.5
Total Outpatient Visits	3,707.3	3,566.7	3,549.1	3,575.3	3,415.7
Outpatient Surgeries	52.0	48.5	47.7	49.0	46.5
Expense per Capita (per person)	$2,831.3	$2,647.4	$2,490.4	$2,427.3	$2,321.4

States

TABLE 6

NEBRASKA

U.S. Registered Community Hospitals
(Nonfederal, short-term general and other special hospitals)

Overview 2009–2013

	2013	2012	2011	2010	2009
Total Community Hospitals in Nebraska.......	87	89	86	88	87
Bed Size Category					
6-24	26	26	24	23	22
25-49	21	21	25	23	22
50-99	21	22	19	23	22
100-199	7	10	8	9	10
200-299	7	5	6	4	6
300-399	4	3	2	4	4
400-499	0	2	1	1	0
500 + ...	1	0	1	1	1
Location					
Hospitals Urban.........................	18	18	16	17	16
Hospitals Rural	69	71	70	71	71
Control					
State and Local Government................	36	38	37	39	40
Not for Profit	49	49	46	46	45
Investor owned	2	2	3	3	2
Physician Models					
Independent Practice Association	4	6	6	6	6
Group Practice without Walls..............	1	2	0	1	2
Open Physician-Hospital Organization	11	11	10	12	13
Closed Physician-Hospital Organization	2	2	1	0	1
Management Service Organization	2	2	2	3	2
Integrated Salary Model....................	20	24	26	27	33
Equity Model	0	0	0	0	0
Foundation..............................	2	2	1	0	1
Insurance Products					
Health Maintenance Organization	4	2	3	3	2
Preferred Provider Organization..............	4	7	12	11	13
Indemnity Fee for Service	0	1	4	3	3
Managed Care Contracts					
Health Maintenance Organization	14	16	15	16	17
Preferred Provider Organization..............	32	43	43	43	50
Affiliations					
Hospitals in a System.....................	28	29	29	26	28
Hospitals in a Network....................	30	30	32	28	33
Hospitals in a Group Purchasing Organization..	36	42	44	47	54

TABLE 6   NEBRASKA

U.S. Registered Community Hospitals
(Nonfederal, short-term general and other special hospitals)

Utilization, Personnel, Revenue and Expenses, Community Health Indicators 2009–2013

	2013	2012	2011	2010	2009
TOTAL FACILITY (Includes Hospital and Nursing Home Units)					
Utilization - Inpatient					
Beds	6,784	6,997	6,592	7,246	7,442
Admissions	199,933	205,065	203,394	208,949	209,750
Inpatient Days	1,335,733	1,411,707	1,313,451	1,461,558	1,552,206
Average Length of Stay	6.7	6.9	6.5	7.0	7.4
Inpatient Surgeries	60,205	81,170	65,592	65,316	67,275
Births	25,323	25,859	25,778	24,575	26,224
Utilization - Outpatient					
Emergency Outpatient Visits	692,717	671,332	716,718	700,818	688,519
Other Outpatient Visits	4,066,743	4,556,326	4,239,738	3,870,823	3,969,589
Total Outpatient Visits	4,759,460	5,227,658	4,956,456	4,571,641	4,658,108
Outpatient Surgeries	119,958	130,932	118,596	112,213	120,310
Personnel					
Full Time RNs	8,332	8,429	7,863	8,038	7,653
Full Time LPNs	617	681	687	856	876
Part Time RNs	3,878	4,274	4,182	4,286	4,111
Part Time LPNs	296	388	393	489	512
Total Full Time	28,467	29,039	27,779	29,024	28,451
Total Part Time	12,462	13,789	13,543	14,502	13,922
Revenue - Inpatient					
Gross Inpatient Revenue	$6,714,985,216	$6,600,070,735	$6,329,607,253	$6,579,976,131	$6,240,788,042
Revenue - Outpatient					
Gross Outpatient Revenue	$6,650,376,967	$6,127,521,502	$5,571,277,484	$5,335,861,059	$4,923,545,533
Revenue and Expenses - Totals					
(Includes Inpatient and Outpatient)					
Total Gross Revenue	$13,365,362,183	$12,727,592,237	$11,900,884,737	$11,915,837,190	$11,164,333,575
Deductions from Revenue	8,104,547,928	7,443,134,120	7,094,550,376	7,060,882,109	6,451,826,044
Net Patient Revenue	5,260,814,255	5,284,458,117	4,806,334,361	4,854,955,081	4,712,507,531
Other Operating Revenue	314,198,761	276,960,199	243,522,454	211,231,348	209,020,415
Other Nonoperating Revenue	175,886,117	61,823,105	203,146,705	132,518,504	-28,338,616
Total Net Revenue	5,750,899,133	5,623,241,421	5,253,003,520	5,198,704,933	4,893,189,330
Total Expenses	4,870,429,742	4,972,245,644	4,659,397,050	4,710,906,183	4,471,302,656
HOSPITAL UNIT (Excludes Separate Nursing Home Units)					
Utilization - Inpatient					
Beds	5,921	5,979	5,817	6,168	6,102
Admissions	197,813	202,588	201,622	206,235	206,131
Inpatient Days	1,074,406	1,097,274	1,082,517	1,128,398	1,144,790
Average Length of Stay	5.4	5.4	5.4	5.5	5.6
Personnel					
Total Full Time	27,928	28,349	27,230	28,177	27,569
Total Part Time	12,190	13,362	13,178	13,927	13,239
Revenue and Expenses - Totals					
(Includes Inpatient and Outpatient)					
Total Net Revenue	$5,689,097,400	$5,554,405,718	$5,207,994,214	$5,123,202,118	$4,790,650,335
Total Expenses	4,798,846,323	4,897,073,033	4,613,479,154	4,634,581,746	4,379,557,407
COMMUNITY HEALTH INDICATORS PER 1000 POPULATION					
Total Population (in thousands)	1,869	1,856	1,843	1,811	1,797
Inpatient					
Beds	3.6	3.8	3.6	4.0	4.1
Admissions	107.0	110.5	110.4	115.4	116.7
Inpatient Days	714.9	760.8	712.8	807.0	864.0
Inpatient Surgeries	32.2	43.7	35.6	36.1	37.4
Births	13.6	13.9	14.0	13.6	14.6
Outpatient					
Emergency Outpatient Visits	370.7	361.8	389.0	387.0	383.2
Other Outpatient Visits	2,176.5	2,455.5	2,300.9	2,137.3	2,209.5
Total Outpatient Visits	2,547.2	2,817.3	2,689.9	2,524.3	2,592.7
Outpatient Surgeries	64.2	70.6	64.4	62.0	67.0
Expense per Capita (per person)	$2,606.6	$2,679.7	$2,528.7	$2,601.2	$2,488.7

States

TABLE 6

NEVADA

U.S. Registered Community Hospitals
(Nonfederal, short-term general and other special hospitals)

Overview 2009–2013

	2013	2012	2011	2010	2009
Total Community Hospitals in Nevada	38	38	38	36	35
Bed Size Category					
6-24	5	5	4	4	4
25-49	7	6	6	6	6
50-99	10	11	12	12	11
100-199	7	7	7	6	6
200-299	3	4	4	3	3
300-399	3	2	2	2	2
400-499	0	0	0	0	0
500 + ...	3	3	3	3	3
Location					
Hospitals Urban.	27	27	27	25	24
Hospitals Rural	11	11	11	11	11
Control					
State and Local Government.	6	6	6	6	6
Not for Profit	12	12	13	13	13
Investor owned	20	20	19	17	16
Physician Models					
Independent Practice Association	1	4	4	2	3
Group Practice without Walls.	1	0	0	0	0
Open Physician-Hospital Organization	3	1	1	1	1
Closed Physician-Hospital Organization	2	2	2	2	2
Management Service Organization	2	1	2	2	4
Integrated Salary Model	8	9	7	2	3
Equity Model	0	0	1	0	0
Foundation.	1	0	0	0	0
Insurance Products					
Health Maintenance Organization	7	6	7	7	5
Preferred Provider Organization.	7	6	7	7	6
Indemnity Fee for Service	6	6	3	4	3
Managed Care Contracts					
Health Maintenance Organization	16	17	20	13	12
Preferred Provider Organization.	16	17	21	15	15
Affiliations					
Hospitals in a System.	27	27	27	25	24
Hospitals in a Network	6	6	6	5	5
Hospitals in a Group Purchasing Organization. .	21	18	22	16	18

TABLE **6**

NEVADA

U.S. Registered Community Hospitals
(Nonfederal, short-term general and other special hospitals)

Utilization, Personnel, Revenue and Expenses, Community Health Indicators 2009–2013

	2013	2012	2011	2010	2009
TOTAL FACILITY (Includes Hospital and Nursing Home Units)					
Utilization - Inpatient					
Beds	5,655	5,504	5,507	5,192	5,119
Admissions	253,822	260,781	249,805	241,296	245,866
Inpatient Days	1,384,938	1,361,402	1,359,447	1,296,929	1,311,084
Average Length of Stay	5.5	5.2	5.4	5.4	5.3
Inpatient Surgeries	62,098	63,184	63,902	69,928	72,737
Births	28,592	26,384	21,822	24,844	30,373
Utilization - Outpatient					
Emergency Outpatient Visits	928,562	865,371	820,812	820,675	820,980
Other Outpatient Visits	1,697,472	2,045,456	1,859,971	1,849,263	1,988,669
Total Outpatient Visits	2,626,034	2,910,827	2,680,783	2,669,938	2,809,649
Outpatient Surgeries	88,318	88,694	98,155	103,406	104,340
Personnel					
Full Time RNs	7,796	6,951	6,582	6,436	6,357
Full Time LPNs	312	322	351	406	404
Part Time RNs	1,900	1,816	2,011	1,439	1,340
Part Time LPNs	72	69	85	68	74
Total Full Time	22,786	21,297	20,545	20,948	20,386
Total Part Time	5,264	4,899	5,339	3,779	3,636
Revenue - Inpatient					
Gross Inpatient Revenue	$13,752,019,901	$12,294,975,694	$11,616,603,674	$10,608,864,288	$10,439,117,032
Revenue - Outpatient					
Gross Outpatient Revenue	$8,132,111,085	$6,990,158,850	$6,466,989,068	$5,826,489,194	$5,312,533,278
Revenue and Expenses - Totals					
(Includes Inpatient and Outpatient)					
Total Gross Revenue	$21,884,130,986	$19,285,134,544	$18,083,592,742	$16,435,353,482	$15,751,650,310
Deductions from Revenue	17,304,616,909	15,017,726,173	14,019,540,936	12,559,876,799	11,866,367,378
Net Patient Revenue	4,579,514,077	4,267,408,371	4,064,051,806	3,875,476,683	3,885,282,932
Other Operating Revenue	151,926,188	102,905,260	107,770,969	97,417,940	98,119,383
Other Nonoperating Revenue	28,598,769	35,498,438	75,853,300	93,314,155	73,065,405
Total Net Revenue	4,760,039,034	4,405,812,069	4,247,676,075	4,066,208,778	4,056,467,720
Total Expenses	4,407,998,320	4,199,882,893	4,070,512,098	3,940,182,337	3,957,622,058
HOSPITAL UNIT (Excludes Separate Nursing Home Units)					
Utilization - Inpatient					
Beds	5,655	5,479	5,443	5,174	5,076
Admissions	253,822	260,768	249,708	241,287	245,844
Inpatient Days	1,384,938	1,354,258	1,341,532	1,291,351	1,298,643
Average Length of Stay	5.5	5.2	5.4	5.4	5.3
Personnel					
Total Full Time	22,786	21,284	20,517	20,939	20,368
Total Part Time	5,264	4,899	5,312	3,779	3,630
Revenue and Expenses - Totals					
(Includes Inpatient and Outpatient)					
Total Net Revenue	$4,760,039,034	$4,403,869,456	$4,243,197,676	$4,065,636,650	$4,053,142,416
Total Expenses	4,407,998,320	4,198,988,696	4,067,942,062	3,939,711,041	3,956,074,612
COMMUNITY HEALTH INDICATORS PER 1000 POPULATION					
Total Population (in thousands)	2,790	2,759	2,723	2,655	2,643
Inpatient					
Beds	2.0	2.0	2.0	2.0	1.9
Admissions	91.0	94.5	91.7	90.9	93.0
Inpatient Days	496.4	493.5	499.2	488.5	496.0
Inpatient Surgeries	22.3	22.9	23.5	26.3	27.5
Births	10.2	9.6	8.0	9.4	11.5
Outpatient					
Emergency Outpatient Visits	332.8	313.7	301.4	309.1	310.6
Other Outpatient Visits	608.4	741.4	683.0	696.6	752.4
Total Outpatient Visits	941.2	1,055.1	984.4	1,005.7	1,063.0
Outpatient Surgeries	31.7	32.1	36.0	39.0	39.5
Expense per Capita (per person)	$1,579.9	$1,522.3	$1,494.7	$1,484.2	$1,497.3

TABLE 6

NEW HAMPSHIRE

U.S. Registered Community Hospitals
(Nonfederal, short-term general and other special hospitals)

Overview 2009–2013

	2013	2012	2011	2010	2009
Total Community Hospitals in New Hampshire	28	28	28	28	28
Bed Size Category					
6-24	1	1	1	1	1
25-49	10	10	10	9	9
50-99	7	7	6	7	7
100-199	6	6	7	7	7
200-299	3	3	3	3	3
300-399	1	1	1	1	1
400-499	0	0	0	0	0
500 +	0	0	0	0	0
Location					
Hospitals Urban	11	11	11	11	11
Hospitals Rural	17	17	17	17	17
Control					
State and Local Government	0	0	0	0	0
Not for Profit	24	24	24	24	24
Investor owned	4	4	4	4	4
Physician Models					
Independent Practice Association	2	2	2	2	2
Group Practice without Walls	2	2	2	2	2
Open Physician-Hospital Organization	4	4	5	9	10
Closed Physician-Hospital Organization	0	0	0	0	0
Management Service Organization	0	0	0	0	1
Integrated Salary Model	19	19	20	17	16
Equity Model	0	0	0	0	0
Foundation	0	0	0	0	0
Insurance Products					
Health Maintenance Organization	0	0	0	0	0
Preferred Provider Organization	0	0	0	0	0
Indemnity Fee for Service	0	0	0	0	0
Managed Care Contracts					
Health Maintenance Organization	19	19	20	23	26
Preferred Provider Organization	18	18	19	21	25
Affiliations					
Hospitals in a System	7	6	6	6	6
Hospitals in a Network	11	12	11	10	11
Hospitals in a Group Purchasing Organization	24	25	25	26	27

TABLE 6

NEW HAMPSHIRE

U.S. Registered Community Hospitals
(Nonfederal, short-term general and other special hospitals)

Utilization, Personnel, Revenue and Expenses, Community Health Indicators 2009–2013

	2013	2012	2011	2010	2009
TOTAL FACILITY (Includes Hospital and Nursing Home Units)					
Utilization - Inpatient					
Beds	2,809	2,831	2,840	2,851	2,863
Admissions	119,566	119,814	122,341	119,971	122,959
Inpatient Days	628,043	627,784	634,954	624,399	655,015
Average Length of Stay	5.3	5.2	5.2	5.2	5.3
Inpatient Surgeries	32,881	33,606	34,281	33,622	33,041
Births	12,664	12,035	12,649	12,630	13,261
Utilization - Outpatient					
Emergency Outpatient Visits	700,141	652,190	677,358	667,605	627,769
Other Outpatient Visits	4,346,816	4,330,937	4,318,549	4,109,910	4,097,077
Total Outpatient Visits	5,046,957	4,983,127	4,995,907	4,777,515	4,724,846
Outpatient Surgeries	89,108	90,715	91,348	92,450	91,495
Personnel					
Full Time RNs	4,648	4,460	4,282	4,298	4,191
Full Time LPNs	283	278	276	278	250
Part Time RNs	2,889	3,068	3,128	3,008	3,017
Part Time LPNs	111	128	126	139	176
Total Full Time	21,980	21,736	21,846	22,066	21,046
Total Part Time	10,181	10,229	10,000	10,151	10,294
Revenue - Inpatient					
Gross Inpatient Revenue	$4,696,146,268	$4,263,267,285	$4,150,081,268	$3,890,334,236	$3,730,906,874
Revenue - Outpatient					
Gross Outpatient Revenue	$6,733,412,770	$6,315,255,279	$5,916,747,273	$5,494,839,267	$4,960,506,458
Revenue and Expenses - Totals					
(Includes Inpatient and Outpatient)					
Total Gross Revenue	$11,429,559,038	$10,578,522,564	$10,066,828,541	$9,385,173,503	$8,691,413,332
Deductions from Revenue	7,139,588,921	6,389,949,615	5,928,255,856	5,410,431,600	4,934,553,834
Net Patient Revenue	4,289,970,117	4,188,572,949	4,138,572,685	3,974,741,903	3,756,859,498
Other Operating Revenue	165,027,209	172,037,917	129,629,985	106,982,372	93,662,673
Other Nonoperating Revenue	87,925,169	65,319,726	296,520	52,157,491	-52,943,319
Total Net Revenue	4,542,922,495	4,425,930,592	4,268,499,190	4,133,881,766	3,797,578,852
Total Expenses	4,089,847,120	4,024,997,567	3,948,270,249	3,781,620,257	3,539,365,267
HOSPITAL UNIT (Excludes Separate Nursing Home Units)					
Utilization - Inpatient					
Beds	2,706	2,728	2,710	2,721	2,683
Admissions	119,473	119,684	121,996	119,391	122,334
Inpatient Days	592,762	592,483	593,304	577,175	602,460
Average Length of Stay	5.0	5.0	4.9	4.8	4.9
Personnel					
Total Full Time	21,933	21,685	21,766	22,003	20,963
Total Part Time	10,159	10,202	9,960	10,110	10,246
Revenue and Expenses - Totals					
(Includes Inpatient and Outpatient)					
Total Net Revenue	$4,535,848,627	$4,417,200,764	$4,256,119,678	$4,120,469,030	$3,781,637,703
Total Expenses	4,083,503,383	4,017,253,998	3,938,257,684	3,770,403,066	3,528,118,615
COMMUNITY HEALTH INDICATORS PER 1000 POPULATION					
Total Population (in thousands)	1,323	1,321	1,318	1,324	1,325
Inpatient					
Beds	2.1	2.1	2.2	2.2	2.2
Admissions	90.3	90.7	92.8	90.6	92.8
Inpatient Days	474.5	475.3	481.7	471.8	494.5
Inpatient Surgeries	24.8	25.4	26.0	25.4	24.9
Births	9.6	9.1	9.6	9.5	10.0
Outpatient					
Emergency Outpatient Visits	529.0	493.8	513.9	504.4	473.9
Other Outpatient Visits	3,284.4	3,279.2	3,276.1	3,105.3	3,093.1
Total Outpatient Visits	3,813.5	3,773.0	3,790.0	3,609.7	3,567.1
Outpatient Surgeries	67.3	68.7	69.3	69.9	69.1
Expense per Capita (per person)	$3,090.3	$3,047.6	$2,995.2	$2,857.2	$2,672.1

States

TABLE 6

NEW JERSEY

U.S. Registered Community Hospitals
(Nonfederal, short-term general and other special hospitals)

Overview 2009–2013

	2013	2012	2011	2010	2009
Total Community Hospitals in New Jersey.....	77	77	73	73	74
Bed Size Category					
6-24	0	0	0	0	0
25-49	2	2	1	2	3
50-99	9	9	7	6	5
100-199	19	20	18	16	19
200-299	16	17	21	20	16
300-399	15	12	10	11	12
400-499	7	9	9	9	11
500 + ...	9	8	7	9	8
Location					
Hospitals Urban..........................	77	77	73	73	74
Hospitals Rural	0	0	0	0	0
Control					
State and Local Government................	4	3	2	3	3
Not for Profit	60	60	61	62	64
Investor owned	13	14	10	8	7
Physician Models					
Independent Practice Association	12	11	10	12	14
Group Practice without Walls................	4	5	1	3	3
Open Physician-Hospital Organization	5	5	3	4	7
Closed Physician-Hospital Organization	5	3	2	2	4
Management Service Organization	15	13	13	12	13
Integrated Salary Model....................	38	27	25	23	22
Equity Model	3	3	0	0	2
Foundation................................	8	8	7	4	3
Insurance Products					
Health Maintenance Organization	17	12	7	6	3
Preferred Provider Organization..............	19	14	7	7	5
Indemnity Fee for Service	11	5	2	3	4
Managed Care Contracts					
Health Maintenance Organization	47	49	48	53	53
Preferred Provider Organization..............	48	49	47	53	54
Affiliations					
Hospitals in a System......................	54	47	42	42	43
Hospitals in a Network	32	30	29	26	28
Hospitals in a Group Purchasing Organization..	59	54	53	54	55

TABLE 6

NEW JERSEY

U.S. Registered Community Hospitals
(Nonfederal, short-term general and other special hospitals)

Utilization, Personnel, Revenue and Expenses, Community Health Indicators 2009–2013

	2013	2012	2011	2010	2009
TOTAL FACILITY (Includes Hospital and Nursing Home Units)					
Utilization - Inpatient					
Beds	21,348	21,162	20,396	21,096	21,054
Admissions	1,005,271	1,047,545	1,050,828	1,067,267	1,094,810
Inpatient Days	5,173,783	5,370,619	5,344,077	5,433,359	5,565,763
Average Length of Stay	5.1	5.1	5.1	5.1	5.1
Inpatient Surgeries	237,735	243,512	243,218	254,003	250,689
Births	99,416	101,599	101,362	100,677	105,841
Utilization - Outpatient					
Emergency Outpatient Visits	3,584,950	3,703,899	3,474,457	3,360,970	3,484,463
Other Outpatient Visits	12,009,026	11,883,599	12,350,842	12,619,644	14,948,039
Total Outpatient Visits	15,593,976	15,587,498	15,825,299	15,980,614	18,432,502
Outpatient Surgeries	361,755	381,289	381,281	378,695	385,028
Personnel					
Full Time RNs	27,680	27,979	27,286	26,849	27,096
Full Time LPNs	692	763	881	976	948
Part Time RNs	13,141	13,111	14,084	12,933	11,792
Part Time LPNs	240	294	321	342	313
Total Full Time	100,545	101,341	100,956	101,574	102,243
Total Part Time	40,840	42,586	43,164	39,829	37,722
Revenue - Inpatient					
Gross Inpatient Revenue	$59,880,957,599	$58,452,281,514	$56,915,377,319	$53,676,558,488	$53,769,546,685
Revenue - Outpatient					
Gross Outpatient Revenue	$34,166,641,289	$31,284,903,340	$27,132,937,292	$25,954,408,517	$23,718,074,694
Revenue and Expenses - Totals **(Includes Inpatient and Outpatient)**					
Total Gross Revenue	$94,047,598,888	$89,737,184,854	$84,048,314,611	$79,630,967,005	$77,487,621,379
Deductions from Revenue	74,483,147,229	70,204,451,132	66,316,458,143	62,268,213,291	60,433,181,540
Net Patient Revenue	19,564,451,659	19,532,733,722	17,731,856,468	17,362,753,714	17,054,439,839
Other Operating Revenue	1,399,525,038	1,217,574,869	1,039,183,060	991,173,520	937,712,136
Other Nonoperating Revenue	561,510,820	398,816,960	157,790,540	355,140,452	506,772,443
Total Net Revenue	21,525,487,517	21,149,125,551	18,928,830,068	18,709,067,686	18,498,924,418
Total Expenses	20,199,975,055	19,790,864,680	18,237,577,704	17,953,893,599	17,724,384,287
HOSPITAL UNIT (Excludes Separate Nursing Home Units)					
Utilization - Inpatient					
Beds	20,929	20,632	19,853	20,533	20,583
Admissions	1,001,500	1,043,187	1,046,456	1,061,552	1,091,384
Inpatient Days	5,037,093	5,189,878	5,168,493	5,258,495	5,408,363
Average Length of Stay	5.0	5.0	4.9	5.0	5.0
Personnel					
Total Full Time	100,231	100,839	100,398	100,902	101,537
Total Part Time	40,689	42,335	42,916	39,482	37,475
Revenue and Expenses - Totals **(Includes Inpatient and Outpatient)**					
Total Net Revenue	$21,472,958,854	$21,088,046,402	$18,869,785,791	$18,584,183,240	$18,453,887,888
Total Expenses	20,160,424,322	19,740,490,336	18,187,967,013	17,859,249,404	17,680,544,335
COMMUNITY HEALTH INDICATORS PER 1000 POPULATION					
Total Population (in thousands)	8,899	8,865	8,821	8,733	8,708
Inpatient					
Beds	2.4	2.4	2.3	2.4	2.4
Admissions	113.0	118.2	119.1	122.2	125.7
Inpatient Days	581.4	605.9	605.8	622.2	639.2
Inpatient Surgeries	26.7	27.5	27.6	29.1	28.8
Births	11.2	11.5	11.5	11.5	12.2
Outpatient					
Emergency Outpatient Visits	402.8	417.8	393.9	384.9	400.2
Other Outpatient Visits	1,349.4	1,340.6	1,400.1	1,445.1	1,716.6
Total Outpatient Visits	1,752.3	1,758.4	1,794.0	1,830.0	2,116.8
Outpatient Surgeries	40.6	43.0	43.2	43.4	44.2
Expense per Capita (per person)	$2,269.8	$2,232.6	$2,067.5	$2,055.9	$2,035.5

States

TABLE 6

NEW MEXICO

U.S. Registered Community Hospitals
(Nonfederal, short-term general and other special hospitals)

Overview 2009–2013

	2013	2012	2011	2010	2009
Total Community Hospitals in New Mexico	37	37	36	36	37
Bed Size Category					
6-24	4	5	4	4	4
25-49	11	9	8	8	8
50-99	10	10	12	12	14
100-199	6	6	7	8	8
200-299	4	5	3	2	1
300-399	0	0	0	0	0
400-499	1	1	0	0	0
500 + ...	1	1	2	2	2
Location					
Hospitals Urban.........................	14	14	14	14	15
Hospitals Rural	23	23	22	22	22
Control					
State and Local Government	6	6	6	6	7
Not for Profit	15	15	15	16	14
Investor owned	16	16	15	14	16
Physician Models					
Independent Practice Association	3	3	3	4	4
Group Practice without Walls..............	0	0	0	0	1
Open Physician-Hospital Organization	2	4	4	3	4
Closed Physician-Hospital Organization	0	0	0	0	0
Management Service Organization	1	0	0	0	0
Integrated Salary Model	15	11	9	11	13
Equity Model	0	0	0	0	1
Foundation.............................	0	0	0	1	2
Insurance Products					
Health Maintenance Organization	8	8	7	6	7
Preferred Provider Organization..............	8	6	7	6	7
Indemnity Fee for Service	8	4	4	5	5
Managed Care Contracts					
Health Maintenance Organization	18	16	13	14	19
Preferred Provider Organization..............	18	16	13	15	19
Affiliations					
Hospitals in a System.....................	29	29	28	28	30
Hospitals in a Network	11	11	11	11	10
Hospitals in a Group Purchasing Organization..	24	22	22	20	26

TABLE 6

NEW MEXICO

U.S. Registered Community Hospitals
(Nonfederal, short-term general and other special hospitals)

Utilization, Personnel, Revenue and Expenses, Community Health Indicators 2009–2013

	2013	2012	2011	2010	2009
TOTAL FACILITY (Includes Hospital and Nursing Home Units)					
Utilization - Inpatient					
Beds	3,806	4,076	4,068	3,975	3,913
Admissions	166,307	177,744	175,112	186,092	183,116
Inpatient Days	771,150	850,391	861,109	831,384	844,787
Average Length of Stay	4.6	4.8	4.9	4.5	4.6
Inpatient Surgeries	43,384	47,292	53,331	49,435	51,319
Births	22,252	23,924	21,537	23,767	26,224
Utilization - Outpatient					
Emergency Outpatient Visits	826,885	793,582	854,871	844,650	829,138
Other Outpatient Visits	3,657,027	3,361,978	3,740,262	3,795,337	3,814,530
Total Outpatient Visits	4,483,912	4,155,560	4,595,133	4,639,987	4,643,668
Outpatient Surgeries	89,154	92,264	93,352	92,079	92,936
Personnel					
Full Time RNs	6,330	6,326	5,549	6,022	5,579
Full Time LPNs	327	353	292	391	455
Part Time RNs	2,221	2,254	2,092	2,065	2,213
Part Time LPNs	109	100	72	124	145
Total Full Time	21,883	21,672	19,318	20,493	21,568
Total Part Time	6,755	6,526	5,387	5,559	6,609
Revenue - Inpatient					
Gross Inpatient Revenue	$6,186,832,999	$6,068,430,416	$5,955,197,886	$5,597,578,195	$5,011,641,495
Revenue - Outpatient					
Gross Outpatient Revenue	$6,581,129,820	$6,116,116,964	$5,493,320,827	$5,288,644,232	$4,601,410,841
Revenue and Expenses - Totals					
(Includes Inpatient and Outpatient)					
Total Gross Revenue	$12,767,962,819	$12,184,547,380	$11,448,518,713	$10,886,222,427	$9,613,052,336
Deductions from Revenue	8,697,316,188	8,059,915,659	7,609,704,329	6,965,889,535	5,938,985,924
Net Patient Revenue	4,070,646,631	4,124,631,721	3,838,814,384	3,920,332,892	3,674,066,412
Other Operating Revenue	220,599,613	229,495,765	211,597,602	193,738,359	179,587,865
Other Nonoperating Revenue	55,758,352	21,327,949	53,311,105	32,566,260	22,192,097
Total Net Revenue	4,347,004,596	4,375,455,435	4,103,723,091	4,146,637,511	3,875,846,374
Total Expenses	3,818,356,732	4,003,331,871	3,713,540,269	3,540,766,412	3,378,281,656
HOSPITAL UNIT (Excludes Separate Nursing Home Units)					
Utilization - Inpatient					
Beds	3,806	4,076	4,068	3,928	3,863
Admissions	166,307	177,744	175,112	186,058	182,956
Inpatient Days	771,150	850,391	861,109	818,802	841,637
Average Length of Stay	4.6	4.8	4.9	4.4	4.6
Personnel					
Total Full Time	21,695	21,499	19,318	20,450	21,545
Total Part Time	6,644	6,433	5,387	5,554	6,606
Revenue and Expenses - Totals					
(Includes Inpatient and Outpatient)					
Total Net Revenue	$4,347,004,596	$4,375,455,435	$4,103,723,091	$4,145,724,111	$3,872,546,211
Total Expenses	3,818,356,732	4,003,331,871	3,713,540,269	3,537,873,415	3,375,982,169
COMMUNITY HEALTH INDICATORS PER 1000 POPULATION					
Total Population (in thousands)	2,085	2,086	2,082	2,034	2,010
Inpatient					
Beds	1.8	2.0	2.0	2.0	1.9
Admissions	79.8	85.2	84.1	91.5	91.1
Inpatient Days	369.8	407.8	413.6	408.8	420.4
Inpatient Surgeries	20.8	22.7	25.6	24.3	25.5
Births	10.7	11.5	10.3	11.7	13.0
Outpatient					
Emergency Outpatient Visits	396.5	380.5	410.6	415.3	412.6
Other Outpatient Visits	1,753.7	1,612.0	1,796.3	1,866.1	1,898.1
Total Outpatient Visits	2,150.3	1,992.6	2,206.8	2,281.4	2,310.7
Outpatient Surgeries	42.8	44.2	44.8	45.3	46.2
Expense per Capita (per person)	$1,831.1	$1,919.6	$1,783.4	$1,740.9	$1,681.0

States

TABLE 6

NEW YORK

U.S. Registered Community Hospitals
(Nonfederal, short-term general and other special hospitals)

Overview 2009–2013

	2013	2012	2011	2010	2009
Total Community Hospitals in New York	177	178	182	185	189
Bed Size Category					
6-24	7	7	6	5	4
25-49	7	7	7	7	7
50-99	17	16	19	18	19
100-199	40	40	41	40	45
200-299	40	39	36	44	40
300-399	20	22	26	25	28
400-499	12	12	14	13	15
500 + ...	34	35	33	33	31
Location					
Hospitals Urban	139	140	145	147	150
Hospitals Rural	38	38	37	38	39
Control					
State and Local Government	25	26	26	25	25
Not for Profit	152	152	156	160	164
Investor owned	0	0	0	0	0
Physician Models					
Independent Practice Association	39	38	35	35	32
Group Practice without Walls	6	7	5	6	4
Open Physician-Hospital Organization	12	15	14	12	9
Closed Physician-Hospital Organization	7	13	10	10	10
Management Service Organization	13	16	15	18	15
Integrated Salary Model	83	77	77	74	63
Equity Model	1	1	2	0	0
Foundation	5	3	3	2	3
Insurance Products					
Health Maintenance Organization	48	42	48	45	39
Preferred Provider Organization	25	13	21	30	22
Indemnity Fee for Service	10	9	10	22	12
Managed Care Contracts					
Health Maintenance Organization	109	114	116	116	111
Preferred Provider Organization	105	108	111	109	101
Affiliations					
Hospitals in a System	94	87	84	82	80
Hospitals in a Network	78	75	83	82	76
Hospitals in a Group Purchasing Organization . .	129	128	134	128	116

TABLE 6

NEW YORK

U.S. Registered Community Hospitals
(Nonfederal, short-term general and other special hospitals)

Utilization, Personnel, Revenue and Expenses, Community Health Indicators 2009–2013

	2013	2012	2011	2010	2009
TOTAL FACILITY (Includes Hospital and Nursing Home Units)					
Utilization - Inpatient					
Beds	56,270	57,148	58,080	59,510	60,400
Admissions	2,331,678	2,444,350	2,491,403	2,509,980	2,533,577
Inpatient Days	15,933,416	16,783,079	16,924,697	17,226,868	17,474,823
Average Length of Stay...........	6.8	6.9	6.8	6.9	6.9
Inpatient Surgeries...............	599,625	615,646	615,656	683,336	653,545
Births......................	232,325	232,967	239,622	238,062	238,647
Utilization - Outpatient					
Emergency Outpatient Visits........	8,616,225	8,379,030	8,432,260	8,063,821	8,542,392
Other Outpatient Visits............	47,693,175	48,264,808	45,578,620	45,586,391	45,702,429
Total Outpatient Visits	56,309,400	56,643,838	54,010,880	53,650,212	54,244,821
Outpatient Surgeries	1,374,086	1,309,661	1,335,088	1,369,360	1,369,632
Personnel					
Full Time RNs	82,755	80,336	81,500	79,270	79,073
Full Time LPNs	5,133	5,110	5,403	5,095	5,781
Part Time RNs..................	23,281	23,613	23,368	24,090	21,651
Part Time LPNs	1,358	1,389	1,427	1,492	1,442
Total Full Time..................	358,347	354,362	350,923	333,121	344,168
Total Part Time	84,342	84,860	85,040	80,711	76,142
Revenue - Inpatient					
Gross Inpatient Revenue...........	$93,765,207,434	$91,398,462,566	$86,312,444,902	$83,446,219,992	$79,742,230,648
Revenue - Outpatient					
Gross Outpatient Revenue	$68,815,204,133	$62,547,461,326	$56,035,192,523	$52,554,490,709	$48,142,548,531
Revenue and Expenses - Totals					
(Includes Inpatient and Outpatient)					
Total Gross Revenue.............	$162,580,411,567	$153,945,923,892	$142,347,637,425	$136,000,710,701	$127,884,779,179
Deductions from Revenue.........	103,028,887,067	95,942,060,347	87,498,353,474	83,151,232,467	77,411,417,932
Net Patient Revenue	59,551,524,500	58,003,863,545	54,849,283,951	52,849,478,234	50,473,361,247
Other Operating Revenue	5,362,994,107	4,732,632,403	4,212,820,400	4,222,330,075	3,824,228,913
Other Nonoperating Revenue	1,788,296,692	758,391,592	541,024,602	925,916,282	1,020,046,507
Total Net Revenue...............	66,702,815,299	63,494,887,540	59,603,128,953	57,997,724,591	55,317,636,667
Total Expenses..................	64,889,138,257	62,122,860,564	58,543,388,525	56,081,000,844	54,164,979,905
HOSPITAL UNIT (Excludes Separate Nursing Home Units)					
Utilization - Inpatient					
Beds	50,184	50,458	51,072	53,436	54,708
Admissions	2,314,517	2,426,083	2,471,603	2,494,952	2,518,427
Inpatient Days	13,831,403	14,420,693	14,460,605	15,107,729	15,475,231
Average Length of Stay...........	6.0	5.9	5.9	6.1	6.1
Personnel					
Total Full Time..................	353,126	348,723	346,182	329,655	339,060
Total Part Time	81,870	82,206	82,889	78,770	73,758
Revenue and Expenses - Totals					
(Includes Inpatient and Outpatient)					
Total Net Revenue...............	$66,062,124,750	$62,830,487,679	$58,992,643,837	$57,401,240,974	$54,761,298,914
Total Expenses..................	64,249,125,162	61,440,662,596	57,946,106,911	55,490,108,946	53,587,952,457
COMMUNITY HEALTH INDICATORS PER 1000 POPULATION					
Total Population (in thousands)	19,651	19,570	19,465	19,578	19,541
Inpatient					
Beds	2.9	2.9	3.0	3.0	3.1
Admissions	118.7	124.9	128.0	128.2	129.7
Inpatient Days	810.8	857.6	869.5	879.9	894.2
Inpatient Surgeries...............	30.5	31.5	31.6	34.9	33.4
Births......................	11.8	11.9	12.3	12.2	12.2
Outpatient					
Emergency Outpatient Visits........	438.5	428.2	433.2	411.9	437.1
Other Outpatient Visits............	2,427.0	2,466.2	2,341.5	2,328.5	2,338.7
Total Outpatient Visits	2,865.5	2,894.4	2,774.7	2,740.4	2,775.9
Outpatient Surgeries	69.9	66.9	68.6	69.9	70.1
Expense per Capita (per person).....	$3,302.1	$3,174.4	$3,007.6	$2,864.5	$2,771.8

States

TABLE 6

NORTH CAROLINA

U.S. Registered Community Hospitals
(Nonfederal, short-term general and other special hospitals)

Overview 2009–2013

	2013	2012	2011	2010	2009
Total Community Hospitals in North Carolina..	117	118	117	117	115
Bed Size Category					
6-24	5	5	3	4	4
25-49	25	26	20	19	18
50-99	23	22	28	25	20
100-199	30	31	31	35	39
200-299	12	12	13	13	13
300-399	7	8	8	6	6
400-499	2	1	1	2	2
500 + ...	13	13	13	13	13
Location					
Hospitals Urban..........................	60	61	59	59	58
Hospitals Rural	57	57	58	58	57
Control					
State and Local Government................	28	30	30	32	32
Not for Profit	72	72	75	73	74
Investor owned	17	16	12	12	9
Physician Models					
Independent Practice Association	8	8	10	10	11
Group Practice without Walls................	3	2	1	2	3
Open Physician-Hospital Organization	9	9	9	10	11
Closed Physician-Hospital Organization	5	5	6	6	7
Management Service Organization	15	14	12	12	14
Integrated Salary Model....................	61	60	57	54	50
Equity Model	1	2	2	4	5
Foundation...............................	1	2	2	3	2
Insurance Products					
Health Maintenance Organization	4	5	6	7	4
Preferred Provider Organization..............	19	14	16	14	10
Indemnity Fee for Service	2	2	6	5	2
Managed Care Contracts					
Health Maintenance Organization	70	75	71	70	71
Preferred Provider Organization..............	81	83	77	75	80
Affiliations					
Hospitals in a System.....................	99	95	90	78	70
Hospitals in a Network.....................	45	46	43	41	39
Hospitals in a Group Purchasing Organization..	96	99	94	90	90

TABLE 6

NORTH CAROLINA

U.S. Registered Community Hospitals
(Nonfederal, short-term general and other special hospitals)

Utilization, Personnel, Revenue and Expenses, Community Health Indicators 2009–2013

	2013	2012	2011	2010	2009
TOTAL FACILITY (Includes Hospital and Nursing Home Units)					
Utilization - Inpatient					
Beds	22,617	22,708	23,136	23,012	22,830
Admissions	1,011,304	1,027,640	1,035,400	1,038,337	1,034,112
Inpatient Days	5,730,722	5,726,216	5,830,425	5,852,967	5,788,671
Average Length of Stay	5.7	5.6	5.6	5.6	5.6
Inpatient Surgeries	278,068	281,357	287,065	293,323	296,668
Births	112,844	114,140	115,013	117,422	122,588
Utilization - Outpatient					
Emergency Outpatient Visits	4,689,431	4,636,192	4,448,191	4,259,853	4,249,375
Other Outpatient Visits	14,969,949	15,094,661	14,180,481	14,026,042	14,071,173
Total Outpatient Visits	19,659,380	19,730,853	18,628,672	18,285,895	18,320,548
Outpatient Surgeries	555,407	549,918	551,009	558,068	561,072
Personnel					
Full Time RNs	40,181	39,539	37,691	37,461	36,051
Full Time LPNs	1,532	1,454	1,457	1,585	1,567
Part Time RNs	13,150	13,727	13,740	13,790	13,892
Part Time LPNs	381	395	433	509	560
Total Full Time	138,355	138,663	134,652	130,456	128,117
Total Part Time	36,141	36,991	36,793	35,766	37,093
Revenue - Inpatient					
Gross Inpatient Revenue	$34,091,849,676	$32,277,023,087	$30,029,780,874	$28,197,730,702	$25,877,825,356
Revenue - Outpatient					
Gross Outpatient Revenue	$34,470,700,452	$31,543,420,298	$27,738,748,951	$24,683,456,547	$22,124,796,442
Revenue and Expenses - Totals					
(Includes Inpatient and Outpatient)					
Total Gross Revenue	$68,562,550,128	$63,820,443,385	$57,768,529,825	$52,881,187,249	$48,002,621,798
Deductions from Revenue	45,661,471,693	40,976,435,538	37,629,541,786	33,708,237,290	29,458,448,362
Net Patient Revenue	22,901,078,435	22,844,007,847	20,138,988,039	19,172,949,959	18,544,173,436
Other Operating Revenue	855,996,247	1,376,765,805	1,235,529,371	1,122,729,376	1,094,994,175
Other Nonoperating Revenue	551,411,198	664,882,512	273,053,042	492,730,856	213,265,535
Total Net Revenue	24,308,485,880	24,885,656,164	21,647,570,452	20,788,410,191	19,852,433,146
Total Expenses	22,436,224,717	22,659,692,061	20,062,914,117	18,847,920,294	18,590,518,185
HOSPITAL UNIT (Excludes Separate Nursing Home Units)					
Utilization - Inpatient					
Beds	21,092	20,823	21,041	20,841	20,811
Admissions	1,004,965	1,020,541	1,027,691	1,030,472	1,026,457
Inpatient Days	5,244,404	5,135,293	5,171,227	5,150,233	5,133,526
Average Length of Stay	5.2	5.0	5.0	5.0	5.0
Personnel					
Total Full Time	137,327	137,311	133,321	128,958	126,542
Total Part Time	35,653	36,455	36,217	35,100	36,425
Revenue and Expenses - Totals					
(Includes Inpatient and Outpatient)					
Total Net Revenue	$24,201,100,219	$24,752,345,760	$21,508,952,533	$20,648,909,546	$19,725,156,052
Total Expenses	22,329,567,069	22,524,391,595	19,925,373,321	18,715,167,064	18,471,921,787
COMMUNITY HEALTH INDICATORS PER 1000 POPULATION					
Total Population (in thousands)	9,848	9,752	9,656	9,459	9,381
Inpatient					
Beds	2.3	2.3	2.4	2.4	2.4
Admissions	102.7	105.4	107.2	109.8	110.2
Inpatient Days	581.9	587.2	603.8	618.8	617.1
Inpatient Surgeries	28.2	28.9	29.7	31.0	31.6
Births	11.5	11.7	11.9	12.4	13.1
Outpatient					
Emergency Outpatient Visits	476.2	475.4	460.6	450.4	453.0
Other Outpatient Visits	1,520.1	1,547.8	1,468.5	1,482.8	1,500.0
Total Outpatient Visits	1,996.3	2,023.2	1,929.2	1,933.2	1,953.0
Outpatient Surgeries	56.4	56.4	57.1	59.0	59.8
Expense per Capita (per person)	$2,278.2	$2,323.6	$2,077.7	$1,992.6	$1,981.7

TABLE 6

NORTH DAKOTA

U.S. Registered Community Hospitals
(Nonfederal, short-term general and other special hospitals)

Overview 2009–2013

	2013	2012	2011	2010	2009
Total Community Hospitals in North Dakota ...	40	44	41	41	41
Bed Size Category					
6-24	15	14	13	10	10
25-49	10	15	14	15	15
50-99	9	8	7	8	9
100-199	1	2	2	3	2
200-299	3	3	3	3	3
300-399	0	0	0	0	0
400-499	2	1	1	1	1
500 + ...	0	1	1	1	1
Location					
Hospitals Urban............................	8	8	8	8	8
Hospitals Rural	32	36	33	33	33
Control					
State and Local Government................	0	0	0	0	0
Not for Profit	38	41	39	39	39
Investor owned	2	3	2	2	2
Physician Models					
Independent Practice Association	2	3	3	4	4
Group Practice without Walls................	0	1	0	0	0
Open Physician-Hospital Organization	1	2	1	1	2
Closed Physician-Hospital Organization	0	0	0	0	0
Management Service Organization	0	0	0	0	0
Integrated Salary Model	10	10	8	10	16
Equity Model	0	0	0	0	1
Foundation...............................	1	1	1	1	2
Insurance Products					
Health Maintenance Organization	4	2	0	1	0
Preferred Provider Organization..............	4	2	5	5	5
Indemnity Fee for Service	0	0	1	2	2
Managed Care Contracts					
Health Maintenance Organization	0	1	2	1	3
Preferred Provider Organization..............	10	10	11	13	17
Affiliations					
Hospitals in a System......................	19	20	19	17	17
Hospitals in a Network.....................	9	9	7	8	12
Hospitals in a Group Purchasing Organization..	19	22	17	19	28

TABLE 6

NORTH DAKOTA

U.S. Registered Community Hospitals
(Nonfederal, short-term general and other special hospitals)

Utilization, Personnel, Revenue and Expenses, Community Health Indicators 2009–2013

	2013	2012	2011	2010	2009
TOTAL FACILITY (Includes Hospital and Nursing Home Units)					
Utilization - Inpatient					
Beds	2,924	3,254	3,145	3,345	3,362
Admissions	94,743	92,940	94,125	94,436	92,593
Inpatient Days	658,748	727,855	701,723	718,950	751,653
Average Length of Stay	7.0	7.8	7.5	7.6	8.1
Inpatient Surgeries	27,930	26,617	28,285	29,558	27,732
Births	11,061	14,625	12,731	12,851	10,552
Utilization - Outpatient					
Emergency Outpatient Visits	328,299	419,652	408,870	353,557	303,190
Other Outpatient Visits	2,007,191	2,566,926	2,540,152	2,722,180	2,059,310
Total Outpatient Visits	2,335,490	2,986,578	2,949,022	3,075,737	2,362,500
Outpatient Surgeries	73,072	68,599	59,702	54,165	56,128
Personnel					
Full Time RNs	3,701	3,651	3,103	2,889	2,497
Full Time LPNs	509	514	501	514	599
Part Time RNs	2,579	2,791	2,485	2,452	2,163
Part Time LPNs	413	441	404	392	361
Total Full Time	16,391	16,049	14,606	13,962	13,326
Total Part Time	8,850	9,429	8,536	8,187	7,909
Revenue - Inpatient					
Gross Inpatient Revenue	$2,807,963,590	$2,688,456,061	$2,320,300,120	$2,092,135,268	$2,019,340,609
Revenue - Outpatient					
Gross Outpatient Revenue	$3,905,959,216	$3,413,782,975	$2,783,603,262	$2,551,094,052	$2,583,127,227
Revenue and Expenses - Totals (Includes Inpatient and Outpatient)					
Total Gross Revenue	$6,713,922,806	$6,102,239,036	$5,103,903,382	$4,643,229,320	$4,602,467,836
Deductions from Revenue	3,821,510,799	3,415,592,851	2,807,521,605	2,493,872,027	2,518,310,749
Net Patient Revenue	2,892,412,007	2,686,646,185	2,296,381,777	2,149,357,293	2,084,157,087
Other Operating Revenue	161,549,912	125,508,307	107,145,231	96,921,743	91,082,749
Other Nonoperating Revenue	28,978,906	24,882,062	22,983,677	33,585,013	13,376,054
Total Net Revenue	3,082,940,825	2,837,036,554	2,426,510,685	2,279,864,049	2,188,615,890
Total Expenses	2,966,838,008	2,666,135,816	2,229,494,218	2,142,846,297	2,133,367,717
HOSPITAL UNIT (Excludes Separate Nursing Home Units)					
Utilization - Inpatient					
Beds	2,422	2,906	2,944	3,063	2,569
Admissions	93,845	91,966	92,902	92,796	90,862
Inpatient Days	495,592	613,301	633,852	634,164	485,393
Average Length of Stay	5.3	6.7	6.8	6.8	5.3
Personnel					
Total Full Time	16,134	15,785	14,472	13,822	12,820
Total Part Time	8,700	9,268	8,439	8,048	7,540
Revenue and Expenses - Totals (Includes Inpatient and Outpatient)					
Total Net Revenue	$3,051,733,992	$2,813,596,727	$2,414,246,674	$2,258,523,169	$2,145,215,671
Total Expenses	2,925,639,027	2,647,960,716	2,223,176,123	2,126,714,369	2,094,921,706
COMMUNITY HEALTH INDICATORS PER 1000 POPULATION					
Total Population (in thousands)	723	700	684	654	647
Inpatient					
Beds	4.0	4.7	4.6	5.1	5.2
Admissions	131.0	132.8	137.6	144.4	143.1
Inpatient Days	910.6	1,040.3	1,026.0	1,099.7	1,162.0
Inpatient Surgeries	38.6	38.0	41.4	45.2	42.9
Births	15.3	20.9	18.6	19.7	16.3
Outpatient					
Emergency Outpatient Visits	453.8	599.8	597.8	540.8	468.7
Other Outpatient Visits	2,774.7	3,669.0	3,714.0	4,163.8	3,183.6
Total Outpatient Visits	3,228.5	4,268.8	4,311.9	4,704.6	3,652.3
Outpatient Surgeries	101.0	98.1	87.3	82.8	86.8
Expense per Capita (per person)	$4,101.3	$3,810.8	$3,259.8	$3,277.6	$3,298.1

States

TABLE 6

OHIO

U.S. Registered Community Hospitals
(Nonfederal, short-term general and other special hospitals)

Overview 2009–2013

	2013	2012	2011	2010	2009
Total Community Hospitals in Ohio..........	183	185	183	183	183
Bed Size Category					
6-24	4	6	2	3	4
25-49	48	47	47	44	45
50-99	29	29	33	33	32
100-199	44	44	40	41	43
200-299	26	25	27	28	25
300-399	8	12	12	12	11
400-499	11	9	9	9	11
500 + ...	13	13	13	13	12
Location					
Hospitals Urban..........................	128	130	128	128	128
Hospitals Rural	55	55	55	55	55
Control					
State and Local Government...............	18	19	19	21	22
Not for Profit	138	140	138	138	138
Investor owned	27	26	26	24	23
Physician Models					
Independent Practice Association	18	13	15	15	19
Group Practice without Walls................	18	6	6	7	8
Open Physician-Hospital Organization	46	44	50	52	46
Closed Physician-Hospital Organization	21	15	15	9	10
Management Service Organization	32	19	33	35	39
Integrated Salary Model....................	79	78	70	71	64
Equity Model.............................	18	8	8	9	7
Foundation..............................	29	20	29	31	28
Insurance Products					
Health Maintenance Organization	24	24	33	36	32
Preferred Provider Organization..............	36	31	39	43	44
Indemnity Fee for Service	13	10	14	16	15
Managed Care Contracts					
Health Maintenance Organization	115	121	114	113	120
Preferred Provider Organization..............	118	117	119	120	129
Affiliations					
Hospitals in a System.....................	123	122	118	114	111
Hospitals in a Network....................	76	77	76	77	77
Hospitals in a Group Purchasing Organization..	128	136	135	133	143

TABLE 6

OHIO

U.S. Registered Community Hospitals
(Nonfederal, short-term general and other special hospitals)

Utilization, Personnel, Revenue and Expenses, Community Health Indicators 2009–2013

	2013	2012	2011	2010	2009
TOTAL FACILITY (Includes Hospital and Nursing Home Units)					
Utilization - Inpatient					
Beds	33,222	33,659	33,828	34,316	33,994
Admissions	1,455,817	1,501,183	1,504,603	1,516,501	1,531,076
Inpatient Days	7,126,702	7,367,870	7,434,042	7,598,267	7,744,235
Average Length of Stay.	4.9	4.9	4.9	5.0	5.1
Inpatient Surgeries.	372,371	383,187	393,731	405,507	407,777
Births.	130,476	128,393	128,695	133,946	141,295
Utilization - Outpatient					
Emergency Outpatient Visits.	6,484,063	6,578,749	6,506,331	6,383,429	6,207,290
Other Outpatient Visits.	30,776,656	30,377,613	29,390,397	29,375,819	28,033,655
Total Outpatient Visits	37,260,719	36,956,362	35,896,728	35,759,248	34,240,945
Outpatient Surgeries	822,722	810,268	803,825	817,556	800,882
Personnel					
Full Time RNs	54,669	54,347	52,672	51,255	48,681
Full Time LPNs	2,789	2,960	3,790	3,309	3,580
Part Time RNs	25,029	25,890	26,034	25,325	24,409
Part Time LPNs	1,407	1,785	1,788	1,808	1,859
Total Full Time.	206,245	205,576	203,689	198,795	198,906
Total Part Time	72,993	76,463	78,003	76,929	75,934
Revenue - Inpatient					
Gross Inpatient Revenue.	$58,384,380,015	$55,828,522,139	$51,716,805,929	$49,069,396,749	$45,306,391,429
Revenue - Outpatient					
Gross Outpatient Revenue	$58,206,812,939	$52,981,694,494	$47,899,777,396	$44,283,440,488	$40,277,248,420
Revenue and Expenses - Totals					
(Includes Inpatient and Outpatient)					
Total Gross Revenue.	$116,591,192,954	$108,810,216,633	$99,616,583,325	$93,352,837,237	$85,583,639,849
Deductions from Revenue.	79,710,922,376	73,204,925,076	67,235,879,337	61,559,545,620	55,069,727,140
Net Patient Revenue	36,880,270,578	35,605,291,557	32,380,703,988	31,793,291,617	30,513,912,709
Other Operating Revenue	2,927,044,680	2,642,307,155	2,439,029,875	2,302,711,954	2,204,346,362
Other Nonoperating Revenue	1,250,816,674	770,720,233	66,768,231	824,057,575	899,809,957
Total Net Revenue.	41,058,131,932	39,018,318,945	34,886,502,094	34,920,061,146	33,618,069,028
Total Expenses.	37,050,070,738	35,772,141,755	32,605,625,518	32,374,139,783	30,929,648,514
HOSPITAL UNIT (Excludes Separate Nursing Home Units)					
Utilization - Inpatient					
Beds	32,570	32,901	32,734	33,157	32,613
Admissions	1,447,101	1,491,784	1,492,180	1,503,171	1,517,223
Inpatient Days	6,909,524	7,117,086	7,086,115	7,219,041	7,292,581
Average Length of Stay.	4.8	4.8	4.7	4.8	4.8
Personnel					
Total Full Time.	205,768	205,033	202,974	197,828	197,669
Total Part Time	72,650	76,040	77,530	76,311	75,222
Revenue and Expenses - Totals					
(Includes Inpatient and Outpatient)					
Total Net Revenue.	$40,990,936,895	$38,920,461,713	$34,777,592,693	$34,807,563,235	$33,478,190,434
Total Expenses.	36,986,993,669	35,672,905,913	32,496,965,573	32,265,651,508	30,795,620,302
COMMUNITY HEALTH INDICATORS PER 1000 POPULATION					
Total Population (in thousands)	11,571	11,544	11,545	11,532	11,543
Inpatient					
Beds	2.9	2.9	2.9	3.0	2.9
Admissions	125.8	130.0	130.3	131.5	132.6
Inpatient Days	615.9	638.2	643.9	658.9	670.9
Inpatient Surgeries.	32.2	33.2	34.1	35.2	35.3
Births.	11.3	11.1	11.1	11.6	12.2
Outpatient					
Emergency Outpatient Visits.	560.4	569.9	563.6	553.5	537.8
Other Outpatient Visits.	2,659.9	2,631.4	2,545.7	2,547.3	2,428.7
Total Outpatient Visits	3,220.2	3,201.3	3,109.3	3,100.8	2,966.5
Outpatient Surgeries	71.1	70.2	69.6	70.9	69.4
Expense per Capita (per person).	$3,202.0	$3,098.7	$2,824.2	$2,807.3	$2,679.6

States

Table 6

OKLAHOMA

U.S. Registered Community Hospitals
(Nonfederal, short-term general and other special hospitals)

Overview 2009–2013

	2013	2012	2011	2010	2009
Total Community Hospitals in Oklahoma......	116	117	115	113	116
Bed Size Category					
6-24..................................	21	21	21	22	20
25-49..................................	46	47	44	41	42
50-99..................................	23	23	24	22	26
100-199..................................	12	13	14	15	15
200-299..................................	4	3	2	2	3
300-399..................................	4	4	4	5	4
400-499..................................	0	0	1	1	1
500 +..................................	6	6	5	5	5
Location					
Hospitals Urban.........................	51	51	49	48	49
Hospitals Rural.........................	65	66	66	65	67
Control					
State and Local Government...............	38	40	41	44	45
Not for Profit...........................	37	37	38	36	36
Investor owned..........................	41	40	36	33	35
Physician Models					
Independent Practice Association............	14	13	16	14	15
Group Practice without Walls...............	6	5	4	6	6
Open Physician-Hospital Organization........	10	12	11	9	11
Closed Physician-Hospital Organization.......	3	3	1	0	0
Management Service Organization...........	9	9	7	7	11
Integrated Salary Model....................	52	52	49	34	26
Equity Model............................	1	1	1	0	0
Foundation.............................	1	2	1	0	1
Insurance Products					
Health Maintenance Organization............	13	13	13	8	7
Preferred Provider Organization..............	14	12	16	10	8
Indemnity Fee for Service	5	5	8	4	4
Managed Care Contracts					
Health Maintenance Organization............	53	52	48	38	38
Preferred Provider Organization..............	77	76	76	63	62
Affiliations					
Hospitals in a System.....................	63	65	60	53	60
Hospitals in a Network....................	39	33	30	22	19
Hospitals in a Group Purchasing Organization..	93	95	91	87	89

TABLE **6**

OKLAHOMA

U.S. Registered Community Hospitals
(Nonfederal, short-term general and other special hospitals)

Utilization, Personnel, Revenue and Expenses, Community Health Indicators 2009–2013

	2013	2012	2011	2010	2009
TOTAL FACILITY (Includes Hospital and Nursing Home Units)					
Utilization - Inpatient					
Beds	11,365	11,349	11,303	11,170	11,316
Admissions	412,225	424,024	424,190	429,096	442,394
Inpatient Days	2,221,235	2,242,204	2,257,353	2,340,946	2,401,771
Average Length of Stay	5.4	5.3	5.3	5.5	5.4
Inpatient Surgeries	102,141	107,089	107,010	109,345	117,362
Births	52,910	50,107	46,583	48,569	53,456
Utilization - Outpatient					
Emergency Outpatient Visits	1,871,330	1,908,047	1,847,389	1,762,821	1,743,802
Other Outpatient Visits	4,741,807	4,866,096	4,175,877	3,895,891	3,827,100
Total Outpatient Visits	6,613,137	6,774,143	6,023,266	5,658,712	5,570,902
Outpatient Surgeries	221,650	223,225	211,753	206,440	200,043
Personnel					
Full Time RNs	13,018	12,313	11,500	11,105	10,929
Full Time LPNs	1,642	1,688	1,612	1,686	1,903
Part Time RNs	3,531	4,277	4,046	3,984	3,654
Part Time LPNs	383	495	464	567	500
Total Full Time	46,292	46,426	44,647	43,629	43,977
Total Part Time	11,446	13,623	13,085	13,056	12,159
Revenue - Inpatient					
Gross Inpatient Revenue	$14,505,192,200	$14,248,526,243	$13,445,502,051	$12,758,064,725	$12,064,230,137
Revenue - Outpatient					
Gross Outpatient Revenue	$13,122,142,376	$11,878,040,440	$10,390,808,413	$9,221,121,763	$8,258,194,596
Revenue and Expenses - Totals					
(Includes Inpatient and Outpatient)					
Total Gross Revenue	$27,627,334,576	$26,126,566,683	$23,836,310,464	$21,979,186,488	$20,322,424,733
Deductions from Revenue	19,789,608,584	18,251,141,886	16,779,981,602	15,258,319,649	13,635,382,267
Net Patient Revenue	7,837,725,992	7,875,424,797	7,056,328,862	6,720,866,839	6,687,042,466
Other Operating Revenue	288,772,295	264,973,762	269,741,536	235,730,490	201,195,524
Other Nonoperating Revenue	244,751,865	27,381,522	185,667,771	102,371,200	-36,278,624
Total Net Revenue	8,371,250,152	8,167,780,081	7,511,738,169	7,058,968,529	6,851,959,366
Total Expenses	7,684,078,335	7,462,798,181	6,782,884,227	6,484,581,837	6,376,319,309
HOSPITAL UNIT (Excludes Separate Nursing Home Units)					
Utilization - Inpatient					
Beds	11,095	11,086	11,033	10,981	11,013
Admissions	411,403	422,856	423,362	427,982	440,886
Inpatient Days	2,143,080	2,164,883	2,183,306	2,280,666	2,277,293
Average Length of Stay	5.2	5.1	5.2	5.3	5.2
Personnel					
Total Full Time	46,006	46,159	44,486	43,532	43,684
Total Part Time	11,382	13,555	13,026	12,983	12,110
Revenue and Expenses - Totals					
(Includes Inpatient and Outpatient)					
Total Net Revenue	$8,358,970,765	$8,133,239,746	$7,501,813,546	$7,049,646,928	$6,836,200,847
Total Expenses	7,672,845,200	7,451,915,559	6,772,484,570	6,475,775,258	6,361,745,192
COMMUNITY HEALTH INDICATORS PER 1000 POPULATION					
Total Population (in thousands)	3,851	3,815	3,792	3,724	3,687
Inpatient					
Beds	3.0	3.0	3.0	3.0	3.1
Admissions	107.1	111.2	111.9	115.2	120.0
Inpatient Days	576.9	587.8	595.4	628.5	651.4
Inpatient Surgeries	26.5	28.1	28.2	29.4	31.8
Births	13.7	13.1	12.3	13.0	14.5
Outpatient					
Emergency Outpatient Visits	486.0	500.2	487.2	473.3	473.0
Other Outpatient Visits	1,231.5	1,275.6	1,101.4	1,046.0	1,038.0
Total Outpatient Visits	1,717.4	1,775.7	1,588.6	1,519.3	1,510.9
Outpatient Surgeries	57.6	58.5	55.8	55.4	54.3
Expense per Capita (per person)	$1,995.6	$1,956.3	$1,789.0	$1,741.1	$1,729.4

TABLE 6

OREGON

U.S. Registered Community Hospitals
(Nonfederal, short-term general and other special hospitals)

Overview 2009–2013

	2013	2012	2011	2010	2009
Total Community Hospitals in Oregon	59	58	59	58	58
Bed Size Category					
6-24	9	8	9	9	8
25-49	20	20	20	20	19
50-99	8	9	10	10	12
100-199	11	10	9	9	9
200-299	4	4	4	4	4
300-399	2	2	2	1	1
400-499	3	3	3	3	3
500 + ...	2	2	2	2	2
Location					
Hospitals Urban........................	30	30	30	29	29
Hospitals Rural	29	28	29	29	29
Control					
State and Local Government................	12	11	12	12	12
Not for Profit	45	45	45	44	44
Investor owned	2	2	2	2	2
Physician Models					
Independent Practice Association	9	10	11	12	13
Group Practice without Walls................	7	8	9	9	8
Open Physician-Hospital Organization	2	5	6	6	6
Closed Physician-Hospital Organization	6	2	2	2	2
Management Service Organization	10	14	13	14	14
Integrated Salary Model	54	41	40	39	35
Equity Model	0	1	0	0	1
Foundation...............................	1	4	4	5	6
Insurance Products					
Health Maintenance Organization	19	14	16	15	15
Preferred Provider Organization..............	19	10	17	19	15
Indemnity Fee for Service	5	0	3	3	3
Managed Care Contracts					
Health Maintenance Organization	39	38	35	34	29
Preferred Provider Organization..............	52	49	52	51	51
Affiliations					
Hospitals in a System.....................	41	41	40	39	39
Hospitals in a Network	30	28	28	27	25
Hospitals in a Group Purchasing Organization..	58	56	58	57	56

TABLE 6

OREGON

U.S. Registered Community Hospitals
(Nonfederal, short-term general and other special hospitals)

Utilization, Personnel, Revenue and Expenses, Community Health Indicators 2009–2013

	2013	2012	2011	2010	2009
TOTAL FACILITY (Includes Hospital and Nursing Home Units)					
Utilization - Inpatient					
Beds	6,778	6,706	6,805	6,420	6,481
Admissions	337,228	336,677	342,649	321,334	323,733
Inpatient Days	1,454,053	1,429,092	1,468,277	1,387,082	1,437,561
Average Length of Stay	4.3	4.2	4.3	4.3	4.4
Inpatient Surgeries	123,905	119,276	123,292	114,683	114,337
Births	42,393	43,472	43,262	41,914	43,940
Utilization - Outpatient					
Emergency Outpatient Visits	1,399,434	1,402,280	1,404,165	1,229,539	1,312,068
Other Outpatient Visits	8,986,321	8,402,499	7,969,367	7,982,714	7,587,931
Total Outpatient Visits	10,385,755	9,804,779	9,373,532	9,212,253	8,899,999
Outpatient Surgeries	192,524	203,622	211,379	205,542	207,341
Personnel					
Full Time RNs	10,997	10,528	10,359	9,293	9,230
Full Time LPNs	142	162	185	189	212
Part Time RNs	7,165	7,366	7,692	7,003	7,068
Part Time LPNs	88	113	154	131	165
Total Full Time	39,732	38,512	39,278	35,968	35,768
Total Part Time	18,834	19,732	20,655	18,954	19,325
Revenue - Inpatient					
Gross Inpatient Revenue	$10,304,742,501	$9,763,893,851	$9,510,397,093	$8,342,718,826	$7,965,180,365
Revenue - Outpatient					
Gross Outpatient Revenue	$9,695,486,581	$9,057,121,305	$8,564,788,044	$7,669,159,468	$7,028,661,629
Revenue and Expenses - Totals					
(Includes Inpatient and Outpatient)					
Total Gross Revenue	$20,000,229,082	$18,821,015,156	$18,075,185,137	$16,011,878,294	$14,993,841,994
Deductions from Revenue	10,889,922,069	9,946,369,291	9,586,390,414	8,389,072,711	7,773,324,462
Net Patient Revenue	9,110,307,013	8,874,645,865	8,488,794,723	7,622,805,583	7,220,517,532
Other Operating Revenue	486,233,283	431,506,659	357,481,939	356,073,198	354,503,423
Other Nonoperating Revenue	116,357,557	120,073,921	115,998,119	164,944,836	-58,115,473
Total Net Revenue	9,712,897,853	9,426,226,445	8,962,274,781	8,143,823,617	7,516,905,482
Total Expenses	9,358,601,796	9,102,609,637	8,726,772,182	7,875,937,042	7,402,240,332
HOSPITAL UNIT (Excludes Separate Nursing Home Units)					
Utilization - Inpatient					
Beds	6,610	6,538	6,618	6,233	6,228
Admissions	337,095	336,526	342,499	321,153	323,516
Inpatient Days	1,412,321	1,387,370	1,426,510	1,338,597	1,373,086
Average Length of Stay	4.2	4.1	4.2	4.2	4.2
Personnel					
Total Full Time	39,667	38,416	39,186	35,872	35,629
Total Part Time	18,780	19,687	20,579	18,863	19,243
Revenue and Expenses - Totals					
(Includes Inpatient and Outpatient)					
Total Net Revenue	$9,702,942,089	$9,416,990,860	$8,952,622,279	$8,133,821,379	$7,504,259,729
Total Expenses	9,350,034,260	9,094,089,019	8,718,381,099	7,866,577,239	7,391,642,279
COMMUNITY HEALTH INDICATORS PER 1000 POPULATION					
Total Population (in thousands)	3,930	3,899	3,872	3,856	3,826
Inpatient					
Beds	1.7	1.7	1.8	1.7	1.7
Admissions	85.8	86.3	88.5	83.3	84.6
Inpatient Days	370.0	366.5	379.2	359.8	375.8
Inpatient Surgeries	31.5	30.6	31.8	29.7	29.9
Births	10.8	11.1	11.2	10.9	11.5
Outpatient					
Emergency Outpatient Visits	356.1	359.6	362.7	318.9	343.0
Other Outpatient Visits	2,286.6	2,154.8	2,058.3	2,070.5	1,983.4
Total Outpatient Visits	2,642.6	2,514.5	2,420.9	2,389.4	2,326.4
Outpatient Surgeries	49.0	52.2	54.6	53.3	54.2
Expense per Capita (per person)	$2,381.3	$2,334.4	$2,253.9	$2,042.8	$1,934.9

States

TABLE 6

PENNSYLVANIA

U.S. Registered Community Hospitals
(Nonfederal, short-term general and other special hospitals)

Overview 2009–2013

	2013	2012	2011	2010	2009
Total Community Hospitals in Pennsylvania ...	190	192	194	196	194
Bed Size Category					
6-24	3	4	3	3	3
25-49	28	27	28	29	29
50-99	37	38	40	42	40
100-199	47	47	47	46	47
200-299	34	35	34	34	37
300-399	18	18	18	17	13
400-499	8	9	10	11	10
500 + ...	15	14	14	14	15
Location					
Hospitals Urban	143	145	146	147	145
Hospitals Rural	47	47	48	49	49
Control					
State and Local Government	2	2	2	2	2
Not for Profit	141	142	145	151	153
Investor owned	47	48	47	43	39
Physician Models					
Independent Practice Association	11	12	8	7	8
Group Practice without Walls	6	5	6	8	13
Open Physician-Hospital Organization	23	22	22	24	25
Closed Physician-Hospital Organization	3	3	3	3	4
Management Service Organization	21	23	19	21	26
Integrated Salary Model	74	78	73	75	73
Equity Model	4	3	1	2	3
Foundation	4	4	8	8	6
Insurance Products					
Health Maintenance Organization	32	37	35	29	24
Preferred Provider Organization	30	38	41	42	39
Indemnity Fee for Service	19	23	19	17	12
Managed Care Contracts					
Health Maintenance Organization	125	132	120	117	115
Preferred Provider Organization	124	128	116	115	109
Affiliations					
Hospitals in a System	129	127	128	118	112
Hospitals in a Network	56	52	51	49	47
Hospitals in a Group Purchasing Organization ..	147	141	134	139	134

TABLE 6

PENNSYLVANIA

U.S. Registered Community Hospitals
(Nonfederal, short-term general and other special hospitals)

Utilization, Personnel, Revenue and Expenses, Community Health Indicators 2009–2013

	2013	2012	2011	2010	2009
TOTAL FACILITY (Includes Hospital and Nursing Home Units)					
Utilization - Inpatient					
Beds	38,970	39,314	39,676	39,889	39,212
Admissions	1,637,872	1,692,087	1,766,191	1,809,935	1,841,550
Inpatient Days	9,147,196	9,287,033	9,659,186	9,769,701	9,865,210
Average Length of Stay	5.6	5.5	5.5	5.4	5.4
Inpatient Surgeries	489,930	545,302	526,338	534,919	540,046
Births	128,950	134,221	132,967	134,404	137,478
Utilization - Outpatient					
Emergency Outpatient Visits	6,263,103	6,239,042	6,221,333	6,120,131	6,009,572
Other Outpatient Visits	31,769,030	32,791,595	31,681,366	32,432,398	31,882,222
Total Outpatient Visits	38,032,133	39,030,637	37,902,699	38,552,529	37,891,794
Outpatient Surgeries	908,695	913,296	895,861	914,558	917,586
Personnel					
Full Time RNs	55,770	55,710	54,899	53,217	51,430
Full Time LPNs	2,617	3,035	3,115	3,406	3,769
Part Time RNs	25,112	25,187	25,473	24,947	25,315
Part Time LPNs	1,078	1,227	1,311	1,558	1,737
Total Full Time	207,082	212,082	211,563	207,153	203,289
Total Part Time	72,723	73,405	73,672	72,508	74,386
Revenue - Inpatient					
Gross Inpatient Revenue	$84,087,084,762	$83,077,919,932	$81,435,847,151	$77,752,923,156	$73,916,497,474
Revenue - Outpatient					
Gross Outpatient Revenue	$66,840,763,963	$65,297,151,073	$58,909,827,289	$52,558,766,166	$47,748,195,221
Revenue and Expenses - Totals					
(Includes Inpatient and Outpatient)					
Total Gross Revenue	$150,927,848,725	$148,375,071,005	$140,345,674,440	$130,311,689,322	$121,664,692,695
Deductions from Revenue	112,764,688,900	110,484,264,654	104,430,760,108	96,372,359,561	89,109,854,967
Net Patient Revenue	38,163,159,825	37,890,806,351	35,914,914,332	33,939,329,761	32,554,837,728
Other Operating Revenue	2,008,282,382	1,891,935,772	1,762,852,582	1,560,413,652	1,478,517,269
Other Nonoperating Revenue	595,823,340	244,155,533	671,813,569	355,838,893	-446,883,805
Total Net Revenue	40,767,265,547	40,026,897,656	38,349,580,483	35,855,582,306	33,586,471,192
Total Expenses	38,184,179,753	37,279,476,131	35,246,467,258	33,929,583,373	32,711,950,307
HOSPITAL UNIT (Excludes Separate Nursing Home Units)					
Utilization - Inpatient					
Beds	37,025	37,482	37,995	38,271	37,446
Admissions	1,620,279	1,674,103	1,748,683	1,793,060	1,822,836
Inpatient Days	8,550,303	8,740,926	9,116,795	9,324,956	9,383,976
Average Length of Stay	5.3	5.2	5.2	5.2	5.1
Personnel					
Total Full Time	206,017	211,038	210,543	205,956	201,932
Total Part Time	72,063	72,757	73,114	71,746	73,493
Revenue and Expenses - Totals					
(Includes Inpatient and Outpatient)					
Total Net Revenue	$40,549,341,944	$39,806,434,073	$38,167,896,294	$35,657,261,435	$33,390,355,912
Total Expenses	38,000,068,482	37,097,937,820	35,082,553,586	33,767,820,668	32,546,735,654
COMMUNITY HEALTH INDICATORS PER 1000 POPULATION					
Total Population (in thousands)	12,774	12,764	12,743	12,633	12,605
Inpatient					
Beds	3.1	3.1	3.1	3.2	3.1
Admissions	128.2	132.6	138.6	143.3	146.1
Inpatient Days	716.1	727.6	758.0	773.4	782.7
Inpatient Surgeries	38.4	42.7	41.3	42.3	42.8
Births	10.1	10.5	10.4	10.6	10.9
Outpatient					
Emergency Outpatient Visits	490.3	488.8	488.2	484.5	476.8
Other Outpatient Visits	2,487.0	2,569.2	2,486.2	2,567.3	2,529.4
Total Outpatient Visits	2,977.4	3,058.0	2,974.4	3,051.8	3,006.1
Outpatient Surgeries	71.1	71.6	70.3	72.4	72.8
Expense per Capita (per person)	$2,989.3	$2,920.8	$2,766.0	$2,685.8	$2,595.2

States

TABLE 6

RHODE ISLAND

U.S. Registered Community Hospitals
(Nonfederal, short-term general and other special hospitals)

Overview 2009–2013

	2013	2012	2011	2010	2009
Total Community Hospitals in Rhode Island ...	11	11	11	11	11
Bed Size Category					
6-24	0	0	0	0	0
25-49	0	0	0	0	0
50-99	2	1	1	1	1
100-199	5	5	5	5	5
200-299	2	3	3	3	3
300-399	1	1	1	1	1
400-499	0	0	0	0	0
500 + ...	1	1	1	1	1
Location					
Hospitals Urban...........................	11	11	11	11	11
Hospitals Rural	0	0	0	0	0
Control					
State and Local Government................	0	0	0	0	0
Not for Profit	10	11	11	11	11
Investor owned	1	0	0	0	0
Physician Models					
Independent Practice Association	5	4	5	5	4
Group Practice without Walls...............	1	1	1	0	0
Open Physician-Hospital Organization	5	4	5	6	6
Closed Physician-Hospital Organization	0	0	0	0	1
Management Service Organization	3	2	2	2	2
Integrated Salary Model	6	6	5	6	5
Equity Model	0	0	0	0	0
Foundation..............................	2	2	2	2	2
Insurance Products					
Health Maintenance Organization	1	1	1	1	1
Preferred Provider Organization..............	0	0	1	0	0
Indemnity Fee for Service	0	0	0	0	0
Managed Care Contracts					
Health Maintenance Organization	7	6	6	7	7
Preferred Provider Organization..............	7	6	7	7	7
Affiliations					
Hospitals in a System.....................	10	6	5	5	5
Hospitals in a Network	5	4	6	6	3
Hospitals in a Group Purchasing Organization..	8	6	7	7	7

States

TABLE **6**

RHODE ISLAND

U.S. Registered Community Hospitals
(Nonfederal, short-term general and other special hospitals)

Utilization, Personnel, Revenue and Expenses, Community Health Indicators 2009–2013

	2013	2012	2011	2010	2009
TOTAL FACILITY (Includes Hospital and Nursing Home Units)					
Utilization - Inpatient					
Beds	2,250	2,461	2,468	2,479	2,512
Admissions	111,406	117,051	120,407	123,188	126,761
Inpatient Days	571,352	580,207	611,837	621,614	654,695
Average Length of Stay	5.1	5.0	5.1	5.0	5.2
Inpatient Surgeries	29,139	32,119	32,737	32,612	39,752
Births	11,352	11,045	11,249	11,492	11,815
Utilization - Outpatient					
Emergency Outpatient Visits	522,861	578,431	542,625	495,149	502,224
Other Outpatient Visits	1,518,166	1,605,322	1,699,025	2,127,266	2,131,290
Total Outpatient Visits	2,041,027	2,183,753	2,241,650	2,622,415	2,633,514
Outpatient Surgeries	66,445	67,537	67,432	66,930	79,583
Personnel					
Full Time RNs	2,322	2,656	2,426	2,251	2,255
Full Time LPNs	50	71	70	58	87
Part Time RNs	2,876	2,780	2,737	2,771	2,705
Part Time LPNs	52	60	60	54	95
Total Full Time	12,542	12,871	12,810	12,686	12,928
Total Part Time	8,313	7,847	7,800	8,001	7,707
Revenue - Inpatient					
Gross Inpatient Revenue	$3,987,915,217	$3,911,358,415	$3,763,721,393	$3,623,363,473	$3,585,072,822
Revenue - Outpatient					
Gross Outpatient Revenue	$4,343,532,799	$4,210,401,437	$3,841,600,497	$3,560,931,543	$3,292,773,520
Revenue and Expenses - Totals					
(Includes Inpatient and Outpatient)					
Total Gross Revenue	$8,331,448,016	$8,121,759,852	$7,605,321,890	$7,184,295,016	$6,877,846,342
Deductions from Revenue	5,499,978,376	5,309,722,108	4,867,608,639	4,555,181,118	4,297,920,625
Net Patient Revenue	2,831,469,640	2,812,037,744	2,737,713,251	2,629,113,898	2,579,925,717
Other Operating Revenue	255,547,838	259,567,063	257,774,487	265,788,290	241,675,005
Other Nonoperating Revenue	18,026,453	26,181,940	10,927,762	6,408,073	6,908,048
Total Net Revenue	3,105,043,931	3,097,786,747	3,006,415,500	2,901,310,261	2,828,508,770
Total Expenses	3,151,478,325	3,067,815,218	3,021,867,827	2,883,693,916	2,812,067,020
HOSPITAL UNIT (Excludes Separate Nursing Home Units)					
Utilization - Inpatient					
Beds	2,250	2,461	2,468	2,479	2,512
Admissions	111,406	117,051	120,407	123,188	126,761
Inpatient Days	571,352	580,207	611,837	621,614	654,695
Average Length of Stay	5.1	5.0	5.1	5.0	5.2
Personnel					
Total Full Time	12,542	12,871	12,810	12,686	12,928
Total Part Time	8,313	7,847	7,800	8,001	7,707
Revenue and Expenses - Totals					
(Includes Inpatient and Outpatient)					
Total Net Revenue	$3,105,043,931	$3,097,786,747	$3,006,415,500	$2,901,310,261	$2,828,508,770
Total Expenses	3,151,478,325	3,067,815,218	3,021,867,827	2,883,693,916	2,812,067,020
COMMUNITY HEALTH INDICATORS PER 1000 POPULATION					
Total Population (in thousands)	1,052	1,050	1,051	1,057	1,053
Inpatient					
Beds	2.1	2.3	2.3	2.3	2.4
Admissions	105.9	111.4	114.5	116.6	120.4
Inpatient Days	543.4	552.4	582.0	588.2	621.6
Inpatient Surgeries	27.7	30.6	31.1	30.9	37.7
Births	10.8	10.5	10.7	10.9	11.2
Outpatient					
Emergency Outpatient Visits	497.2	550.7	516.1	468.5	476.9
Other Outpatient Visits	1,443.8	1,528.5	1,616.1	2,012.8	2,023.6
Total Outpatient Visits	1,941.0	2,079.2	2,132.3	2,481.3	2,500.5
Outpatient Surgeries	63.2	64.3	64.1	63.3	75.6
Expense per Capita (per person)	$2,997.1	$2,920.9	$2,874.4	$2,728.5	$2,670.0

States

TABLE **6**

SOUTH CAROLINA

U.S. Registered Community Hospitals
(Nonfederal, short-term general and other special hospitals)

Overview 2009–2013

	2013	2012	2011	2010	2009
Total Community Hospitals in South Carolina	69	67	66	67	70
Bed Size Category					
6-24	2	1	2	1	2
25-49	16	16	17	19	18
50-99	13	13	11	10	13
100-199	14	14	14	13	13
200-299	9	9	8	9	10
300-399	5	6	6	7	7
400-499	5	4	3	3	2
500 +	5	4	5	5	5
Location					
Hospitals Urban	45	43	41	42	45
Hospitals Rural	24	24	25	25	25
Control					
State and Local Government	18	18	19	17	20
Not for Profit	28	26	23	24	25
Investor owned	23	23	24	26	25
Physician Models					
Independent Practice Association	6	6	6	5	5
Group Practice without Walls	1	1	1	1	1
Open Physician-Hospital Organization	3	5	4	4	7
Closed Physician-Hospital Organization	3	2	2	1	0
Management Service Organization	1	1	0	2	1
Integrated Salary Model	19	20	20	19	15
Equity Model	2	2	1	0	0
Foundation	0	0	0	0	0
Insurance Products					
Health Maintenance Organization	4	1	6	7	7
Preferred Provider Organization	3	6	9	10	10
Indemnity Fee for Service	0	0	1	6	6
Managed Care Contracts					
Health Maintenance Organization	42	40	43	39	45
Preferred Provider Organization	43	40	43	38	46
Affiliations					
Hospitals in a System	51	50	44	44	47
Hospitals in a Network	13	12	12	12	12
Hospitals in a Group Purchasing Organization	61	55	60	59	58

TABLE 6

SOUTH CAROLINA

U.S. Registered Community Hospitals
(Nonfederal, short-term general and other special hospitals)

Utilization, Personnel, Revenue and Expenses, Community Health Indicators 2009–2013

	2013	2012	2011	2010	2009
TOTAL FACILITY (Includes Hospital and Nursing Home Units)					
Utilization - Inpatient					
Beds	12,758	12,539	12,253	12,495	12,483
Admissions	498,344	506,072	508,652	522,793	528,204
Inpatient Days	2,864,513	2,861,439	2,878,860	3,002,541	2,960,134
Average Length of Stay	5.7	5.7	5.7	5.7	5.6
Inpatient Surgeries	194,834	197,921	194,171	194,895	205,119
Births	52,388	53,353	53,530	54,894	57,559
Utilization - Outpatient					
Emergency Outpatient Visits	1,575,728	1,435,010	1,687,578	1,453,696	2,171,925
Other Outpatient Visits	5,134,748	5,114,768	4,732,533	4,922,633	4,147,745
Total Outpatient Visits	6,710,476	6,549,778	6,420,111	6,376,329	6,319,670
Outpatient Surgeries	317,318	309,250	298,549	289,794	300,093
Personnel					
Full Time RNs	18,693	17,934	17,357	17,476	17,451
Full Time LPNs	722	775	947	1,062	1,170
Part Time RNs	4,641	4,652	4,897	5,184	5,246
Part Time LPNs	174	227	280	347	395
Total Full Time	60,317	60,411	58,183	58,567	58,933
Total Part Time	13,327	13,579	13,721	14,343	14,332
Revenue - Inpatient					
Gross Inpatient Revenue	$21,575,477,093	$20,007,919,363	$19,216,509,155	$18,371,422,174	$17,448,319,308
Revenue - Outpatient					
Gross Outpatient Revenue	$17,600,043,070	$15,551,458,526	$14,306,685,453	$12,660,946,189	$11,900,471,047
Revenue and Expenses - Totals					
(Includes Inpatient and Outpatient)					
Total Gross Revenue	$39,175,520,163	$35,559,377,889	$33,523,194,608	$31,032,368,363	$29,348,790,355
Deductions from Revenue	28,456,657,258	25,246,098,981	23,252,635,242	21,049,743,519	19,883,727,173
Net Patient Revenue	10,718,862,905	10,313,278,908	10,270,559,366	9,982,624,844	9,465,063,182
Other Operating Revenue	321,252,507	308,030,013	243,603,622	249,339,525	236,614,730
Other Nonoperating Revenue	293,338,530	277,725,354	141,294,623	210,607,769	190,176,135
Total Net Revenue	11,333,453,942	10,899,034,275	10,655,457,611	10,442,572,138	9,891,854,047
Total Expenses	10,033,330,821	9,729,644,756	9,707,103,556	9,349,824,264	9,264,970,348
HOSPITAL UNIT (Excludes Separate Nursing Home Units)					
Utilization - Inpatient					
Beds	12,027	11,656	11,479	11,611	11,739
Admissions	495,189	502,923	504,604	518,130	524,147
Inpatient Days	2,653,359	2,585,730	2,632,449	2,729,473	2,685,104
Average Length of Stay	5.4	5.1	5.2	5.3	5.1
Personnel					
Total Full Time	59,621	59,664	57,533	57,811	58,169
Total Part Time	13,133	13,328	13,382	14,118	13,998
Revenue and Expenses - Totals					
(Includes Inpatient and Outpatient)					
Total Net Revenue	$11,269,144,355	$10,842,235,748	$10,577,543,806	$10,354,825,713	$9,821,499,987
Total Expenses	9,974,428,391	9,666,217,448	9,635,628,294	9,272,925,368	9,204,773,809
COMMUNITY HEALTH INDICATORS PER 1000 POPULATION					
Total Population (in thousands)	4,775	4,724	4,679	4,597	4,561
Inpatient					
Beds	2.7	2.7	2.6	2.7	2.7
Admissions	104.4	107.1	108.7	113.7	115.8
Inpatient Days	599.9	605.8	615.2	653.2	649.0
Inpatient Surgeries	40.8	41.9	41.5	42.4	45.0
Births	11.0	11.3	11.4	11.9	12.6
Outpatient					
Emergency Outpatient Visits	330.0	303.8	360.7	316.2	476.2
Other Outpatient Visits	1,075.4	1,082.8	1,011.4	1,070.8	909.3
Total Outpatient Visits	1,405.4	1,386.6	1,372.0	1,387.1	1,385.5
Outpatient Surgeries	66.5	65.5	63.8	63.0	65.8
Expense per Capita (per person)	$2,101.3	$2,059.7	$2,074.5	$2,033.9	$2,031.2

States

TABLE **6**

SOUTH DAKOTA

U.S. Registered Community Hospitals
(Nonfederal, short-term general and other special hospitals)

Overview 2009–2013

	2013	2012	2011	2010	2009
Total Community Hospitals in South Dakota...	54	54	53	53	53
Bed Size Category					
6-24	20	19	19	17	16
25-49	11	13	12	14	14
50-99	11	10	10	10	11
100-199	7	7	7	7	7
200-299	2	2	2	2	2
300-399	0	1	1	1	1
400-499	2	1	2	2	2
500 + ...	1	1	0	0	0
Location					
Hospitals Urban.	11	11	11	11	11
Hospitals Rural	43	43	42	42	42
Control					
State and Local Government	4	4	4	4	3
Not for Profit	46	46	45	45	46
Investor owned	4	4	4	4	4
Physician Models					
Independent Practice Association	7	9	10	8	12
Group Practice without Walls.	1	2	2	1	3
Open Physician-Hospital Organization	1	3	4	3	6
Closed Physician-Hospital Organization	1	3	3	2	3
Management Service Organization	0	2	3	1	2
Integrated Salary Model	24	25	27	23	28
Equity Model	2	3	2	1	2
Foundation.	2	3	3	2	1
Insurance Products					
Health Maintenance Organization	14	13	13	16	17
Preferred Provider Organization.	10	12	13	11	10
Indemnity Fee for Service	6	5	8	6	9
Managed Care Contracts					
Health Maintenance Organization	22	27	25	23	24
Preferred Provider Organization.	25	31	30	27	29
Affiliations					
Hospitals in a System.	39	39	37	37	38
Hospitals in a Network	23	23	24	21	22
Hospitals in a Group Purchasing Organization. .	36	43	46	39	45

TABLE 6

SOUTH DAKOTA

U.S. Registered Community Hospitals
(Nonfederal, short-term general and other special hospitals)

Utilization, Personnel, Revenue and Expenses, Community Health Indicators 2009–2013

	2013	2012	2011	2010	2009
TOTAL FACILITY (Includes Hospital and Nursing Home Units)					
Utilization - Inpatient					
Beds	4,161	4,188	4,084	4,108	4,142
Admissions	101,878	108,263	101,867	101,128	102,335
Inpatient Days	934,748	960,652	956,044	935,410	1,005,265
Average Length of Stay	9.2	8.9	9.4	9.2	9.8
Inpatient Surgeries	27,820	29,636	31,220	30,363	32,416
Births	12,782	12,242	11,976	11,437	11,848
Utilization - Outpatient					
Emergency Outpatient Visits	291,177	282,899	251,769	259,364	240,618
Other Outpatient Visits	1,972,035	1,979,362	1,862,618	1,782,993	1,698,830
Total Outpatient Visits	2,263,212	2,262,261	2,114,387	2,042,357	1,939,448
Outpatient Surgeries	51,305	76,606	69,535	67,743	71,571
Personnel					
Full Time RNs	4,796	4,457	4,068	3,633	3,596
Full Time LPNs	340	267	270	216	191
Part Time RNs	1,889	1,948	1,951	1,736	2,003
Part Time LPNs	128	124	144	129	132
Total Full Time	16,960	16,543	15,443	14,483	15,119
Total Part Time	7,099	6,807	6,954	6,316	7,357
Revenue - Inpatient					
Gross Inpatient Revenue	$3,410,939,910	$3,259,110,943	$2,969,819,139	$2,779,376,912	$2,534,795,960
Revenue - Outpatient					
Gross Outpatient Revenue	$3,299,557,436	$3,103,567,011	$2,643,342,592	$2,405,199,211	$2,107,192,538
Revenue and Expenses - Totals (Includes Inpatient and Outpatient)					
Total Gross Revenue	$6,710,497,346	$6,362,677,954	$5,613,161,731	$5,184,576,123	$4,641,988,498
Deductions from Revenue	4,030,372,232	3,649,680,422	3,130,649,704	2,884,612,400	2,468,508,414
Net Patient Revenue	2,680,125,114	2,712,997,532	2,482,512,027	2,299,963,723	2,173,480,084
Other Operating Revenue	176,424,473	146,318,931	129,361,349	122,786,678	113,185,811
Other Nonoperating Revenue	73,485,535	34,097,686	101,197,230	34,907,740	-20,449,611
Total Net Revenue	2,930,035,122	2,893,414,149	2,713,070,606	2,457,658,141	2,266,216,284
Total Expenses	2,672,087,974	2,494,970,877	2,353,418,704	2,194,315,958	2,075,750,158
HOSPITAL UNIT (Excludes Separate Nursing Home Units)					
Utilization - Inpatient					
Beds	2,811	2,847	2,602	2,869	2,728
Admissions	100,616	106,941	100,451	99,824	100,901
Inpatient Days	488,235	503,324	443,426	505,190	507,150
Average Length of Stay	4.9	4.7	4.4	5.1	5.0
Personnel					
Total Full Time	16,072	15,690	14,561	13,753	14,238
Total Part Time	6,571	6,221	6,292	5,684	6,607
Revenue and Expenses - Totals (Includes Inpatient and Outpatient)					
Total Net Revenue	$2,846,625,100	$2,806,088,891	$2,626,079,779	$2,382,414,150	$2,185,615,059
Total Expenses	2,602,036,829	2,410,336,333	2,278,140,332	2,128,257,681	2,002,334,795
COMMUNITY HEALTH INDICATORS PER 1000 POPULATION					
Total Population (in thousands)	845	833	824	820	812
Inpatient					
Beds	4.9	5.0	5.0	5.0	5.1
Admissions	120.6	129.9	123.6	123.3	126.0
Inpatient Days	1,106.4	1,152.8	1,160.1	1,140.6	1,237.4
Inpatient Surgeries	32.9	35.6	37.9	37.0	39.9
Births	15.1	14.7	14.5	13.9	14.6
Outpatient					
Emergency Outpatient Visits	344.6	339.5	305.5	316.3	296.2
Other Outpatient Visits	2,334.1	2,375.2	2,260.2	2,174.2	2,091.2
Total Outpatient Visits	2,678.7	2,714.6	2,565.7	2,490.4	2,387.4
Outpatient Surgeries	60.7	91.9	84.4	82.6	88.1
Expense per Capita (per person)	$3,162.7	$2,993.9	$2,855.8	$2,675.7	$2,555.1

States

TABLE **6**

TENNESSEE

U.S. Registered Community Hospitals
(Nonfederal, short-term general and other special hospitals)

Overview 2009–2013

	2013	2012	2011	2010	2009
Total Community Hospitals in Tennessee	130	132	133	134	137
Bed Size Category					
6-24	9	9	7	6	6
25-49	32	34	36	35	36
50-99	33	31	32	32	32
100-199	24	26	26	29	30
200-299	13	13	13	12	13
300-399	8	7	7	6	7
400-499	2	3	3	5	6
500 + ...	9	9	9	9	7
Location					
Hospitals Urban.	76	77	78	78	81
Hospitals Rural	54	55	55	56	56
Control					
State and Local Government	22	21	21	20	22
Not for Profit	49	49	50	56	59
Investor owned	59	62	62	58	56
Physician Models					
Independent Practice Association	14	16	17	19	17
Group Practice without Walls.	4	4	5	4	3
Open Physician-Hospital Organization	17	17	11	11	11
Closed Physician-Hospital Organization	3	4	3	3	3
Management Service Organization	12	14	17	16	18
Integrated Salary Model	34	30	29	31	26
Equity Model	3	0	0	0	0
Foundation.	6	2	3	4	7
Insurance Products					
Health Maintenance Organization	12	9	8	8	5
Preferred Provider Organization.	24	13	17	17	16
Indemnity Fee for Service	10	7	3	3	2
Managed Care Contracts					
Health Maintenance Organization	56	56	68	66	67
Preferred Provider Organization.	63	62	69	72	75
Affiliations					
Hospitals in a System.	107	107	105	101	103
Hospitals in a Network	37	31	38	41	41
Hospitals in a Group Purchasing Organization. .	66	68	70	69	77

States

TABLE 6

TENNESSEE

U.S. Registered Community Hospitals
(Nonfederal, short-term general and other special hospitals)

Utilization, Personnel, Revenue and Expenses, Community Health Indicators 2009–2013

	2013	2012	2011	2010	2009
TOTAL FACILITY (Includes Hospital and Nursing Home Units)					
Utilization - Inpatient					
Beds	20,259	20,154	20,042	20,830	20,959
Admissions	819,116	823,781	805,805	832,554	859,191
Inpatient Days	4,525,456	4,500,597	4,465,285	4,579,402	4,799,858
Average Length of Stay	5.5	5.5	5.5	5.5	5.6
Inpatient Surgeries	227,285	241,056	234,368	249,367	255,557
Births	66,249	64,660	64,202	70,685	79,804
Utilization - Outpatient					
Emergency Outpatient Visits	3,378,159	3,260,802	3,113,164	3,130,660	3,301,872
Other Outpatient Visits	8,534,100	8,519,980	7,799,873	8,299,669	8,281,474
Total Outpatient Visits	11,912,259	11,780,782	10,913,037	11,430,329	11,583,346
Outpatient Surgeries	430,284	448,279	405,105	411,688	413,202
Personnel					
Full Time RNs	26,540	26,169	25,298	24,475	25,846
Full Time LPNs	2,139	2,252	2,503	2,706	2,938
Part Time RNs	7,626	9,110	9,124	9,222	8,514
Part Time LPNs	518	610	652	767	742
Total Full Time	90,588	91,851	89,424	88,145	93,028
Total Part Time	20,281	25,175	23,382	25,539	24,476
Revenue - Inpatient					
Gross Inpatient Revenue	$31,762,517,052	$28,979,229,922	$27,704,113,354	$26,846,357,974	$25,367,667,093
Revenue - Outpatient					
Gross Outpatient Revenue	$26,898,593,106	$24,221,902,571	$20,574,396,531	$19,276,589,146	$17,453,642,146
Revenue and Expenses - Totals					
(Includes Inpatient and Outpatient)					
Total Gross Revenue	$58,661,110,158	$53,201,132,493	$48,278,509,885	$46,122,947,120	$42,821,309,239
Deductions from Revenue	43,023,032,783	37,978,697,915	34,865,417,816	32,931,211,533	29,947,998,235
Net Patient Revenue	15,638,077,375	15,222,434,578	13,413,092,069	13,191,735,587	12,873,311,004
Other Operating Revenue	631,573,575	546,985,739	445,637,920	409,743,303	432,326,528
Other Nonoperating Revenue	159,509,587	108,447,768	158,051,242	268,674,837	-81,972,728
Total Net Revenue	16,429,160,537	15,877,868,085	14,016,781,231	13,870,153,727	13,223,664,804
Total Expenses	15,002,528,839	14,708,134,735	12,769,264,645	12,699,265,618	12,694,504,650
HOSPITAL UNIT (Excludes Separate Nursing Home Units)					
Utilization - Inpatient					
Beds	19,058	19,052	19,080	19,750	19,682
Admissions	811,908	816,107	797,947	825,283	850,278
Inpatient Days	4,171,201	4,178,131	4,182,726	4,244,905	4,400,598
Average Length of Stay	5.1	5.1	5.2	5.1	5.2
Personnel					
Total Full Time	89,727	90,895	88,534	87,258	91,886
Total Part Time	20,073	24,986	23,260	25,367	24,274
Revenue and Expenses - Totals					
(Includes Inpatient and Outpatient)					
Total Net Revenue	$16,338,297,498	$15,793,027,961	$13,930,291,003	$13,791,578,759	$13,131,489,651
Total Expenses	14,923,551,273	14,632,776,271	12,708,497,514	12,630,190,370	12,619,381,549
COMMUNITY HEALTH INDICATORS PER 1000 POPULATION					
Total Population (in thousands)	6,496	6,456	6,403	6,338	6,296
Inpatient					
Beds	3.1	3.1	3.1	3.3	3.3
Admissions	126.1	127.6	125.8	131.4	136.5
Inpatient Days	696.7	697.1	697.3	722.5	762.3
Inpatient Surgeries	35.0	37.3	36.6	39.3	40.6
Births	10.2	10.0	10.0	11.2	12.7
Outpatient					
Emergency Outpatient Visits	520.0	505.1	486.2	493.9	524.4
Other Outpatient Visits	1,313.8	1,319.6	1,218.1	1,309.5	1,315.3
Total Outpatient Visits	1,833.8	1,824.7	1,704.3	1,803.4	1,839.7
Outpatient Surgeries	66.2	69.4	63.3	65.0	65.6
Expense per Capita (per person)	$2,309.5	$2,278.1	$1,994.2	$2,003.6	$2,016.2

States

TABLE **6**

TEXAS

U.S. Registered Community Hospitals
(Nonfederal, short-term general and other special hospitals)

Overview 2009–2013

	2013	2012	2011	2010	2009
Total Community Hospitals in Texas..........	424	425	420	426	428
Bed Size Category					
6-24	74	74	70	73	69
25-49	108	107	109	107	111
50-99	86	87	82	86	79
100-199	55	55	58	61	66
200-299	41	42	43	41	43
300-399	22	23	19	20	21
400-499	13	13	15	14	16
500 + ...	25	24	24	24	23
Location					
Hospitals Urban...........................	277	276	269	275	277
Hospitals Rural	147	149	151	151	151
Control					
State and Local Government...............	103	106	110	113	116
Not for Profit	154	151	149	148	147
Investor owned	167	168	161	165	165
Physician Models					
Independent Practice Association	54	58	62	72	69
Group Practice without Walls...............	19	15	15	15	24
Open Physician-Hospital Organization	75	83	79	82	84
Closed Physician-Hospital Organization	26	26	20	19	18
Management Service Organization	55	62	71	73	74
Integrated Salary Model....................	122	115	114	97	95
Equity Model	7	8	9	13	13
Foundation...............................	40	37	37	35	33
Insurance Products					
Health Maintenance Organization	68	60	65	66	62
Preferred Provider Organization..............	61	50	79	84	75
Indemnity Fee for Service	18	13	22	26	22
Managed Care Contracts					
Health Maintenance Organization	337	331	318	318	323
Preferred Provider Organization..............	370	362	357	358	361
Affiliations					
Hospitals in a System.....................	283	283	272	278	286
Hospitals in a Network....................	117	116	115	114	106
Hospitals in a Group Purchasing Organization..	408	407	399	398	386

TABLE 6

TEXAS

U.S. Registered Community Hospitals
(Nonfederal, short-term general and other special hospitals)

Utilization, Personnel, Revenue and Expenses, Community Health Indicators 2009–2013

	2013	2012	2011	2010	2009
TOTAL FACILITY (Includes Hospital and Nursing Home Units)					
Utilization - Inpatient					
Beds	61,600	61,290	60,755	61,357	62,069
Admissions	2,522,455	2,548,864	2,534,688	2,580,401	2,621,436
Inpatient Days	13,173,092	13,170,816	13,062,644	13,331,491	13,590,044
Average Length of Stay	5.2	5.2	5.2	5.2	5.2
Inpatient Surgeries	718,822	729,749	736,841	761,437	781,093
Births	376,859	369,860	364,901	381,038	397,979
Utilization - Outpatient					
Emergency Outpatient Visits	10,404,119	10,439,383	9,889,631	9,739,066	9,438,151
Other Outpatient Visits	29,734,004	30,271,030	29,375,051	28,541,761	26,584,907
Total Outpatient Visits	40,138,123	40,710,413	39,264,682	38,280,827	36,023,058
Outpatient Surgeries	1,058,968	1,024,211	1,034,126	1,061,053	1,049,368
Personnel					
Full Time RNs	87,202	83,746	79,968	82,490	80,537
Full Time LPNs	7,258	7,679	8,278	9,113	9,798
Part Time RNs	24,170	22,853	22,557	20,107	20,901
Part Time LPNs	1,481	1,674	1,683	2,103	2,416
Total Full Time	283,921	278,323	274,534	280,656	280,533
Total Part Time	68,650	64,880	63,938	59,204	61,186
Revenue - Inpatient					
Gross Inpatient Revenue	$121,281,645,571	$114,321,510,363	$105,598,575,282	$100,476,401,353	$95,184,048,332
Revenue - Outpatient					
Gross Outpatient Revenue	$89,812,997,830	$82,221,757,827	$72,395,257,221	$66,131,968,217	$58,578,510,903
Revenue and Expenses - Totals					
(Includes Inpatient and Outpatient)					
Total Gross Revenue	$211,094,643,401	$196,543,268,190	$177,993,832,503	$166,608,369,570	$153,762,559,235
Deductions from Revenue	157,784,347,806	144,431,424,185	132,820,105,328	122,345,151,455	111,061,711,464
Net Patient Revenue	53,310,295,595	52,111,844,005	45,173,727,175	44,263,218,115	42,700,847,771
Other Operating Revenue	5,363,702,261	5,301,391,230	4,676,074,781	4,492,462,311	4,384,346,385
Other Nonoperating Revenue	937,753,455	842,027,514	1,373,986,299	1,120,744,597	304,258,670
Total Net Revenue	59,611,751,311	58,255,262,749	51,223,788,255	49,876,425,023	47,389,452,826
Total Expenses	53,271,177,348	51,154,019,956	45,556,147,376	44,225,750,333	43,410,205,109
HOSPITAL UNIT (Excludes Separate Nursing Home Units)					
Utilization - Inpatient					
Beds	60,802	60,350	59,835	60,497	61,160
Admissions	2,513,915	2,539,148	2,525,028	2,570,756	2,610,941
Inpatient Days	12,946,382	12,898,573	12,794,132	13,090,722	13,329,807
Average Length of Stay	5.1	5.1	5.1	5.1	5.1
Personnel					
Total Full Time	283,250	277,484	273,785	279,998	279,502
Total Part Time	68,503	64,773	63,837	59,051	61,033
Revenue and Expenses - Totals					
(Includes Inpatient and Outpatient)					
Total Net Revenue	$59,524,322,308	$58,163,406,060	$51,125,792,174	$49,780,310,157	$47,305,885,374
Total Expenses	53,205,672,674	51,073,523,904	45,465,619,488	44,132,923,562	43,327,541,508
COMMUNITY HEALTH INDICATORS PER 1000 POPULATION					
Total Population (in thousands)	26,448	26,059	25,675	25,213	24,782
Inpatient					
Beds	2.3	2.4	2.4	2.4	2.5
Admissions	95.4	97.8	98.7	102.3	105.8
Inpatient Days	498.1	505.4	508.8	528.7	548.4
Inpatient Surgeries	27.2	28.0	28.7	30.2	31.5
Births	14.2	14.2	14.2	15.1	16.1
Outpatient					
Emergency Outpatient Visits	393.4	400.6	385.2	386.3	380.8
Other Outpatient Visits	1,124.2	1,161.6	1,144.1	1,132.0	1,072.7
Total Outpatient Visits	1,517.6	1,562.2	1,529.3	1,518.3	1,453.6
Outpatient Surgeries	40.0	39.3	40.3	42.1	42.3
Expense per Capita (per person)	$2,014.2	$1,963.0	$1,774.4	$1,754.1	$1,751.7

States

TABLE 6

UTAH

U.S. Registered Community Hospitals
(Nonfederal, short-term general and other special hospitals)

Overview 2009–2013

	2013	2012	2011	2010	2009
Total Community Hospitals in Utah...........	47	47	46	44	44
Bed Size Category					
6-24	10	9	8	8	6
25-49	15	16	16	15	15
50-99	3	3	4	3	6
100-199	10	10	9	8	8
200-299	5	4	4	5	4
300-399	2	3	3	3	3
400-499	1	1	2	2	1
500 + ...	1	1	0	0	1
Location					
Hospitals Urban..........................	28	28	28	26	26
Hospitals Rural	19	19	18	18	18
Control					
State and Local Government...............	6	6	6	6	6
Not for Profit............................	26	26	25	23	23
Investor owned	15	15	15	15	15
Physician Models					
Independent Practice Association	3	4	4	4	6
Group Practice without Walls...............	2	2	2	1	1
Open Physician-Hospital Organization	2	1	1	1	3
Closed Physician-Hospital Organization	2	2	3	2	2
Management Service Organization	2	2	2	2	2
Integrated Salary Model....................	16	19	18	13	13
Equity Model.............................	1	1	1	1	1
Foundation...............................	1	1	1	1	2
Insurance Products					
Health Maintenance Organization	16	16	17	15	15
Preferred Provider Organization..............	14	9	15	13	13
Indemnity Fee for Service	4	4	7	5	7
Managed Care Contracts					
Health Maintenance Organization	15	13	12	14	13
Preferred Provider Organization..............	20	18	18	17	17
Affiliations					
Hospitals in a System.....................	38	38	38	36	36
Hospitals in a Network....................	15	8	11	11	16
Hospitals in a Group Purchasing Organization..	29	21	25	22	21

TABLE **6**

UTAH

U.S. Registered Community Hospitals
(Nonfederal, short-term general and other special hospitals)

Utilization, Personnel, Revenue and Expenses, Community Health Indicators 2009–2013

	2013	2012	2011	2010	2009
TOTAL FACILITY (Includes Hospital and Nursing Home Units)					
Utilization - Inpatient					
Beds	5,216	5,212	5,135	5,086	4,973
Admissions	229,492	241,436	236,131	224,264	226,239
Inpatient Days	979,856	992,015	993,098	979,963	1,003,710
Average Length of Stay	4.3	4.1	4.2	4.4	4.4
Inpatient Surgeries	68,077	71,909	71,272	70,503	71,568
Births	47,854	51,575	52,695	49,392	52,189
Utilization - Outpatient					
Emergency Outpatient Visits	888,611	894,661	855,152	834,897	865,286
Other Outpatient Visits	5,292,520	5,459,212	4,999,514	4,642,827	4,609,086
Total Outpatient Visits	6,181,131	6,353,873	5,854,666	5,477,724	5,474,372
Outpatient Surgeries	174,163	166,063	174,376	166,870	155,162
Personnel					
Full Time RNs	8,280	7,273	7,462	7,303	6,961
Full Time LPNs	304	299	337	358	367
Part Time RNs	4,486	4,801	4,362	4,353	4,454
Part Time LPNs	148	171	181	187	222
Total Full Time	29,048	26,395	26,733	26,111	26,390
Total Part Time	13,993	14,612	13,696	13,418	14,135
Revenue - Inpatient					
Gross Inpatient Revenue	$8,689,472,055	$8,253,048,052	$7,051,376,726	$6,581,097,114	$5,718,543,491
Revenue - Outpatient					
Gross Outpatient Revenue	$7,762,738,220	$6,983,551,734	$6,027,847,868	$5,300,499,527	$4,667,222,276
Revenue and Expenses - Totals					
(Includes Inpatient and Outpatient)					
Total Gross Revenue	$16,452,210,275	$15,236,599,786	$13,079,224,594	$11,881,596,641	$10,385,765,767
Deductions from Revenue	10,308,471,435	9,233,540,993	7,638,050,195	6,906,546,426	5,568,409,487
Net Patient Revenue	6,143,738,840	6,003,058,793	5,441,174,399	4,975,050,215	4,817,356,280
Other Operating Revenue	229,460,960	221,419,572	265,484,132	243,975,154	228,925,055
Other Nonoperating Revenue	24,760,128	9,983,495	10,166,250	31,741,257	12,752,174
Total Net Revenue	6,397,959,928	6,234,461,860	5,716,824,781	5,250,766,626	5,059,033,509
Total Expenses	5,364,834,918	5,117,473,502	4,679,558,728	4,470,510,613	4,263,844,434
HOSPITAL UNIT (Excludes Separate Nursing Home Units)					
Utilization - Inpatient					
Beds	5,089	5,080	5,008	4,931	4,808
Admissions	228,932	240,784	235,615	223,117	224,928
Inpatient Days	946,093	951,874	954,737	935,962	961,475
Average Length of Stay	4.1	4.0	4.1	4.2	4.3
Personnel					
Total Full Time	28,977	26,322	26,670	26,037	26,296
Total Part Time	13,944	14,549	13,647	13,364	14,068
Revenue and Expenses - Totals					
(Includes Inpatient and Outpatient)					
Total Net Revenue	$6,390,793,512	$6,225,430,738	$5,708,620,280	$5,239,992,029	$5,050,316,084
Total Expenses	5,360,928,383	5,110,023,379	4,672,187,702	4,461,414,330	4,255,351,046
COMMUNITY HEALTH INDICATORS PER 1000 POPULATION					
Total Population (in thousands)	2,901	2,855	2,817	2,831	2,785
Inpatient					
Beds	1.8	1.8	1.8	1.8	1.8
Admissions	79.1	84.6	83.8	79.2	81.2
Inpatient Days	337.8	347.4	352.5	346.2	360.5
Inpatient Surgeries	23.5	25.2	25.3	24.9	25.7
Births	16.5	18.1	18.7	17.4	18.7
Outpatient					
Emergency Outpatient Visits	306.3	313.3	303.5	294.9	310.7
Other Outpatient Visits	1,824.5	1,912.0	1,774.6	1,640.1	1,655.2
Total Outpatient Visits	2,130.8	2,225.3	2,078.2	1,935.1	1,966.0
Outpatient Surgeries	60.0	58.2	61.9	58.9	55.7
Expense per Capita (per person)	$1,849.4	$1,792.3	$1,661.1	$1,579.3	$1,531.2

States

TABLE 6

VERMONT

U.S. Registered Community Hospitals
(Nonfederal, short-term general and other special hospitals)

Overview 2009–2013

	2013	2012	2011	2010	2009
Total Community Hospitals in Vermont	14	14	14	14	14
Bed Size Category					
6-24	1	2	2	1	1
25-49	7	6	6	6	6
50-99	3	3	3	4	4
100-199	1	1	1	1	1
200-299	1	1	1	1	1
300-399	0	0	0	0	0
400-499	1	1	1	1	1
500 + ...	0	0	0	0	0
Location					
Hospitals Urban.	2	2	2	2	2
Hospitals Rural	12	12	12	12	12
Control					
State and Local Government.	0	0	0	0	0
Not for Profit	14	14	14	14	14
Investor owned	0	0	0	0	0
Physician Models					
Independent Practice Association	0	0	0	0	0
Group Practice without Walls.	1	0	0	0	0
Open Physician-Hospital Organization	1	3	3	3	2
Closed Physician-Hospital Organization	0	0	1	1	1
Management Service Organization	0	0	0	0	0
Integrated Salary Model.	5	6	7	8	7
Equity Model	0	0	0	0	0
Foundation.	0	0	0	0	0
Insurance Products					
Health Maintenance Organization	1	2	2	2	3
Preferred Provider Organization.	1	1	1	0	0
Indemnity Fee for Service	1	2	1	0	0
Managed Care Contracts					
Health Maintenance Organization	3	2	5	6	6
Preferred Provider Organization.	3	3	5	5	4
Affiliations					
Hospitals in a System.	1	1	1	1	1
Hospitals in a Network	4	5	5	5	5
Hospitals in a Group Purchasing Organization. .	11	10	10	10	10

TABLE 6

VERMONT

U.S. Registered Community Hospitals
(Nonfederal, short-term general and other special hospitals)

Utilization, Personnel, Revenue and Expenses, Community Health Indicators 2009–2013

	2013	2012	2011	2010	2009
TOTAL FACILITY (Includes Hospital and Nursing Home Units)					
Utilization - Inpatient					
Beds	1,201	1,231	1,218	1,288	1,296
Admissions	48,464	48,887	48,941	49,449	50,922
Inpatient Days	303,555	307,154	310,510	305,289	321,741
Average Length of Stay	6.3	6.3	6.3	6.2	6.3
Inpatient Surgeries	12,785	13,036	13,258	13,950	15,557
Births	5,246	5,250	12,755	5,604	5,829
Utilization - Outpatient					
Emergency Outpatient Visits	302,264	302,030	296,666	352,808	357,793
Other Outpatient Visits	2,779,607	2,740,382	2,788,192	2,999,812	2,997,816
Total Outpatient Visits	3,081,871	3,042,412	3,084,858	3,352,620	3,355,609
Outpatient Surgeries	46,251	46,671	48,381	48,158	48,673
Personnel					
Full Time RNs	2,006	1,852	1,720	1,748	1,671
Full Time LPNs	150	148	159	166	163
Part Time RNs	1,646	1,553	1,595	1,311	1,262
Part Time LPNs	91	104	128	149	110
Total Full Time	10,374	9,967	9,724	9,629	9,738
Total Part Time	4,657	4,590	4,930	4,078	3,920
Revenue - Inpatient					
Gross Inpatient Revenue	$1,435,938,955	$1,089,276,425	$1,055,321,773	$1,154,115,173	$1,055,165,310
Revenue - Outpatient					
Gross Outpatient Revenue	$3,197,627,776	$3,001,872,051	$2,665,042,545	$2,538,622,333	$2,313,816,425
Revenue and Expenses - Totals					
(Includes Inpatient and Outpatient)					
Total Gross Revenue	$4,633,566,731	$4,091,148,476	$3,720,364,318	$3,692,737,506	$3,368,981,735
Deductions from Revenue	2,565,323,969	2,173,153,296	1,901,314,973	1,982,861,871	1,719,852,956
Net Patient Revenue	2,068,242,762	1,917,995,180	1,819,049,345	1,709,875,635	1,649,128,779
Other Operating Revenue	102,107,130	71,915,614	57,250,217	56,110,764	51,534,989
Other Nonoperating Revenue	68,713,604	39,281,120	18,547,865	35,893,255	-10,009,965
Total Net Revenue	2,239,063,496	2,029,191,914	1,894,847,427	1,801,879,654	1,690,653,803
Total Expenses	2,042,602,482	1,931,290,820	1,776,728,126	1,714,899,646	1,660,403,783
HOSPITAL UNIT (Excludes Separate Nursing Home Units)					
Utilization - Inpatient					
Beds	1,048	1,053	1,010	1,080	1,118
Admissions	48,129	48,477	48,523	49,078	50,549
Inpatient Days	249,025	248,986	241,161	233,003	259,463
Average Length of Stay	5.2	5.1	5.0	4.7	5.1
Personnel					
Total Full Time	10,247	9,791	9,591	9,493	9,397
Total Part Time	4,601	4,502	4,811	3,963	3,708
Revenue and Expenses - Totals					
(Includes Inpatient and Outpatient)					
Total Net Revenue	$2,222,318,627	$2,012,967,016	$1,876,507,339	$1,783,366,299	$1,669,557,556
Total Expenses	2,026,117,019	1,915,144,417	1,759,323,094	1,697,709,912	1,635,099,616
COMMUNITY HEALTH INDICATORS PER 1000 POPULATION					
Total Population (in thousands)	627	626	626	622	622
Inpatient					
Beds	1.9	2.0	1.9	2.1	2.1
Admissions	77.3	78.1	78.1	79.4	81.9
Inpatient Days	484.4	490.7	495.7	490.5	517.5
Inpatient Surgeries	20.4	20.8	21.2	22.4	25.0
Births	8.4	8.4	20.4	9.0	9.4
Outpatient					
Emergency Outpatient Visits	482.4	482.5	473.6	566.8	575.5
Other Outpatient Visits	4,435.8	4,377.5	4,450.9	4,819.5	4,821.5
Total Outpatient Visits	4,918.2	4,860.0	4,924.5	5,386.3	5,397.0
Outpatient Surgeries	73.8	74.6	77.2	77.4	78.3
Expense per Capita (per person)	$3,259.7	$3,085.1	$2,836.3	$2,755.2	$2,670.5

TABLE **6**

VIRGINIA

U.S. Registered Community Hospitals
(Nonfederal, short-term general and other special hospitals)

Overview 2009–2013

	2013	2012	2011	2010	2009
Total Community Hospitals in Virginia	93	94	89	89	90
Bed Size Category					
6-24	6	5	5	5	3
25-49	16	16	15	14	15
50-99	18	17	15	15	17
100-199	23	26	23	25	27
200-299	12	12	13	12	11
300-399	5	5	6	6	5
400-499	5	5	5	5	5
500 + ...	8	8	7	7	7
Location					
Hospitals Urban	64	64	59	59	60
Hospitals Rural	29	30	30	30	30
Control					
State and Local Government	5	5	4	4	4
Not for Profit	65	65	65	64	66
Investor owned	23	24	20	21	20
Physician Models					
Independent Practice Association	11	13	12	13	12
Group Practice without Walls	9	9	9	10	8
Open Physician-Hospital Organization	14	14	8	9	7
Closed Physician-Hospital Organization	3	2	2	2	1
Management Service Organization	15	16	17	18	15
Integrated Salary Model	44	45	47	51	40
Equity Model	9	9	8	8	7
Foundation	1	2	2	1	1
Insurance Products					
Health Maintenance Organization	28	18	18	15	13
Preferred Provider Organization	30	15	20	18	12
Indemnity Fee for Service	15	9	9	2	1
Managed Care Contracts					
Health Maintenance Organization	60	55	59	55	48
Preferred Provider Organization	61	57	61	59	54
Affiliations					
Hospitals in a System	81	78	73	70	69
Hospitals in a Network	44	41	44	44	37
Hospitals in a Group Purchasing Organization . .	65	64	65	70	57

TABLE 6

VIRGINIA

U.S. Registered Community Hospitals
(Nonfederal, short-term general and other special hospitals)

Utilization, Personnel, Revenue and Expenses, Community Health Indicators 2009–2013

	2013	2012	2011	2010	2009
TOTAL FACILITY (Includes Hospital and Nursing Home Units)					
Utilization - Inpatient					
Beds	17,975	18,150	17,797	17,747	17,538
Admissions	780,153	796,004	788,441	776,678	793,145
Inpatient Days	4,436,963	4,516,303	4,391,769	4,310,430	4,375,451
Average Length of Stay	5.7	5.7	5.6	5.5	5.5
Inpatient Surgeries	213,323	209,255	210,890	223,354	234,981
Births	93,002	93,114	98,141	99,623	96,209
Utilization - Outpatient					
Emergency Outpatient Visits	3,626,500	3,600,733	3,407,824	3,256,956	3,199,466
Other Outpatient Visits	12,187,544	11,952,608	10,710,596	10,524,980	10,959,387
Total Outpatient Visits	15,814,044	15,553,341	14,118,420	13,781,936	14,158,853
Outpatient Surgeries	501,555	451,407	446,691	439,146	448,650
Personnel					
Full Time RNs	26,044	24,712	24,546	24,035	23,711
Full Time LPNs	1,935	2,104	2,062	2,226	2,231
Part Time RNs	10,775	10,964	11,202	11,030	10,025
Part Time LPNs	521	611	614	703	684
Total Full Time	85,502	83,946	83,312	82,310	82,332
Total Part Time	29,524	29,934	29,682	30,091	28,083
Revenue - Inpatient					
Gross Inpatient Revenue	$29,611,485,772	$28,228,430,166	$25,657,236,400	$24,373,894,322	$22,941,847,825
Revenue - Outpatient					
Gross Outpatient Revenue	$28,296,364,383	$25,551,564,541	$22,821,731,869	$21,205,056,723	$18,818,269,487
Revenue and Expenses - Totals					
(Includes Inpatient and Outpatient)					
Total Gross Revenue	$57,907,850,155	$53,779,994,707	$48,478,968,269	$45,578,951,045	$41,760,117,312
Deductions from Revenue	39,950,040,314	36,089,745,615	32,415,072,411	30,139,978,214	26,616,556,088
Net Patient Revenue	17,957,809,841	17,690,249,092	16,063,895,858	15,438,972,831	15,143,561,224
Other Operating Revenue	685,703,799	614,154,152	538,832,905	425,128,846	422,020,787
Other Nonoperating Revenue	484,708,430	354,593,302	170,711,732	253,492,718	10,537,285
Total Net Revenue	19,128,222,070	18,658,996,546	16,773,440,495	16,117,594,395	15,576,119,296
Total Expenses	17,002,869,179	16,505,378,259	15,341,349,476	14,709,796,266	14,456,123,508
HOSPITAL UNIT (Excludes Separate Nursing Home Units)					
Utilization - Inpatient					
Beds	16,327	16,467	16,091	16,163	16,422
Admissions	773,930	789,746	781,788	770,195	788,427
Inpatient Days	3,879,122	3,951,225	3,823,198	3,775,706	3,995,348
Average Length of Stay	5.0	5.0	4.9	4.9	5.1
Personnel					
Total Full Time	84,464	82,960	82,422	81,441	81,316
Total Part Time	29,137	29,503	29,292	29,637	27,710
Revenue and Expenses - Totals					
(Includes Inpatient and Outpatient)					
Total Net Revenue	$18,989,222,239	$18,515,704,755	$16,629,452,446	$15,986,427,239	$15,479,330,448
Total Expenses	16,873,364,471	16,368,213,160	15,208,955,950	14,592,391,811	14,367,593,188
COMMUNITY HEALTH INDICATORS PER 1000 POPULATION					
Total Population (in thousands)	8,260	8,186	8,097	7,952	7,883
Inpatient					
Beds	2.2	2.2	2.2	2.2	2.2
Admissions	94.4	97.2	97.4	97.7	100.6
Inpatient Days	537.1	551.7	542.4	542.0	555.1
Inpatient Surgeries	25.8	25.6	26.0	28.1	29.8
Births	11.3	11.4	12.1	12.5	12.2
Outpatient					
Emergency Outpatient Visits	439.0	439.9	420.9	409.6	405.9
Other Outpatient Visits	1,475.4	1,460.2	1,322.9	1,323.5	1,390.3
Total Outpatient Visits	1,914.4	1,900.0	1,743.7	1,733.1	1,796.2
Outpatient Surgeries	60.7	55.1	55.2	55.2	56.9
Expense per Capita (per person)	$2,058.4	$2,016.3	$1,894.8	$1,849.8	$1,833.9

States

TABLE 6

WASHINGTON

U.S. Registered Community Hospitals
(Nonfederal, short-term general and other special hospitals)

Overview 2009–2013

	2013	2012	2011	2010	2009
Total Community Hospitals in Washington	90	87	85	86	87
Bed Size Category					
6-24	9	8	8	7	7
25-49	27	27	27	29	30
50-99	16	14	11	10	11
100-199	16	15	16	16	16
200-299	11	12	12	13	13
300-399	5	4	5	6	5
400-499	4	5	4	3	3
500 + ...	2	2	2	2	2
Location					
Hospitals Urban............................	56	55	53	53	53
Hospitals Rural	34	32	32	33	34
Control					
State and Local Government................	40	38	38	39	41
Not for Profit	44	42	41	42	41
Investor owned	6	7	6	5	5
Physician Models					
Independent Practice Association	1	1	1	2	2
Group Practice without Walls...............	2	3	4	4	4
Open Physician-Hospital Organization	2	3	6	5	4
Closed Physician-Hospital Organization	0	1	1	0	0
Management Service Organization	2	3	4	6	6
Integrated Salary Model....................	36	39	40	39	42
Equity Model.............................	3	3	3	4	4
Foundation...............................	6	4	4	5	7
Insurance Products					
Health Maintenance Organization	4	4	7	4	5
Preferred Provider Organization..............	9	9	14	11	12
Indemnity Fee for Service	1	2	1	0	1
Managed Care Contracts					
Health Maintenance Organization	31	38	35	34	36
Preferred Provider Organization..............	34	40	37	38	44
Affiliations					
Hospitals in a System......................	42	40	39	35	32
Hospitals in a Network.....................	24	17	20	19	19
Hospitals in a Group Purchasing Organization..	51	44	51	48	60

TABLE 6

WASHINGTON

U.S. Registered Community Hospitals
(Nonfederal, short-term general and other special hospitals)

Utilization, Personnel, Revenue and Expenses, Community Health Indicators 2009–2013

	2013	2012	2011	2010	2009
TOTAL FACILITY (Includes Hospital and Nursing Home Units)					
Utilization - Inpatient					
Beds	12,180	12,132	11,670	11,537	11,322
Admissions	600,519	597,338	576,214	588,855	588,889
Inpatient Days	2,763,826	2,731,437	2,613,217	2,638,779	2,660,901
Average Length of Stay	4.6	4.6	4.5	4.5	4.5
Inpatient Surgeries	170,566	165,978	167,254	170,895	185,833
Births	77,904	76,089	77,238	78,216	80,667
Utilization - Outpatient					
Emergency Outpatient Visits	2,338,002	2,390,525	2,321,612	2,290,953	2,509,243
Other Outpatient Visits	10,120,396	10,576,020	10,136,318	9,515,677	8,996,667
Total Outpatient Visits	12,458,398	12,966,545	12,457,930	11,806,630	11,505,910
Outpatient Surgeries	299,228	265,920	261,623	261,997	266,107
Personnel					
Full Time RNs	18,241	18,981	16,121	16,109	15,789
Full Time LPNs	826	946	774	825	870
Part Time RNs	14,128	12,219	13,423	13,848	13,205
Part Time LPNs	545	509	560	616	665
Total Full Time	74,227	75,760	65,087	68,163	64,767
Total Part Time	41,067	37,294	39,667	39,185	36,879
Revenue - Inpatient					
Gross Inpatient Revenue	$27,370,345,005	$25,728,322,501	$21,352,251,400	$21,516,174,379	$19,988,875,344
Revenue - Outpatient					
Gross Outpatient Revenue	$25,026,435,484	$22,312,583,270	$19,065,026,947	$18,594,056,137	$16,200,972,533
Revenue and Expenses - Totals (Includes Inpatient and Outpatient)					
Total Gross Revenue	$52,396,780,489	$48,040,905,771	$40,417,278,347	$40,110,230,516	$36,189,847,877
Deductions from Revenue	34,820,455,823	31,116,500,841	25,612,881,399	25,534,351,330	22,273,010,097
Net Patient Revenue	17,576,324,666	16,924,404,930	14,804,396,948	14,575,879,186	13,916,837,780
Other Operating Revenue	1,020,203,756	972,579,978	842,178,249	804,026,112	755,280,721
Other Nonoperating Revenue	249,956,325	210,144,087	300,691,951	226,341,197	188,342,686
Total Net Revenue	18,846,484,747	18,107,128,995	15,947,267,148	15,606,246,495	14,860,461,187
Total Expenses	17,864,679,102	16,739,742,990	14,869,963,274	14,641,932,019	13,773,406,044
HOSPITAL UNIT (Excludes Separate Nursing Home Units)					
Utilization - Inpatient					
Beds	11,997	11,914	11,453	11,382	10,974
Admissions	600,198	597,051	575,796	587,786	587,527
Inpatient Days	2,686,606	2,655,788	2,530,869	2,589,013	2,549,787
Average Length of Stay	4.5	4.4	4.4	4.4	4.3
Personnel					
Total Full Time	74,098	75,610	64,968	68,113	64,470
Total Part Time	40,938	37,137	39,509	39,097	36,649
Revenue and Expenses - Totals (Includes Inpatient and Outpatient)					
Total Net Revenue	$18,825,783,157	$18,084,028,525	$15,927,548,095	$15,586,259,128	$14,821,016,445
Total Expenses	17,844,227,960	16,718,398,352	14,852,332,389	14,623,738,440	13,737,554,929
COMMUNITY HEALTH INDICATORS PER 1000 POPULATION					
Total Population (in thousands)	6,971	6,897	6,830	6,746	6,664
Inpatient					
Beds	1.7	1.8	1.7	1.7	1.7
Admissions	86.1	86.6	84.4	87.3	88.4
Inpatient Days	396.5	396.0	382.6	391.2	399.3
Inpatient Surgeries	24.5	24.1	24.5	25.3	27.9
Births	11.2	11.0	11.3	11.6	12.1
Outpatient					
Emergency Outpatient Visits	335.4	346.6	339.9	339.6	376.5
Other Outpatient Visits	1,451.7	1,533.4	1,484.1	1,410.5	1,350.0
Total Outpatient Visits	1,787.1	1,880.0	1,824.0	1,750.1	1,726.5
Outpatient Surgeries	42.9	38.6	38.3	38.8	39.9
Expense per Capita (per person)	$2,562.6	$2,427.1	$2,177.1	$2,170.4	$2,066.8

TABLE 6

WEST VIRGINIA

U.S. Registered Community Hospitals
(Nonfederal, short-term general and other special hospitals)

Overview 2009–2013

	2013	2012	2011	2010	2009
Total Community Hospitals in West Virginia ...	55	55	55	56	56
Bed Size Category					
6-24	3	3	3	3	3
25-49	17	16	15	14	14
50-99	11	12	13	13	13
100-199	12	12	11	14	14
200-299	8	7	8	9	8
300-399	2	2	2	1	2
400-499	0	1	1	0	0
500 + ...	2	2	2	2	2
Location					
Hospitals Urban...........................	26	26	26	27	27
Hospitals Rural	29	29	29	29	29
Control					
State and Local Government................	7	8	8	8	10
Not for Profit	34	33	33	34	32
Investor owned	14	14	14	14	14
Physician Models					
Independent Practice Association	2	2	2	3	4
Group Practice without Walls..............	1	0	0	0	0
Open Physician-Hospital Organization	11	12	14	13	14
Closed Physician-Hospital Organization	1	1	1	3	3
Management Service Organization	1	2	2	2	3
Integrated Salary Model....................	27	27	25	25	25
Equity Model	0	0	0	0	0
Foundation...............................	0	0	0	0	0
Insurance Products					
Health Maintenance Organization	4	5	5	6	5
Preferred Provider Organization..............	8	6	10	10	9
Indemnity Fee for Service	4	4	2	3	2
Managed Care Contracts					
Health Maintenance Organization	29	31	28	31	31
Preferred Provider Organization..............	41	40	40	42	42
Affiliations					
Hospitals in a System......................	30	30	30	29	25
Hospitals in a Network.....................	20	20	21	21	22
Hospitals in a Group Purchasing Organization..	53	53	52	53	53

TABLE 6

WEST VIRGINIA

U.S. Registered Community Hospitals
(Nonfederal, short-term general and other special hospitals)

Utilization, Personnel, Revenue and Expenses, Community Health Indicators 2009–2013

	2013	2012	2011	2010	2009
TOTAL FACILITY (Includes Hospital and Nursing Home Units)					
Utilization - Inpatient					
Beds	7,054	7,212	7,365	7,298	7,408
Admissions	265,292	276,114	282,194	278,221	280,252
Inpatient Days	1,549,653	1,587,250	1,632,308	1,612,811	1,648,197
Average Length of Stay	5.8	5.7	5.8	5.8	5.9
Inpatient Surgeries	80,580	82,602	82,491	83,992	80,776
Births	20,974	20,758	20,639	20,487	21,010
Utilization - Outpatient					
Emergency Outpatient Visits	1,164,759	1,224,551	1,216,780	1,207,918	1,221,485
Other Outpatient Visits	5,732,531	5,585,774	5,544,015	5,446,482	5,463,158
Total Outpatient Visits	6,897,290	6,810,325	6,760,795	6,654,400	6,684,643
Outpatient Surgeries	231,365	228,957	222,505	212,434	215,853
Personnel					
Full Time RNs	9,300	8,852	8,593	8,532	8,282
Full Time LPNs	1,098	1,130	1,099	1,217	1,298
Part Time RNs	3,325	3,251	3,252	3,395	3,447
Part Time LPNs	325	332	396	419	403
Total Full Time	35,411	34,272	33,119	33,349	32,751
Total Part Time	10,751	10,125	9,903	10,143	10,082
Revenue - Inpatient					
Gross Inpatient Revenue	$6,598,503,203	$6,272,466,443	$6,028,967,872	$5,597,580,327	$5,174,519,813
Revenue - Outpatient					
Gross Outpatient Revenue	$6,837,148,779	$6,361,117,278	$5,824,592,215	$5,444,045,714	$5,161,162,251
Revenue and Expenses - Totals					
(Includes Inpatient and Outpatient)					
Total Gross Revenue	$13,435,651,982	$12,633,583,721	$11,853,560,087	$11,041,626,041	$10,335,682,064
Deductions from Revenue	8,165,212,258	7,391,004,309	7,049,221,237	6,386,501,669	5,787,332,486
Net Patient Revenue	5,270,439,724	5,242,579,412	4,804,338,850	4,655,124,372	4,548,349,578
Other Operating Revenue	222,761,392	182,070,517	133,361,426	126,269,003	168,034,621
Other Nonoperating Revenue	191,330,033	86,836,379	-338,296	63,579,778	54,115,339
Total Net Revenue	5,684,531,149	5,511,486,308	4,937,361,980	4,844,973,153	4,770,499,538
Total Expenses	5,371,862,686	5,151,427,691	4,724,080,410	4,689,352,987	4,584,221,488
HOSPITAL UNIT (Excludes Separate Nursing Home Units)					
Utilization - Inpatient					
Beds	6,270	6,423	6,554	6,454	6,575
Admissions	261,148	271,352	277,659	272,471	274,341
Inpatient Days	1,303,200	1,329,793	1,378,567	1,340,666	1,371,913
Average Length of Stay	5.0	4.9	5.0	4.9	5.0
Personnel					
Total Full Time	34,840	33,683	32,566	32,752	32,152
Total Part Time	10,370	9,785	9,508	9,781	9,787
Revenue and Expenses - Totals					
(Includes Inpatient and Outpatient)					
Total Net Revenue	$5,617,231,970	$5,439,544,951	$4,873,165,838	$4,774,505,282	$4,700,079,381
Total Expenses	5,329,382,003	5,097,076,501	4,670,781,412	4,637,567,799	4,529,683,828
COMMUNITY HEALTH INDICATORS PER 1000 POPULATION					
Total Population (in thousands)	1,854	1,855	1,855	1,826	1,820
Inpatient					
Beds	3.8	3.9	4.0	4.0	4.1
Admissions	143.1	148.8	152.1	152.4	154.0
Inpatient Days	835.7	855.5	879.8	883.5	905.7
Inpatient Surgeries	43.5	44.5	44.5	46.0	44.4
Births	11.3	11.2	11.1	11.2	11.5
Outpatient					
Emergency Outpatient Visits	628.1	660.0	655.8	661.7	671.2
Other Outpatient Visits	3,091.5	3,010.5	2,988.1	2,983.5	3,002.1
Total Outpatient Visits	3,719.6	3,670.5	3,643.9	3,645.2	3,673.3
Outpatient Surgeries	124.8	123.4	119.9	116.4	118.6
Expense per Capita (per person)	$2,897.0	$2,776.4	$2,546.2	$2,568.8	$2,519.1

States

TABLE 6

WISCONSIN

U.S. Registered Community Hospitals
(Nonfederal, short-term general and other special hospitals)

Overview 2009–2013

	2013	2012	2011	2010	2009
Total Community Hospitals in Wisconsin......	129	128	125	124	126
Bed Size Category					
6-24	23	21	15	13	12
25-49	32	33	36	37	37
50-99	32	33	31	31	32
100-199	22	20	22	21	25
200-299	12	11	11	13	11
300-399	4	7	7	5	6
400-499	1	0	1	2	2
500 + ...	3	3	2	2	1
Location					
Hospitals Urban.........................	73	72	69	68	69
Hospitals Rural	56	56	56	56	57
Control					
State and Local Government...............	2	2	2	2	2
Not for Profit	121	121	119	117	118
Investor owned	6	5	4	5	6
Physician Models					
Independent Practice Association	8	11	11	9	13
Group Practice without Walls...............	1	0	3	3	3
Open Physician-Hospital Organization	8	6	4	4	3
Closed Physician-Hospital Organization	4	3	4	4	2
Management Service Organization	1	2	2	2	3
Integrated Salary Model....................	54	62	56	38	34
Equity Model	11	7	6	9	12
Foundation..............................	2	2	2	2	2
Insurance Products					
Health Maintenance Organization	43	41	36	20	23
Preferred Provider Organization..............	45	41	36	31	35
Indemnity Fee for Service	18	19	15	15	16
Managed Care Contracts					
Health Maintenance Organization	120	118	118	116	116
Preferred Provider Organization..............	122	121	120	118	118
Affiliations					
Hospitals in a System.....................	76	75	72	72	74
Hospitals in a Network....................	45	44	43	37	36
Hospitals in a Group Purchasing Organization..	124	126	123	118	116

TABLE 6

WISCONSIN

U.S. Registered Community Hospitals
(Nonfederal, short-term general and other special hospitals)

Utilization, Personnel, Revenue and Expenses, Community Health Indicators 2009–2013

	2013	2012	2011	2010	2009
TOTAL FACILITY (Includes Hospital and Nursing Home Units)					
Utilization - Inpatient					
Beds	12,760	13,020	13,134	13,520	13,637
Admissions	566,368	578,239	573,077	588,592	609,329
Inpatient Days	2,808,943	2,855,397	2,873,295	2,966,909	3,125,349
Average Length of Stay	5.0	4.9	5.0	5.0	5.1
Inpatient Surgeries	172,640	214,146	214,111	228,469	256,942
Births	64,598	65,632	66,783	67,843	70,129
Utilization - Outpatient					
Emergency Outpatient Visits	2,098,324	2,171,739	2,130,925	2,160,341	2,080,601
Other Outpatient Visits	14,400,592	13,957,038	13,379,041	12,444,617	12,847,067
Total Outpatient Visits	16,498,916	16,128,777	15,509,966	14,604,958	14,927,668
Outpatient Surgeries	454,518	526,585	531,355	522,864	535,955
Personnel					
Full Time RNs	15,560	15,095	15,048	14,476	14,345
Full Time LPNs	617	537	622	673	711
Part Time RNs	15,965	15,972	14,982	15,552	16,139
Part Time LPNs	689	645	706	794	908
Total Full Time	64,634	63,722	63,544	63,254	63,168
Total Part Time	49,311	48,388	46,533	48,472	51,235
Revenue - Inpatient					
Gross Inpatient Revenue	$17,961,771,456	$17,011,582,655	$16,185,500,212	$15,357,857,584	$15,634,706,846
Revenue - Outpatient					
Gross Outpatient Revenue	$22,326,935,702	$20,638,540,030	$18,798,615,788	$16,468,660,136	$14,805,407,754
Revenue and Expenses - Totals					
(Includes Inpatient and Outpatient)					
Total Gross Revenue	$40,288,707,158	$37,650,122,685	$34,984,116,000	$31,826,517,720	$30,440,114,600
Deductions from Revenue	24,091,152,555	21,459,464,213	19,455,297,266	16,996,231,064	16,618,465,592
Net Patient Revenue	16,197,554,603	16,190,658,472	15,528,818,734	14,830,286,656	13,821,649,008
Other Operating Revenue	715,806,300	751,235,572	644,957,778	630,341,533	716,584,248
Other Nonoperating Revenue	456,057,518	322,542,557	288,307,316	285,539,514	-26,443,242
Total Net Revenue	17,369,418,421	17,264,436,601	16,462,083,828	15,746,167,703	14,511,790,014
Total Expenses	15,412,000,677	15,601,708,952	14,997,018,589	14,230,620,575	13,496,778,176
HOSPITAL UNIT (Excludes Separate Nursing Home Units)					
Utilization - Inpatient					
Beds	11,611	11,775	11,814	12,092	12,049
Admissions	563,976	575,966	570,650	586,022	606,542
Inpatient Days	2,450,661	2,439,508	2,453,855	2,511,474	2,597,929
Average Length of Stay	4.3	4.2	4.3	4.3	4.3
Personnel					
Total Full Time	64,288	63,255	62,919	62,460	62,376
Total Part Time	48,766	47,770	45,754	47,543	50,255
Revenue and Expenses - Totals					
(Includes Inpatient and Outpatient)					
Total Net Revenue	$17,289,048,577	$17,182,065,794	$16,360,856,116	$15,640,069,501	$14,399,372,197
Total Expenses	15,332,364,550	15,523,090,630	14,902,736,502	14,124,128,291	13,393,867,097
COMMUNITY HEALTH INDICATORS PER 1000 POPULATION					
Total Population (in thousands)	5,743	5,726	5,712	5,669	5,655
Inpatient					
Beds	2.2	2.3	2.3	2.4	2.4
Admissions	98.6	101.0	100.3	103.8	107.8
Inpatient Days	489.1	498.6	503.0	523.4	552.7
Inpatient Surgeries	30.1	37.4	37.5	40.3	45.4
Births	11.2	11.5	11.7	12.0	12.4
Outpatient					
Emergency Outpatient Visits	365.4	379.3	373.1	381.1	367.9
Other Outpatient Visits	2,507.6	2,437.3	2,342.4	2,195.4	2,271.9
Total Outpatient Visits	2,873.0	2,816.6	2,715.4	2,576.5	2,639.8
Outpatient Surgeries	79.1	92.0	93.0	92.2	94.8
Expense per Capita (per person)	$2,683.7	$2,724.5	$2,625.6	$2,510.5	$2,386.8

States

TABLE 6

WYOMING

U.S. Registered Community Hospitals
(Nonfederal, short-term general and other special hospitals)

Overview 2009–2013

	2013	2012	2011	2010	2009
Total Community Hospitals in Wyoming.......	24	24	24	24	24
Bed Size Category					
6-24	0	0	0	0	0
25-49	11	11	11	11	11
50-99	6	6	6	6	6
100-199	6	5	4	4	4
200-299	1	2	3	3	3
300-399	0	0	0	0	0
400-499	0	0	0	0	0
500 + ...	0	0	0	0	0
Location					
Hospitals Urban...........................	2	2	2	2	2
Hospitals Rural	22	22	22	22	22
Control					
State and Local Government................	16	16	16	16	16
Not for Profit	5	5	5	5	5
Investor owned	3	3	3	3	3
Physician Models					
Independent Practice Association	3	2	2	2	3
Group Practice without Walls................	0	0	0	0	0
Open Physician-Hospital Organization	2	1	1	1	1
Closed Physician-Hospital Organization	1	1	1	1	1
Management Service Organization	2	2	1	2	2
Integrated Salary Model.....................	11	10	9	10	11
Equity Model	0	0	0	0	0
Foundation................................	0	0	0	0	0
Insurance Products					
Health Maintenance Organization	2	2	2	1	1
Preferred Provider Organization..............	1	1	3	3	1
Indemnity Fee for Service	0	0	0	0	0
Managed Care Contracts					
Health Maintenance Organization	5	5	4	3	4
Preferred Provider Organization..............	17	17	14	14	14
Affiliations					
Hospitals in a System......................	12	12	12	12	12
Hospitals in a Network.....................	4	5	4	4	5
Hospitals in a Group Purchasing Organization..	22	22	21	21	21

TABLE 6

WYOMING

U.S. Registered Community Hospitals
(Nonfederal, short-term general and other special hospitals)

Utilization, Personnel, Revenue and Expenses, Community Health Indicators 2009–2013

	2013	2012	2011	2010	2009
TOTAL FACILITY (Includes Hospital and Nursing Home Units)					
Utilization - Inpatient					
Beds	1,920	1,923	1,958	1,958	2,002
Admissions	44,574	44,180	45,697	49,704	52,232
Inpatient Days	372,237	375,036	378,227	398,850	411,717
Average Length of Stay	8.4	8.5	8.3	8.0	7.9
Inpatient Surgeries	11,419	11,959	12,872	14,159	13,801
Births	6,404	6,364	6,363	6,920	7,305
Utilization - Outpatient					
Emergency Outpatient Visits	233,648	229,649	228,140	231,261	236,213
Other Outpatient Visits	1,029,872	976,926	890,706	866,984	823,944
Total Outpatient Visits	1,263,520	1,206,575	1,118,846	1,098,245	1,060,157
Outpatient Surgeries	26,232	28,021	29,019	29,260	26,180
Personnel					
Full Time RNs	1,864	1,798	1,721	1,680	1,561
Full Time LPNs	101	113	116	117	127
Part Time RNs	604	578	556	455	526
Part Time LPNs	43	50	52	54	76
Total Full Time	7,803	7,546	7,404	7,338	7,094
Total Part Time	2,211	2,166	2,067	2,005	2,310
Revenue - Inpatient					
Gross Inpatient Revenue	$1,146,334,560	$1,129,646,064	$1,079,479,758	$1,072,618,270	$967,170,829
Revenue - Outpatient					
Gross Outpatient Revenue	$1,448,039,841	$1,327,536,898	$1,216,235,177	$1,103,760,780	$946,462,599
Revenue and Expenses - Totals					
(Includes Inpatient and Outpatient)					
Total Gross Revenue	$2,594,374,401	$2,457,182,962	$2,295,714,935	$2,176,379,050	$1,913,633,428
Deductions from Revenue	1,320,845,075	1,211,190,965	1,180,144,790	1,096,026,956	955,291,698
Net Patient Revenue	1,273,529,326	1,245,991,997	1,115,570,145	1,080,352,094	958,341,730
Other Operating Revenue	82,996,786	74,346,388	69,049,844	74,157,196	66,460,224
Other Nonoperating Revenue	38,510,265	4,294,457	26,792,888	19,130,354	-798,016
Total Net Revenue	1,395,036,377	1,324,632,842	1,211,412,877	1,173,639,644	1,024,003,938
Total Expenses	1,233,698,322	1,182,216,845	1,046,675,080	1,031,425,657	980,632,479
HOSPITAL UNIT (Excludes Separate Nursing Home Units)					
Utilization - Inpatient					
Beds	1,292	1,245	1,281	1,303	1,303
Admissions	43,817	43,484	44,155	48,206	50,673
Inpatient Days	177,813	167,355	169,461	196,510	188,014
Average Length of Stay	4.1	3.8	3.8	4.1	3.7
Personnel					
Total Full Time	7,420	7,150	7,004	6,925	6,618
Total Part Time	2,020	1,957	1,888	1,841	2,117
Revenue and Expenses - Totals					
(Includes Inpatient and Outpatient)					
Total Net Revenue	$1,353,272,060	$1,282,240,814	$1,170,074,150	$1,133,360,264	$984,238,688
Total Expenses	1,198,106,925	1,141,742,073	1,006,052,821	991,627,019	938,219,346
COMMUNITY HEALTH INDICATORS PER 1000 POPULATION					
Total Population (in thousands)	583	576	568	548	544
Inpatient					
Beds	3.3	3.3	3.4	3.6	3.7
Admissions	76.5	76.6	80.4	90.8	96.0
Inpatient Days	638.9	650.6	665.7	728.3	756.5
Inpatient Surgeries	19.6	20.7	22.7	25.9	25.4
Births	11.0	11.0	11.2	12.6	13.4
Outpatient					
Emergency Outpatient Visits	401.0	398.4	401.5	422.3	434.0
Other Outpatient Visits	1,767.5	1,694.8	1,567.7	1,583.1	1,513.9
Total Outpatient Visits	2,168.5	2,093.3	1,969.3	2,005.4	1,947.9
Outpatient Surgeries	45.0	48.6	51.1	53.4	48.1
Expense per Capita (per person)	$2,117.4	$2,051.0	$1,842.2	$1,883.4	$1,801.7

States

Table 7

Table	Page

7   Facilities and Services in the U. S. Census Divisions and States for 2013   155

The facilities and services presented in Table 7 are listed below in alphabetical order by major heading (where applicable).

Table 7

2013 Facilities and Services in the U.S. Census Divisions and States

These data include only hospital-based facilities and services as reported by responding hospitals in Section C of the 2013 AHA Annual Survey, beginning on page 215. All hospitals are represented with Community Hospitals listed separately under United States. No estimates have been made for nonresponding hospitals. Definitions of facilities and services are listed in the Glossary, page 201.

CLASSIFICATION	HOSPITALS REPORTING	ADULT DAY CARE PROGRAM Number	Percent	AIRBORNE INFECTION ISOLATION ROOM Number	Percent	ALCOHOL/DRUG ABUSE OR DEPENDENCY INPATIENT CARE UNITS Number	Percent	ALCOHOL/DRUG ABUSE OR DEPENDENCY OUTPATIENT SERVICES Number	Percent	ALZHEIMER CENTER Number	Percent	AMBULANCE SERVICE Number	Percent	AMBULATORY SURGERY CENTER Number	Percent	ARTHRITIS TREATMENT CENTER Number	Percent	ASSISTED LIVING Number	Percent
UNITED STATES	4,780	188	3.9	3,718	77.8	454	9.5	681	14.2	209	4.4	717	15.0	1,243	26.0	290	6.1	172	3.6
COMMUNITY HOSPITALS	4,053	161	4.0	3,383	83.5	312	7.7	516	12.7	192	4.7	694	17.1	1,186	29.3	277	6.8	161	4.0
CENSUS DIVISION 1, NEW ENGLAND	190	9	4.7	143	75.3	16	8.4	60	31.6	17	8.9	21	11.1	68	35.8	18	9.5	4	2.1
Connecticut	34	1	2.9	26	76.5	3	8.8	16	47.1	4	11.8	3	8.8	16	47.1	6	17.6	1	2.9
Maine	37	1	2.7	26	70.3	4	10.8	13	35.1	4	10.8	6	16.2	12	32.4	0	0.0	1	2.7
Massachusetts	66	4	6.1	46	69.7	5	7.6	22	33.3	5	7.6	6	9.1	23	34.8	8	12.1	0	0.0
New Hampshire	26	2	7.7	24	92.3	1	3.8	2	7.7	1	3.8	4	15.4	5	19.2	2	7.7	1	3.8
Rhode Island	13	0	0.0	11	84.6	1	7.7	4	30.8	2	15.4	1	7.7	8	61.5	0	0.0	0	0.0
Vermont	14	1	7.1	10	71.4	2	14.3	3	21.4	1	7.1	1	7.1	4	28.6	2	14.3	1	7.1
CENSUS DIVISION 2, MIDDLE ATLANTIC	423	34	8.0	344	81.3	69	16.3	92	21.7	34	8.0	76	18.0	186	44.0	59	13.9	13	3.1
New Jersey	72	8	11.1	57	79.2	10	13.9	18	25.0	6	8.3	20	27.8	25	34.7	9	12.5	3	4.2
New York	156	19	12.2	135	86.5	43	27.6	48	30.8	15	9.6	27	17.3	103	66.0	32	20.5	1	0.6
Pennsylvania	195	7	3.6	152	77.9	16	8.2	26	13.3	13	6.7	29	14.9	58	29.7	18	9.2	9	4.6
CENSUS DIVISION 3, SOUTH ATLANTIC	682	20	2.9	558	81.8	74	10.9	100	14.7	33	4.8	94	13.8	178	26.1	43	6.3	11	1.6
Delaware	8	2	25.0	5	62.5	0	0.0	0	0.0	1	12.5	2	25.0	5	62.5	1	12.5	0	0.0
District of Columbia	11	0	0.0	10	90.9	1	9.1	3	27.3	1	9.1	2	18.2	4	36.4	3	27.3	1	9.1
Florida	170	3	1.8	140	82.4	21	12.4	19	11.2	10	5.9	16	9.4	52	30.6	8	4.7	1	0.6
Georgia	110	2	1.8	82	74.5	9	8.2	11	10.0	4	3.6	20	18.2	22	20.0	2	1.8	3	2.7
Maryland	52	4	7.7	45	86.5	6	11.5	16	30.8	5	9.6	2	3.8	15	28.8	8	15.4	1	1.9
North Carolina	112	3	2.7	99	88.4	13	11.6	19	17.0	4	3.6	21	18.8	33	29.5	8	7.1	1	1.8
South Carolina	73	1	1.4	60	82.2	10	13.7	8	11.0	3	4.1	10	13.7	12	16.4	3	4.1	0	0.0
Virginia	84	5	6.0	70	83.3	9	10.7	18	21.4	5	6.0	13	15.5	27	32.1	6	7.1	3	3.6
West Virginia	62	0	0.0	47	75.8	5	8.1	6	9.7	0	0.0	8	12.9	8	12.9	4	6.5	0	0.0
CENSUS DIVISION 4, EAST NORTH CENTRAL	725	31	4.3	605	83.4	99	13.7	163	22.5	55	7.6	104	14.3	209	28.8	66	9.1	25	3.4
Illinois	163	13	8.0	140	85.9	17	10.4	42	25.8	8	4.9	18	11.0	38	23.3	14	8.6	4	2.5
Indiana	128	1	0.8	99	77.3	14	10.9	26	20.3	3	2.3	27	21.1	36	28.1	5	3.9	4	3.1
Michigan	131	4	3.1	111	84.7	17	13.0	26	19.8	9	6.9	20	15.3	29	22.1	14	10.7	2	1.5
Ohio	156	3	1.9	132	84.6	17	10.9	33	21.2	10	6.4	26	16.7	50	32.1	15	9.6	2	1.3
Wisconsin	147	10	6.8	123	83.7	34	23.1	36	24.5	25	17.0	13	8.8	56	38.1	18	12.2	13	8.8
CENSUS DIVISION 5, EAST SOUTH CENTRAL	383	6	1.6	270	70.5	37	9.7	38	9.9	6	1.6	50	13.1	71	18.5	9	2.3	7	1.8
Alabama	94	1	1.1	64	68.1	5	5.3	8	8.5	2	2.1	8	8.5	17	18.1	2	2.1	1	1.1
Kentucky	90	3	3.3	72	80.0	9	10.0	11	12.2	1	1.1	9	10.0	20	22.2	3	3.3	2	2.2
Mississippi	112	0	0.0	66	58.9	15	13.4	7	6.3	1	0.9	16	14.3	15	13.4	0	0.0	2	1.8
Tennessee	87	2	2.3	68	78.2	8	9.2	12	13.8	2	2.3	17	19.5	19	21.8	4	4.6	2	2.3
CENSUS DIVISION 6, WEST NORTH CENTRAL	651	35	5.4	475	73.0	59	9.1	73	11.2	27	4.1	160	24.6	121	18.6	29	4.5	62	9.5
Iowa	126	4	3.2	88	69.8	11	8.7	20	15.9	4	3.2	55	43.7	26	20.6	3	2.4	12	9.5
Kansas	152	10	6.6	108	71.1	6	3.9	4	2.6	3	2.0	19	12.5	14	9.2	3	2.0	12	7.9
Minnesota	104	10	9.6	78	75.0	10	9.6	17	16.3	8	7.7	34	32.7	27	26.0	6	5.8	15	14.4
Missouri	146	1	0.7	121	82.9	23	15.8	20	13.7	5	3.4	25	17.1	24	16.4	10	6.8	2	1.4
Nebraska	50	1	2.0	34	68.0	5	10.0	5	10.0	3	6.0	6	12.0	12	24.0	2	4.0	5	10.0
North Dakota	30	3	10.0	18	60.0	3	10.0	3	10.0	0	0.0	10	33.3	8	26.7	4	13.3	3	10.0
South Dakota	43	6	14.0	28	65.1	1	2.3	4	9.3	4	9.3	11	25.6	10	23.3	1	2.3	13	30.2
CENSUS DIVISION 7, WEST SOUTH CENTRAL	896	10	1.1	695	77.6	45	5.0	53	5.9	6	0.7	102	11.4	143	16.0	17	1.9	20	1.9
Arkansas	96	2	2.1	76	79.2	3	3.1	6	6.3	0	0.0	13	13.5	16	16.7	2	2.1	2	2.1
Louisiana	99	4	4.0	61	61.6	4	4.0	6	6.1	1	1.0	6	6.1	21	21.2	3	3.0	3	3.0
Oklahoma	127	1	0.8	101	79.5	5	3.9	8	6.3	1	0.8	15	11.8	28	22.0	2	1.6	3	2.4
Texas	574	3	0.5	457	79.6	33	5.7	33	5.7	4	0.7	68	11.8	78	13.6	10	1.7	10	2.3
CENSUS DIVISION 8, MOUNTAIN	349	22	6.3	257	73.6	21	6.0	45	12.9	15	4.3	69	19.8	95	27.2	17	4.9	21	6.0
Arizona	68	1	1.5	48	70.6	2	2.9	10	14.7	2	2.9	2	2.9	15	22.1	3	4.4	3	4.4
Colorado	72	3	4.2	59	81.9	5	6.9	8	11.1	3	4.2	17	23.6	21	29.2	4	5.6	5	6.9
Idaho	29	4	13.8	20	69.0	3	10.3	5	17.2	1	3.4	11	37.9	12	41.4	4	13.8	2	6.9
Montana	55	13	23.6	36	65.5	3	5.5	4	7.3	4	7.3	13	23.6	11	20.0	1	1.8	11	20.0
Nevada	30	0	0.0	20	66.7	3	10.0	5	16.7	0	0.0	3	10.0	6	20.0	0	0.0	1	3.3
New Mexico	33	0	0.0	20	75.8	0	0.0	3	9.1	0	0.0	7	21.2	11	33.3	2	6.1	0	0.0
Utah	35	1	2.9	28	80.0	4	11.4	5	14.3	2	5.7	7	20.0	16	45.7	3	8.6	3	8.6
Wyoming	27	0	0.0	21	77.8	1	3.7	5	18.5	3	11.1	9	33.3	3	11.1	0	0.0	2	7.4
CENSUS DIVISION 9, PACIFIC	481	21	4.4	371	77.1	34	7.1	57	11.9	16	3.3	41	8.5	172	35.8	32	6.7	9	1.9
Alaska	15	0	0.0	9	60.0	2	13.3	3	20.0	0	0.0	0	0.0	2	13.3	0	0.0	0	0.0
California	309	14	4.5	238	77.0	22	7.1	39	12.6	14	4.5	21	6.8	123	39.8	21	6.8	3	1.0
Hawaii	18	0	0.0	13	72.2	3	16.7	1	5.6	0	0.0	1	5.6	5	27.8	1	5.6	0	0.0
Oregon	61	3	4.9	55	90.2	1	1.6	5	8.2	1	1.6	8	13.1	13	21.3	4	6.6	2	3.3
Washington	78	4	5.1	56	71.8	6	7.7	9	11.5	1	1.3	11	14.1	29	37.2	6	7.7	4	5.1

Table 7 (Continued)

These data include only hospital-based facilities and services as reported by responding hospitals in Section C of the 2013 AHA Annual Survey, beginning on page 215. All hospitals are represented with Community Hospitals listed separately under United States. No estimates have been made for nonresponding hospitals. Definitions of facilities and services are listed in the Glossary, page 201.

CLASSIFICATION	HOSPITALS REPORTING	AUXILIARY Number	AUXILIARY Percent	BARIATRIC/ WEIGHT CONTROL SERVICES Number	Percent	BIRTHING/ LDR/ LDRP ROOM Number	Percent	BLOOD DONOR CENTER Number	Percent	BREAST CANCER SCREENING Number	Percent	BURN CARE UNITS Number	Percent	CASE MANAGEMENT Number	Percent	CHAPLAINCY/ PASTORAL CARE SERVICES Number	Percent	CHEMOTHERAPY Number	Percent
UNITED STATES	4,760	2,671	55.9	1,205	25.2	2,537	53.1	314	6.6	3,284	68.7	187	3.9	4,154	86.9	3,113	65.1	2,419	50.6
COMMUNITY HOSPITALS	4,053	2,601	64.2	1,131	27.9	2,504	61.8	308	7.6	3,205	79.1	180	4.4	3,666	90.5	2,828	69.8	2,338	57.7
CENSUS DIVISION 1. NEW ENGLAND	190	105	55.3	66	34.7	119	62.6	31	16.3	140	73.7	10	5.3	182	95.8	147	77.4	126	66.3
Connecticut	34	19	55.9	17	50.0	23	67.6	5	14.7	25	73.5	1	2.9	33	97.1	31	91.2	21	61.8
Maine	37	22	59.5	7	18.9	26	70.3	0	0.0	30	81.1	1	2.7	35	94.6	28	75.8	25	67.6
Massachusetts	66	31	47.0	30	45.5	38	57.6	21	31.8	44	66.7	6	9.1	62	93.9	50	75.8	42	63.6
New Hampshire	26	17	65.4	7	26.9	17	65.4	4	15.4	21	80.8	0	0.0	25	96.2	20	76.9	18	69.2
Rhode Island	13	7	53.8	3	23.1	5	38.5	0	0.0	9	69.2	1	7.7	13	100.0	10	76.9	10	76.9
Vermont	14	9	64.3	2	14.3	10	71.4	1	7.1	11	78.6	1	7.1	14	100.0	10	71.4	10	71.4
CENSUS DIVISION 2. MIDDLE ATLANTIC	423	259	61.2	181	42.8	240	56.7	64	15.1	326	77.1	25	5.9	387	91.5	324	76.6	273	64.5
New Jersey	72	51	70.8	41	56.9	44	61.1	11	15.3	52	72.2	4	5.6	66	91.7	60	83.3	48	66.7
New York	156	103	66.0	72	46.2	107	68.6	36	23.1	135	86.5	14	9.0	149	95.5	128	82.1	117	75.0
Pennsylvania	195	105	53.8	68	34.9	89	45.6	17	8.7	139	71.3	7	3.6	172	88.2	136	69.7	108	55.4
CENSUS DIVISION 3. SOUTH ATLANTIC	682	418	61.3	187	27.4	362	53.1	52	7.6	502	73.6	27	4.0	621	91.1	520	76.2	378	55.4
Delaware	8	5	62.5	4	50.0	4	50.0	0	0.0	4	50.0	0	0.0	6	75.0	7	87.5	5	62.5
District of Columbia	11	3	27.3	7	63.6	7	63.6	3	27.3	7	63.6	1	9.1	10	90.9	11	100.0	7	63.6
Florida	170	97	57.1	52	30.6	76	44.7	10	5.9	115	67.6	11	6.5	160	94.1	123	72.4	102	60.0
Georgia	110	73	66.4	26	23.6	53	48.2	4	3.6	82	74.5	2	1.8	98	89.1	76	69.1	47	42.7
Maryland	52	42	80.8	18	34.6	31	59.6	13	25.0	37	71.2	3	5.8	46	88.5	47	90.4	43	82.7
North Carolina	112	68	60.7	31	27.7	78	69.6	7	6.3	89	79.5	3	2.7	102	91.1	95	84.8	68	60.7
South Carolina	73	39	53.4	14	19.2	42	57.5	5	6.8	54	74.0	4	5.5	67	91.8	47	64.4	28	38.4
Virginia	84	53	63.1	24	28.6	44	52.4	9	10.7	66	78.6	4	4.8	81	96.4	69	82.1	53	63.1
West Virginia	62	38	61.3	11	17.7	27	43.5	1	1.6	48	77.4	1	1.6	51	82.3	45	72.6	25	40.3
CENSUS DIVISION 4. EAST NORTH CENTRAL	725	448	61.8	195	26.9	447	61.7	40	5.5	584	80.6	32	4.4	660	91.0	543	74.9	465	64.1
Illinois	163	108	66.3	51	31.3	106	65.0	12	7.4	143	87.7	8	4.9	158	96.9	134	82.2	118	72.4
Indiana	128	61	47.7	26	20.3	77	60.2	3	2.3	94	73.4	3	2.3	118	92.2	96	75.0	72	56.3
Michigan	131	92	70.2	49	37.4	75	57.3	8	6.1	108	82.4	7	5.3	115	87.8	91	69.5	88	67.2
Ohio	156	105	67.3	39	25.0	94	60.3	14	9.0	129	82.7	8	5.1	141	90.4	129	82.7	107	68.6
Wisconsin	147	82	55.8	30	20.4	95	64.6	3	2.0	110	74.8	6	4.1	128	87.1	93	63.3	80	54.4
CENSUS DIVISION 5. EAST SOUTH CENTRAL	383	175	45.7	75	19.6	165	43.1	9	2.3	250	65.3	14	3.7	314	82.0	231	60.3	131	34.2
Alabama	94	48	51.1	24	25.5	43	45.7	3	3.2	60	63.8	4	4.3	80	85.1	53	56.4	29	30.9
Kentucky	90	53	58.9	22	24.4	39	43.3	4	4.4	69	76.7	6	6.7	81	90.0	69	76.7	43	47.8
Mississippi	112	33	29.5	15	13.4	43	38.4	0	0.0	57	50.9	1	0.9	72	64.3	38	33.9	23	20.5
Tennessee	87	41	47.1	14	16.1	40	46.0	2	2.3	64	73.6	3	3.4	81	93.1	71	81.6	36	41.4
CENSUS DIVISION 6. WEST NORTH CENTRAL	651	419	64.4	123	18.9	350	53.8	21	3.2	476	73.1	30	4.6	502	77.1	344	52.8	350	53.8
Iowa	126	109	86.5	17	13.5	77	61.1	3	2.4	113	89.7	5	4.0	107	84.9	56	44.4	88	69.8
Kansas	152	78	51.3	22	14.5	69	45.4	1	0.7	82	53.9	7	4.6	96	63.2	69	45.4	50	32.9
Minnesota	104	72	69.2	31	29.8	78	75.0	5	4.8	88	84.6	3	2.9	83	79.8	59	56.7	71	68.3
Missouri	146	99	67.8	28	19.2	69	47.3	7	4.8	103	70.5	9	6.2	131	89.7	102	69.9	72	49.3
Nebraska	50	27	54.0	15	30.0	31	62.0	1	2.0	42	84.0	4	8.0	38	76.0	28	56.0	34	68.0
North Dakota	30	15	50.0	5	16.7	10	33.3	2	6.7	18	60.0	0	0.0	22	73.3	14	46.7	11	36.7
South Dakota	43	19	44.2	5	11.6	16	37.2	2	4.7	30	69.8	1	2.3	25	58.1	16	37.2	24	55.8
CENSUS DIVISION 7. WEST SOUTH CENTRAL	896	408	45.5	184	20.5	351	39.2	31	3.5	433	48.3	21	2.3	767	85.6	455	50.8	238	26.6
Arkansas	96	62	64.6	16	16.7	40	41.7	4	4.2	53	55.2	2	2.1	83	86.5	45	46.9	29	30.2
Louisiana	99	34	34.3	21	21.2	38	38.4	6	6.1	57	57.6	5	5.1	83	83.8	50	50.5	35	35.4
Oklahoma	127	63	49.6	20	15.7	54	42.5	5	3.9	68	53.5	2	1.6	109	85.8	71	55.9	27	21.3
Texas	574	249	43.4	127	22.1	219	38.2	16	2.8	255	44.4	12	2.1	492	85.7	289	50.3	147	25.6
CENSUS DIVISION 8. MOUNTAIN	349	188	53.9	71	20.3	208	59.6	17	4.9	231	66.2	9	2.6	294	84.2	193	55.3	175	50.1
Arizona	68	30	44.1	12	17.6	33	48.5	1	1.5	36	52.9	1	1.5	66	97.1	45	66.2	31	45.6
Colorado	72	44	61.1	23	31.9	47	65.3	9	12.5	56	77.8	1	1.4	65	90.3	47	65.3	49	68.1
Idaho	29	22	75.9	9	31.0	19	65.5	2	6.9	19	65.5	1	3.4	22	75.9	18	62.1	14	48.3
Montana	55	29	52.7	4	7.3	27	49.1	0	0.0	34	61.8	1	1.8	34	61.8	21	38.2	22	40.0
Nevada	30	9	30.0	7	23.3	13	43.3	0	0.0	16	53.3	1	3.3	27	90.0	14	46.7	14	46.7
New Mexico	33	20	60.6	2	6.1	21	63.6	2	6.1	21	63.6	3	9.1	29	87.9	24	72.7	11	33.3
Utah	35	17	48.6	11	31.4	28	80.0	3	8.6	29	82.9	1	2.9	29	82.9	13	37.1	19	54.3
Wyoming	27	17	63.0	3	11.1	20	74.1	0	0.0	20	74.1	0	0.0	22	81.5	11	40.7	15	55.6
CENSUS DIVISION 9. PACIFIC	481	251	52.2	123	25.6	295	61.3	49	10.2	342	71.1	19	4.0	427	88.8	356	74.0	283	58.8
Alaska	15	4	26.7	1	6.7	8	53.3	0	0.0	10	66.7	0	0.0	11	73.3	10	66.7	8	53.3
California	309	160	51.8	85	27.5	182	58.9	47	15.2	212	68.6	14	4.5	280	90.6	227	73.5	184	59.5
Hawaii	18	5	27.8	6	33.3	7	38.9	1	5.6	12	66.7	3	16.7	15	83.3	8	44.4	11	61.1
Oregon	61	45	73.8	16	26.2	51	83.6	1	1.6	54	88.5	1	1.6	56	91.8	51	83.6	40	65.6
Washington	78	37	47.4	15	19.2	47	60.3	0	0.0	54	69.2	1	1.3	65	83.3	60	76.9	40	51.3

Table 7 (Continued)

These data include only hospital-based facilities and services as reported by responding hospitals in Section C of the 2013 AHA Annual Survey, beginning on page 215. All hospitals are represented with Community Hospitals listed separately under United States. No estimates have been made for nonresponding hospitals. Definitions of facilities and services are listed in the Glossary, page 201.

CLASSIFICATION	HOSPITALS REPORTING	CHILDREN'S WELLNESS PROGRAM Number	CHILDREN'S WELLNESS PROGRAM Percent	CHIROPRACTIC SERVICES Number	CHIROPRACTIC SERVICES Percent	COMMUNITY OUTREACH Number	COMMUNITY OUTREACH Percent	COMPLEMENTARY AND ALTERNATIVE MEDICINE SERVICES Number	COMPLEMENTARY AND ALTERNATIVE MEDICINE SERVICES Percent	COMPUTER ASSISTED ORTHOPEDIC SURGERY (CAOS) Number	COMPUTER ASSISTED ORTHOPEDIC SURGERY (CAOS) Percent	CRISIS PREVENTION Number	CRISIS PREVENTION Percent	DENTAL SERVICES Number	DENTAL SERVICES Percent	ENABLING SERVICES Number	ENABLING SERVICES Percent	ENROLLMENT ASSISTANCE SERVICES Number	ENROLLMENT ASSISTANCE SERVICES Percent	EXTRACORPOREAL SHOCK WAVE LITHOTRIPTER (ESWL) Number	EXTRACORPOREAL SHOCK WAVE LITHOTRIPTER (ESWL) Percent
UNITED STATES	4,780	918	19.2	132	2.8	3,260	68.2	927	19.4	733	15.3	1,047	21.9	987	20.6	1,219	25.5	2,639	55.2	1,291	27.0
COMMUNITY HOSPITALS	4,053	889	21.9	100	2.5	3,031	74.8	872	21.5	713	17.6	909	22.4	842	20.8	1,138	28.1	2,468	60.9	1,237	30.5
CENSUS DIVISION 1, NEW ENGLAND	190	62	32.6	6	3.2	152	80.0	83	43.7	38	20.0	76	40.0	53	27.9	76	40.0	144	75.8	95	50.0
Connecticut	34	11	32.4	0	0.0	29	85.3	21	61.8	8	23.5	22	64.7	15	44.1	13	38.2	27	79.4	18	52.9
Maine	37	10	27.0	1	2.7	28	75.7	12	32.4	2	5.4	8	21.6	4	10.8	12	32.4	23	62.2	17	45.9
Massachusetts	66	24	36.4	3	4.5	50	75.8	27	40.9	14	21.2	27	40.9	17	25.8	26	39.4	53	80.3	33	50.0
New Hampshire	26	11	42.3	1	3.8	22	84.6	13	50.0	7	26.9	8	30.8	10	38.5	11	42.3	20	76.9	13	50.0
Rhode Island	13	3	23.1	1	7.7	13	100.0	3	50.0	4	30.8	7	53.8	3	23.1	8	61.5	11	84.6	8	61.5
Vermont	14	3	21.4	0	0.0	10	71.4	7	50.0	3	21.4	4	28.6	4	28.6	6	42.9	10	71.4	6	42.9
CENSUS DIVISION 2, MIDDLE ATLANTIC	423	140	33.1	22	5.2	330	78.0	128	30.3	91	21.5	171	40.4	169	40.0	161	38.1	284	67.1	150	35.5
New Jersey	72	31	43.1	4	5.6	58	80.6	29	40.3	19	26.4	42	58.3	30	41.7	35	48.6	51	70.8	21	29.2
New York	156	65	41.7	13	8.3	136	87.2	57	36.5	39	25.0	81	51.9	80	51.3	59	37.8	114	73.1	61	39.1
Pennsylvania	195	44	22.6	5	2.6	136	69.7	42	21.5	33	16.9	48	24.6	59	30.3	67	34.4	119	61.0	68	34.9
CENSUS DIVISION 3, SOUTH ATLANTIC	682	116	17.0	15	2.2	492	72.1	130	19.1	133	19.5	155	22.7	163	23.9	208	30.5	414	60.7	224	32.8
Delaware	8	5	62.5	0	0.0	5	62.5	2	25.0	1	12.5	3	37.5	3	37.5	2	25.0	5	62.5	3	37.5
District of Columbia	11	5	45.5	1	9.1	10	90.9	4	36.4	3	27.3	3	27.3	6	54.5	5	45.5	8	72.7	3	27.3
Florida	170	19	11.2	7	4.1	117	68.8	28	16.5	41	24.1	31	18.2	25	14.7	45	26.5	96	56.5	72	42.4
Georgia	110	11	10.0	2	1.8	71	64.5	18	16.4	26	23.6	23	20.9	18	16.4	28	25.5	66	60.0	31	28.2
Maryland	52	15	28.8	0	0.0	43	82.7	24	46.2	13	25.0	22	42.3	21	40.4	29	55.8	41	78.8	25	48.1
North Carolina	112	18	16.1	1	0.9	81	72.3	19	17.0	17	15.2	23	20.5	34	30.4	35	31.3	65	58.0	19	17.0
South Carolina	73	16	21.9	0	0.0	57	78.1	4	5.5	8	11.0	6	8.2	15	20.5	9	12.3	35	47.9	22	30.1
Virginia	84	14	16.7	2	2.4	64	76.2	26	31.0	20	23.8	30	35.7	27	32.1	43	51.2	66	78.6	33	39.3
West Virginia	62	13	21.0	2	3.2	44	71.0	5	8.1	4	6.5	14	22.6	14	22.6	12	19.4	32	51.6	16	25.8
CENSUS DIVISION 4, EAST NORTH CENTRAL	725	201	27.7	30	4.1	573	79.0	221	30.5	130	17.9	215	29.7	141	19.4	264	36.4	485	66.9	221	30.5
Illinois	163	50	30.7	4	2.5	133	81.6	43	26.4	39	23.9	61	37.4	44	27.0	61	37.4	111	68.1	44	27.0
Indiana	128	32	25.0	4	3.1	103	80.5	24	18.8	12	9.4	29	22.7	18	14.1	24	18.8	81	63.3	34	26.6
Michigan	131	48	36.6	5	3.8	107	81.7	50	38.2	21	16.0	45	34.4	33	25.2	64	48.9	99	75.6	45	34.4
Ohio	156	31	19.9	11	7.1	128	82.1	47	30.1	31	19.9	46	29.5	46	29.5	58	37.2	106	67.9	62	39.7
Wisconsin	147	40	27.2	6	4.1	102	69.4	57	38.8	27	18.4	34	23.1	0	0.0	57	38.8	88	59.9	36	24.5
CENSUS DIVISION 5, EAST SOUTH CENTRAL	383	44	11.5	7	1.8	241	62.9	26	6.8	42	10.6	48	12.5	72	18.8	64	16.7	163	42.6	92	24.0
Alabama	94	8	8.5	3	3.2	49	52.1	3	3.2	10	10.6	9	9.6	6	6.4	8	8.5	44	46.8	23	24.5
Kentucky	90	12	13.3	2	2.2	66	73.3	12	13.3	13	14.4	12	13.3	18	20.0	22	24.4	55	61.1	26	28.9
Mississippi	112	13	11.6	2	1.8	66	58.9	4	3.6	8	7.1	8	7.1	32	28.6	9	8.0	19	17.0	17	15.2
Tennessee	87	11	12.6	0	0.0	60	69.0	7	8.0	11	12.6	19	21.8	16	18.4	25	28.7	45	51.7	26	29.9
CENSUS DIVISION 6, WEST NORTH CENTRAL	651	111	17.1	21	3.2	418	64.2	109	16.7	54	8.3	117	18.0	115	17.7	130	20.0	309	47.5	109	16.7
Iowa	126	25	19.8	3	2.4	95	75.4	27	21.4	11	8.7	31	24.6	24	19.0	32	25.4	77	61.1	14	11.1
Kansas	152	13	8.6	1	0.7	65	42.8	9	5.9	6	3.9	6	3.9	15	9.9	12	7.9	54	35.5	20	13.2
Minnesota	104	22	21.2	9	8.7	76	73.1	30	28.8	10	9.6	24	23.1	18	17.3	21	20.2	51	49.0	19	18.3
Missouri	146	29	19.9	4	2.7	97	66.4	24	16.4	13	8.9	33	22.6	43	29.5	48	32.9	77	52.7	36	24.7
Nebraska	50	10	20.0	0	0.0	39	78.0	8	16.0	10	20.0	12	24.0	7	14.0	9	18.0	25	50.0	12	24.0
North Dakota	30	7	23.3	3	10.0	17	56.7	5	16.7	3	10.0	5	16.7	3	10.0	5	16.7	15	50.0	3	10.0
South Dakota	43	5	11.6	1	2.3	29	67.4	6	14.0	1	2.3	6	14.0	5	11.6	3	7.0	10	23.3	5	11.6
CENSUS DIVISION 7, WEST SOUTH CENTRAL	896	100	11.2	7	0.8	455	50.8	52	5.8	93	10.4	88	9.8	120	13.4	116	12.9	356	39.7	165	18.4
Arkansas	96	8	8.3	0	0.0	55	57.3	5	5.2	5	5.2	13	13.5	8	8.3	8	8.3	44	45.8	15	15.6
Louisiana	99	19	19.2	1	1.0	57	57.6	5	5.1	14	14.1	16	16.2	17	17.2	12	12.1	49	49.5	17	17.2
Oklahoma	127	14	11.0	3	2.4	66	52.0	5	3.9	10	7.9	11	8.7	19	15.0	10	7.9	44	34.6	23	18.1
Texas	574	59	10.3	3	0.5	277	48.3	37	6.4	64	11.1	48	8.4	76	13.2	86	15.0	219	38.2	110	19.2
CENSUS DIVISION 8, MOUNTAIN	349	66	18.9	9	2.6	232	66.5	73	20.9	56	16.0	75	21.5	69	19.8	76	21.8	194	55.6	81	23.2
Arizona	68	15	22.1	2	2.9	37	54.4	21	30.9	18	26.5	13	19.1	12	17.6	22	32.4	40	58.8	22	32.4
Colorado	72	8	11.1	4	5.6	58	80.6	23	31.9	12	16.7	13	18.1	13	18.1	18	25.0	47	65.3	13	18.1
Idaho	29	7	24.1	1	3.4	23	79.3	6	20.7	10	34.5	5	17.2	9	31.0	5	17.2	15	51.7	3	10.3
Montana	55	12	21.8	1	1.8	34	61.8	10	18.2	5	9.1	10	18.2	5	9.1	6	10.9	31	56.4	7	12.7
Nevada	30	7	23.3	0	0.0	16	53.3	1	3.3	2	6.7	6	20.0	4	13.3	6	20.0	13	43.3	5	16.7
New Mexico	33	6	18.2	0	0.0	21	63.6	3	9.1	2	6.1	5	15.2	9	27.3	4	12.1	20	60.6	13	39.4
Utah	35	8	22.9	1	2.9	26	74.3	6	17.1	6	17.1	17	48.6	14	40.0	12	34.3	20	57.1	13	37.1
Wyoming	27	3	11.1	0	0.0	17	63.0	3	11.1	1	3.7	6	22.2	3	11.1	3	11.1	8	29.6	5	18.5
CENSUS DIVISION 9, PACIFIC	481	78	16.2	15	3.1	367	76.3	105	21.8	96	20.0	102	21.2	85	17.7	124	25.8	290	60.3	154	32.0
Alaska	15	1	6.7	0	0.0	6	40.0	1	6.7	0	0.0	3	20.0	4	26.7	2	13.3	7	46.7	3	20.0
California	309	46	14.9	10	3.2	237	76.7	66	21.4	60	19.4	60	19.4	61	19.7	78	25.2	176	57.0	104	33.7
Hawaii	18	2	11.1	1	5.6	11	61.1	4	22.2	1	5.6	3	16.7	4	22.2	5	27.8	8	44.4	5	27.8
Oregon	61	12	19.7	1	1.6	55	90.2	17	27.9	20	32.8	11	18.0	5	8.2	19	31.1	48	78.7	21	34.4
Washington	78	17	21.8	3	3.8	58	74.4	17	21.8	15	19.2	25	32.1	11	14.1	20	25.6	51	65.4	21	26.9

Table 7 (Continued)

These data include only hospital-based facilities and services as reported by responding hospitals in Section C of the 2013 AHA Annual Survey, beginning on page 215. All hospitals are represented with Community Hospitals listed separately under United States. No estimates have been made for nonresponding hospitals. Definitions of facilities and services are listed in the Glossary, page 201.

CLASSIFICATION	HOSPITALS REPORTING	FERTILITY CLINIC Number	FERTILITY CLINIC Percent	FITNESS CENTER Number	FITNESS CENTER Percent	FREESTANDING OUTPATIENT CARE CENTER Number	FREESTANDING OUTPATIENT CARE CENTER Percent	GENETIC TESTING/ COUNSELING Number	GENETIC TESTING/ COUNSELING Percent	GERIATRIC SERVICES Number	GERIATRIC SERVICES Percent	HEALTH FAIR Number	HEALTH FAIR Percent	COMMUNITY HEALTH EDUCATION Number	COMMUNITY HEALTH EDUCATION Percent	HEALTH RESEARCH Number	HEALTH RESEARCH Percent	HEALTH SCREENINGS Number	HEALTH SCREENINGS Percent	HEMODIALYSIS Number	HEMODIALYSIS Percent	HIV/AIDS SERVICES Number	HIV/AIDS SERVICES Percent
UNITED STATES	4,780	247	5.2	1,368	28.6	1,490	31.2	731	15.3	1,818	38.0	3,447	72.1	3,569	74.7	1,148	24.0	3,570	74.7	1,460	30.5	1,076	22.5
COMMUNITY HOSPITALS	4,053	242	6.0	1,273	31.4	1,378	34.0	706	17.4	1,646	40.6	3,242	80.0	3,324	82.0	1,054	26.0	3,355	82.8	1,370	33.8	994	24.5
CENSUS DIVISION 1, NEW ENGLAND	190	24	12.6	63	33.2	88	46.3	55	28.9	87	45.8	150	78.9	157	82.6	82	43.2	157	82.6	55	28.9	82	43.2
Connecticut	34	6	17.6	17	50.0	22	64.7	12	35.3	17	50.0	26	76.5	27	79.4	20	58.8	27	79.4	10	29.4	16	47.1
Maine	37	3	8.1	12	32.4	15	40.5	6	16.2	11	29.7	29	78.4	30	81.1	9	24.3	32	86.5	6	16.2	13	35.1
Massachusetts	66	9	13.6	15	22.7	30	45.5	24	36.4	31	47.0	51	77.3	51	77.3	32	48.5	52	78.8	27	40.9	31	47.0
New Hampshire	26	3	11.5	8	30.8	10	38.5	5	19.2	14	53.8	23	88.5	25	96.2	7	26.9	23	88.5	3	11.5	12	46.2
Rhode Island	13	1	7.7	5	38.5	7	53.8	3	23.1	9	69.2	12	92.3	11	84.6	9	69.2	11	84.6	7	53.8	6	46.2
Vermont	14	2	14.3	6	42.9	4	28.6	5	35.7	5	35.7	9	64.3	13	92.9	5	35.7	12	85.7	2	14.3	4	28.6
CENSUS DIVISION 2, MIDDLE ATLANTIC	423	48	11.3	127	30.0	220	52.0	140	33.1	236	55.8	338	79.9	344	81.3	163	38.5	347	82.0	205	48.5	176	41.6
New Jersey	72	10	13.9	22	30.6	41	56.9	32	44.4	47	65.3	54	75.0	58	80.6	34	47.2	55	76.4	47	65.3	36	50.0
New York	156	26	16.7	51	32.7	95	60.9	65	41.7	99	63.5	139	89.1	138	88.5	71	45.5	142	91.0	96	61.5	83	53.2
Pennsylvania	195	12	6.2	54	27.7	84	43.1	43	22.1	90	46.2	145	74.4	148	75.9	58	29.7	150	76.9	62	31.8	57	29.2
CENSUS DIVISION 3, SOUTH ATLANTIC	682	35	5.1	199	29.2	262	38.4	128	18.8	255	37.4	527	77.3	533	78.2	196	28.7	542	79.5	288	42.2	195	28.6
Delaware	8	0	0.0	3	37.5	4	50.0	4	50.0	2	25.0	5	62.5	6	75.0	5	62.5	6	75.0	4	50.0	4	50.0
District of Columbia	11	2	18.2	2	18.2	6	54.5	6	54.5	6	54.5	9	81.8	10	90.9	7	63.6	9	81.8	7	63.6	7	63.6
Florida	170	10	5.9	51	30.0	62	36.5	40	23.5	53	31.2	127	74.7	135	79.4	57	33.5	126	74.1	84	49.4	43	25.3
Georgia	110	4	3.6	27	24.5	43	39.1	14	12.7	37	33.6	74	67.3	76	69.1	26	23.6	84	76.4	42	38.2	26	23.6
Maryland	52	5	9.6	14	26.9	20	38.5	22	42.3	35	67.3	45	86.5	42	80.8	28	53.8	45	86.5	37	71.2	26	50.0
North Carolina	112	6	5.4	42	37.5	42	37.5	16	14.3	46	41.1	90	80.4	93	83.0	27	24.1	95	84.8	36	32.1	26	23.2
South Carolina	73	2	2.7	21	28.8	22	30.1	6	8.2	30	41.1	54	74.0	54	74.0	14	19.2	53	72.6	29	39.7	24	32.9
Virginia	84	4	4.8	19	22.6	41	48.8	15	17.9	27	32.1	69	82.1	67	79.8	23	27.4	69	82.1	32	38.1	29	34.5
West Virginia	62	2	3.2	20	32.3	22	35.5	5	8.1	19	30.6	54	87.1	50	80.6	9	14.5	55	88.7	17	27.4	10	16.1
CENSUS DIVISION 4, EAST NORTH CENTRAL	725	43	5.9	267	36.8	288	39.7	118	16.3	349	48.1	569	78.5	620	85.5	219	30.2	596	82.2	232	32.0	172	23.7
Illinois	163	12	7.4	53	32.5	66	40.5	27	16.6	82	50.3	143	87.7	145	89.0	56	34.4	147	90.2	50	30.7	49	30.1
Indiana	128	5	3.9	39	30.5	46	35.9	15	11.7	42	32.8	97	75.8	102	79.7	31	24.2	97	75.8	33	25.8	18	14.1
Michigan	131	11	8.4	50	38.2	61	46.6	24	18.3	69	52.7	107	81.7	114	87.0	53	40.5	116	88.5	46	35.1	49	37.4
Ohio	156	11	7.1	65	41.7	68	43.6	30	19.2	60	38.5	125	80.1	136	87.2	55	35.3	135	86.5	71	45.5	49	31.4
Wisconsin	147	4	2.7	60	40.8	47	32.0	22	15.0	96	65.3	97	66.0	123	83.7	24	16.3	101	68.7	32	21.8	7	4.8
CENSUS DIVISION 5, EAST SOUTH CENTRAL	383	13	3.4	97	25.3	85	22.2	28	7.3	122	31.9	258	67.4	248	64.8	64	16.7	252	65.8	93	24.3	68	17.8
Alabama	94	3	3.2	26	27.7	21	22.3	6	6.4	32	34.0	65	69.1	57	60.6	15	16.0	66	70.2	30	31.9	14	14.9
Kentucky	90	2	2.2	18	20.0	26	28.9	9	10.0	31	34.4	72	80.0	74	82.2	20	22.2	74	82.2	23	25.6	14	15.6
Mississippi	112	2	1.8	31	27.7	12	10.7	2	1.8	21	18.8	55	49.1	55	49.1	6	5.4	48	42.9	15	13.4	20	17.9
Tennessee	87	6	6.9	22	25.3	26	29.9	11	12.6	38	43.7	66	75.9	62	71.3	23	26.4	64	73.6	25	28.7	20	23.0
CENSUS DIVISION 6, WEST NORTH CENTRAL	651	30	4.6	230	35.3	115	17.7	65	10.0	243	37.3	456	70.0	491	75.4	97	14.9	521	80.0	137	21.0	107	16.4
Iowa	126	3	2.4	48	38.1	18	14.3	9	7.1	56	44.4	105	83.3	111	88.1	14	11.1	119	94.4	21	16.7	21	16.7
Kansas	152	3	2.0	41	27.0	15	9.9	10	6.6	47	30.9	82	53.9	78	51.3	11	7.2	89	58.6	19	12.5	15	9.9
Minnesota	104	7	6.7	36	34.6	20	19.2	17	16.3	45	43.3	73	70.2	89	85.6	17	16.3	86	82.7	23	22.1	21	20.2
Missouri	146	9	6.2	55	37.7	44	30.1	18	12.3	52	35.6	107	73.3	113	77.4	33	22.6	117	80.1	45	30.8	33	22.6
Nebraska	50	4	8.0	21	42.0	9	18.0	6	12.0	18	36.0	34	68.0	40	80.0	13	26.0	43	86.0	12	24.0	8	16.0
North Dakota	30	3	10.0	12	40.0	5	16.7	3	10.0	15	50.0	21	70.0	24	80.0	5	16.7	25	83.3	7	23.3	4	13.3
South Dakota	43	1	2.3	17	39.5	4	9.3	2	4.7	10	23.3	34	79.1	36	83.7	4	9.3	42	97.7	10	23.3	3	7.0
CENSUS DIVISION 7, WEST SOUTH CENTRAL	896	19	2.1	190	21.2	178	19.9	60	6.7	248	27.7	549	61.3	542	60.5	105	11.7	539	60.2	180	20.1	98	10.9
Arkansas	96	1	1.0	21	21.9	14	14.6	4	4.2	31	32.3	67	69.8	62	64.6	10	10.4	71	74.0	13	13.5	12	12.5
Louisiana	99	2	2.0	16	16.2	28	28.3	9	9.1	34	34.3	65	65.7	65	65.7	18	18.2	57	57.6	19	19.2	16	16.2
Oklahoma	127	3	2.4	24	18.9	19	15.0	8	6.3	28	22.0	77	60.6	83	65.4	16	12.6	79	62.2	23	18.1	11	8.7
Texas	574	13	2.3	129	22.5	117	20.4	39	6.8	155	27.0	340	59.2	332	57.8	61	10.6	332	57.8	125	21.8	59	10.3
CENSUS DIVISION 8, MOUNTAIN	349	11	3.2	92	26.4	93	26.6	46	13.2	111	31.8	259	74.2	265	75.9	70	20.1	266	76.2	91	26.1	64	18.3
Arizona	68	2	2.9	20	29.4	16	23.5	8	11.8	14	20.6	42	61.8	52	76.5	22	32.4	46	67.6	30	44.1	20	29.4
Colorado	72	3	4.2	27	37.5	27	37.5	23	31.9	20	27.8	56	77.8	63	87.5	21	29.2	57	79.2	21	29.2	15	20.8
Idaho	29	1	3.4	9	31.0	10	34.5	5	17.2	12	41.4	24	82.8	24	82.8	6	20.7	25	86.2	5	17.2	4	13.8
Montana	55	0	0.0	9	16.4	9	16.4	4	7.3	26	47.3	49	89.1	38	69.1	5	9.1	48	87.3	4	7.3	9	16.4
Nevada	30	0	0.0	2	6.7	6	20.0	0	0.0	8	26.7	17	56.7	17	56.7	4	13.3	15	50.0	6	20.0	4	13.3
New Mexico	33	0	0.0	9	27.3	8	24.2	0	0.0	9	27.3	23	69.7	20	60.6	2	6.1	25	75.8	6	21.2	4	12.1
Utah	35	4	11.4	13	37.1	14	40.0	6	17.1	13	37.1	28	80.0	30	85.7	10	28.6	28	80.0	12	34.3	7	20.0
Wyoming	27	0	0.0	3	11.1	3	11.1	0	0.0	9	33.3	20	74.1	21	77.8	0	0.0	22	81.5	6	22.2	1	3.7
CENSUS DIVISION 9, PACIFIC	481	24	5.0	103	21.4	161	33.5	91	18.9	167	34.7	341	70.9	369	76.7	152	31.6	350	72.8	179	37.2	114	23.7
Alaska	15	0	0.0	3	20.0	2	13.3	0	0.0	1	6.7	8	53.3	11	73.3	1	6.7	10	66.7	1	6.7	1	6.7
California	309	17	5.5	61	19.7	110	35.6	66	21.4	114	36.9	212	68.6	225	72.8	105	34.0	220	71.2	132	42.7	84	27.2
Hawaii	18	1	5.6	3	16.7	4	22.2	3	16.7	5	27.8	11	61.1	13	72.2	8	44.4	12	66.7	6	33.3	2	11.1
Oregon	61	1	1.6	20	32.8	22	36.1	6	9.8	21	34.4	52	85.2	55	90.2	13	21.3	52	85.2	18	29.5	14	23.0
Washington	78	5	6.4	16	20.5	23	29.5	16	20.5	26	33.3	58	74.4	65	83.3	25	32.1	56	71.8	22	28.2	13	16.7

Table 7 (Continued)

These data include only hospital-based facilities and services as reported by responding hospitals in Section C of the 2013 AHA Annual Survey, beginning on page 215. All hospitals are represented with Community Hospitals listed separately under United States. No estimates have been made for nonresponding hospitals. Definitions of facilities and services are listed in the Glossary, page 201.

CLASSIFICATION	HOSPITALS REPORTING	HOME HEALTH SERVICES Number	Percent	HOSPICE Number	Percent	HOSPITAL-BASED OUTPATIENT CARE CENTER SERVICES Number	Percent	IMMUNIZATION PROGRAM Number	Percent	INDIGENT CARE CLINIC Number	Percent	LINGUISTIC/TRANSLATION SERVICES Number	Percent	MEALS ON WHEELS Number	Percent	MOBILE HEALTH SERVICES Number	Percent	NEONATAL INTERMEDIATE CARE UNITS Number	Percent	NEUROLOGICAL SERVICES Number	Percent	NUTRITION PROGRAMS CENTER Number	Percent
UNITED STATES	4,780	1,222	25.6	968	20.3	3,452	72.2	1,935	40.5	785	16.4	2,640	55.2	407	8.5	532	11.1	714	14.9	2,326	48.7	3,509	73.4
COMMUNITY HOSPITALS	4,053	1,160	28.6	900	22.2	3,201	79.0	1,784	44.0	751	18.5	2,429	59.9	395	9.7	497	12.3	707	17.4	2,172	53.6	3,180	78.5
CENSUS DIVISION 1, NEW ENGLAND	190	35	18.4	49	25.8	163	85.8	116	61.1	49	25.8	125	65.8	7	3.7	25	13.2	25	13.2	127	66.8	171	90.0
Connecticut	34	3	8.8	14	41.2	29	85.3	22	64.7	13	38.2	23	67.6	1	2.9	7	20.6	5	14.7	24	70.6	30	88.2
Maine	37	6	16.2	6	16.2	30	81.1	26	70.3	8	21.6	18	48.6	2	5.4	4	10.8	3	8.1	18	48.6	35	94.6
Massachusetts	66	17	25.8	15	22.7	57	86.4	37	56.1	13	19.7	50	75.8	1	1.5	8	12.1	13	19.7	47	71.2	59	89.4
New Hampshire	26	5	19.2	7	26.9	24	92.3	15	57.7	7	26.9	16	61.5	1	3.8	4	15.4	2	7.7	20	76.9	25	96.2
Rhode Island	13	3	23.1	3	23.1	12	92.3	9	69.2	5	38.5	11	84.6	0	0.0	1	7.7	1	7.7	11	84.6	11	84.6
Vermont	14	1	7.1	4	28.6	11	78.6	7	50.0	3	21.4	7	50.0	2	14.3	1	7.1	1	7.1	7	50.0	11	78.6
CENSUS DIVISION 2, MIDDLE ATLANTIC	423	114	27.0	114	27.0	344	81.3	227	53.7	152	35.9	274	64.8	36	8.5	73	17.3	116	27.4	296	70.0	346	81.8
New Jersey	72	16	22.2	18	25.0	60	83.3	37	51.4	40	55.6	54	75.0	12	16.7	24	33.3	39	54.2	59	81.9	62	86.1
New York	156	37	23.7	46	29.5	139	89.1	99	63.5	69	44.2	117	75.0	13	8.3	35	22.4	54	34.6	119	76.3	134	85.9
Pennsylvania	195	61	31.3	50	25.6	145	74.4	91	46.7	43	22.1	103	52.8	11	5.6	14	7.2	23	11.8	118	60.5	150	76.9
CENSUS DIVISION 3, SOUTH ATLANTIC	682	154	22.6	126	18.5	505	74.0	237	34.8	120	17.6	392	57.5	30	4.4	110	16.1	144	21.1	401	58.8	518	76.0
Delaware	8	3	37.5	1	12.5	5	62.5	5	62.5	1	12.5	6	75.0	0	0.0	0	0.0	2	25.0	5	62.5	6	75.0
District of Columbia	11	1	9.1	1	9.1	10	90.9	9	81.8	5	45.5	10	90.9	1	9.1	6	54.5	4	36.4	10	90.9	11	100.0
Florida	170	40	23.5	21	12.4	115	67.6	47	27.6	29	17.1	90	52.9	2	1.2	24	14.1	28	16.5	117	68.8	119	70.0
Georgia	110	14	12.7	17	15.5	70	63.6	25	22.7	14	12.7	62	56.4	1	0.9	13	11.8	27	24.5	53	48.2	84	76.4
Maryland	52	8	15.4	14	26.9	44	84.6	33	63.5	23	44.2	39	75.0	5	9.6	12	23.1	5	9.6	42	80.8	46	88.5
North Carolina	112	29	25.9	19	17.0	92	82.1	37	33.0	17	15.2	67	59.8	4	3.6	22	19.6	36	32.1	60	53.6	85	75.9
South Carolina	73	14	19.2	9	12.3	53	72.6	19	26.0	7	9.6	37	50.7	5	6.8	11	15.1	26	35.6	33	45.2	50	68.5
Virginia	84	29	34.5	37	44.0	66	78.6	32	38.1	18	21.4	56	66.7	8	9.5	19	22.6	15	17.9	52	61.9	69	82.1
West Virginia	62	16	25.8	7	11.3	50	80.6	30	48.4	6	9.7	25	40.3	4	6.5	3	4.8	1	1.6	29	46.8	48	77.4
CENSUS DIVISION 4, EAST NORTH CENTRAL	725	220	30.3	191	26.3	571	78.8	349	48.1	162	22.3	453	62.5	121	16.7	91	12.6	86	11.9	420	57.9	617	85.1
Illinois	163	53	32.5	48	29.4	131	80.4	68	41.7	31	19.0	103	63.2	29	17.8	19	11.7	32	19.6	104	63.8	137	84.0
Indiana	128	40	31.3	32	25.0	93	72.7	51	39.8	23	18.0	71	55.5	28	21.9	16	12.5	18	14.1	64	50.0	103	80.5
Michigan	131	46	35.1	44	33.6	112	85.5	84	64.1	39	29.8	89	67.9	13	9.9	15	11.5	11	8.4	83	63.4	115	87.8
Ohio	156	53	34.0	44	28.2	121	77.6	74	47.4	46	29.5	103	66.0	18	11.5	23	14.7	25	16.0	103	66.0	136	87.2
Wisconsin	147	28	19.0	23	15.6	114	77.6	72	49.0	23	15.6	87	59.2	33	22.4	18	12.2	0	0.0	66	44.9	126	85.7
CENSUS DIVISION 5, EAST SOUTH CENTRAL	383	80	20.9	45	11.7	213	55.6	93	24.3	32	8.4	169	44.1	10	2.6	32	8.4	68	17.8	144	37.6	215	56.1
Alabama	94	22	23.4	9	9.6	56	59.6	17	18.1	6	6.4	40	42.6	3	3.2	5	5.3	10	10.6	39	41.5	49	52.1
Kentucky	90	26	28.9	10	11.1	60	66.7	19	21.1	10	11.1	50	55.6	5	5.6	11	12.2	14	15.6	46	51.1	65	72.2
Mississippi	112	10	8.9	8	7.1	44	39.3	34	30.4	9	8.0	32	28.6	1	0.9	6	5.4	31	27.7	23	20.5	39	34.8
Tennessee	87	22	25.3	18	20.7	53	60.9	23	26.4	7	8.0	47	54.0	1	1.1	10	11.5	13	14.9	36	41.4	62	71.3
CENSUS DIVISION 6, WEST NORTH CENTRAL	651	242	37.2	177	27.2	500	76.8	292	44.9	52	8.0	312	47.9	105	16.1	63	9.7	79	12.1	202	31.0	466	71.6
Iowa	126	56	44.4	52	41.3	110	87.3	66	52.4	13	10.3	69	54.8	32	25.4	11	8.7	11	8.7	36	28.6	112	88.9
Kansas	152	47	30.9	19	12.5	111	73.0	43	28.3	5	3.3	56	36.8	29	19.1	15	9.9	15	9.9	28	18.4	79	52.0
Minnesota	104	38	36.5	39	37.5	84	80.8	56	53.8	7	6.7	49	47.1	14	13.5	8	7.7	9	8.7	33	31.7	81	77.9
Missouri	146	52	35.6	29	19.9	107	73.3	65	44.5	20	13.7	83	56.8	14	9.6	20	13.7	30	20.5	73	50.0	116	79.5
Nebraska	50	24	48.0	17	34.0	38	76.0	23	46.0	2	4.0	30	60.0	7	14.0	4	8.0	7	14.0	20	40.0	37	74.0
North Dakota	30	8	26.7	8	26.7	20	66.7	16	53.3	2	6.7	11	36.7	2	6.7	3	10.0	3	10.0	5	16.7	17	56.7
South Dakota	43	17	39.5	13	30.2	30	69.8	23	53.5	3	7.0	14	32.6	7	16.3	8	18.6	4	9.3	7	16.3	24	55.8
CENSUS DIVISION 7, WEST SOUTH CENTRAL	896	164	18.3	83	9.3	544	60.7	257	28.7	74	8.3	389	43.4	44	4.9	52	5.8	97	10.8	325	36.3	563	62.8
Arkansas	96	35	36.5	9	9.4	61	63.5	16	16.7	2	2.1	38	39.6	5	5.2	8	8.3	13	13.5	27	28.1	58	60.4
Louisiana	99	12	12.1	5	5.1	52	52.5	33	33.3	13	13.1	31	31.3	2	2.0	7	7.1	9	9.1	41	41.4	62	62.6
Oklahoma	127	33	26.0	16	12.6	74	58.3	42	33.1	7	5.5	59	46.5	17	13.4	6	4.7	8	6.3	38	29.9	64	50.4
Texas	574	84	14.6	53	9.2	357	62.2	166	28.9	52	9.1	261	45.5	20	3.5	31	5.4	67	11.7	219	38.2	379	66.0
CENSUS DIVISION 8, MOUNTAIN	349	83	23.8	77	22.1	247	70.8	133	38.1	51	14.6	204	58.5	31	8.9	26	7.4	39	11.2	143	41.0	253	72.5
Arizona	68	9	13.2	10	14.7	43	63.2	17	25.0	10	14.7	40	58.8	5	7.4	5	7.4	8	11.8	34	50.0	51	75.0
Colorado	72	19	26.4	12	16.7	60	83.3	25	34.7	14	19.4	50	69.4	8	11.1	5	6.9	12	16.7	38	52.8	57	79.2
Idaho	29	7	24.1	8	27.6	21	72.4	12	41.4	3	10.3	12	65.5	6	20.7	6	20.7	2	6.9	10	34.5	19	65.5
Montana	55	17	30.9	21	38.2	41	74.5	28	50.9	8	14.5	22	40.0	10	18.2	4	7.3	2	3.6	13	23.6	39	70.9
Nevada	30	4	13.3	3	10.0	16	53.3	12	40.0	4	13.3	17	56.7	0	0.0	0	0.0	3	10.0	13	43.3	20	66.7
New Mexico	33	9	27.3	7	21.2	24	72.7	16	48.5	4	12.1	21	63.6	2	6.1	1	3.0	4	12.1	10	30.3	23	69.7
Utah	35	9	25.7	9	25.7	26	74.3	14	40.0	5	14.3	23	65.7	2	5.7	2	5.7	6	17.1	16	45.7	27	77.1
Wyoming	27	9	33.3	7	25.9	16	59.3	9	33.3	3	11.1	12	44.4	2	7.4	3	11.1	2	7.4	9	33.3	17	63.0
CENSUS DIVISION 9, PACIFIC	481	130	27.0	106	22.0	365	75.9	231	48.0	93	19.3	322	66.9	23	4.8	60	12.5	60	12.5	268	55.7	360	74.8
Alaska	15	4	26.7	3	20.0	9	60.0	6	40.0	2	13.3	8	53.3	1	6.7	0	0.0	0	0.0	4	26.7	4	26.7
California	309	76	24.6	63	20.4	232	75.1	152	49.2	64	20.7	209	67.6	16	5.2	41	13.3	35	11.3	186	60.2	224	72.5
Hawaii	18	5	27.8	3	16.7	11	61.1	5	27.8	2	11.1	11	61.1	2	11.1	2	11.1	3	16.7	11	61.1	15	83.3
Oregon	61	26	42.6	22	36.1	54	88.5	26	42.6	10	16.4	46	75.4	1	1.6	7	11.5	4	6.6	25	41.0	55	90.2
Washington	78	19	24.4	15	19.2	59	75.6	42	53.8	15	19.2	48	61.5	3	3.8	10	12.8	18	23.1	42	53.8	57	73.1

Table 7 (Continued)

These data include only hospital-based facilities and services as reported by responding hospitals in Section C of the 2013 AHA Annual Survey, beginning on page 215. All hospitals are represented with Community Hospitals listed separately under United States. No estimates have been made for nonresponding hospitals. Definitions of facilities and services are listed in the Glossary, page 201.

CLASSIFICATION	HOSPITALS REPORTING	OBSTETRICS INPATIENT CARE UNITS Number	Percent	OCCUPATIONAL HEALTH SERVICES Number	Percent	ONCOLOGY SERVICES Number	Percent	ORTHOPEDIC SERVICES Number	Percent	OTHER SPECIAL CARE UNITS Number	Percent	OUTPATIENT SURGERY Number	Percent	PAIN MANAGEMENT PROGRAM Number	Percent	PALLIATIVE CARE PROGRAM Number	Percent	PALLIATIVE CARE INPATIENT UNIT Number	Percent	PATIENT CONTROLLED ANALGESIA (PCA) Number	Percent	PATIENT EDUCATION CENTER Number	Percent
UNITED STATES	4,780	2,471	51.7	3,007	62.9	2,411	50.4	3,260	68.2	768	16.1	3,777	79.0	2,446	51.2	1,697	35.5	467	9.8	3,240	67.8	2,549	53.3
COMMUNITY HOSPITALS	4,053	2,438	60.2	2,790	68.8	2,334	57.6	3,063	75.6	733	18.1	3,573	88.2	2,253	55.6	1,603	39.6	413	10.2	3,016	74.4	2,319	57.2
CENSUS DIVISION 1, NEW ENGLAND	190	118	62.1	143	75.3	133	70.0	152	80.0	26	13.7	153	80.5	122	64.2	100	52.6	31	16.3	145	76.3	118	62.1
Connecticut	34	23	67.6	19	55.9	25	73.5	24	70.6	10	29.4	25	73.5	20	58.8	24	70.6	7	20.6	25	73.5	17	50.0
Maine	37	26	70.3	24	64.9	25	67.6	33	89.2	7	18.9	32	86.5	20	54.1	17	45.9	6	16.2	30	81.1	19	51.4
Massachusetts	66	38	57.6	53	80.3	44	66.7	50	75.8	4	6.1	50	75.8	48	72.7	27	40.9	9	13.6	47	71.2	47	71.2
New Hampshire	26	17	65.4	23	88.5	19	73.1	24	92.3	4	15.4	23	88.5	16	61.5	16	61.5	6	23.1	23	88.5	17	65.4
Rhode Island	13	5	38.5	12	92.3	10	76.9	9	69.2	0	0.0	11	84.6	10	76.9	8	61.5	0	0.0	9	69.2	10	76.9
Vermont	14	9	64.3	12	85.7	10	71.4	12	85.7	1	7.1	12	85.7	8	57.1	8	57.1	3	21.4	11	78.6	8	57.1
CENSUS DIVISION 2, MIDDLE ATLANTIC	423	237	56.0	316	74.7	289	68.3	345	81.6	79	18.7	354	83.7	301	71.2	230	54.4	72	17.0	325	76.8	268	63.4
New Jersey	72	44	61.1	52	72.2	53	73.6	58	80.6	11	15.3	57	79.2	57	79.2	44	61.1	14	19.4	53	73.6	52	72.2
New York	156	103	66.0	127	81.4	123	78.8	137	87.8	32	20.5	146	93.6	116	74.4	107	68.6	41	26.3	131	84.0	100	64.1
Pennsylvania	195	90	46.2	137	70.3	113	57.9	150	76.9	36	18.5	151	77.4	128	65.6	79	40.5	17	8.7	141	72.3	116	59.5
CENSUS DIVISION 3, SOUTH ATLANTIC	682	361	52.9	468	68.6	380	55.7	516	75.7	145	21.3	545	79.9	384	56.3	264	38.7	68	10.0	487	71.4	405	59.4
Delaware	8	3	37.5	4	50.0	4	50.0	5	62.5	2	25.0	5	62.5	3	37.5	4	50.0	4	50.0	5	62.5	5	62.5
District of Columbia	11	7	63.6	8	72.7	7	63.6	9	81.8	3	27.3	8	72.7	8	72.7	7	63.6	4	36.4	8	72.7	10	90.9
Florida	170	79	46.5	103	60.6	102	60.0	131	77.1	48	28.2	135	79.4	93	54.7	66	38.8	20	11.8	120	70.6	94	55.3
Georgia	110	53	48.2	72	65.5	49	44.5	69	62.7	17	15.5	82	74.5	57	51.8	31	28.2	9	8.2	66	60.0	56	50.9
Maryland	52	31	59.6	42	80.8	43	82.7	45	86.5	11	21.2	44	88.5	43	82.7	38	73.1	8	15.4	46	88.5	36	69.2
North Carolina	112	76	67.9	87	77.7	70	62.5	92	82.1	28	25.0	100	89.3	80	71.4	39	34.8	11	9.8	86	76.8	69	61.6
South Carolina	73	42	57.5	50	68.5	28	38.4	57	78.1	19	26.0	55	75.3	30	41.1	21	28.8	2	2.7	53	72.6	45	61.6
Virginia	84	43	51.2	66	78.6	52	61.9	66	78.6	15	17.9	68	81.0	49	58.3	39	46.4	9	10.7	66	78.6	54	64.3
West Virginia	62	27	43.5	36	58.1	25	40.3	42	67.7	2	3.2	46	74.2	21	33.9	19	30.6	4	6.5	37	59.7	36	58.1
CENSUS DIVISION 4, EAST NORTH CENTRAL	725	425	58.6	507	69.9	465	64.1	558	77.0	207	28.6	631	87.0	469	64.7	302	41.7	93	12.8	566	78.1	495	68.3
Illinois	163	102	62.6	110	67.5	113	69.3	130	79.8	17	10.4	150	92.0	118	72.4	71	43.6	14	8.6	134	82.2	98	60.1
Indiana	128	68	53.1	85	66.4	68	53.1	92	71.9	24	18.8	103	80.5	66	51.6	41	32.0	12	9.4	99	77.3	76	59.4
Michigan	131	72	55.0	101	77.1	91	69.5	106	80.9	29	22.1	115	87.8	84	64.1	57	43.5	19	14.5	103	78.6	85	64.9
Ohio	156	87	55.8	118	75.6	110	70.5	132	84.6	26	16.7	137	87.8	110	70.5	67	42.9	30	19.2	123	78.8	105	67.3
Wisconsin	147	96	65.3	93	63.3	83	56.5	98	66.7	111	75.5	126	85.7	91	61.9	66	44.9	18	12.2	107	72.8	131	89.1
CENSUS DIVISION 5, EAST SOUTH CENTRAL	383	165	43.1	183	47.8	141	36.8	204	53.3	57	14.9	280	73.1	124	32.4	86	22.5	25	6.5	201	52.5	173	45.2
Alabama	94	44	46.8	46	48.9	32	34.0	54	57.4	10	10.6	68	72.3	39	41.5	18	19.1	5	4.3	50	53.2	41	43.6
Kentucky	90	38	42.2	45	50.0	46	51.1	63	70.0	13	14.4	74	82.2	51	56.7	27	30.0	5	5.6	58	64.4	47	52.2
Mississippi	112	42	37.5	35	31.3	26	23.2	34	30.4	14	12.5	70	62.5	3	2.7	17	15.2	6	5.4	39	34.8	46	41.1
Tennessee	87	41	47.1	57	65.5	37	42.5	53	60.9	20	23.0	68	78.2	31	35.6	24	27.6	10	11.5	54	62.1	39	44.8
CENSUS DIVISION 6, WEST NORTH CENTRAL	651	331	50.8	435	66.8	296	45.5	399	61.3	76	11.7	548	84.2	296	45.5	198	30.4	45	6.9	426	65.4	316	48.5
Iowa	126	73	57.9	92	73.0	75	59.5	92	73.0	11	8.7	118	93.7	67	53.2	39	31.0	5	4.0	95	75.4	68	54.0
Kansas	152	63	41.4	83	54.6	39	25.7	67	44.1	12	7.9	119	78.3	57	37.5	28	18.4	6	3.9	81	53.3	53	34.9
Minnesota	104	73	70.2	84	80.8	53	51.0	69	66.3	12	11.5	99	95.2	45	43.3	40	38.5	8	7.7	74	71.2	51	49.0
Missouri	146	69	47.3	101	69.2	76	52.1	103	70.5	30	20.5	108	74.0	74	50.7	54	37.0	11	7.5	108	74.0	86	58.9
Nebraska	50	27	54.0	31	62.0	32	64.0	40	80.0	6	12.0	47	94.0	28	56.0	19	38.0	7	14.0	33	66.0	25	50.0
North Dakota	30	10	33.3	15	50.0	8	26.7	10	33.3	2	6.7	23	76.7	11	36.7	7	23.3	5	16.7	15	50.0	13	43.3
South Dakota	43	16	37.2	29	67.4	13	30.2	18	41.9	3	7.0	34	79.1	14	32.6	11	25.6	3	7.0	20	46.5	20	46.5
CENSUS DIVISION 7, WEST SOUTH CENTRAL	896	339	37.8	432	48.2	260	29.0	478	53.3	84	9.4	581	64.8	314	35.0	153	17.1	38	4.2	516	57.6	367	41.0
Arkansas	99	36	37.5	47	49.0	33	34.4	48	50.0	6	6.3	66	68.8	21	21.9	16	16.7	3	3.1	52	54.2	34	35.4
Louisiana	99	37	37.4	50	50.5	35	35.4	53	53.5	7	7.1	66	66.7	28	28.3	22	22.2	3	3.0	55	55.6	40	40.4
Oklahoma	127	51	40.2	54	42.5	29	22.8	67	52.8	11	8.7	93	73.2	43	33.9	22	17.3	10	7.9	69	54.3	38	29.9
Texas	574	215	37.5	281	49.0	163	28.4	310	54.0	60	10.5	356	62.0	222	38.7	93	16.2	22	3.8	340	59.2	255	44.4
CENSUS DIVISION 8, MOUNTAIN	349	197	56.4	207	59.3	160	45.8	235	67.3	35	10.0	277	79.4	173	49.6	119	34.1	32	9.2	227	65.0	158	45.3
Arizona	68	32	47.1	40	58.8	33	48.5	46	67.6	11	16.2	51	75.0	37	54.4	25	36.8	5	7.4	48	70.6	33	48.5
Colorado	72	48	66.7	51	70.8	47	65.3	55	76.4	12	16.7	64	88.9	42	58.3	33	45.8	5	6.9	56	77.8	35	48.6
Idaho	55	19	65.5	19	65.5	11	37.9	22	75.9	3	10.3	27	93.1	14	48.3	9	31.0	4	13.8	20	69.0	20	69.0
Montana	30	23	41.8	28	50.9	18	32.7	26	47.3	1	1.8	36	65.5	23	41.8	19	34.5	6	10.9	24	43.6	10	34.5
Nevada	33	12	40.0	19	63.3	13	43.3	21	70.0	1	3.3	19	63.3	11	36.7	9	30.0	2	6.7	16	53.3	8	24.2
New Mexico	35	20	60.6	15	45.5	12	36.4	20	60.6	1	3.0	26	78.8	9	27.3	7	21.2	5	15.2	22	66.7	22	62.9
Utah	35	25	71.4	20	57.1	16	45.7	25	71.4	5	14.3	32	91.4	24	68.6	11	31.4	4	11.4	25	71.4	11	40.7
Wyoming	27	18	66.7	15	55.6	10	37.0	20	74.1	1	3.7	22	81.5	13	48.1	6	22.2	1	3.7	16	59.3		
CENSUS DIVISION 9, PACIFIC	481	298	62.0	316	65.7	287	59.7	373	77.5	59	12.3	408	84.8	263	54.7	245	50.9	63	13.1	347	72.1	249	51.8
Alaska	15	9	60.0	7	46.7	5	33.3	7	46.7	1	6.7	10	66.7	2	13.3	4	26.7	0	0.0	9	60.0	5	33.3
California	309	183	59.2	204	66.0	189	61.2	246	79.6	35	11.3	265	85.8	180	58.3	167	54.0	40	12.9	218	70.6	161	52.1
Hawaii	18	10	55.6	15	83.3	12	66.7	14	77.8	3	16.7	13	72.2	6	33.3	8	44.4	2	11.1	11	61.1	8	44.4
Oregon	61	50	82.0	40	65.6	39	63.9	51	83.6	5	8.2	57	93.4	35	57.4	28	45.9	10	16.4	55	90.2	37	60.7
Washington	78	46	59.0	50	64.1	42	53.8	55	70.5	15	19.2	63	80.8	40	51.3	38	48.7	11	14.1	54	69.2	38	48.7

Table 7 (Continued)

These data include only hospital-based facilities and services as reported by responding hospitals in Section C of the 2012 AHA Annual Survey, beginning on page 215. All hospitals are represented with Community Hospitals listed separately under United States. No estimates have been made for nonresponding hospitals. Definitions of facilities and services are listed in the Glossary, page 201.

CLASSIFICATION	HOSPITALS REPORTING	PATIENT REPRESENTATIVE SERVICES		PHYSICAL REHABILITATION INPATIENT CARE UNITS		PRIMARY CARE DEPARTMENT		PSYCHIATRIC INPATIENT CARE UNITS		RETIREMENT HOUSING		ROBOTIC SURGERY		RURAL HEALTH CLINIC		SLEEP CENTER		SOCIAL WORK SERVICES		SPORTS MEDICINE		SUPPORT GROUPS	
		Number	Percent	Number	Percent	Number	Percent	Number	Percent	Number	Percent	Number	Percent	Number	Percent	Number	Percent	Number	Percent	Number	Percent	Number	Percent
UNITED STATES	4,780	3,163	66.2	1,431	29.9	1,903	39.8	1,617	33.8	135	2.8	1,213	25.4	1,020	21.3	2,221	46.5	4,023	84.2	1,885	39.4	2,980	62.3
COMMUNITY HOSPITALS	4,053	2,854	70.4	1,330	32.8	1,787	44.1	1,234	30.4	132	3.3	1,174	29.0	953	23.5	2,149	53.0	3,510	86.6	1,825	45.0	2,722	67.2
CENSUS DIVISION 1, NEW ENGLAND	190	148	77.9	45	23.7	110	57.9	102	53.7	4	2.1	55	28.9	28	14.7	100	52.6	182	95.8	109	57.4	162	85.3
Connecticut	34	28	82.4	10	29.4	18	52.9	27	79.4	1	2.9	17	50.0			22	64.7	33	97.1	20	58.8	29	85.3
Maine	37	27	73.0	9	24.3	29	78.4	14	37.8	1	2.7	3	8.1	14	37.8	19	51.4	35	94.6	15	40.5	34	91.9
Massachusetts	66	51	77.3	11	16.7	29	43.9	39	59.1	0	0.0	22	33.3	2	3.0	33	50.0	62	93.9	39	59.1	55	83.3
New Hampshire	26	21	80.8	7	26.9	18	69.2	8	30.8	1	3.8	6	23.1	7	26.9	16	61.5	26	100.0	19	73.1	21	80.8
Rhode Island	13	11	84.6	5	38.5	9	69.2	8	61.5	0	0.0	6	46.2	0	0.0	6	46.2	13	100.0	6	46.2	13	100.0
Vermont	14	10	71.4	3	21.4	7	50.0	6	42.9	1	7.1	1	7.1	5	35.7	4	28.6	13	92.9	10	71.4	10	71.4
CENSUS DIVISION 2, MIDDLE ATLANTIC	423	323	76.4	159	37.6	237	56.0	232	54.8	7	1.7	157	37.1	34	8.0	236	55.8	393	92.9	211	49.9	330	78.0
New Jersey	72	60	83.3	19	26.4	45	62.5	41	56.9	2	2.8	35	48.6	2	2.8	46	63.9	69	95.8	33	45.8	57	79.2
New York	156	137	87.8	66	42.3	114	73.1	95	60.9	2	1.3	63	40.4	20	12.8	79	50.6	146	93.6	91	58.3	133	85.3
Pennsylvania	195	126	64.6	74	37.9	78	40.0	96	49.2	3	1.5	59	30.3	12	6.2	111	56.9	178	91.3	87	44.6	140	71.8
CENSUS DIVISION 3, SOUTH ATLANTIC	682	482	70.7	218	32.0	263	38.6	251	36.8	6	0.9	224	32.8	97	14.2	363	53.2	575	84.3	270	39.6	459	67.3
Delaware	8	6	75.0	3	37.5	3	37.5	4	50.0	0	0.0	3	37.5	0	0.0	4	50.0	7	87.5	3	37.5	6	75.0
District of Columbia	11	9	81.8	3	27.3	7	63.6	10	90.9	0	0.0	6	54.5	0	0.0	7	63.6	11	100.0	7	63.6	9	81.8
Florida	170	112	65.9	49	28.8	57	33.5	55	32.4	0	0.0	76	44.7	18	10.6	76	44.7	132	77.6	72	42.4	116	68.2
Georgia	110	71	64.5	24	21.8	33	30.0	29	26.4	4	3.6	32	29.1	21	19.1	60	54.5	83	75.5	30	27.3	59	53.6
Maryland	52	46	88.5	16	30.8	25	48.1	33	63.5	0	0.0	22	42.3	1	1.9	37	71.2	49	94.2	21	40.4	44	84.6
North Carolina	112	82	73.2	34	30.4	45	40.2	49	43.8	1	0.9	40	35.7	17	15.2	65	58.0	101	90.2	53	47.3	81	72.3
South Carolina	73	45	61.6	52	71.2	19	26.0	20	27.4	0	0.0	12	16.4	14	19.2	34	46.6	61	83.6	22	30.1	43	58.9
Virginia	84	68	81.0	25	29.8	40	47.6	33	39.3	1	1.2	24	28.6	8	9.5	47	56.0	76	90.5	42	50.0	64	76.2
West Virginia	62	43	69.4	12	19.4	34	54.8	18	29.0	0	0.0	9	14.5	17	27.4	33	53.2	55	88.7	20	32.3	37	59.7
CENSUS DIVISION 4, EAST NORTH CENTRAL	725	562	77.5	267	36.8	356	49.1	279	38.5	23	3.2	216	29.8	138	19.0	456	62.9	665	91.7	395	54.5	573	79.0
Illinois	163	129	79.1	54	33.1	76	46.6	66	40.5	9	5.5	59	36.2	41	25.2	111	68.1	149	91.4	88	54.0	135	82.8
Indiana	128	88	68.8	45	35.2	44	34.4	45	35.2	2	1.6	28	21.9	12	9.4	79	61.7	107	83.6	49	38.3	100	78.1
Michigan	131	104	79.4	45	34.4	86	65.6	55	42.0	3	2.3	46	35.1	42	32.1	85	64.9	122	93.1	84	64.1	117	89.3
Ohio	156	126	80.8	51	32.7	78	50.0	71	45.5	2	1.3	52	33.3	15	9.6	106	67.9	151	96.8	97	62.2	121	77.6
Wisconsin	147	115	78.2	72	49.0	72	49.0	42	28.6	7	4.8	31	21.1	28	19.0	75	51.0	136	92.5	77	52.4	100	68.0
CENSUS DIVISION 5, EAST SOUTH CENTRAL	383	233	60.8	123	32.1	106	27.7	144	37.6	5	1.3	85	22.2	86	22.5	159	41.5	304	79.4	114	29.8	191	49.9
Alabama	94	45	47.9	21	22.3	20	21.3	39	41.5	3	3.2	24	25.5	15	16.0	37	39.4	61	64.9	34	36.2	45	47.9
Kentucky	90	65	72.2	27	30.0	38	42.2	33	36.7	1	1.1	15	16.7	32	35.6	51	56.7	73	81.1	31	34.4	55	61.1
Mississippi	112	65	58.0	52	46.4	22	19.6	42	37.5	0	0.0	22	19.6	33	29.5	26	23.2	100	89.3	21	18.8	39	34.8
Tennessee	87	58	66.7	23	26.4	26	29.9	30	34.5	1	1.1	24	27.6	6	6.9	45	51.7	70	80.5	28	32.2	52	59.8
CENSUS DIVISION 6, WEST NORTH CENTRAL	651	374	57.5	203	31.2	288	44.2	178	27.3	66	10.1	92	14.1	263	40.4	317	48.7	537	82.5	288	44.2	401	61.6
Iowa	126	73	57.9	28	22.2	70	55.6	36	28.6	18	14.3	18	14.3	48	38.1	70	55.6	109	86.5	62	49.2	95	75.4
Kansas	152	69	45.4	31	20.4	54	35.5	28	18.4	12	7.9	14	9.2	68	44.7	39	25.7	110	72.4	49	32.2	55	36.2
Minnesota	104	62	59.6	23	22.1	53	51.0	28	26.9	15	14.4	17	16.3	28	26.9	57	54.8	97	93.3	50	48.1	83	79.8
Missouri	146	108	74.0	89	61.0	57	39.0	61	41.8	2	1.4	24	16.4	61	41.8	89	61.0	132	90.4	68	46.6	95	65.1
Nebraska	50	26	52.0	16	32.0	19	38.0	12	24.0	2	4.0	11	22.0	24	48.0	34	68.0	41	82.0	28	56.0	32	64.0
North Dakota	30	17	56.7	9	30.0	18	60.0	8	26.7	6	20.0	3	10.0	17	56.7	12	40.0	23	76.7	15	50.0	16	53.3
South Dakota	43	19	44.2	7	16.3	17	39.5	5	11.6	11	25.6	5	11.6	17	39.5	16	37.2	25	58.1	16	37.2	25	58.1
CENSUS DIVISION 7, WEST SOUTH CENTRAL	896	499	55.7	228	25.4	196	21.9	211	23.5	11	1.2	163	18.2	183	20.4	286	31.9	676	75.4	213	23.8	379	42.3
Arkansas	96	50	52.1	26	27.1	20	20.8	34	35.4	1	1.0	14	14.6	22	22.9	42	43.8	73	76.0	24	25.0	42	43.8
Louisiana	99	46	46.5	34	34.3	29	29.3	37	37.4	4	4.0	21	21.2	21	21.2	28	28.3	75	75.8	24	24.2	42	42.4
Oklahoma	127	69	54.3	33	26.0	29	22.8	33	26.0	3	2.4	17	13.4	28	22.0	55	43.3	87	68.5	31	24.4	46	36.2
Texas	574	334	58.2	135	23.5	118	20.6	107	18.6	3	0.5	111	19.3	112	19.5	161	28.0	441	76.8	130	22.6	249	43.4
CENSUS DIVISION 8, MOUNTAIN	349	223	63.9	82	23.5	152	43.6	85	24.4	8	2.3	81	23.2	108	30.9	150	43.0	271	77.7	135	38.7	193	55.3
Arizona	68	45	66.2	20	29.4	17	25.0	19	27.9	0	0.0	20	29.4	12	17.6	17	25.0	50	73.5	18	26.5	39	57.4
Colorado	72	52	72.2	21	29.2	47	65.3	11	15.3	1	1.4	27	37.5	28	38.9	50	69.4	54	75.0	36	50.0	47	65.3
Idaho	29	23	79.3	7	24.1	15	51.7	8	27.6	0	0.0	7	24.1	15	51.7	14	48.3	24	82.8	14	48.3	16	55.2
Montana	55	28	50.9	8	14.5	30	54.5	9	16.4	5	9.1	9	16.4	32	58.2	19	34.5	44	80.0	24	43.6	24	43.6
Nevada	30	15	50.0	8	26.7	5	16.7	9	30.0	0	0.0	7	23.3	5	16.7	4	13.3	22	73.3	7	23.3	15	50.0
New Mexico	33	18	54.5	7	21.2	11	33.3	11	33.3	0	0.0	4	12.1	7	21.2	11	33.3	27	81.8	5	15.2	17	51.5
Utah	35	26	74.3	9	25.7	14	40.0	12	34.3	0	0.0	5	14.3	5	14.3	18	51.4	27	77.1	19	54.3	20	57.1
Wyoming	27	16	59.3	2	7.4	13	48.1	6	22.2	1	3.7	2	7.4	4	14.8	17	63.0	23	85.2	12	44.4	14	51.9
CENSUS DIVISION 9, PACIFIC	481	319	66.3	106	22.0	195	40.5	135	28.1	5	1.0	140	29.1	83	17.3	154	32.0	420	87.3	150	31.2	292	60.7
Alaska	15	6	40.0	1	6.7	6	40.0	5	33.3	0	0.0	2	13.3	0	0.0	7	46.7	12	80.0	3	20.0	5	33.3
California	309	204	66.0	74	23.9	102	33.0	86	27.8	2	0.6	92	29.8	40	12.9	73	23.6	278	90.0	81	26.2	182	58.9
Hawaii	18	9	50.0	3	16.7	7	38.9	8	44.4	0	0.0	4	22.2	4	22.2	5	27.8	17	94.4	7	38.9	12	66.7
Oregon	61	47	77.0	10	16.4	34	55.7	17	27.9	1	1.6	17	27.9	16	26.2	30	49.2	50	82.0	26	42.6	51	83.6
Washington	78	53	67.9	18	23.1	46	59.0	19	24.4	2	2.6	25	32.1	23	29.5	39	50.0	63	80.8	33	42.3	42	53.8

Table 7 (Continued)

These data include only hospital-based facilities and services as reported by responding hospitals in Section C of the 2013 AHA Annual Survey, beginning on page 215. All hospitals are represented with Community Hospitals listed separately under United States. No estimates have been made for nonresponding hospitals. Definitions of facilities and services are listed in the Glossary, page 201.

CLASSIFICATION	HOSPITALS REPORTING	SWING BED SERVICES Number	Percent	TEEN OUTREACH SERVICES Number	Percent	TOBACCO TREATMENT/ CESSATION PROGRAM Number	Percent	TRANSPORTATION TO HEALTH FACILITIES Number	Percent	URGENT CARE CENTER Number	Percent	VIRTUAL COLONOSCOPY Number	Percent	VOLUNTEER SERVICES DEPARTMENT Number	Percent	WOMEN'S HEALTH SERVICES Number	Percent	WOUND MANAGEMENT SERVICES Number	Percent
UNITED STATES	4,780	1,482	31.0	603	12.6	2,382	49.8	1,083	22.7	1,074	22.5	790	16.5	3,456	72.3	2,322	48.6	3,165	66.2
COMMUNITY HOSPITALS	4,053	1,432	35.3	573	14.1	2,189	54.0	927	22.9	1,013	25.0	765	18.9	3,221	79.5	2,222	54.8	2,918	72.0
CENSUS DIVISION 1, NEW ENGLAND	190	45	23.7	54	28.4	133	70.0	54	28.4	70	36.8	45	23.7	169	88.9	131	68.9	141	74.2
Connecticut	34	2	5.9	14	41.2	22	64.7	4	11.8	16	47.1	16	47.1	29	85.3	19	55.9	26	76.5
Maine	37	13	35.1	6	16.2	27	73.0	7	18.9	13	35.1	6	16.2	33	89.2	27	73.0	28	75.7
Massachusetts	66	5	7.6	21	31.8	41	62.1	27	40.9	27	40.9	15	22.7	58	87.9	43	65.2	50	75.8
New Hampshire	26	15	57.7	8	30.8	20	76.9	6	23.1	8	30.8	4	15.4	25	96.2	23	88.5	17	65.4
Rhode Island	13	1	7.7	3	23.1	11	84.6	5	38.5	3	23.1	2	15.4	11	84.6	10	76.9	10	76.9
Vermont	14	9	64.3	2	14.3	12	85.7	5	35.7	3	21.4	2	14.3	13	92.9	9	64.3	10	71.4
CENSUS DIVISION 2, MIDDLE ATLANTIC	423	69	16.3	111	26.2	274	64.8	140	33.1	109	25.8	102	24.1	368	87.0	284	67.1	305	72.1
New Jersey	72	6	8.3	31	43.1	43	59.7	39	54.2	20	27.8	18	25.0	62	86.1	51	70.8	59	81.9
New York	156	25	16.0	38	24.4	118	75.6	51	32.7	53	34.0	49	31.4	145	92.9	121	77.6	116	74.4
Pennsylvania	195	38	19.5	42	21.5	113	57.9	50	25.6	36	18.5	35	17.9	161	82.6	112	57.4	130	66.7
CENSUS DIVISION 3, SOUTH ATLANTIC	682	136	19.9	83	12.2	375	55.0	156	22.9	144	21.1	128	18.8	553	81.1	373	54.7	488	71.6
Delaware	8			4	50.0	4	50.0	4	50.0	2	25.0	1	12.5	6	75.0	4	50.0	6	75.0
District of Columbia	11	2	18.2	4	36.4	4	36.4	3	27.3	1	9.1	2	18.2	11	100.0	7	63.6	11	100.0
Florida	170	23	13.5	16	9.4	83	48.8	38	22.4	42	24.7	29	17.1	130	76.5	88	51.8	122	71.8
Georgia	110	32	29.1	11	10.0	55	50.0	23	20.9	21	19.1	12	10.9	79	71.8	57	51.8	78	70.9
Maryland	52	1	1.9	16	30.8	34	65.4	16	30.8	15	28.8	13	25.0	48	92.3	30	57.7	39	75.0
North Carolina	112	24	21.4	11	9.8	71	63.4	28	25.0	25	22.3	29	25.9	103	92.0	64	57.1	77	68.8
South Carolina	73	10	13.7	8	11.0	39	53.4	11	15.1	9	12.3	11	15.1	53	72.6	43	58.9	48	65.8
Virginia	84	20	23.8	9	10.7	49	58.3	19	22.6	18	21.4	22	26.2	72	85.7	48	57.1	68	81.0
West Virginia	62	24	38.7	4	6.5	36	58.1	14	22.6	11	17.7	9	14.5	51	82.3	32	51.6	39	62.9
CENSUS DIVISION 4, EAST NORTH CENTRAL	725	207	28.6	114	15.7	462	63.7	191	26.3	284	39.2	166	22.9	613	84.6	417	57.5	516	71.2
Illinois	163	48	29.4	30	18.4	92	56.4	49	30.1	52	31.9	45	27.6	144	88.3	97	59.5	113	69.3
Indiana	128	38	29.7	20	15.6	80	62.5	23	18.0	42	32.8	23	18.0	104	81.3	71	55.5	84	65.6
Michigan	131	24	18.3	22	16.8	90	68.7	35	26.7	50	38.2	29	22.1	118	90.1	83	63.4	102	77.9
Ohio	156	37	23.7	27	17.3	115	73.7	52	33.3	55	35.3	37	23.7	139	89.1	99	63.5	115	73.7
Wisconsin	147	60	40.8	15	10.2	85	57.8	32	21.8	85	57.8	32	21.8	108	73.5	67	45.6	102	69.4
CENSUS DIVISION 5, EAST SOUTH CENTRAL	383	135	35.2	33	8.6	158	41.3	63	16.4	52	13.6	35	9.1	205	53.5	143	37.3	186	48.6
Alabama	94	21	22.3	7	7.4	36	38.3	16	17.0	12	12.8	5	5.3	60	63.8	36	38.3	45	47.9
Kentucky	90	36	40.0	8	8.9	49	54.4	13	14.4	14	15.6	11	12.2	68	75.6	45	50.0	49	54.4
Mississippi	112	55	49.1	9	8.0	32	28.6	18	16.1	13	11.6	10	8.9	8	7.1	30	26.8	36	32.1
Tennessee	87	23	26.4	9	10.3	41	47.1	16	18.4	13	14.9	9	10.3	69	79.3	32	36.8	56	64.4
CENSUS DIVISION 6, WEST NORTH CENTRAL	651	389	59.8	59	9.1	301	46.2	156	24.0	133	20.4	87	13.4	431	66.2	244	37.5	412	63.3
Iowa	126	90	71.4	16	12.7	81	64.3	23	18.3	24	19.0	16	12.7	97	77.0	50	39.7	88	69.8
Kansas	152	101	66.4	5	3.3	46	30.3	31	20.4	19	12.5	17	11.2	75	49.3	39	25.7	86	56.6
Minnesota	104	58	55.8	11	10.6	53	51.0	20	19.2	37	35.6	19	18.3	81	77.9	42	40.4	72	69.2
Missouri	146	51	34.9	18	12.3	75	51.4	54	37.0	35	24.0	18	12.3	103	70.5	70	47.9	99	67.8
Nebraska	50	30	60.0	6	12.0	23	46.0	12	24.0	4	8.0	12	24.0	34	68.0	20	40.0	29	58.0
North Dakota	30	22	73.3	0	0.0	11	36.7	10	33.3	9	30.0	3	10.0	21	70.0	11	36.7	12	40.0
South Dakota	43	37	86.0	3	7.0	12	27.9	6	14.0	5	11.6	2	4.7	21	48.8	12	27.9	26	60.5
CENSUS DIVISION 7, WEST SOUTH CENTRAL	896	242	27.0	46	5.1	285	31.8	125	14.0	89	9.9	83	9.3	485	54.1	301	33.6	545	60.8
Arkansas	96	37	38.5	7	7.3	32	33.3	16	16.7	11	11.5	7	7.3	57	59.4	31	32.3	52	54.2
Louisiana	99	24	24.2	7	7.1	43	43.4	19	19.2	12	12.1	3	3.0	50	50.5	36	36.4	56	56.6
Oklahoma	127	56	44.1	4	3.1	51	40.2	23	18.1	15	11.8	13	10.2	85	66.9	47	37.0	74	58.3
Texas	574	125	21.8	28	4.9	159	27.7	67	11.7	51	8.9	60	10.5	293	51.0	187	32.6	363	63.2
CENSUS DIVISION 8, MOUNTAIN	349	152	43.6	37	10.6	174	49.9	79	22.6	84	24.1	61	17.5	243	69.6	180	51.6	224	64.2
Arizona	68	14	20.6	8	11.8	36	52.9	11	16.2	13	19.1	9	12.5	48	70.6	33	48.5	45	66.2
Colorado	72	31	43.1	9	12.5	37	51.4	14	19.4	14	19.4	9	12.5	56	77.8	46	63.9	59	81.9
Idaho	29	17	58.6	6	20.7	16	55.2	9	31.0	9	31.0	4	13.8	24	82.8	14	48.3	15	51.7
Montana	55	44	80.0	4	7.3	25	45.5	23	41.8	18	32.7	14	25.5	37	67.3	22	40.0	30	54.5
Nevada	30	4	13.3	0	0.0	12	40.0	7	23.3	5	16.7	2	6.7	16	53.3	12	40.0	18	60.0
New Mexico	33	10	30.3	2	6.1	14	42.4	4	12.1	8	24.2	3	9.1	18	54.5	16	48.5	20	60.6
Utah	35	12	34.3	6	17.1	15	42.9	6	17.1	8	22.9	4	11.4	26	74.3	23	65.7	23	65.7
Wyoming	27	20	74.1	2	7.4	19	70.4	5	18.5	9	33.3	6	22.2	18	66.7	14	51.9	14	51.9
CENSUS DIVISION 9, PACIFIC	481	107	22.2	66	13.7	220	45.7	119	24.7	109	22.7	83	17.3	389	80.9	249	51.8	348	72.3
Alaska	15	7	46.7	1	6.7	4	26.7	0	0.0	1	6.7	1	6.7	8	53.3	3	20.0	10	66.7
California	309	36	11.7	42	13.6	120	38.8	80	25.9	63	20.4	53	17.2	252	81.6	152	49.2	222	71.8
Hawaii	18	7	38.9	3	16.7	11	61.1	6	33.3	3	16.7	4	22.2	15	83.3	11	61.1	13	72.2
Oregon	61	30	49.2	6	9.8	44	72.1	18	29.5	18	29.5	12	19.7	53	86.9	41	67.2	53	86.9
Washington	78	27	34.6	14	17.9	41	52.6	15	19.2	24	30.8	13	16.7	61	78.2	42	53.8	50	64.1

Table 7 (Continued)

These data include only hospital-based facilities and services as reported by responding hospitals in Section C of the 2013 AHA Annual Survey, beginning on page 215. All hospitals are represented with Community Hospitals listed separately under United States. No estimates have been made for nonresponding hospitals. Definitions of facilities and services are listed in the Glossary, page 201.

Column groups: **General Medical Surgical Care** = Adult Units, Pediatric Units. **Intensive Care Units** = Cardiac, Medical Surgical, Neonatal, Other, Pediatric. **Long-Term Care Units** = Skilled Nursing, Intermediate Nursing, Other Long-Term.

Classification	Hospitals Reporting	Adult Units No.	Adult Units %	Pediatric Units No.	Pediatric Units %	Cardiac ICU No.	Cardiac ICU %	Med-Surg ICU No.	Med-Surg ICU %	Neonatal ICU No.	Neonatal ICU %	Other ICU No.	Other ICU %	Pediatric ICU No.	Pediatric ICU %	Acute LTC No.	Acute LTC %	Skilled Nursing No.	Skilled Nursing %	Intermediate Nursing No.	Intermediate Nursing %	Other LTC No.	Other LTC %
UNITED STATES	4,780	3,999	83.7	1,893	39.6	1,283	26.8	2,955	61.8	983	20.6	554	11.2	422	8.8	369	7.7	1,060	22.2	376	7.9	256	5.4
COMMUNITY HOSPITALS	4,053	3,740	92.3	1,854	45.7	1,250	30.8	2,833	69.9	969	23.9	518	12.8	413	10.2	258	6.4	981	24.2	345	8.5	210	5.2
CENSUS DIVISION 1, NEW ENGLAND	190	152	80.0	96	50.5	50	26.3	135	71.1	30	15.8	13	6.8	14	7.4	8	4.2	35	18.4	19	10.0	6	3.2
Connecticut	34	26	76.5	16	47.1	11	32.4	25	73.5	11	32.4	3	8.8	1	2.9	2	5.9	5	14.7	1	2.9	0	0.0
Maine	37	32	86.5	17	45.9	6	16.2	29	78.4	4	10.8	4	10.8	3	8.1	1	2.7	12	32.4	8	21.6	4	10.8
Massachusetts	66	47	71.2	40	60.6	21	31.8	44	66.7	11	16.7	4	6.1	7	10.6	5	7.6	5	7.6	2	3.0	0	0.0
New Hampshire	26	23	88.5	13	50.0	6	23.1	20	76.9	2	7.7	0	0.0	1	3.8	0	0.0	8	30.8	7	26.9	0	0.0
Rhode Island	13	11	84.6	5	38.5	4	30.8	8	61.5	1	7.7	2	15.4	1	7.7	0	0.0	1	7.7	1	7.7	0	0.0
Vermont	14	13	92.9	5	35.7	2	14.3	9	64.3	1	7.1	0	0.0	1	7.1	0	0.0	4	28.6	0	0.0	0	0.0
CENSUS DIVISION 2, MIDDLE ATLANTIC	423	357	84.4	194	45.9	170	40.2	313	74.0	124	29.3	55	13.0	51	12.1	24	5.7	101	23.9	15	3.5	21	5.0
New Jersey	72	57	79.2	39	54.2	29	40.3	57	79.2	22	30.6	8	11.1	14	19.4	4	5.6	11	15.3	4	5.6	6	8.3
New York	156	149	95.5	89	57.1	81	51.9	131	84.0	59	37.8	22	14.1	30	19.2	9	5.8	47	30.1	7	4.5	11	7.1
Pennsylvania	195	151	77.4	66	33.8	60	30.8	125	64.1	43	22.1	25	12.8	7	3.6	11	5.6	43	22.1	4	2.1	4	2.1
CENSUS DIVISION 3, SOUTH ATLANTIC	682	569	83.4	282	41.3	213	31.2	485	71.1	158	23.2	96	14.1	73	10.7	77	11.3	159	23.3	61	8.9	52	7.6
Delaware	8	4	50.0	4	50.0	5	62.5	4	50.0	3	37.5	0	0.0	2	25.0	1	12.5	0	0.0	2	25.0	0	0.0
District of Columbia	11	7	63.6	3	27.3	5	45.5	7	63.6	6	54.5	1	9.1	2	18.2	0	0.0	2	18.2	0	0.0	3	27.3
Florida	170	139	81.8	58	34.1	67	39.4	128	75.3	49	28.8	26	15.3	30	17.6	17	10.0	26	15.3	15	8.8	8	4.7
Georgia	110	92	83.6	30	27.3	25	22.7	62	56.4	25	22.7	10	9.1	4	3.6	10	9.1	23	20.9	5	4.5	3	2.7
Maryland	52	46	88.5	32	61.5	19	36.5	46	88.5	16	30.8	5	9.6	4	7.7	5	9.6	13	25.0	2	3.8	3	5.8
North Carolina	112	101	90.2	52	46.4	30	26.8	86	76.8	23	20.5	15	13.4	12	10.7	5	4.5	27	24.1	11	9.8	1	0.9
South Carolina	73	60	82.2	46	63.0	23	31.5	53	72.6	11	15.1	27	37.0	7	9.6	28	38.4	30	41.1	7	9.6	26	35.6
Virginia	84	68	81.0	30	35.7	22	26.2	63	75.0	21	25.0	8	9.5	8	9.5	4	4.8	14	16.7	8	9.5	4	4.8
West Virginia	62	52	83.9	27	43.5	16	25.8	36	58.1	4	6.5	4	6.5	4	6.5	5	8.1	24	38.7	9	14.5	4	6.5
CENSUS DIVISION 4, EAST NORTH CENTRAL	725	624	86.1	354	48.8	218	30.1	482	66.5	129	17.8	126	17.4	71	9.8	42	5.8	130	17.9	35	4.8	36	5.0
Illinois	163	149	91.4	95	58.3	41	25.2	119	73.0	29	17.8	15	9.2	20	12.3	7	4.3	41	25.2	8	4.9	10	6.1
Indiana	128	99	77.3	50	39.1	27	21.1	75	58.6	22	17.2	6	4.7	9	7.0	8	6.3	14	10.9	11	8.6	2	1.6
Michigan	131	116	88.5	58	44.3	41	31.3	90	68.7	22	16.8	17	13.0	10	7.6	7	5.3	27	20.6	4	3.1	6	4.6
Ohio	156	134	85.9	55	35.3	50	32.1	124	79.5	26	16.7	19	12.2	10	6.4	8	5.1	26	16.7	6	3.8	11	7.1
Wisconsin	147	126	85.7	96	65.3	59	40.1	74	50.3	30	20.4	69	46.9	22	15.0	12	8.2	22	15.0	6	4.1	7	4.8
CENSUS DIVISION 5, EAST SOUTH CENTRAL	383	328	85.6	160	41.8	109	28.5	270	70.5	61	15.9	85	22.2	33	8.6	31	8.1	83	21.7	25	6.5	31	8.1
Alabama	94	73	77.7	29	30.9	23	24.5	56	59.6	15	16.0	10	10.6	6	6.4	10	10.6	10	10.6	7	7.4	3	3.2
Kentucky	90	75	83.3	35	38.9	27	30.0	58	64.4	17	18.9	15	16.7	8	8.9	10	11.1	26	28.9	8	8.9	7	7.8
Mississippi	112	107	95.5	72	64.3	39	34.8	106	94.6	16	14.3	47	42.0	12	10.7	5	4.5	25	22.3	0	0.0	19	17.0
Tennessee	87	73	83.9	24	27.6	20	23.0	50	57.5	13	14.9	13	14.9	7	8.0	6	6.9	22	25.3	10	11.5	2	2.3
CENSUS DIVISION 6, WEST NORTH CENTRAL	651	589	90.5	273	41.9	138	21.2	314	48.2	91	14.0	53	8.1	51	7.8	38	5.8	261	40.1	127	19.5	62	9.5
Iowa	126	119	94.4	56	44.4	21	16.7	66	52.4	18	14.3	9	7.1	10	7.9	6	4.8	55	43.7	38	30.2	14	11.1
Kansas	152	134	88.2	44	28.9	18	11.8	55	36.2	17	11.2	9	5.9	11	7.2	10	6.6	67	44.1	48	31.6	19	12.5
Minnesota	104	99	95.2	45	43.3	25	24.0	58	55.8	10	9.6	5	4.8	8	7.7	2	1.9	41	39.4	4	3.8	2	1.9
Missouri	146	120	82.2	80	54.8	41	28.1	81	55.5	22	15.1	19	13.0	8	5.5	10	6.8	38	26.0	16	11.0	10	6.8
Nebraska	50	47	94.0	21	42.0	16	32.0	23	46.0	14	28.0	5	10.0	6	12.0	5	10.0	24	48.0	8	16.0	6	12.0
North Dakota	30	28	93.3	11	36.7	8	26.7	11	36.7	6	20.0	1	3.3	4	13.3	2	6.7	11	36.7	4	13.3	2	6.7
South Dakota	43	42	97.7	16	37.2	9	20.9	20	46.5	4	9.3	5	11.6	4	9.3	3	7.0	25	58.1	9	20.9	9	20.9
CENSUS DIVISION 7, WEST SOUTH CENTRAL	896	652	72.8	230	25.7	147	16.4	403	45.0	159	17.7	49	5.5	49	5.5	111	12.4	95	10.6	29	3.2	14	1.6
Arkansas	96	54	76.0	27	28.1	27	28.1	46	47.9	13	13.5	3	3.1	1	1.0	9	9.4	15	15.6	3	3.1	0	0.0
Louisiana	99	71	71.7	34	34.3	21	21.2	51	51.5	27	27.3	6	6.1	12	12.1	14	14.1	20	20.2	7	7.1	5	5.1
Oklahoma	127	108	85.0	36	28.3	19	15.0	49	38.6	12	9.4	8	6.3	4	3.1	10	7.9	23	18.1	7	5.5	4	3.1
Texas	574	400	69.7	133	23.2	80	13.9	257	44.8	107	18.6	32	5.6	32	5.6	78	13.6	37	6.4	12	2.1	5	0.9
CENSUS DIVISION 8, MOUNTAIN	349	308	88.3	129	37.0	70	20.1	203	58.2	79	22.6	19	5.4	32	9.2	13	3.7	88	25.2	31	8.9	18	5.2
Arizona	68	54	79.4	21	25.0	21	30.9	41	60.3	15	22.1	3	4.4	7	10.3	3	4.4	16	23.5	1	1.5	1	1.5
Colorado	72	67	93.1	30	41.7	14	19.4	49	68.1	24	33.3	5	6.9	6	8.3	2	2.8	16	22.2	5	6.9	4	5.6
Idaho	29	27	93.1	12	41.4	5	17.2	15	51.7	8	27.6	2	6.9	3	10.3	1	3.4	11	37.9	4	13.8	1	3.4
Montana	55	53	96.4	23	41.8	11	20.0	22	40.0	7	12.7	2	3.6	5	9.1	3	5.5	30	54.5	6	10.9	5	9.1
Nevada	30	20	66.7	8	26.7	6	20.0	16	53.3	6	20.0	2	6.7	4	13.3	3	10.0	0	0.0	0	0.0	0	0.0
New Mexico	33	30	90.9	15	45.5	4	12.1	22	66.7	5	15.2	1	3.0	3	9.1	0	0.0	2	6.1	3	9.1	2	6.1
Utah	35	32	91.4	17	48.6	9	25.7	20	57.1	13	37.1	3	8.6	3	8.6	0	0.0	11	31.4	3	8.6	1	2.9
Wyoming	27	25	92.6	7	25.9	0	0.0	18	66.7	1	3.7	1	3.7	1	3.7	0	0.0	13	48.1	4	14.8	6	22.2
CENSUS DIVISION 9, PACIFIC	481	420	87.3	175	36.4	168	34.9	350	72.8	152	31.6	38	7.9	48	10.0	25	5.2	108	22.5	34	7.1	16	3.3
Alaska	15	12	80.0	2	13.3	0	0.0	7	46.7	0	0.0	1	6.7	0	0.0	0	0.0	8	53.3	5	33.3	1	6.7
California	309	266	86.1	110	35.6	126	40.8	231	74.8	124	40.1	26	8.4	37	12.0	20	6.5	75	24.3	11	3.6	11	3.6
Hawaii	18	14	77.8	6	33.3	8	44.4	13	72.2	4	22.2	2	11.1	3	16.7	2	11.1	7	38.9	5	27.8	1	5.6
Oregon	61	59	96.7	26	42.6	16	26.2	50	82.0	8	13.1	3	4.9	3	4.9	1	1.6	9	14.8	9	14.8	0	0.0
Washington	78	69	88.5	31	39.7	18	23.1	49	62.8	16	20.5	6	7.7	5	6.4	2	2.6	9	11.5	4	5.1	3	3.8

Table 7 (Continued)

These data include only hospital-based facilities and services as reported by responding hospitals in Section C of the 2013 AHA Annual Survey, beginning on page 215. All hospitals are represented with Community Hospitals listed separately under United States. No estimates have been made for nonresponding hospitals. Definitions of facilities and services are listed in the Glossary, page 201.

CARDIOLOGY AND CARDIAC SERVICES

CLASSIFICATION	HOSPITALS REPORTING	Adult Cardiology Services No.	%	Pediatric Cardiology Services No.	%	Adult Diagnostic Catheterization No.	%	Pediatric Diagnostic Catheterization No.	%	Adult Interventional Cardiac Catheterization No.	%	Pediatric Interventional Cardiac Catheterization No.	%	Adult Cardiac Surgery No.	%	Pediatric Cardiac Surgery No.	%	Adult Cardiac Electro-Physiology No.	%	Pediatric Cardiac Electro-Physiology No.	%	Cardiac Rehabilitation No.	%
UNITED STATES	4,780	2,377	49.7	412	8.6	1,813	37.9	199	4.2	1,564	32.7	179	3.7	1,133	23.7	176	3.7	1,335	27.9	210	4.4	2,471	51.7
COMMUNITY HOSPITALS	4,053	2,274	56.1	407	10.0	1,748	43.1	195	4.8	1,507	37.2	177	4.4	1,094	27.0	174	4.3	1,288	31.8	207	5.1	2,401	59.2
CENSUS DIVISION 1, NEW ENGLAND	190	117	61.6	17	8.9	72	37.9	9	4.7	52	27.4	9	4.7	40	21.1	8	4.2	59	31.1	6	3.2	123	64.7
Connecticut	34	23	67.6	3	8.8	15	44.1	1	2.9	14	41.2	1	2.9	13	38.2	1	2.9	11	32.4	1	2.9	23	67.6
Maine	37	19	51.4	4	10.8	11	29.7	1	2.7	5	13.5	1	2.7	3	8.1	1	2.7	8	21.6	1	2.7	27	73.0
Massachusetts	66	44	66.7	6	9.1	30	45.5	3	4.5	21	31.8	3	4.5	17	25.8	4	6.1	25	37.9	3	4.5	40	60.6
New Hampshire	26	15	57.7	2	7.7	8	30.8	2	7.7	7	26.9	1	3.8	3	11.5	1	3.8	7	26.9	1	3.8	19	73.1
Rhode Island	13	9	69.2	1	7.7	5	38.5	1	7.7	3	23.1	1	7.7	2	15.4	0	0.0	5	38.5	0	0.0	5	38.5
Vermont	14	7	50.0	1	7.1	3	21.4	1	7.1	2	14.3	2	14.3	2	14.3	1	7.1	3	21.4	0	0.0	9	64.3
CENSUS DIVISION 2, MIDDLE ATLANTIC	423	294	69.5	81	19.1	209	49.4	24	5.7	173	40.9	22	5.2	119	28.1	18	4.3	152	35.9	32	7.6	234	55.3
New Jersey	72	53	73.6	21	29.2	50	69.4	3	4.2	39	54.2	2	2.8	17	23.6	2	2.8	24	33.3	5	6.9	41	56.9
New York	156	123	78.8	41	26.3	71	45.5	16	10.3	59	37.8	15	9.6	38	24.4	11	7.1	61	39.1	18	11.5	85	54.5
Pennsylvania	195	118	60.5	19	9.7	88	45.1	5	2.6	75	38.5	5	2.6	64	32.8	5	2.6	67	34.4	9	4.6	108	55.4
CENSUS DIVISION 3, SOUTH ATLANTIC	682	413	60.6	58	8.5	332	48.7	28	4.1	264	38.7	26	3.8	164	24.0	28	4.1	244	35.8	28	4.1	368	54.0
Delaware	8	4	50.0	1	12.5	4	50.0	1	12.5	4	50.0	1	12.5	3	37.5	1	12.5	3	37.5	1	12.5	5	62.5
District of Columbia	11	8	72.7	1	9.1	6	54.5	1	9.1	4	36.4	1	9.1	3	27.3	1	9.1	5	45.5	1	9.1	4	36.4
Florida	170	120	70.6	22	12.9	98	57.6	12	7.1	85	50.0	10	5.9	57	33.5	11	6.5	73	42.9	9	5.3	79	46.5
Georgia	110	50	45.5	3	2.7	46	41.8	1	0.9	37	33.6	1	0.9	18	16.4	2	1.8	34	30.9	1	0.9	44	40.0
Maryland	52	40	76.9	5	9.6	35	67.3	2	3.8	25	48.1	2	3.8	10	19.2	2	3.8	32	61.5	3	5.8	32	61.5
North Carolina	112	73	65.2	13	11.6	52	46.4	5	4.5	41	36.6	5	4.5	26	23.2	5	4.5	38	33.9	6	5.4	76	67.9
South Carolina	73	37	50.7	2	2.7	30	41.1	1	1.4	18	24.7	1	1.4	19	26.0	1	1.4	18	24.7	2	2.7	38	52.1
Virginia	84	53	63.1	9	10.7	40	47.6	4	4.8	36	42.9	4	4.8	22	26.2	4	4.8	33	39.3	4	4.8	59	70.2
West Virginia	62	28	45.2	2	3.2	21	33.9	1	1.6	14	22.6	1	1.6	6	9.7	1	1.6	8	12.9	1	1.6	31	50.0
CENSUS DIVISION 4, EAST NORTH CENTRAL	725	428	59.0	72	9.9	325	44.8	28	3.9	283	39.0	25	3.4	217	29.9	28	3.9	259	35.7	34	4.7	518	71.4
Illinois	163	111	68.1	32	19.6	67	53.4	8	4.9	83	50.9	8	4.9	62	38.0	9	5.5	72	44.2	14	8.6	131	80.4
Indiana	128	64	50.0	10	7.8	50	39.1	5	3.9	47	36.7	4	3.1	34	26.6	5	3.9	36	28.1	4	3.1	82	64.1
Michigan	131	74	56.5	12	9.2	57	43.5	3	2.3	45	34.4	3	2.3	33	25.2	4	3.1	51	38.9	5	3.8	84	64.1
Ohio	156	111	71.2	11	7.1	83	53.2	8	5.1	63	40.4	6	3.8	55	35.3	6	3.8	62	39.7	6	3.8	109	69.9
Wisconsin	147	68	46.3	7	4.8	48	32.7	4	2.7	45	30.6	4	2.7	33	22.4	4	2.7	38	25.9	5	3.4	112	76.2
CENSUS DIVISION 5, EAST SOUTH CENTRAL	383	160	41.8	27	7.0	126	32.9	16	4.2	105	27.4	13	3.4	77	20.1	14	3.7	82	21.4	17	4.4	151	39.4
Alabama	94	36	38.3	5	5.3	33	35.1	4	4.3	30	31.9	3	3.2	23	24.5	3	3.2	27	28.7	4	4.3	35	37.2
Kentucky	90	45	50.0	6	6.7	36	40.0	2	2.2	29	32.2	2	2.2	19	21.1	3	3.3	20	22.2	3	3.3	49	54.4
Mississippi	112	30	26.8	6	5.4	20	17.9	2	1.8	16	14.3	1	0.9	15	13.4	2	1.8	12	10.7	3	2.7	24	21.4
Tennessee	87	49	56.3	10	11.5	37	42.5	8	9.2	30	34.5	7	8.0	20	23.0	7	8.0	23	26.4	7	8.0	43	49.4
CENSUS DIVISION 6, WEST NORTH CENTRAL	651	229	35.2	38	5.8	154	23.7	16	2.5	147	22.6	15	2.3	96	14.7	16	2.5	112	17.2	20	3.1	459	70.5
Iowa	126	43	34.1	4	3.2	27	21.4	2	1.6	27	21.4	2	1.6	12	9.5	2	1.6	21	16.7	2	1.6	108	85.7
Kansas	152	35	23.0	6	3.9	25	16.4	2	1.3	24	15.8	2	1.3	16	10.5	1	0.7	14	9.2	3	2.0	70	46.1
Minnesota	104	38	36.5	9	8.7	20	19.2	3	2.9	19	18.3	3	2.9	16	15.4	3	2.9	23	22.1	6	5.8	89	85.6
Missouri	146	76	52.1	8	5.5	55	37.7	4	2.7	52	35.6	3	2.1	36	24.7	6	4.1	38	26.0	5	3.4	92	63.0
Nebraska	50	18	36.0	4	8.0	15	30.0	1	2.0	14	28.0	1	2.0	7	14.0	1	2.0	10	20.0	1	2.0	42	84.0
North Dakota	30	8	26.7	3	10.0	5	16.7	2	6.7	5	16.7	2	6.7	5	16.7	2	6.7	3	10.0	2	6.7	20	66.7
South Dakota	43	11	25.6	4	9.3	7	16.3	2	4.7	6	14.0	2	4.7	4	9.3	1	2.3	3	7.0	1	2.3	38	88.4
CENSUS DIVISION 7, WEST SOUTH CENTRAL	896	327	36.5	38	4.2	267	29.8	24	2.7	246	27.5	21	2.3	195	21.8	19	2.1	183	20.4	22	2.5	276	30.8
Arkansas	96	38	39.6	3	3.1	26	27.1	1	1.0	25	26.0	1	1.0	21	21.9	1	1.0	15	15.6	1	1.0	32	33.3
Louisiana	99	43	43.4	9	9.1	39	39.4	5	5.1	35	35.4	3	3.0	26	26.3	3	3.0	29	29.3	3	3.0	32	32.3
Oklahoma	127	47	37.0	3	2.4	32	25.2	2	1.6	29	22.8	2	1.6	18	14.2	2	1.6	18	14.2	2	1.6	35	27.6
Texas	574	199	34.7	23	4.0	170	29.6	16	2.8	157	27.4	15	2.6	130	22.6	13	2.3	121	21.1	14	2.4	177	30.8
CENSUS DIVISION 8, MOUNTAIN	349	147	42.1	25	7.2	115	33.0	19	5.4	110	31.5	18	5.2	73	20.9	17	4.9	79	22.6	18	5.2	158	45.3
Arizona	68	40	58.8	6	8.8	30	44.1	3	4.4	31	45.6	3	4.4	20	29.4	3	4.4	24	35.3	6	8.8	29	42.6
Colorado	72	38	52.8	5	6.9	34	47.2	3	4.2	33	45.8	3	4.2	20	27.8	3	4.2	21	29.2	3	4.2	44	61.1
Idaho	29	12	41.4	3	10.3	9	31.0	2	6.9	9	31.0	2	6.9	5	17.2	1	3.4	5	17.2	1	3.4	10	34.5
Montana	55	9	16.4	2	3.6	8	14.5	1	1.8	8	14.5	1	1.8	5	9.1	1	1.8	6	10.9	2	3.6	28	50.9
Nevada	30	13	43.3	3	10.0	12	40.0	4	13.3	10	33.3	4	13.3	8	26.7	3	10.0	8	26.7	3	10.0	10	33.3
New Mexico	33	13	39.4	4	12.1	9	27.3	3	9.1	7	21.2	2	6.1	7	21.2	2	6.1	7	21.2	2	6.1	8	24.2
Utah	35	16	45.7	2	5.7	11	31.4	3	8.6	10	28.6	3	8.6	7	20.0	4	11.4	6	17.1	1	2.9	13	37.1
Wyoming	27	6	22.2	0	0.0	2	7.4	0	0.0	2	7.4	0	0.0	3	11.1	0	0.0	2	7.4	0	0.0	16	59.3
CENSUS DIVISION 9, PACIFIC	481	262	54.5	56	11.6	213	44.3	35	7.3	184	38.3	30	6.2	152	31.6	28	5.8	165	34.3	33	6.9	184	38.3
Alaska	15	3	20.0	1	6.7	2	13.3	0	0.0	2	13.3	0	0.0	0	0.0	0	0.0	1	6.7	0	0.0	5	33.3
California	309	183	59.2	41	13.3	148	47.9	21	6.8	129	41.7	20	6.5	113	36.6	19	6.1	118	38.2	21	6.8	118	38.2
Hawaii	18	10	55.6	2	11.1	8	44.4	3	16.7	7	38.9	3	11.1	6	33.3	1	5.6	7	38.9	3	11.1	5	27.8
Oregon	61	28	45.9	8	13.1	23	37.7	6	9.8	19	31.1	4	6.6	16	26.2	4	6.6	17	27.9	5	8.2	27	44.3
Washington	78	38	48.7	4	5.1	32	41.0	5	6.4	27	34.6	4	5.1	17	21.8	4	5.1	22	28.2	5	6.4	29	37.2

Table 7 (Continued)

These data include only hospital-based facilities and services as reported by responding hospitals in Section C of the 2013 AHA Annual Survey, beginning on page 215. All hospitals are represented with Community Hospitals listed separately under United States. No estimates have been made for nonresponding hospitals. Definitions of facilities and services are listed in the Glossary, page 201.

CLASSIFICATION	HOSPITALS REPORTING (Number)	EMERGENCY SERVICES — EMERGENCY DEPARTMENT Number	Percent	PEDIATRIC EMERGENCY DEPARTMENT Number	Percent	FREESTANDING/SATELLITE EMERGENCY DEPARTMENT Number	Percent	TRAUMA CENTER (CERTIFIED) Number	Percent	ENDOSCOPIC SERVICES — ENDOSCOPIC ULTRASOUND Number	Percent	ABLATION OF BARRETT'S ESOPHAGUS Number	Percent	ESOPHAGEAL IMPEDANCE STUDY Number	Percent	ENDOSCOPIC RETROGRADE CHOLANGIO-PANCREATOGRAPHY Number	Percent	OPTICAL COLONOSCOPY Number	Percent
UNITED STATES	4,780	3,925	82.1	713	14.9	326	6.8	1,696	35.5	1,563	32.7	1,150	24.1	1,072	22.4	1,967	41.2	2,966	62.1
COMMUNITY HOSPITALS	4,053	3,696	91.2	685	16.9	312	7.7	1,663	41.0	1,501	37.0	1,103	27.2	1,034	25.5	1,899	46.9	2,818	69.5
CENSUS DIVISION 1, NEW ENGLAND	190	150	78.9	33	17.4	20	10.5	58	30.5	73	38.4	54	28.4	54	28.4	93	48.9	129	67.9
Connecticut	34	25	73.5	4	11.8	6	17.6	11	32.4	15	44.1	17	50.0	14	41.2	22	64.7	25	73.5
Maine	37	32	86.5	5	13.5	5	13.5	11	29.7	9	24.3	4	10.8	8	21.6	8	21.6	26	70.3
Massachusetts	66	46	69.7	15	22.7	3	4.5	17	25.8	27	40.9	18	27.3	18	27.3	35	53.0	41	62.1
New Hampshire	26	23	88.5	7	26.9	5	19.2	14	53.8	10	38.5	8	30.8	5	19.2	13	50.0	18	69.2
Rhode Island	13	11	84.6	1	7.7	1	7.7	1	7.7	9	69.2	5	38.5	6	46.2	9	69.2	8	61.5
Vermont	14	13	92.9	1	7.1	0	0.0	4	28.6	3	21.4	2	14.3	3	21.4	6	42.9	11	78.6
CENSUS DIVISION 2, MIDDLE ATLANTIC	423	342	80.9	97	22.9	29	6.9	111	26.2	195	46.1	134	31.7	115	27.2	264	62.4	289	68.3
New Jersey	72	57	79.2	32	44.4	9	12.5	18	25.0	46	63.9	34	47.2	32	44.4	52	72.2	47	65.3
New York	156	142	91.0	50	32.1	11	7.1	57	36.5	80	51.3	57	36.5	41	26.3	107	68.6	124	79.5
Pennsylvania	195	143	73.3	15	7.7	9	4.6	36	18.5	69	35.4	43	22.1	42	21.5	105	53.8	118	60.5
CENSUS DIVISION 3, SOUTH ATLANTIC	682	550	80.6	112	16.4	56	8.2	148	21.7	250	36.7	188	27.6	203	29.8	346	50.7	463	67.9
Delaware	8	5	62.5	2	25.0	3	37.5	5	62.5	1	12.5	3	37.5	4	50.0	4	50.0	3	37.5
District of Columbia	11	8	72.7	2	18.2	2	18.2	5	45.5	7	63.6	4	36.4	5	45.5	7	63.6	7	63.6
Florida	170	135	79.4	37	21.8	12	7.1	24	14.1	71	41.8	56	32.9	54	31.8	105	61.8	122	71.8
Georgia	110	87	79.1	10	9.1	1	0.9	13	11.8	39	35.5	26	23.6	28	25.5	47	42.7	71	64.5
Maryland	52	44	84.6	20	38.5	6	11.5	12	23.1	28	53.8	15	28.8	17	32.7	34	65.4	38	73.1
North Carolina	112	98	87.5	12	10.7	13	11.6	21	18.8	37	33.0	30	26.8	36	32.1	56	50.0	87	77.7
South Carolina	73	55	75.3	5	6.8	3	4.1	17	23.3	20	27.4	17	23.3	15	20.5	27	37.0	35	47.9
Virginia	84	69	82.1	19	22.6	15	17.9	19	22.6	32	38.1	25	29.8	29	34.5	47	56.0	62	73.8
West Virginia	62	49	79.0	5	8.1	1	1.6	32	51.6	15	24.2	12	19.4	15	24.2	21	33.9	38	61.3
CENSUS DIVISION 4, EAST NORTH CENTRAL	725	615	84.8	110	15.2	79	10.9	265	36.6	278	38.3	224	30.9	198	27.3	333	45.9	493	68.0
Illinois	163	152	93.3	33	20.2	12	7.4	61	37.4	69	42.3	62	38.0	47	28.8	100	61.3	124	76.1
Indiana	128	94	73.4	10	7.8	6	4.7	14	10.9	42	32.8	34	26.6	23	18.0	51	39.8	84	65.6
Michigan	131	111	84.7	19	14.5	15	11.5	46	35.1	53	40.5	30	22.9	31	23.7	56	42.7	92	70.2
Ohio	156	134	85.9	25	16.0	27	17.3	44	28.2	66	42.3	52	33.3	54	34.6	76	48.7	100	64.1
Wisconsin	147	124	84.4	23	15.6	19	12.9	100	68.0	48	32.7	46	31.3	43	29.3	50	34.0	93	63.3
CENSUS DIVISION 5, EAST SOUTH CENTRAL	383	310	80.9	45	11.7	27	7.0	146	38.1	86	22.5	73	19.1	77	20.1	123	32.1	183	47.8
Alabama	94	74	78.7	9	9.6	9	9.6	35	37.2	19	20.2	16	17.0	19	20.2	31	33.0	48	51.1
Kentucky	90	77	85.6	5	5.6	9	10.0	22	24.4	27	30.0	23	25.6	21	23.3	43	47.8	47	52.2
Mississippi	112	88	78.6	14	12.5	11	9.8	76	67.9	15	13.4	15	13.4	15	13.4	19	17.0	39	34.8
Tennessee	87	71	81.6	17	19.5	5	5.7	13	14.9	25	28.7	19	21.8	22	25.3	30	34.5	49	56.3
CENSUS DIVISION 6, WEST NORTH CENTRAL	651	579	88.9	84	12.9	22	3.4	285	43.8	134	20.6	88	13.5	98	15.1	151	23.2	411	63.1
Iowa	126	119	94.4	16	12.7	1	0.8	92	73.0	29	23.0	14	11.1	17	13.5	22	17.5	89	70.6
Kansas	152	127	83.6	11	7.2	4	2.0	22	14.5	18	11.8	13	8.6	15	9.9	25	16.4	90	59.2
Minnesota	104	97	93.3	15	14.4	4	3.8	75	72.1	29	27.9	16	15.4	16	15.4	25	24.0	69	66.3
Missouri	146	116	79.5	20	13.7	9	6.2	30	20.5	34	23.3	28	19.2	26	17.8	54	37.0	83	56.8
Nebraska	50	47	94.0	8	16.0	2	4.0	28	56.0	14	28.0	12	24.0	14	28.0	14	28.0	36	72.0
North Dakota	30	30	100.0	7	23.3	3	10.0	16	53.3	2	6.7	2	6.7	4	13.3	6	20.0	18	60.0
South Dakota	43	43	100.0	7	16.3	0	0.0	22	51.2	8	18.6	3	7.0	6	14.0	5	11.6	26	60.5
CENSUS DIVISION 7, WEST SOUTH CENTRAL	896	671	74.9	86	9.6	47	5.2	356	39.7	206	23.0	152	17.0	122	13.6	278	31.0	452	50.4
Arkansas	96	71	74.0	6	6.3	1	1.0	52	54.2	18	18.8	11	11.5	14	14.6	21	21.9	53	55.2
Louisiana	99	64	64.6	9	9.1	3	3.0	14	14.1	33	33.3	17	17.2	18	18.2	32	32.3	49	49.5
Oklahoma	127	117	92.1	15	11.8	3	2.4	49	38.6	22	17.3	19	15.0	13	10.2	36	28.3	73	57.5
Texas	574	419	73.0	56	9.8	40	7.0	241	42.0	133	23.2	105	18.3	77	13.4	189	32.9	277	48.3
CENSUS DIVISION 8, MOUNTAIN	349	299	85.7	63	18.1	27	7.7	162	46.4	110	31.5	77	22.1	82	23.5	126	36.1	217	62.2
Arizona	68	51	75.0	20	29.4	6	8.8	20	29.4	30	44.1	23	33.8	18	26.5	36	52.9	38	55.9
Colorado	72	67	93.1	10	13.9	13	18.1	56	77.8	25	34.7	20	27.8	23	31.9	34	47.2	55	76.4
Idaho	29	27	93.1	5	17.2	2	6.9	6	20.7	9	31.0	6	20.7	5	17.2	8	27.6	19	65.5
Montana	55	52	94.5	8	14.5	1	1.8	32	58.2	7	12.7	3	5.5	6	10.9	8	14.5	28	50.9
Nevada	30	19	63.3	4	13.3	1	3.3	6	20.0	9	30.0	7	23.3	4	13.3	12	40.0	16	53.3
New Mexico	33	28	84.8	4	12.1	0	0.0	9	27.3	11	33.3	8	24.2	8	24.2	10	30.3	21	63.6
Utah	35	30	85.7	8	22.9	4	11.4	16	45.7	11	31.4	7	20.0	12	34.3	14	40.0	23	65.7
Wyoming	27	25	92.6	4	14.8	0	0.0	17	63.0	8	29.6	3	11.1	6	22.2	4	14.8	17	63.0
CENSUS DIVISION 9, PACIFIC	481	409	85.0	83	17.3	19	4.0	165	34.3	231	48.0	160	33.3	123	25.6	253	52.6	329	68.4
Alaska	15	13	86.7	1	6.7	0	0.0	4	26.7	6	40.0	2	13.3	2	13.3	1	6.7	9	60.0
California	309	251	81.2	53	17.2	10	3.2	67	21.7	155	50.2	112	36.2	87	28.2	190	61.5	207	67.0
Hawaii	18	14	77.8	3	16.7	0	0.0	5	27.8	7	38.9	6	33.3	4	22.2	8	44.4	8	44.4
Oregon	61	59	96.7	9	14.8	2	3.3	40	65.6	32	52.5	21	34.4	10	16.4	22	36.1	49	80.3
Washington	78	72	92.3	17	21.8	7	9.0	49	62.8	31	39.7	19	24.4	20	25.6	32	41.0	57	73.1

Table 7 (Continued)

These data include only hospital-based facilities and services as reported by responding hospitals in Section C of the 2013 AHA Annual Survey, beginning on page 215. All hospitals are represented with Community Hospitals listed separately under United States. No estimates have been made for nonresponding hospitals. Definitions of facilities and services are listed in the Glossary, page 201.

Columns under **PHYSICAL REHABILITATION SERVICES**: Assistive Technology Center, Electro-Diagnostic Services, Physical Rehabilitation Outpatient Services, Prosthetic Orthotic Services, Robot Assisted Walking Therapy, Simulated Rehabilitation Environment. Columns under **PSYCHIATRIC SERVICES**: Child/Adolescent Services, Consultation/Liaison Services, Education Services, Emergency Services, Geriatric Services.

CLASSIFICATION	HOSPITALS REPORTING	Assistive Technology Center No.	%	Electro-Diagnostic Services No.	%	Physical Rehab. Outpatient Services No.	%	Prosthetic Orthotic Services No.	%	Robot Assisted Walking Therapy No.	%	Simulated Rehab. Environment No.	%	Child/Adolescent Services No.	%	Consultation/Liaison Services No.	%	Education Services No.	%	Emergency Services No.	%	Geriatric Services No.	%
UNITED STATES	4,780	932	19.5	1,220	25.5	3,459	72.4	874	18.3	205	4.3	1,235	25.8	857	17.9	1,546	32.3	1,158	24.2	1,574	32.9	1,469	30.7
COMMUNITY HOSPITALS	4,053	813	20.1	1,146	28.3	3,273	80.8	787	19.4	185	4.6	1,137	28.1	636	15.7	1,305	32.2	887	21.9	1,360	33.6	1,180	29.1
CENSUS DIVISION 1, NEW ENGLAND	190	46	24.2	59	31.1	157	82.6	48	25.3	12	6.3	59	31.1	65	34.2	104	54.7	77	40.5	96	50.5	84	44.2
Connecticut	34	11	32.4	12	35.3	25	73.5	12	35.3	4	11.8	15	44.1	17	50.0	23	67.6	18	52.9	24	70.6	20	58.8
Maine	37	8	21.6	8	21.6	30	81.1	5	13.5	1	2.7	12	32.4	9	24.3	11	29.7	9	24.3	10	27.0	9	24.3
Massachusetts	66	17	25.8	24	36.4	55	83.3	15	22.7	4	6.1	17	25.8	24	36.4	41	62.1	31	47.0	34	51.5	32	48.5
New Hampshire	26	4	15.4	6	23.1	24	92.3	8	30.8	2	7.7	8	30.8	4	15.4	13	50.0	8	30.8	11	42.3	8	30.8
Rhode Island	13	4	30.8	6	46.2	10	76.9	3	23.1	0	0.0	2	15.4	4	30.8	9	69.2	6	46.2	10	76.9	9	69.2
Vermont	14	2	14.3	3	21.4	13	92.9	5	35.7	1	7.1	5	35.7	3	21.4	7	50.0	5	35.7	7	50.0	6	42.9
CENSUS DIVISION 2, MIDDLE ATLANTIC	423	121	28.6	201	47.5	333	78.7	124	29.3	38	9.0	155	36.6	132	31.2	240	56.7	163	38.5	224	53.0	205	48.5
New Jersey	72	28	38.9	38	52.8	61	84.7	28	38.9	8	11.1	32	44.4	29	40.3	49	68.1	34	47.2	48	66.7	36	50.0
New York	156	45	28.8	79	50.6	136	87.2	58	37.2	10	6.4	56	35.9	58	37.2	100	64.1	70	44.9	91	58.3	85	54.5
Pennsylvania	195	48	24.6	84	43.1	136	69.7	38	19.5	20	10.3	67	34.4	45	23.1	91	46.7	59	30.3	85	43.6	84	43.1
CENSUS DIVISION 3, SOUTH ATLANTIC	682	145	21.3	193	28.3	502	73.6	172	25.2	41	6.0	196	28.7	116	17.0	241	35.3	180	26.4	258	37.8	221	32.4
Delaware	8	1	12.5	2	25.0	5	62.5	3	37.5	0	0.0	1	12.5	4	50.0	5	62.5	4	50.0	3	37.5	4	50.0
District of Columbia	11	5	45.5	7	63.6	9	81.8	5	45.5	4	36.4	7	63.6	4	36.4	7	63.6	3	27.3	8	72.7	6	54.5
Florida	170	53	31.2	45	26.5	132	77.6	39	22.9	13	7.6	48	28.2	28	16.5	59	34.7	41	24.1	61	35.9	46	27.1
Georgia	110	10	9.1	14	12.7	76	69.1	14	12.7	1	0.9	22	20.0	6	5.5	28	25.5	19	17.3	22	20.0	26	23.6
Maryland	52	12	23.1	28	53.8	40	76.9	18	34.6	3	5.8	21	40.4	17	32.7	34	65.4	25	48.1	38	73.1	30	57.7
North Carolina	112	29	25.9	39	34.8	92	82.1	20	17.9	6	5.4	40	35.7	19	17.0	39	34.8	36	32.1	47	42.0	45	40.2
South Carolina	73	5	6.8	8	11.0	37	50.7	44	60.3	6	8.2	14	19.2	10	13.7	21	28.8	13	17.8	23	31.5	18	24.7
Virginia	84	24	28.6	34	40.5	67	79.8	21	25.0	6	7.1	33	39.3	16	19.0	32	38.1	24	28.6	40	47.6	28	33.3
West Virginia	62	6	9.7	16	25.8	44	71.0	8	12.9	2	3.2	10	16.1	12	19.4	16	25.8	15	24.2	16	25.8	18	29.0
CENSUS DIVISION 4, EAST NORTH CENTRAL	725	145	20.0	252	34.8	587	81.0	163	22.5	20	2.8	273	37.7	158	21.8	295	40.7	230	31.7	288	39.7	262	36.1
Illinois	163	31	19.0	64	39.3	145	89.0	35	21.5	5	3.1	65	39.9	47	28.8	70	42.9	63	38.7	76	46.6	67	41.1
Indiana	128	26	20.3	31	24.2	94	73.4	23	18.0	2	1.6	42	32.8	28	21.9	37	28.9	31	24.2	39	30.5	42	32.8
Michigan	131	31	23.7	55	42.0	107	81.7	26	19.8	7	5.3	49	37.4	26	19.8	65	49.6	49	37.4	64	48.9	49	37.4
Ohio	156	33	21.2	57	36.5	121	77.6	37	23.7	5	3.2	56	35.9	25	16.0	66	42.3	49	31.4	62	39.7	58	37.2
Wisconsin	147	24	16.3	45	30.6	120	81.6	42	28.6	1	0.7	61	41.5	32	21.8	57	38.8	38	25.9	47	32.0	46	31.3
CENSUS DIVISION 5, EAST SOUTH CENTRAL	383	40	10.4	73	19.1	256	66.8	42	11.0	19	5.0	65	17.0	42	11.0	85	22.2	69	18.0	100	26.1	133	34.7
Alabama	94	12	12.8	15	16.0	62	66.0	14	14.9	7	7.4	15	16.0	12	12.8	23	24.5	18	19.1	27	28.7	37	39.4
Kentucky	90	10	11.1	23	25.6	66	73.3	9	10.0	5	5.6	16	17.8	9	10.0	27	30.0	21	23.3	28	31.1	21	23.3
Mississippi	112	6	5.4	15	13.4	61	54.5	9	8.0	3	2.7	16	14.3	8	7.1	16	14.3	14	12.5	17	15.2	44	39.3
Tennessee	87	12	13.8	20	23.0	67	77.0	10	11.5	4	4.6	18	20.7	12	13.8	19	21.8	16	18.4	28	32.2	31	35.6
CENSUS DIVISION 6, WEST NORTH CENTRAL	651	97	14.9	129	19.8	520	79.9	102	15.7	15	2.3	142	21.8	115	17.7	163	25.0	138	21.2	182	28.0	168	25.8
Iowa	126	26	20.6	22	17.5	103	81.7	14	11.1	1	0.8	30	23.8	27	21.4	33	26.2	32	25.4	43	34.1	35	27.8
Kansas	152	12	7.9	16	10.5	116	76.3	12	7.9	4	2.6	21	13.8	9	5.9	15	9.9	15	9.9	26	17.1	28	18.4
Minnesota	104	19	18.3	24	23.1	91	87.5	18	17.3	3	2.9	21	20.2	25	24.0	38	36.5	28	26.9	35	33.7	33	31.7
Missouri	146	17	11.6	34	23.3	106	72.6	33	22.6	5	3.4	47	32.2	30	20.5	54	37.0	41	28.1	55	37.7	49	33.6
Nebraska	50	11	22.0	14	28.0	43	86.0	13	26.0	1	2.0	12	24.0	12	24.0	12	24.0	8	16.0	6	12.0	10	20.0
North Dakota	30	6	20.0	8	26.7	26	86.7	5	16.7	1	3.3	6	20.0	8	26.7	8	26.7	8	26.7	9	30.0	9	30.0
South Dakota	43	6	14.0	11	25.6	35	81.4	7	16.3	0	0.0	5	11.6	4	9.3	4	9.3	6	14.0	8	18.6	4	9.3
CENSUS DIVISION 7, WEST SOUTH CENTRAL	896	179	20.0	109	12.2	525	58.6	80	8.9	31	3.5	172	19.2	87	9.7	154	17.2	124	13.8	159	17.7	202	22.5
Arkansas	96	20	20.8	11	11.5	62	64.6	6	6.3	5	5.2	14	14.6	13	13.5	20	20.8	13	13.5	23	24.0	31	32.3
Louisiana	99	20	20.2	13	13.1	47	47.5	9	9.1	1	1.0	21	21.2	9	9.1	19	19.2	17	17.2	25	25.3	32	32.3
Oklahoma	127	25	19.7	20	15.7	84	66.1	16	12.6	1	0.8	22	17.3	10	7.9	28	22.0	16	12.6	25	19.7	28	22.0
Texas	574	114	19.9	65	11.3	332	57.8	49	8.5	24	4.2	115	20.0	55	9.6	87	15.2	78	13.6	86	15.0	111	19.3
CENSUS DIVISION 8, MOUNTAIN	349	74	21.2	71	20.3	245	70.2	55	15.8	13	3.7	70	20.1	55	15.8	97	27.8	74	21.2	111	31.8	88	25.2
Arizona	68	17	25.0	21	30.9	38	55.9	14	20.6	4	5.9	18	26.5	8	11.8	29	42.6	17	25.0	24	35.3	18	26.5
Colorado	72	14	19.4	18	25.0	60	83.3	14	19.4	4	5.6	19	26.4	10	13.9	17	23.6	12	16.7	17	23.6	11	15.3
Idaho	29	7	24.1	6	20.7	21	72.4	3	10.3	0	0.0	8	27.6	4	13.8	7	24.1	7	24.1	8	27.6	6	20.7
Montana	55	10	18.2	9	16.4	45	81.8	7	12.7	0	0.0	5	9.1	9	16.4	14	25.5	10	18.2	20	36.4	15	27.3
Nevada	30	4	13.3	3	10.0	16	53.3	1	3.3	2	6.7	5	16.7	6	20.0	4	13.3	6	20.0	11	36.7	8	26.7
New Mexico	33	7	21.2	5	15.2	25	75.8	2	6.1	2	6.1	5	15.2	6	18.2	8	24.2	7	21.2	16	48.5	13	39.4
Utah	35	11	31.4	8	22.9	23	65.7	10	28.6	2	5.7	7	20.0	6	17.1	12	34.3	10	28.6	13	37.1	9	25.7
Wyoming	27	4	14.8	1	3.7	17	63.0	4	14.8	0	0.0	3	11.1	6	22.2	6	22.2	5	18.5	10	37.0	8	29.6
CENSUS DIVISION 9, PACIFIC	481	85	17.7	133	27.7	334	69.4	88	18.3	16	3.3	103	21.4	87	18.1	167	34.7	103	21.4	156	32.4	106	22.0
Alaska	15	1	6.7	1	6.7	12	80.0	2	13.3	0	0.0	1	6.7	7	46.7	6	40.0	2	13.3	4	26.7	4	26.7
California	309	51	16.5	82	26.5	201	65.0	58	18.8	9	2.9	64	20.7	55	17.8	110	35.6	70	22.7	91	29.4	74	23.9
Hawaii	18	5	27.8	4	22.2	13	72.2	4	22.2	1	5.6	4	22.2	4	22.2	6	33.3	6	33.3	6	33.3	6	33.3
Oregon	61	12	19.7	20	32.8	51	83.6	9	14.8	1	3.3	8	13.1	8	13.1	20	32.8	8	13.1	25	41.0	7	11.5
Washington	78	16	20.5	26	33.3	57	73.1	15	19.2	4	5.1	26	33.3	13	16.7	25	32.1	17	21.8	30	38.5	15	19.2

Table 7 (Continued)

These data include only hospital-based facilities and services as reported by responding hospitals in Section C of the 2013 AHA Annual Survey, beginning on page 215. All hospitals are represented with Community Hospitals listed separately under United States. No estimates have been made for nonresponding hospitals. Definitions of facilities and services are listed in the Glossary, page 201.

PSYCHIATRIC SERVICES — RADIOLOGY, DIAGNOSTIC

CLASSIFICATION	HOSPITALS REPORTING	OUTPATIENT SERVICES Number	Percent	PARTIAL HOSPITALIZATION PROGRAM Number	Percent	RESIDENTIAL TREATMENT Number	Percent	CT SCANNER Number	Percent	DIAGNOSTIC RADIOISOTOPE FACILITY Number	Percent	ELECTRON BEAM COMPUTED TOMOGRAPHY (EBCT) Number	Percent	FULL-FIELD DIGITAL MAMMOGRAPHY (FFDM) Number	Percent	MAGNETIC RESONANCE IMAGING (MRI) Number	Percent	INTRAOPERATIVE MAGNETIC IMAGING Number	Percent	MAGNETO-ENCEPHALO-GRAPHY Number	Percent	MULTI-SLICE SPIRAL COMPUTED TOMOGRAPHY (<64 SLICE CT) Number	Percent
UNITED STATES	4,780	1,305	27.3	735	15.4	309	6.5	3,949	82.6	2,658	55.6	338	7.1	2,598	54.4	3,105	65.0	223	4.7	152	3.2	2,727	57.1
COMMUNITY HOSPITALS	4,053	1,049	25.9	548	13.5	159	3.9	3,723	91.9	2,561	63.2	318	7.8	2,538	62.6	2,940	72.5	208	5.1	146	3.6	2,598	64.1
CENSUS DIVISION 1, NEW ENGLAND	190	104	54.7	63	33.2	17	8.9	152	80.0	127	66.8	10	5.3	122	64.2	122	64.2	11	5.8	8	4.2	112	58.9
Connecticut	34	23	67.6	17	50.0	6	17.6	25	73.5	23	67.6	5	14.7	21	61.8	24	70.6	2	5.9	0	0.0	20	58.8
Maine	37	12	32.4	7	18.9	0	0.0	32	86.5	27	73.0	0	0.0	24	64.9	23	62.2	2	5.4	0	0.0	19	51.4
Massachusetts	66	37	56.1	22	33.3	6	9.1	49	74.2	45	68.2	4	6.1	43	65.2	38	57.6	5	7.6	6	9.1	40	60.6
New Hampshire	26	12	46.2	7	26.9	0	0.0	23	88.5	13	50.0	0	0.0	18	69.2	15	57.7	1	3.8	2	7.7	16	61.5
Rhode Island	13	10	76.9	7	53.8	2	15.4	10	76.9	9	69.2	1	7.7	8	61.5	10	76.9	1	7.7	0	0.0	10	76.9
Vermont	14	10	71.4	3	21.4	3	21.4	13	92.9	10	71.4	0	0.0	8	57.1	12	85.7	0	0.0	0	0.0	7	50.0
CENSUS DIVISION 2, MIDDLE ATLANTIC	423	166	39.2	90	21.3	42	9.9	363	85.8	305	72.1	58	13.7	283	66.9	321	75.9	23	5.4	16	3.8	260	61.5
New Jersey	72	34	47.2	29	40.3	13	18.1	59	81.9	53	73.6	14	19.4	47	65.3	56	77.8	7	9.7	4	5.6	52	72.2
New York	156	80	51.3	30	19.2	17	10.9	149	95.5	121	77.6	21	13.5	123	78.8	129	82.7	7	4.5	5	3.2	100	64.1
Pennsylvania	195	52	26.7	31	15.9	12	6.2	155	79.5	131	67.2	23	11.8	113	57.9	136	69.7	9	4.6	7	3.6	108	55.4
CENSUS DIVISION 3, SOUTH ATLANTIC	682	176	25.8	112	16.4	46	6.7	570	83.6	444	65.1	55	8.1	411	60.3	486	71.3	30	4.4	21	3.1	445	65.2
Delaware	8	4	50.0	2	25.0	1	12.5	5	62.5	4	50.0	1	12.5	4	50.0	5	62.5	0	0.0	0	0.0	5	62.5
District of Columbia	11	6	54.5	4	36.4	1	9.1	8	72.7	7	63.6	3	27.3	6	54.5	8	72.7	4	36.4	1	9.1	7	63.6
Florida	170	40	23.5	22	12.9	10	5.9	141	82.9	114	67.1	24	14.1	103	60.6	129	75.9	10	5.9	8	4.7	120	70.6
Georgia	110	20	18.2	13	11.8	4	3.6	93	84.5	62	56.4	2	1.8	66	60.0	76	69.1	4	3.6	3	2.7	63	57.3
Maryland	52	29	55.8	26	50.0	5	9.6	46	88.5	40	76.9	3	5.8	32	61.5	40	76.9	3	5.8	1	1.9	38	73.1
North Carolina	112	31	27.7	13	11.6	8	7.1	100	89.3	78	69.6	10	8.9	71	63.4	87	77.7	5	4.5	5	4.5	83	74.1
South Carolina	73	15	20.5	10	13.7	5	6.8	56	76.7	44	60.3	2	2.7	43	58.9	47	64.4	1	1.4	2	2.7	46	63.0
Virginia	84	20	23.8	18	21.4	8	9.5	70	83.3	57	67.9	8	9.5	55	65.5	60	71.4	3	3.6	1	1.2	48	57.1
West Virginia	62	11	17.7	4	6.5	4	6.5	51	82.3	38	61.3	2	3.2	31	50.0	34	54.8	0	0.0	0	0.0	35	56.5
CENSUS DIVISION 4, EAST NORTH CENTRAL	725	241	33.2	157	21.7	60	8.3	630	86.9	491	67.7	67	9.2	483	66.6	518	71.4	49	6.8	28	3.9	431	59.4
Illinois	163	69	42.3	48	29.4	13	8.0	155	95.1	113	69.3	10	6.1	122	74.8	117	71.8	7	4.3	5	3.1	107	65.6
Indiana	128	32	25.0	23	18.0	16	12.5	104	81.3	79	61.7	13	10.2	77	60.2	96	75.0	7	5.5	7	5.5	67	52.3
Michigan	131	45	34.4	24	18.3	7	5.3	114	87.0	100	76.3	8	6.1	87	66.4	91	69.5	6	4.6	5	3.8	83	63.4
Ohio	156	50	32.1	39	25.0	9	5.8	136	87.2	116	74.4	23	14.7	111	71.2	123	78.8	11	7.1	7	4.5	111	71.2
Wisconsin	147	45	30.6	23	15.6	15	10.2	121	82.3	83	56.5	13	8.8	86	58.5	91	61.9	18	12.2	4	2.7	63	42.9
CENSUS DIVISION 5, EAST SOUTH CENTRAL	383	77	20.1	45	11.7	26	6.8	306	79.9	205	53.5	20	5.2	170	44.4	239	62.4	15	3.9	9	2.3	191	49.9
Alabama	94	24	25.5	13	13.8	6	6.4	75	78.7	49	52.1	4	4.3	36	38.3	60	63.8	2	2.1	2	2.1	51	54.3
Kentucky	90	16	17.8	11	12.2	4	4.4	75	83.3	52	57.8	3	3.3	48	53.3	68	75.6	3	3.3	2	2.2	50	55.6
Mississippi	112	16	14.3	8	7.1	11	9.8	85	75.9	53	47.3	6	5.4	35	31.3	51	45.5	4	3.6	1	0.9	41	36.6
Tennessee	87	21	24.1	13	14.9	5	5.7	72	82.8	51	58.6	7	8.0	51	58.6	60	69.0	6	6.9	4	4.6	49	56.3
CENSUS DIVISION 6, WEST NORTH CENTRAL	651	172	26.4	61	9.4	38	5.8	565	86.8	250	38.4	24	3.7	340	52.2	383	58.8	20	3.1	12	1.8	367	56.4
Iowa	126	34	27.0	11	8.7	6	4.8	114	90.5	44	34.9	5	4.0	82	65.1	76	60.3	0	0.0	2	1.6	82	65.1
Kansas	152	15	9.9	6	3.9	5	3.3	123	80.9	49	32.2	3	2.0	48	31.6	58	38.2	3	2.0	1	0.7	76	50.0
Minnesota	104	40	38.5	15	14.4	8	7.7	99	95.2	43	41.3	5	4.8	67	64.4	70	67.3	7	6.7	5	4.8	58	55.8
Missouri	146	55	37.7	15	10.3	12	8.2	117	80.1	72	49.3	6	4.1	77	52.7	112	76.7	6	4.1	3	2.1	84	57.5
Nebraska	50	14	28.0	6	12.0	4	8.0	46	92.0	23	46.0	5	10.0	34	68.0	36	72.0	3	6.0	0	0.0	31	62.0
North Dakota	30	9	30.0	7	23.3	3	10.0	26	86.7	9	30.0	0	0.0	14	46.7	13	43.3	1	3.3	1	3.3	16	53.3
South Dakota	43	5	11.6	1	2.3	0	0.0	40	93.0	10	23.3	0	0.0	18	41.9	18	41.9	0	0.0	0	0.0	20	46.5
CENSUS DIVISION 7, WEST SOUTH CENTRAL	896	151	16.9	83	9.3	37	4.1	647	72.2	356	39.7	35	3.9	337	37.6	472	52.7	31	3.5	18	2.0	425	47.4
Arkansas	96	20	20.8	10	10.4	8	8.3	73	76.0	38	39.6	3	3.1	36	37.5	36	37.5	6	6.3	2	2.1	47	49.0
Louisiana	98	26	26.3	15	15.2	4	4.0	66	66.7	46	46.5	9	9.1	53	53.5	52	52.5	2	2.0	3	3.0	41	41.4
Oklahoma	127	23	18.1	6	4.7	12	9.4	103	81.1	47	37.0	4	3.1	58	45.7	78	61.4	2	1.6	2	1.6	62	48.8
Texas	574	82	14.3	52	9.1	13	2.3	405	70.6	225	39.2	19	3.3	190	33.1	284	49.5	21	3.7	11	1.9	275	47.9
CENSUS DIVISION 8, MOUNTAIN	349	85	24.4	45	12.9	20	5.7	296	84.8	173	49.6	22	6.3	184	52.7	232	66.5	15	4.3	18	5.2	200	57.3
Arizona	68	18	26.5	9	13.2	2	2.9	51	75.0	34	50.0	2	2.9	29	42.6	47	69.1	2	2.9	7	10.3	40	58.8
Colorado	72	16	22.2	6	8.3	3	4.2	67	93.1	44	61.1	5	6.9	45	62.5	59	81.9	5	6.9	3	4.2	47	65.3
Idaho	29	8	27.6	2	6.9	3	10.3	28	96.6	15	51.7	2	6.9	13	44.8	22	75.9	1	3.4	1	3.4	19	65.5
Montana	55	12	21.8	8	14.5	3	5.5	45	81.8	20	36.4	0	0.0	28	50.9	24	43.6	0	0.0	2	3.6	25	45.5
Nevada	30	9	30.0	5	16.7	3	10.0	20	66.7	16	53.3	1	3.3	11	36.7	19	63.3	1	3.3	1	3.3	15	50.0
New Mexico	33	8	24.2	2	6.1	2	6.1	29	87.9	16	48.5	3	9.1	16	48.5	19	57.6	3	9.1	2	6.1	19	57.6
Utah	35	8	22.9	8	22.9	4	11.4	31	88.6	17	48.6	7	20.0	26	74.3	25	71.4	3	8.6	2	5.7	20	57.1
Wyoming	27	6	22.2	5	18.5	2	7.4	25	92.6	11	40.7	2	7.4	16	59.3	17	63.0	0	0.0	0	0.0	15	55.6
CENSUS DIVISION 9, PACIFIC	481	133	27.7	79	16.4	23	4.8	420	87.3	307	63.8	47	9.8	268	55.7	332	69.0	29	6.0	22	4.6	296	61.5
Alaska	15	5	33.3	3	20.0	2	13.3	13	86.7	5	33.3	0	0.0	9	60.0	8	53.3	0	0.0	0	0.0	8	53.3
California	309	90	29.1	55	17.8	11	3.6	266	86.1	205	66.3	37	12.0	157	50.8	217	70.2	22	7.1	18	5.8	184	59.5
Hawaii	18	6	33.3	4	22.2	3	16.7	13	72.2	10	55.6	1	5.6	11	61.1	11	61.1	0	0.0	0	0.0	6	33.3
Oregon	61	10	16.4	5	8.2	1	1.6	58	95.1	42	68.9	3	4.9	46	75.4	45	73.8	4	6.6	1	1.6	47	77.0
Washington	78	22	28.2	12	15.4	6	7.7	70	89.7	45	57.7	6	7.7	45	57.7	51	65.4	3	3.8	3	3.8	51	65.4

Table 7 (Continued)

These data include only hospital-based facilities and services as reported by responding hospitals in Section C of the 2013 AHA Annual Survey, beginning on page 215. All hospitals are represented with Community Hospitals listed separately under United States. No estimates have been made for nonresponding hospitals. Definitions of facilities and services are listed in the Glossary, page 201.

| | | RADIOLOGY, DIAGNOSTIC | | | | | | | | | | RADIOLOGY, THERAPEUTIC | | | | | | | | | |
CLASSIFICATION	HOSPITALS REPORTING	MULTI-SLICE SPIRAL COMPUTED TOMOGRAPHY (64+ SLICE CT) Number	Percent	POSITRON EMISSION TOMOGRAPHY (PET) Number	Percent	POSITRON EMISSION TOMOGRAPHY/CT (PET/CT) Number	Percent	SINGLE PHOTON EMISSION COMPUTERIZED TOMOGRAPHY (SPECT) Number	Percent	ULTRASOUND Number	Percent	IMAGE-GUIDED RADIATION THERAPY (IGRT) Number	Percent	INTENSITY-MODULATED RADIATION THERAPY (IMRT) Number	Percent	PROTON BEAM THERAPY Number	Percent	SHAPED BEAM RADIATION SYSTEM Number	Percent	STEREOTACTIC RADIOSURGERY Number	Percent
UNITED STATES	4,780	2,193	45.9	801	16.8	1,021	21.4	1,750	36.6	3,824	80.0	1,016	21.3	1,124	23.5	101	2.1	904	18.9	848	17.7
COMMUNITY HOSPITALS	4,053	2,099	51.8	765	18.9	980	24.2	1,699	41.9	3,610	89.1	983	24.3	1,093	27.0	93	2.3	877	21.6	830	20.5
CENSUS DIVISION 1, NEW ENGLAND	190	101	53.2	38	20.0	51	26.8	99	52.1	160	84.2	50	26.3	55	28.9	4	2.1	48	25.3	48	25.3
Connecticut	34	19	55.9	12	35.3	17	50.0	22	64.7	27	79.4	17	50.0	17	50.0	1	2.9	15	44.1	16	47.1
Maine	37	18	48.6	3	8.1	17	45.9	17	45.9	32	86.5	4	10.8	6	16.2	0	0.0	4	10.8	4	10.8
Massachusetts	66	40	60.6	14	21.2	18	27.3	32	48.5	55	83.3	23	34.8	25	37.9	3	4.5	22	33.3	22	33.3
New Hampshire	26	11	42.3	3	11.5	4	15.4	13	50.0	23	88.5	4	15.4	5	19.2	0	0.0	4	15.4	4	15.4
Rhode Island	13	5	38.5	3	23.1	2	15.4	7	53.8	10	76.9	1	7.7	1	7.7	0	0.0	1	7.7	1	7.7
Vermont	14	8	57.1	3	21.4	3	21.4	8	57.1	13	92.9	1	7.1	1	7.1	0	0.0	1	7.1	1	7.1
CENSUS DIVISION 2, MIDDLE ATLANTIC	423	244	57.7	102	24.1	126	29.8	224	53.0	363	85.8	143	33.8	170	40.2	12	2.8	133	31.4	108	25.5
New Jersey	72	39	54.2	22	30.6	26	36.1	42	58.3	62	86.1	31	43.1	37	51.4	0	0.0	34	47.2	22	30.6
New York	156	105	67.3	35	22.4	42	26.9	82	52.6	148	94.9	52	33.3	65	41.7	7	4.5	50	32.1	39	25.0
Pennsylvania	195	100	51.3	45	23.1	58	29.7	100	51.3	153	78.5	60	30.8	68	34.9	5	2.6	49	25.1	47	24.1
CENSUS DIVISION 3, SOUTH ATLANTIC	682	366	53.7	126	18.5	168	24.6	307	45.0	568	83.3	192	28.2	203	29.8	14	2.1	168	24.6	150	22.0
Delaware	8	5	62.5	2	25.0	4	50.0	4	50.0	5	62.5	4	50.0	4	50.0	0	0.0	4	50.0	4	50.0
District of Columbia	11	5	45.5	4	36.4	5	45.5	6	54.5	9	81.8	4	36.4	4	36.4	0	0.0	5	45.5	4	36.4
Florida	170	104	61.2	43	25.3	52	30.6	71	41.8	136	80.0	48	28.2	46	27.1	3	1.8	42	24.7	50	29.4
Georgia	110	51	46.4	16	14.5	26	23.6	32	29.1	94	85.5	27	24.5	26	23.6	2	1.8	23	20.9	20	18.2
Maryland	52	38	73.1	11	21.2	13	25.0	32	61.5	45	86.5	25	48.1	24	46.2	1	1.9	17	32.7	16	30.8
North Carolina	112	56	50.0	18	16.1	27	24.1	61	54.5	102	91.1	36	32.1	41	36.6	7	6.3	34	30.4	20	17.9
South Carolina	73	30	41.1	5	6.8	11	15.1	25	34.2	58	79.5	8	11.0	14	19.2	0	0.0	8	11.0	9	12.3
Virginia	84	51	60.7	16	19.0	21	25.0	53	63.1	69	82.1	32	38.1	34	40.5	1	1.2	26	31.0	19	22.6
West Virginia	62	26	41.9	11	17.7	9	14.5	23	37.1	50	80.6	8	12.9	10	16.1	0	0.0	9	14.5	8	12.9
CENSUS DIVISION 4, EAST NORTH CENTRAL	725	417	57.5	177	24.4	210	29.0	337	46.5	619	85.4	207	28.6	225	31.0	18	2.5	189	26.1	162	22.3
Illinois	163	108	66.3	30	18.4	44	27.0	72	44.2	147	90.2	50	30.7	57	35.0	4	2.5	44	27.0	39	23.9
Indiana	128	64	50.0	30	23.4	35	27.3	47	36.7	103	80.5	40	31.3	43	33.6	4	3.1	35	27.3	23	18.0
Michigan	131	88	67.2	27	20.6	38	29.0	62	47.3	119	90.8	37	28.2	39	29.8	2	1.5	36	27.5	37	28.2
Ohio	156	82	52.6	51	32.7	58	37.2	90	57.7	137	87.8	45	28.8	47	30.1	4	2.6	43	27.6	38	24.4
Wisconsin	147	75	51.0	39	26.5	35	23.8	66	44.9	113	76.9	35	23.8	39	26.5	4	2.7	31	21.1	25	17.0
CENSUS DIVISION 5, EAST SOUTH CENTRAL	383	143	37.3	59	15.4	81	21.1	132	34.5	309	80.7	62	16.2	72	18.8	6	1.6	52	13.6	52	13.6
Alabama	94	34	36.2	15	16.0	21	22.3	25	26.6	75	79.8	13	13.8	16	17.0	2	2.1	11	11.7	9	9.6
Kentucky	90	39	43.3	13	14.4	20	22.2	37	41.1	76	84.4	15	16.7	18	20.0	1	1.1	13	14.4	14	15.6
Mississippi	112	32	28.6	17	15.2	18	16.1	34	30.4	85	75.9	14	12.5	12	10.7	1	0.9	9	8.0	8	7.1
Tennessee	87	38	43.7	14	16.1	22	25.3	36	41.4	73	83.9	20	23.0	26	29.9	2	2.3	19	21.8	21	24.1
CENSUS DIVISION 6, WEST NORTH CENTRAL	651	221	33.9	67	10.3	105	16.1	178	27.3	513	78.8	96	14.7	110	16.9	12	1.8	81	12.4	79	12.1
Iowa	126	41	32.5	13	10.3	14	11.1	36	28.6	113	89.7	14	11.1	16	12.7	1	0.8	15	11.9	14	11.1
Kansas	152	30	19.7	11	5.3	11	7.2	23	15.1	99	65.1	13	8.6	16	10.5	3	2.0	14	9.2	9	5.9
Minnesota	104	54	51.9	11	10.6	20	19.2	32	30.8	91	87.5	18	17.3	20	19.2	2	1.9	12	11.5	15	14.4
Missouri	146	65	44.5	17	11.6	37	25.3	55	37.7	116	79.5	28	19.2	34	23.3	3	2.1	17	11.6	20	13.7
Nebraska	50	17	34.0	10	20.0	15	30.0	16	32.0	42	84.0	14	28.0	12	24.0	2	4.0	11	22.0	13	26.0
North Dakota	30	5	16.7	3	10.0	5	16.7	6	20.0	19	63.3	3	10.0	4	13.3	0	0.0	4	13.3	4	13.3
South Dakota	43	9	20.9	5	11.6	3	7.0	10	23.3	33	76.7	6	14.0	8	18.6	1	2.3	6	14.0	4	9.3
CENSUS DIVISION 7, WEST SOUTH CENTRAL	896	287	32.0	76	8.5	96	10.7	196	21.9	597	66.6	90	10.0	97	10.8	8	0.9	73	8.1	99	11.0
Arkansas	96	32	33.3	8	8.3	9	9.4	22	22.9	68	70.8	10	10.4	8	8.3	2	2.0	4	4.2	13	13.5
Louisiana	99	37	37.4	12	12.1	19	19.2	21	21.2	65	65.7	15	15.2	14	14.1	2	2.0	11	11.1	15	15.2
Oklahoma	127	40	31.5	16	12.6	20	15.7	24	18.9	93	73.2	19	15.0	20	15.7	0	0.0	17	13.4	14	11.0
Texas	574	178	31.0	40	7.0	48	8.4	129	22.5	371	64.6	46	8.0	55	9.6	4	0.7	41	7.1	57	9.9
CENSUS DIVISION 8, MOUNTAIN	349	168	48.1	56	16.0	64	18.3	98	28.1	284	81.4	57	16.3	64	18.3	11	3.2	55	15.8	51	14.6
Arizona	68	32	47.1	12	17.6	16	23.5	28	41.2	52	76.5	11	16.2	11	16.2	1	1.5	11	16.2	10	14.7
Colorado	72	47	65.3	16	22.2	18	25.0	19	26.4	66	91.7	15	20.8	18	25.0	3	4.2	18	25.0	15	20.8
Idaho	29	12	41.4	3	10.3	4	13.8	9	31.0	25	86.2	7	24.1	6	20.7	1	3.4	5	17.2	5	17.2
Montana	55	20	36.4	7	12.7	8	14.5	12	21.8	42	76.4	9	16.4	8	14.5	3	5.5	6	10.9	6	10.9
Nevada	30	11	36.7	2	6.7	2	6.7	6	20.0	19	63.3	3	10.0	3	10.0	0	0.0	2	6.7	4	13.3
New Mexico	33	19	57.6	5	15.2	5	15.2	9	27.3	27	81.8	4	12.1	7	21.2	2	6.1	5	15.2	5	15.2
Utah	35	19	54.3	8	22.9	10	28.6	10	28.6	29	82.9	7	20.0	7	20.0	1	2.9	6	17.1	4	11.4
Wyoming	27	8	29.6	3	11.1	1	3.7	5	18.5	24	88.9	4	14.8	4	14.8	0	0.0	2	7.4	2	7.4
CENSUS DIVISION 9, PACIFIC	481	246	51.1	100	20.8	120	24.9	179	37.2	411	85.4	119	24.7	128	26.6	16	3.3	105	21.8	99	20.6
Alaska	15	5	33.3	0	0.0	0	0.0	0	0.0	13	86.7	0	0.0	1	6.7	0	0.0	0	0.0	1	6.7
California	309	167	54.0	71	23.0	85	27.5	124	40.1	264	85.4	80	25.9	84	27.2	12	3.9	67	21.7	70	22.7
Hawaii	18	10	55.6	2	11.1	4	22.2	4	22.2	14	77.8	2	11.1	4	22.2	0	0.0	2	11.1	2	11.1
Oregon	61	29	47.5	11	18.0	13	21.3	29	47.5	59	96.7	15	24.6	15	24.6	3	4.9	14	23.0	9	14.8
Washington	78	35	44.9	16	20.5	18	23.1	22	28.2	61	78.2	20	25.6	24	30.8	1	1.3	22	28.2	17	21.8

Table 7 (Continued)

Facilities and Services

These data include only hospital-based facilities and services as reported by responding hospitals in Section C of the 2013 AHA Annual Survey, beginning on page 215. All hospitals are represented with Community Hospitals listed separately under United States. No estimates have been made for nonresponding hospitals. Definitions of facilities and services are listed in the Glossary, page 201.

Columns under **TRANSPLANT**: HEART, KIDNEY, LIVER, LUNG.

CLASSIFICATION	HOSPITALS REPORTING	BONE MARROW Number	BONE MARROW Percent	HEART Number	HEART Percent	KIDNEY Number	KIDNEY Percent	LIVER Number	LIVER Percent	LUNG Number	LUNG Percent	TISSUE Number	TISSUE Percent	OTHER Number	OTHER Percent
UNITED STATES	4,780	206	4.3	136	2.8	220	4.6	129	2.7	74	1.5	379	7.9	250	5.2
COMMUNITY HOSPITALS	4,053	203	5.0	133	3.3	217	5.4	127	3.1	73	1.8	361	8.9	244	6.0
CENSUS DIVISION 1, NEW ENGLAND	190	13	6.8	6	3.2	15	7.9	7	3.7	3	1.6	21	11.1	16	8.4
Connecticut	34	1	2.9	2	5.9	2	5.9	2	5.9	0	0.0	4	11.8	4	11.8
Maine	37	0	0.0	0	0.0	1	2.7	0	0.0	0	0.0	1	2.7	0	0.0
Massachusetts	66	9	13.6	4	6.1	9	13.6	5	7.6	3	4.5	11	16.7	8	12.1
New Hampshire	26	1	3.8	0	0.0	1	3.8	0	0.0	0	0.0	2	7.7	2	7.7
Rhode Island	13	1	7.7	0	0.0	1	7.7	0	0.0	0	0.0	1	7.7	1	7.7
Vermont	14	1	7.1	0	0.0	1	7.1	0	0.0	0	0.0	2	14.3	1	7.1
CENSUS DIVISION 2, MIDDLE ATLANTIC	423	24	5.7	16	3.8	33	7.8	19	4.5	8	1.9	58	13.7	38	9.0
New Jersey	72	2	2.8	2	2.8	5	6.9	2	2.8	1	1.4	8	11.1	6	8.3
New York	156	12	7.7	5	3.2	12	7.7	6	3.8	1	0.6	25	16.0	15	9.6
Pennsylvania	195	10	5.1	9	4.6	16	8.2	11	5.6	6	3.1	25	12.8	17	8.7
CENSUS DIVISION 3, SOUTH ATLANTIC	682	39	5.7	25	3.7	32	4.7	22	3.2	14	2.1	59	8.7	44	6.5
Delaware	8	2	25.0	1	12.5	2	25.0	1	12.5	0	0.0	0	0.0	0	0.0
District of Columbia	11	3	27.3	2	18.2	3	27.3	2	18.2	0	0.0	4	36.4	3	27.3
Florida	170	11	6.5	7	4.1	8	4.7	7	4.1	5	2.9	13	7.6	7	4.1
Georgia	110	5	4.5	3	2.7	4	3.6	3	2.7	2	1.8	9	8.2	5	4.5
Maryland	52	4	7.7	2	3.8	2	3.8	2	3.8	2	3.8	6	11.5	7	13.5
North Carolina	112	4	3.6	4	3.6	5	4.5	4	3.6	2	1.8	10	8.9	10	8.9
South Carolina	73	4	5.5	1	1.4	1	1.4	1	1.4	1	1.4	6	8.2	4	5.5
Virginia	84	5	6.0	5	6.0	6	7.1	2	2.4	2	2.4	11	13.1	7	8.3
West Virginia	62	1	1.6	0	0.0	1	1.6	0	0.0	0	0.0	4	6.5	1	1.6
CENSUS DIVISION 4, EAST NORTH CENTRAL	725	32	4.4	24	3.3	35	4.8	21	2.9	16	2.2	73	10.1	34	4.7
Illinois	163	10	6.1	6	3.7	9	5.5	6	3.7	2	1.2	17	10.4	11	6.7
Indiana	128	1	0.8	3	2.3	3	2.3	1	0.8	1	0.8	7	5.5	3	2.3
Michigan	131	8	6.1	6	4.6	10	7.6	6	4.6	5	3.8	24	18.3	8	6.1
Ohio	156	9	5.8	5	3.2	9	5.8	5	3.2	4	2.6	20	12.8	6	3.8
Wisconsin	147	4	2.7	4	2.7	4	2.7	3	2.0	4	2.7	5	3.4	6	4.1
CENSUS DIVISION 5, EAST SOUTH CENTRAL	383	16	4.2	10	2.6	12	3.1	7	1.8	4	1.0	20	5.2	16	4.2
Alabama	94	2	2.1	2	2.1	2	2.1	2	2.1	1	1.1	4	4.3	4	4.3
Kentucky	90	5	5.6	3	3.3	3	3.3	2	2.2	2	2.2	5	5.6	3	3.3
Mississippi	112	1	0.9	1	0.9	2	1.8	1	0.9	0	0.0	2	1.8	1	0.9
Tennessee	87	8	9.2	4	4.6	5	5.7	2	2.3	1	1.1	9	10.3	8	9.2
CENSUS DIVISION 6, WEST NORTH CENTRAL	651	16	2.5	10	1.5	21	3.2	11	1.7	5	0.8	36	5.5	26	4.0
Iowa	126	1	0.8	1	0.8	3	2.4	1	0.8	1	0.8	2	1.6	3	2.4
Kansas	152	2	1.3	0	0.0	3	2.0	1	0.7	0	0.0	3	2.0	3	2.0
Minnesota	104	4	3.8	3	2.9	4	3.8	2	1.9	2	1.9	10	9.6	3	2.9
Missouri	146	5	3.4	4	2.7	8	5.5	6	4.1	2	1.4	11	7.5	10	6.8
Nebraska	50	3	6.0	2	4.0	1	2.0	1	2.0	0	0.0	5	10.0	3	6.0
North Dakota	30	0	0.0	0	0.0	0	0.0	0	0.0	0	0.0	2	6.7	2	6.7
South Dakota	43	1	2.3	0	0.0	2	4.7	0	0.0	0	0.0	3	7.0	2	4.7
CENSUS DIVISION 7, WEST SOUTH CENTRAL	896	20	2.2	18	2.0	31	3.5	15	1.7	10	1.1	35	3.9	26	2.9
Arkansas	99	3	3.0	2	2.0	3	3.1	2	2.0	1	1.0	3	3.1	3	2.9
Louisiana	127	2	1.6	2	1.6	5	3.9	1	0.8	1	0.8	9	7.1	3	2.4
Oklahoma	96	3	3.1	1	0.8	2	2.0	1	1.0	0	0.0	4	3.1	2	2.0
Texas	574	12	2.1	13	2.3	21	3.7	11	1.9	8	1.4	21	3.7	20	3.5
CENSUS DIVISION 8, MOUNTAIN	349	18	5.2	9	2.6	15	4.3	10	2.9	5	1.4	24	6.9	15	4.3
Arizona	68	8	11.8	2	2.9	4	5.9	3	4.4	2	2.9	6	8.8	6	8.8
Colorado	72	3	4.2	2	2.8	4	5.6	3	4.2	1	1.4	6	8.3	2	2.8
Idaho	29	1	3.4	1	3.4	0	0.0	0	0.0	0	0.0	2	6.9	1	3.4
Montana	55	2	3.6	0	0.0	1	1.8	1	1.8	0	0.0	3	5.5	1	1.8
Nevada	30	0	0.0	0	0.0	1	3.3	0	0.0	0	0.0	1	3.3	0	0.0
New Mexico	33	1	3.0	0	0.0	2	6.1	0	0.0	0	0.0	1	3.0	2	6.1
Utah	35	3	8.6	4	11.4	3	8.6	3	8.6	1	2.9	3	8.6	3	8.6
Wyoming	27	0	0.0	0	0.0	0	0.0	0	0.0	0	0.0	0	0.0	0	0.0
CENSUS DIVISION 9, PACIFIC	481	28	5.8	18	3.7	26	5.4	17	3.5	9	1.9	53	11.0	35	7.3
Alaska	15	0	0.0	0	0.0	0	0.0	0	0.0	0	0.0	0	0.0	0	0.0
California	309	21	6.8	13	4.2	18	5.8	12	3.9	8	2.6	40	12.9	26	8.4
Hawaii	18	0	0.0	0	0.0	1	5.6	1	5.6	0	0.0	0	0.0	1	5.6
Oregon	61	2	3.3	2	3.3	2	3.3	1	1.6	0	0.0	5	8.2	4	6.6
Washington	78	5	6.4	3	3.8	5	6.4	3	3.8	1	1.3	8	10.3	4	5.1

Table 8

Table		Page

MSAs

Metropolitan Statistical Areas

Metropolitan Statistical Areas (MSAs) definitions announced by the U.S. Office of Management and Budget (OMB) effective June 6, 2003 were added with the 2006 edition.

According to the OMB, an MSA is a geographical designation that represents an integrated social and economic unit with a large population nucleus. Under these standards, an area qualifies for recognition as an MSA if there is a city within the area of at least 50,000 with a total metropolitan population of at least 100,000. MSAs are defined as entire counties. In addition to the county containing the main city, an MSA also includes additional counties having strong economic and social ties to the central county. Such counties must have a specified level of commuting to the central counties and must meet certain standards regarding metropolitan character, such as population density.

When an MSA encompasses two or more central cities, up to three cities may be specified in the MSA title. They will be listed in order of population size. When a single central city exists, the MSA is named for that particular city. A MSA may extend beyond a single state.

An MSA containing a single core with a population of 2.5 million or more may be subdivided to form smaller groupings of counties referred to as Metropolitan Divisions. Where they exist the Metropolitan Divisions are shown in this table rather than the entire MSA.

2013 Utilization, Personnel and Finances

CLASSIFICATION	Hospitals	Beds	Admissions	Inpatient Days	Adjusted Inpatient Days	Average Daily Census	Adjusted Average Daily Census	Average Stay (days)	Surgical Operations	NEWBORNS Bassinets	NEWBORNS Births	OUTPATIENT VISITS Emergency	OUTPATIENT VISITS Total
UNITED STATES	4,974	795,603	33,609,083	182,370,189	362,566,276	500,222	962,267	5.4	26,566,037	56,342	3,699,411	133,611,670	677,951,120
Nonmetropolitan	1,971	130,332	3,839,423	24,309,871	69,408,427	66,633	181,025	6.3	3,948,240	10,447	436,830	23,881,030	127,477,109
Metropolitan................	3,003	665,271	29,769,660	158,060,318	293,157,849	433,589	781,242	5.3	22,617,797	45,895	3,262,581	109,730,640	550,474,011
CENSUS DIVISION 1, NEW ENGLAND	203	34,028	1,597,809	8,611,159	19,550,817	23,584	52,720	5.4	1,358,559	2,414	146,765	7,168,129	48,697,288
Nonmetropolitan	57	3,657	142,647	857,579	2,664,694	2,346	6,941	6.0	160,679	360	13,645	1,034,481	8,867,234
Metropolitan................	146	30,371	1,455,162	7,753,580	16,886,123	21,238	45,779	5.3	1,197,880	2,054	133,120	6,133,648	39,830,054
Connecticut..................	33	7,811	391,394	2,144,945	4,289,281	5,876	11,593	5.5	323,181	503	36,851	1,626,044	9,275,025
Nonmetropolitan	5	353	18,958	84,579	234,032	232	642	4.5	20,076	35	1,919	157,340	738,007
Metropolitan................	28	7,458	372,436	2,060,366	4,055,249	5,644	10,951	5.5	303,105	468	34,932	1,468,704	8,537,018
Bridgeport-Stamford-Norwalk	6	1,874	87,579	466,309	973,823	1,277	2,668	5.3	63,463	165	11,029	368,271	2,263,741
Hartford-West Hartford-East Hartford	11	2,661	135,968	764,992	1,465,631	2,096	4,014	5.6	113,685	125	12,008	551,674	3,453,734
New Haven-Milford	9	2,483	124,138	707,921	1,350,485	1,939	3,542	5.7	106,395	146	9,945	412,346	2,077,733
Norwich-New London	2	440	24,751	121,144	265,310	332	727	4.9	19,562	32	1,950	136,413	741,810
Maine	35	3,474	139,976	782,150	2,011,035	2,145	5,272	5.6	144,025	278	11,687	795,374	7,154,254
Nonmetropolitan	21	1,243	41,231	276,121	925,694	757	2,512	6.7	41,432	132	4,144	366,386	3,507,279
Metropolitan................	14	2,231	98,745	506,029	1,085,341	1,388	2,760	5.1	102,593	146	7,543	428,988	3,646,975
Bangor	4	498	27,794	131,334	275,528	361	715	4.7	30,678	20	1,794	79,589	578,563
Lewiston-Auburn	2	361	16,032	70,332	181,072	193	496	4.4	11,913	35	1,327	74,291	1,062,037
Portland-South Portland-Biddeford.	8	1,372	54,919	304,363	628,741	834	1,549	5.5	60,002	91	4,422	275,108	2,006,375
Massachusetts................	82	16,483	787,003	4,181,114	9,370,538	11,448	25,548	5.3	614,744	1,113	68,965	3,221,445	22,098,154
Nonmetropolitan	2	44	2,010	7,567	40,294	20	62	3.8	2,241	10	249	25,609	116,358
Metropolitan................	80	16,439	784,993	4,173,547	9,330,244	11,428	25,486	5.3	612,503	1,103	68,716	3,195,836	21,981,796
Barnstable Town	3	414	28,709	103,020	310,399	282	851	3.6	14,134	18	1,221	123,197	810,531
Boston-Cambridge-Quincy......	50	11,068	522,037	2,855,769	6,323,490	7,820	17,249	5.5	416,544	728	46,954	1,874,608	14,057,763
Pittsfield.................	2	294	13,807	61,559	170,029	168	466	4.5	12,618	24	746	69,592	541,546
Providence-New Bedford-Fall River	4	1,028	57,152	279,368	589,417	765	1,616	4.9	36,290	72	4,409	367,551	1,501,066
Springfield	12	1,933	79,468	451,651	951,627	1,236	2,606	5.7	62,176	114	7,113	339,538	2,603,246
Worcester................	9	1,702	83,820	422,180	985,282	1,157	2,698	5.0	70,741	147	8,273	421,350	2,467,644
New Hampshire	28	2,809	119,566	628,043	1,718,361	1,718	4,667	5.3	121,989	270	12,664	700,141	5,046,957
Nonmetropolitan	17	1,297	54,519	311,150	957,760	850	2,583	5.7	61,365	112	4,578	262,439	2,870,630
Metropolitan................	11	1,512	65,047	316,893	760,601	868	2,084	4.9	60,624	158	8,086	437,702	2,176,327
Manchester-Nashua	5	823	37,339	173,848	421,454	476	1,155	4.7	30,416	96	4,507	230,348	1,180,669
Rockingham County-Strafford County	6	689	27,708	143,045	339,147	392	929	5.2	30,208	62	3,579	207,354	995,658
Rhode Island	11	2,250	111,406	571,352	1,214,062	1,567	3,327	5.1	95,584	148	11,352	522,861	2,041,027
Metropolitan................	11	2,250	111,406	571,352	1,214,062	1,567	3,327	5.1	95,584	148	11,352	522,861	2,041,027
Providence-New Bedford-Fall River	11	2,250	111,406	571,352	1,214,062	1,567	3,327	5.1	95,584	148	11,352	522,861	2,041,027
Vermont....................	14	1,201	48,464	303,555	947,540	830	2,313	6.3	59,036	102	5,246	302,264	3,081,871
Nonmetropolitan	12	720	25,929	178,162	506,914	487	1,142	6.9	35,565	71	2,755	222,707	1,634,960
Metropolitan................	2	481	22,535	125,393	440,626	343	1,171	5.6	23,471	31	2,491	79,557	1,446,911
Burlington-South Burlington.....	2	481	22,535	125,393	440,626	343	1,171	5.6	23,471	31	2,491	79,557	1,446,911

MSAs

TABLE 8

U.S. CENSUS DIVISION 1, NEW ENGLAND

U.S. Community Hospitals
(Nonfederal, short-term general and other special hospitals)

2013 Utilization, Personnel and Finances

FULL-TIME EQUIVALENT PERSONNEL					FULL-TIME EQUIV. TRAINEES			EXPENSES						
								LABOR				TOTAL		
Physicians and Dentists	Registered Nurses	Licensed Practical Nurses	Other Salaried Personnel	Total Personnel	Medical and Dental Residents	Other Trainees	Total Trainees	Payroll (in thousands)	Employee Benefits (in thousands)	Total (in thousands)	Percent of Total	Amount (in thousands)	Adjusted per Admission	Adjusted per Inpatient Day
122,119	1,366,402	78,164	3,219,402	4,786,087	107,029	9,592	120,142	$303,635,275	$83,520,086	$387,155,349	49.5	$782,035,350	$11,650.90	$2,156.94
16,394	163,074	23,407	470,243	673,118	1,951	433	2,686	36,502,464	9,848,281	46,350,747	52.0	89,112,057	8,086.11	1,283.88
105,725	1,203,328	54,757	2,749,159	4,112,969	105,078	9,159	117,456	267,132,811	73,671,804	340,804,602	49.2	692,923,293	12,351.15	2,363.65
13,455	67,430	2,404	200,120	283,409	9,655	1,323	11,161	19,761,116	5,333,277	25,094,391	51.4	48,855,355	12,942.97	2,498.89
1,725	7,679	506	24,719	34,629	444	18	471	2,406,128	655,026	3,061,154	56.8	5,387,170	11,640.39	2,021.68
11,730	59,751	1,898	175,401	248,780	9,211	1,305	10,690	17,354,989	4,678,250	22,033,237	50.7	43,468,185	13,124.99	2,574.20
1,152	14,126	335	37,853	53,466	1,675	116	1,826	4,151,959	1,263,753	5,415,709	52.1	10,399,557	12,972.06	2,424.55
46	668	26	1,967	2,707	1	0	1	212,252	62,062	274,313	56.1	488,566	9,151.23	2,087.60
1,106	13,458	309	35,886	50,759	1,674	116	1,825	3,939,707	1,201,691	5,141,396	51.9	9,910,991	13,244.66	2,443.99
277	2,932	32	8,301	11,542	422	14	436	964,153	298,596	1,262,748	52.0	2,426,561	13,098.70	2,491.79
579	4,950	119	14,471	20,119	166	37	211	1,476,429	466,744	1,943,172	55.2	3,521,691	13,298.38	2,402.85
172	4,828	133	10,946	16,079	1,070	30	1,114	1,252,867	373,967	1,626,833	48.1	3,381,274	13,903.38	2,503.75
78	748	25	2,168	3,019	16	35	64	246,259	62,384	308,643	53.1	581,466	10,566.34	2,191.65
1,605	7,261	301	20,622	29,789	333	12	363	1,982,391	526,533	2,508,926	55.7	4,501,337	12,103.72	2,238.32
521	2,476	117	8,237	11,351	9	5	19	695,523	167,986	863,508	56.6	1,524,561	10,404.07	1,646.94
1,084	4,785	184	12,385	18,438	324	7	344	1,286,868	358,547	1,645,418	55.3	2,976,776	13,208.86	2,742.71
291	1,272	38	3,073	4,674	28	4	32	319,195	87,097	406,293	52.8	768,848	12,640.95	2,790.45
227	669	66	1,814	2,776	19	0	19	201,352	40,402	241,754	53.0	456,430	11,174.67	2,520.71
566	2,844	80	7,498	10,988	277	3	293	766,321	231,049	997,371	56.9	1,751,498	14,159.81	2,785.72
8,352	33,358	1,156	102,529	145,395	6,028	1,107	7,228	9,533,174	2,423,076	11,956,247	48.5	24,670,533	13,195.16	2,632.78
40	81	9	350	480	0	0	0	40,186	9,232	49,418	51.8	95,436	7,962.99	2,368.50
8,312	33,277	1,147	102,179	144,915	6,028	1,107	7,228	9,492,989	2,413,843	11,906,829	48.5	24,575,097	13,228.92	2,633.92
65	537	17	1,628	2,247	0	1	10	230,282	72,056	302,338	53.6	563,738	6,353.70	1,816.17
6,957	24,350	801	75,386	107,494	4,973	1,058	6,085	6,924,182	1,734,809	8,658,990	46.9	18,466,680	15,099.58	2,920.33
80	562	41	1,574	2,257	83	21	104	177,724	46,253	223,977	61.3	365,674	9,467.78	2,150.66
52	1,935	58	4,934	6,979	10	1	21	506,988	137,569	644,557	65.0	991,431	8,175.27	1,682.05
525	2,942	127	9,284	12,878	355	0	370	750,030	168,985	919,013	50.8	1,807,434	9,986.26	1,899.31
633	2,951	103	9,373	13,060	607	26	638	903,782	254,172	1,157,954	48.7	2,380,140	11,606.25	2,415.69
1,027	6,094	339	19,128	26,588	466	14	503	1,800,028	483,027	2,283,057	55.8	4,089,847	12,370.53	2,380.09
805	3,171	233	9,962	14,171	431	11	442	1,054,168	299,965	1,354,133	58.7	2,307,721	13,832.27	2,409.50
222	2,923	106	9,166	12,417	35	3	61	745,861	183,062	928,924	52.1	1,782,127	10,881.49	2,343.05
150	1,763	59	5,049	7,021	26	2	51	410,560	96,483	507,044	52.5	965,490	10,409.37	2,290.86
72	1,160	47	4,117	5,396	9	1	10	335,301	86,579	421,880	51.7	816,636	11,498.03	2,407.91
488	3,761	77	11,500	15,826	832	38	880	1,392,063	383,865	1,775,928	56.4	3,151,478	13,220.62	2,595.81
488	3,761	77	11,500	15,826	832	38	880	1,392,063	383,865	1,775,928	56.4	3,151,478	13,220.62	2,595.81
488	3,761	77	11,500	15,826	832	38	880	1,392,063	383,865	1,775,928	56.4	3,151,478	13,220.62	2,595.81
831	2,830	196	8,489	12,346	321	36	361	901,501	253,023	1,154,524	56.5	2,042,602	12,575.74	2,155.69
313	1,283	121	4,203	5,920	3	2	9	404,000	115,782	519,782	53.5	970,887	11,550.47	1,915.29
518	1,547	75	4,286	6,426	318	34	352	497,501	137,241	634,742	59.2	1,071,716	13,675.43	2,432.26
518	1,547	75	4,286	6,426	318	34	352	497,501	137,241	634,742	59.2	1,071,716	13,675.43	2,432.26

MSAs

TABLE 8

U.S. CENSUS DIVISION 2, MIDDLE ATLANTIC

U.S. Community Hospitals
(Nonfederal, short-term general and other special hospitals)

2013 Utilization, Personnel and Finances

CLASSIFICATION	Hospitals	Beds	Admissions	Inpatient Days	Adjusted Inpatient Days	Average Daily Census	Adjusted Average Daily Census	Average Stay (days)	Surgical Operations	NEWBORNS Bassinets	Births	OUTPATIENT VISITS Emergency	Total
UNITED STATES	4,974	795,603	33,609,083	182,370,189	362,566,276	500,222	962,267	5.4	26,566,037	56,342	3,699,411	133,611,670	677,951,120
Nonmetropolitan	1,971	130,332	3,839,423	24,309,871	69,408,427	66,633	181,025	6.3	3,948,240	10,447	436,830	23,881,030	127,477,109
Metropolitan	3,003	665,271	29,769,660	158,060,318	293,157,849	433,589	781,242	5.3	22,617,797	45,895	3,262,581	109,730,640	550,474,011
CENSUS DIVISION 2, MIDDLE ATLANTIC.	444	116,588	4,974,821	30,254,395	55,610,187	83,162	149,020	6.1	3,971,826	6,375	460,691	18,464,278	109,935,509
Nonmetropolitan	85	10,561	319,351	2,361,458	6,210,925	6,476	16,255	7.4	359,445	657	28,183	1,894,890	12,960,650
Metropolitan	359	106,027	4,655,470	27,892,937	49,399,262	76,686	132,765	6.0	3,612,381	5,718	432,508	16,569,388	96,974,859
New Jersey.	77	21,348	1,005,271	5,173,783	8,322,156	14,188	22,341	5.1	599,490	1,440	99,416	3,584,950	15,593,976
Metropolitan	77	21,348	1,005,271	5,173,783	8,322,156	14,188	22,341	5.1	599,490	1,440	99,416	3,584,950	15,593,976
Allentown-Bethlehem-Easton	2	251	9,240	41,280	87,521	113	240	4.5	15,713	12	747	42,865	181,459
Atlantic City	4	842	42,671	197,548	324,247	542	889	4.6	19,169	56	3,419	177,447	417,679
Camden.	10	2,839	140,922	684,218	1,064,711	1,875	2,917	4.9	81,576	145	12,418	581,646	1,562,043
Edison.	17	4,964	234,102	1,251,610	1,918,268	3,429	5,257	5.3	130,066	398	24,741	772,386	2,635,370
New York-White Plains-Wayne. . .	13	4,458	230,905	1,025,037	1,617,562	2,820	4,447	4.4	131,735	338	23,577	728,412	5,140,040
Newark-Union	19	5,783	250,926	1,491,149	2,400,657	4,085	6,405	5.9	156,639	349	25,704	899,729	3,526,402
Ocean City	1	180	7,541	29,113	63,712	80	175	3.9	3,821	16	449	45,245	175,876
Trenton-Ewing	6	1,388	62,093	314,711	594,493	863	1,357	5.1	39,335	94	5,941	230,902	1,551,419
Vineland-Millville-Bridgeton	2	376	18,898	97,760	182,984	268	501	5.2	14,667	24	1,894	68,226	288,553
Wilmington	3	267	7,973	41,357	68,001	113	153	5.2	6,769	8	526	38,092	115,135
New York	177	56,270	2,331,678	15,933,416	29,569,147	43,908	79,661	6.8	1,973,711	3,082	232,325	8,616,225	56,309,400
Nonmetropolitan	38	4,776	128,827	1,171,813	3,217,565	3,212	8,713	9.1	156,348	293	13,533	818,545	5,919,727
Metropolitan	139	51,494	2,202,851	14,761,603	26,351,582	40,696	70,948	6.7	1,817,363	2,789	218,792	7,797,680	50,389,673
Albany-Schenectady-Troy	9	2,395	103,247	674,097	1,325,224	1,847	3,630	6.5	91,807	110	7,908	435,371	2,687,015
Binghamton	2	610	27,520	149,454	399,976	409	1,096	5.4	34,046	46	2,762	101,705	2,371,338
Buffalo-Niagara Falls.	10	4,425	139,031	1,293,725	2,172,088	3,543	5,949	9.3	183,100	194	12,885	492,337	3,598,935
Elmira	2	466	16,065	106,551	201,385	292	292	6.6	11,796	20	1,400	76,920	375,574
Glens Falls	1	363	14,913	71,955	180,299	197	494	4.8	14,440	20	1,330	49,954	823,658
Ithaca	1	193	6,418	27,862	95,117	76	261	4.3	7,432	19	850	30,061	205,363
Kingston	3	295	12,623	71,473	121,256	196	291	5.7	6,371	13	417	47,429	117,407
Nassau-Suffolk	23	7,778	395,814	2,386,326	4,032,359	6,541	10,886	6.0	322,320	457	36,047	1,113,935	5,954,111
New York-White Plains-Wayne. . .	60	27,469	1,185,697	7,982,262	13,628,218	22,123	37,096	6.7	884,249	1,428	124,725	4,364,914	24,637,029
Poughkeepsie-Newburgh-Middletown . .	7	1,544	64,036	383,594	706,550	1,050	1,478	6.0	52,134	90	6,820	264,634	1,034,289
Rochester.	10	3,041	120,892	836,585	1,917,221	2,292	5,252	6.9	111,920	173	11,900	445,922	5,276,709
Syracuse	6	1,939	83,800	528,853	969,080	1,448	2,571	6.3	69,941	147	8,137	249,925	2,079,041
Utica-Rome.	5	976	32,795	248,866	602,809	682	1,652	7.6	27,807	72	3,611	124,573	1,229,204
Pennsylvania	190	38,970	1,637,872	9,147,196	17,718,884	25,066	47,018	5.6	1,398,625	1,853	128,950	6,263,103	38,032,133
Nonmetropolitan	47	5,785	190,524	1,189,645	2,993,360	3,264	7,542	6.2	203,097	364	14,650	1,076,345	7,040,923
Metropolitan	143	33,185	1,447,348	7,957,551	14,725,524	21,802	39,476	5.5	1,195,528	1,489	114,300	5,186,758	30,991,210
Allentown-Bethlehem-Easton	8	2,303	105,114	596,939	1,113,576	1,635	2,989	5.7	76,478	88	8,947	372,789	2,133,722
Altoona	4	530	22,247	116,879	246,220	321	675	5.3	21,562	30	1,516	85,118	523,356
Erie	6	1,081	39,786	218,574	385,675	599	1,005	5.5	33,683	73	3,232	167,196	504,219
Harrisburg-Carlisle	9	1,837	82,992	460,616	861,905	1,261	2,312	5.6	70,283	74	7,334	308,317	2,081,378
Johnstown	3	624	24,142	141,922	277,558	389	761	5.9	24,966	14	1,546	76,476	556,912
Lancaster.	4	1,059	46,197	211,381	427,523	580	1,171	4.6	50,333	84	5,949	179,415	1,947,005
Lebanon	1	164	7,708	39,337	103,809	108	284	5.1	9,558	19	848	53,486	272,348
Philadelphia	46	11,989	569,917	2,979,272	5,102,819	8,160	13,567	5.2	449,934	572	45,815	1,921,682	10,205,157
Pittsburgh.	35	8,777	352,191	2,101,210	3,939,030	5,759	10,750	6.0	300,711	297	22,182	1,195,701	7,228,497
Reading.	3	959	39,286	219,812	417,769	602	1,145	5.6	24,934	56	4,061	180,153	1,150,084
Scranton--Wilkes-Barre	12	1,746	71,602	392,641	746,699	1,075	2,015	5.5	54,384	55	4,756	307,818	1,855,910
State College	2	333	12,678	62,052	133,061	170	328	4.9	12,592	5	1,363	49,119	290,385
Williamsport	3	386	13,837	107,569	268,093	295	735	7.8	18,473	22	1,241	75,151	263,888
York-Hanover	4	848	41,111	212,110	449,823	581	1,176	5.2	23,203	71	4,292	130,739	1,271,731
Youngstown-Warren-Boardman . .	3	549	18,540	97,237	251,964	267	563	5.2	24,434	29	1,218	83,598	706,618

TABLE 8

U.S. CENSUS DIVISION 2, MIDDLE ATLANTIC

U.S. Community Hospitals
(Nonfederal, short-term general and other special hospitals)

2013 Utilization, Personnel and Finances

	FULL-TIME EQUIVALENT PERSONNEL				FULL-TIME EQUIV. TRAINEES			EXPENSES						
								LABOR				TOTAL		
Physicians and Dentists	Registered Nurses	Licensed Practical Nurses	Other Salaried Personnel	Total Personnel	Medical and Dental Residents	Other Trainees	Total Trainees	Payroll (in thousands)	Employee Benefits (in thousands)	Total (in thousands)	Percent of Total	Amount (in thousands)	Adjusted per Admission	Adjusted per Inpatient Day
122,119	1,366,402	78,164	3,219,402	4,786,087	107,029	9,592	120,142	$303,635,275	$83,520,086	$387,155,349	49.5	$782,035,350	$11,650.90	$2,156.94
16,394	163,074	23,407	470,243	673,118	1,951	433	2,686	36,502,464	9,848,281	46,350,747	52.0	89,112,057	8,086.11	1,283.88
105,725	1,203,328	54,757	2,749,159	4,112,969	105,078	9,159	117,456	267,132,811	73,671,804	340,804,602	49.2	692,923,293	12,351.15	2,363.65
25,026	196,975	9,779	507,942	739,722	29,490	1,128	31,232	50,833,265	14,998,415	65,831,672	53.4	123,273,293	13,486.52	2,216.74
1,454	12,795	1,864	39,268	55,381	463	38	600	3,012,588	837,131	3,849,713	53.9	7,141,441	8,441.46	1,149.82
23,572	184,180	7,915	468,674	684,341	29,027	1,090	30,632	47,820,677	14,161,284	61,981,959	53.4	116,131,852	14,001.10	2,350.88
2,786	34,250	810	80,862	118,708	3,137	55	3,425	8,396,595	2,129,741	10,526,337	52.1	20,199,975	12,426.80	2,427.25
2,786	34,250	810	80,862	118,708	3,137	55	3,425	8,396,595	2,129,741	10,526,337	52.1	20,199,975	12,426.80	2,427.25
22	379	18	980	1,399	18	1	23	86,357	25,707	112,065	52.0	215,638	11,026.14	2,463.85
99	1,572	24	3,480	5,175	42	1	47	363,254	112,615	475,869	54.0	880,473	12,647.02	2,715.44
606	4,047	120	10,728	15,501	450	12	507	1,003,110	253,476	1,256,585	45.6	2,754,074	12,610.00	2,586.69
385	8,502	183	17,828	26,898	514	6	641	1,881,902	480,996	2,362,896	52.1	4,531,894	12,598.99	2,362.49
663	7,203	114	18,042	26,022	555	20	607	1,947,066	454,279	2,401,346	52.7	4,558,026	12,478.48	2,817.84
799	9,430	229	22,469	32,927	1,355	5	1,387	2,389,265	595,988	2,985,255	54.6	5,465,254	13,533.25	2,276.57
0	194	1	618	813	0	3	3	47,308	20,448	67,756	61.5	110,086	6,670.68	1,727.87
207	2,185	74	5,189	7,655	102	7	109	472,191	123,383	595,575	48.8	1,220,937	10,127.38	2,053.74
0	485	31	1,012	1,528	98	0	98	145,924	46,744	192,667	59.1	325,794	8,807.87	1,780.45
5	253	16	516	790	3	0	3	60,217	16,106	76,323	55.4	137,797	9,141.37	2,026.40
14,548	94,400	5,815	267,527	382,290	17,875	387	18,488	28,276,022	8,924,354	37,200,375	57.3	64,889,138	15,088.00	2,194.49
766	5,256	915	17,097	24,034	122	5	154	1,336,233	350,315	1,686,547	56.7	2,976,490	8,349.81	925.08
13,782	89,144	4,900	250,431	358,257	17,753	382	18,334	26,939,789	8,574,039	35,513,828	57.4	61,912,649	15,696.99	2,349.49
293	4,473	199	11,122	16,087	487	4	504	899,040	175,674	1,074,713	48.1	2,232,498	10,985.03	1,684.62
244	1,222	145	3,740	5,351	89	1	90	309,559	92,994	402,554	51.8	777,272	10,102.97	1,943.30
422	6,717	463	14,306	21,908	92	90	191	1,469,510	585,259	2,054,769	57.8	3,553,844	15,248.10	1,636.14
61	745	35	1,803	2,644	29	1	40	197,748	54,422	252,170	60.8	414,600	13,654.78	2,058.74
79	519	53	1,622	2,273	0	0	0	147,072	33,378	180,450	58.9	306,583	8,204.42	1,700.41
9	331	3	802	1,145	1	0	1	63,114	25,376	88,490	51.9	170,506	7,782.09	1,792.59
4	401	22	1,095	1,522	0	1	1	74,721	19,860	94,581	51.4	184,105	8,763.96	1,518.31
3,276	15,651	421	48,589	67,937	3,321	20	3,425	4,971,667	1,337,528	6,309,195	60.3	10,469,515	15,587.87	2,596.37
8,081	45,868	2,352	134,897	191,198	12,426	253	12,726	15,849,221	5,335,332	21,184,552	57.5	36,814,556	18,005.34	2,701.35
122	2,200	68	4,661	7,051	56	5	87	487,408	182,450	669,858	49.8	1,343,947	11,621.52	1,902.13
972	6,184	626	16,343	24,125	646	7	663	1,383,338	376,355	1,759,693	57.4	3,065,755	11,293.70	1,599.06
110	3,558	360	7,890	11,918	568	0	568	782,744	268,363	1,051,107	55.1	1,906,697	13,185.28	1,967.53
109	1,275	153	3,561	5,098	38	0	38	304,647	87,049	391,696	58.2	672,772	9,298.08	1,116.06
7,692	68,325	3,154	159,553	238,724	8,478	686	9,319	14,160,648	3,944,320	18,104,960	47.4	38,184,180	11,879.65	2,155.00
688	7,539	949	22,171	31,347	341	33	446	1,676,355	486,816	2,163,166	51.9	4,164,952	8,508.20	1,391.40
7,004	60,786	2,205	137,382	207,377	8,137	653	8,873	12,484,293	3,457,504	15,941,794	46.9	34,019,228	12,485.37	2,310.22
662	4,643	98	9,863	15,266	510	40	550	840,671	205,388	1,046,060	46.3	2,260,590	11,946.45	2,030.03
37	847	66	1,736	2,686	29	0	29	172,255	51,358	223,613	53.8	415,737	8,205.11	1,688.48
140	1,677	93	3,615	5,525	130	2	132	243,316	67,367	310,683	44.2	703,615	9,915.10	1,824.37
917	3,553	290	10,447	15,207	755	132	887	789,335	220,772	1,010,107	46.9	2,153,534	13,682.61	2,498.57
13	948	91	2,867	3,919	79	0	79	165,896	47,887	213,782	52.1	410,153	8,405.13	1,477.72
185	1,838	136	5,037	7,196	61	4	65	450,352	130,786	581,138	53.4	1,088,415	11,499.25	2,545.86
29	247	24	891	1,191	0	0	0	58,577	19,166	77,744	45.5	170,707	8,392.25	1,644.43
3,533	24,731	438	53,057	81,759	4,869	220	5,121	5,700,841	1,582,102	7,282,942	49.8	14,617,040	14,782.16	2,864.50
1,089	15,207	401	30,765	47,462	1,364	248	1,636	2,466,322	661,007	3,127,328	39.5	7,912,727	11,442.78	2,008.80
118	1,506	97	4,677	6,398	104	0	104	372,175	110,623	482,799	51.8	931,435	12,311.62	2,229.55
141	2,274	215	6,594	9,224	28	2	48	500,883	128,284	629,169	46.8	1,343,562	9,530.50	1,799.33
11	364	20	1,089	1,484	0	0	0	132,634	36,358	168,992	52.1	324,394	11,722.41	2,437.94
12	570	75	1,088	1,745	21	0	21	111,560	31,030	142,589	45.7	312,072	9,960.50	1,164.04
78	1,626	105	4,029	5,838	174	0	174	356,935	132,424	489,358	47.7	1,025,828	11,661.65	2,280.52
39	755	56	1,627	2,477	13	5	27	122,540	32,950	155,490	44.5	349,417	7,167.09	1,386.77

MSAs

TABLE 8

U.S. CENSUS DIVISION 3, SOUTH ATLANTIC

U.S. Community Hospitals
(Nonfederal, short-term general and other special hospitals)

2013 Utilization, Personnel and Finances

MSAs

CLASSIFICATION	Hospitals	Beds	Admissions	Inpatient Days	Adjusted Inpatient Days	Average Daily Census	Adjusted Average Daily Census	Average Stay (days)	Surgical Operations	NEWBORNS Bassinets	Births	OUTPATIENT VISITS Emergency	Total
UNITED STATES	4,974	795,603	33,609,083	182,370,189	362,566,276	500,222	962,267	5.4	26,566,037	56,342	3,699,411	133,611,670	677,951,120
Nonmetropolitan	1,971	130,332	3,839,423	24,309,871	69,408,427	66,633	181,025	6.3	3,948,240	10,447	436,830	23,881,030	127,477,109
Metropolitan	3,003	665,271	29,769,660	158,060,318	293,157,849	433,589	781,242	5.3	22,617,797	45,895	3,262,581	109,730,640	550,474,011
CENSUS DIVISION 3, SOUTH ATLANTIC.	758	156,366	6,775,396	37,330,440	71,108,569	102,367	189,240	5.5	5,288,633	10,323	688,383	27,180,478	103,189,238
Nonmetropolitan	237	22,773	750,240	4,706,969	11,696,385	12,903	30,879	6.3	724,956	1,671	71,122	4,703,997	17,096,594
Metropolitan	521	133,593	6,025,156	32,623,471	59,412,184	89,464	158,361	5.4	4,563,677	8,652	617,261	22,476,481	86,092,644
Delaware	7	2,034	104,769	538,590	1,022,693	1,476	2,802	5.1	94,508	97	11,037	441,756	2,090,410
Nonmetropolitan	2	253	14,438	57,377	128,526	157	352	4.0	15,899	23	1,712	84,319	612,391
Metropolitan	5	1,781	90,331	481,213	894,167	1,319	2,450	5.3	78,609	74	9,325	357,437	1,478,019
Dover	1	326	18,235	95,153	211,959	261	581	5.2	13,427	11	2,226	90,142	553,696
Wilmington	4	1,455	72,096	386,060	682,208	1,058	1,869	5.4	65,182	63	7,099	267,295	924,323
District of Columbia	11	3,609	132,633	946,679	1,544,606	2,594	3,971	7.1	115,605	222	13,718	482,319	2,578,298
Metropolitan	11	3,609	132,633	946,679	1,544,606	2,594	3,971	7.1	115,605	222	13,718	482,319	2,578,298
Washington-Arlington-Alexandria. .	11	3,609	132,633	946,679	1,544,606	2,594	3,971	7.1	115,605	222	13,718	482,319	2,578,298
Florida	212	53,198	2,407,117	12,063,283	20,440,299	33,049	54,668	5.0	1,440,768	2,848	198,157	8,436,473	23,994,950
Nonmetropolitan	30	1,983	89,537	406,761	890,819	1,115	2,312	4.5	64,805	105	4,560	526,745	1,460,662
Metropolitan	182	51,215	2,317,580	11,656,522	19,549,480	31,934	52,356	5.0	1,375,963	2,743	193,597	7,909,728	22,534,288
Cape Coral-Fort Myers	4	1,563	78,014	399,320	746,705	1,094	1,133	5.1	40,220	112	6,390	201,035	495,808
Deltona-Daytona Beach-Ormond Beach . .	5	1,305	56,302	271,302	512,664	743	1,404	4.8	33,830	64	3,929	303,044	705,890
Fort Lauderdale-Pompano Beach-Deerfield Beach	19	5,624	238,232	1,197,521	1,985,637	3,281	5,441	5.0	134,586	263	21,534	894,316	2,340,406
Fort Walton Beach-Crestview-Destin	3	405	20,410	88,905	151,026	243	365	4.4	10,864	32	1,659	96,485	238,786
Gainesville	3	1,441	69,360	386,007	581,475	1,057	1,593	5.6	57,910	49	5,584	152,762	1,011,408
Jacksonville	13	4,054	186,754	962,353	1,629,779	2,637	4,463	5.2	131,545	286	16,905	697,324	1,973,800
Lakeland	5	1,681	74,987	335,120	613,823	918	1,682	4.5	38,222	51	5,784	304,911	627,736
Miami-Miami Beach-Kendall	25	7,465	306,180	1,652,105	2,693,952	4,527	7,257	5.4	160,963	357	25,482	982,848	3,215,088
Naples-Marco Island	2	786	33,066	149,059	234,141	408	642	4.5	14,833	36	2,954	111,112	328,937
North Port-Bradenton-Sarasota. . .	8	1,974	77,680	384,315	668,144	1,054	1,830	4.9	44,889	59	4,377	245,438	948,119
Ocala	3	721	37,155	170,002	265,624	466	727	4.6	19,278	26	1,847	107,303	258,496
Orlando-Kissimmee.	11	5,390	293,194	1,474,569	2,357,547	4,040	6,459	5.0	173,183	434	29,166	1,040,033	2,461,179
Palm Bay-Melbourne-Titusville . . .	7	1,436	58,377	303,309	519,633	831	1,422	5.2	36,478	122	4,623	259,546	674,055
Palm Coast.	1	99	6,879	29,705	72,177	81	198	4.3	6,328	0	0	38,090	104,092
Panama City-Lynn Haven	4	554	28,440	140,795	245,550	386	673	5.0	18,261	37	3,576	80,822	299,561
Pensacola-Ferry Pass-Brent	7	1,366	62,951	282,719	532,039	775	1,458	4.5	40,855	63	6,698	268,305	1,000,179
Port St. Lucie-Fort Pierce	3	846	45,510	205,151	362,009	562	992	4.5	30,449	50	3,652	144,861	243,917
Punta Gorda	3	742	25,546	130,608	195,382	358	535	5.1	20,767	8	1,302	61,148	147,307
Sebastian-Vero Beach	3	469	20,158	102,873	171,935	282	420	5.1	12,111	22	1,102	59,515	147,879
Tallahassee	4	794	40,975	201,814	359,239	553	984	4.9	22,028	62	4,584	104,436	700,766
Tampa-St. Petersburg-Clearwater .	35	8,827	384,261	1,973,533	3,287,015	5,404	9,007	5.1	235,370	420	27,914	1,265,777	3,169,305
West Palm Beach-Boca Raton-Boynton Beach	14	3,673	173,149	815,437	1,363,984	2,234	3,671	4.7	92,993	190	14,535	490,617	1,441,574
Georgia	144	24,729	947,299	6,034,948	12,164,263	16,540	30,852	6.4	727,539	1,884	119,564	4,221,105	16,022,609
Nonmetropolitan	60	5,818	135,251	1,218,490	3,084,765	3,346	7,868	9.0	143,170	359	16,719	930,494	3,294,500
Metropolitan	84	18,911	812,048	4,816,458	9,079,498	13,194	22,984	5.9	584,369	1,525	102,845	3,290,611	12,728,109
Albany.	2	542	23,326	126,861	281,428	348	771	5.4	13,097	42	2,794	113,082	1,040,877
Athens-Clarke County	2	506	28,213	122,024	240,357	334	658	4.3	22,522	52	3,272	106,750	440,190
Atlanta-Sandy Springs-Marietta . .	43	9,867	445,497	2,602,545	4,795,768	7,128	11,337	5.8	314,383	849	66,215	1,821,958	6,338,814
Augusta-Richmond County	8	1,517	60,730	350,555	615,889	960	1,688	5.8	56,780	123	5,663	281,372	1,248,446
Brunswick.	1	494	12,149	136,752	294,579	375	807	11.3	10,168	17	1,336	53,218	199,501
Chattanooga	1	185	6,219	60,623	134,093	166	367	9.7	5,175	15	669	22,311	105,063
Columbus.	5	1,127	38,631	240,586	448,713	659	1,229	6.2	25,069	46	1,855	99,614	394,252
Dalton	2	263	9,673	38,146	82,702	104	137	3.9	4,751	40	1,807	69,791	291,786
Gainesville	1	773	28,329	215,950	397,260	592	1,088	7.6	18,490	64	3,541	107,531	351,388
Hinesville-Fort Stewart	1	25	1,874	6,999	27,082	19	74	3.7	890	6	345	5,557	32,661
Macon	5	1,072	47,368	263,576	427,229	723	1,172	5.6	26,055	96	3,232	125,792	553,613
Rome	3	593	25,940	139,355	265,636	382	727	5.4	18,266	30	2,155	119,585	353,651
Savannah.	5	1,219	51,168	332,201	681,361	910	1,867	6.5	41,645	71	5,677	197,724	778,513
Valdosta	3	452	16,321	103,233	219,838	283	603	6.3	14,174	40	2,169	86,390	321,732
Warner Robins	2	276	16,610	77,052	167,563	211	459	4.6	12,904	34	2,115	79,936	277,622

TABLE 8

U.S. CENSUS DIVISION 3, SOUTH ATLANTIC

U.S. Community Hospitals
(Nonfederal, short-term general and other special hospitals)

2013 Utilization, Personnel and Finances

	FULL-TIME EQUIVALENT PERSONNEL				FULL-TIME EQUIV. TRAINEES			EXPENSES						
								LABOR				TOTAL		
Physicians and Dentists	Registered Nurses	Licensed Practical Nurses	Other Salaried Personnel	Total Personnel	Medical and Dental Residents	Other Trainees	Total Trainees	Payroll (in thousands)	Employee Benefits (in thousands)	Total (in thousands)	Percent of Total	Amount (in thousands)	Adjusted per Admission	Adjusted per Inpatient Day
122,119	1,366,402	78,164	3,219,402	4,786,087	107,029	9,592	120,142	$303,635,275	$83,520,086	$387,155,349	49.5	$782,035,350	$11,650.90	$2,156.94
16,394	163,074	23,407	470,243	673,118	1,951	433	2,686	36,502,464	9,848,281	46,350,747	52.0	89,112,057	8,086.11	1,283.88
105,725	1,203,328	54,757	2,749,159	4,112,969	105,078	9,159	117,456	267,132,811	73,671,804	340,804,602	49.2	692,923,293	12,351.15	2,363.65
16,791	266,158	13,060	575,635	871,644	17,211	723	18,690	51,336,464	13,091,863	64,428,337	47.4	135,926,142	10,458.43	1,911.53
1,911	28,997	3,220	74,310	108,438	289	45	381	5,487,884	1,431,723	6,919,609	49.8	13,891,818	7,344.46	1,187.70
14,880	237,161	9,840	501,325	763,206	16,922	678	18,309	45,848,580	11,660,141	57,508,728	47.1	122,034,324	10,988.80	2,054.03
509	5,196	195	11,784	17,684	311	1	317	1,192,822	390,047	1,582,870	57.7	2,744,800	13,630.90	2,683.89
64	708	8	1,685	2,465	0	0	0	135,746	49,360	185,106	50.5	366,656	11,299.81	2,852.78
445	4,488	187	10,099	15,219	311	1	317	1,057,077	340,687	1,397,764	58.8	2,378,144	14,078.69	2,659.62
45	881	59	1,889	2,874	0	0	0	200,176	56,596	256,772	59.4	432,187	10,639.76	2,039.01
400	3,607	128	8,210	12,345	311	1	317	856,901	284,091	1,140,992	58.6	1,945,957	15,167.48	2,852.44
1,465	6,702	203	15,722	24,092	1,424	29	1,471	1,794,410	358,203	2,152,612	54.5	3,946,218	18,074.14	2,554.84
1,465	6,702	203	15,722	24,092	1,424	29	1,471	1,794,410	358,203	2,152,612	54.5	3,946,218	18,074.14	2,554.84
1,465	6,702	203	15,722	24,092	1,424	29	1,471	1,794,410	358,203	2,152,612	54.5	3,946,218	18,074.14	2,554.84
4,149	82,607	3,460	165,802	256,018	5,255	215	5,821	15,143,102	3,738,615	18,881,721	46.0	41,035,030	9,912.39	2,007.56
150	2,801	298	6,707	9,956	17	5	22	522,911	112,350	635,261	47.3	1,342,070	6,620.90	1,506.56
3,999	79,806	3,162	159,095	246,062	5,238	210	5,799	14,620,191	3,626,264	18,246,460	46.0	39,692,960	10,081.85	2,030.38
217	2,793	149	6,467	9,626	547	32	696	604,694	195,156	799,850	51.7	1,548,186	10,545.94	2,073.36
164	1,818	73	4,944	6,999	29	0	29	387,277	97,791	485,068	49.0	989,668	9,226.04	1,930.44
637	8,080	351	14,578	23,646	306	15	353	1,382,363	297,504	1,679,867	46.9	3,585,337	8,915.84	1,805.64
25	572	32	892	1,521	11	0	11	79,865	18,232	98,097	45.1	217,411	6,187.54	1,439.56
4	2,926	60	5,910	8,900	573	6	579	487,395	137,435	624,831	43.9	1,423,836	13,440.02	2,448.66
496	6,660	153	11,688	18,997	578	29	629	1,043,902	313,576	1,357,479	42.5	3,196,971	9,929.37	1,961.60
30	2,328	99	5,339	7,796	8	1	9	417,436	87,991	505,428	51.6	979,297	7,127.29	1,595.41
563	11,217	500	24,213	36,493	1,638	29	1,680	2,415,476	544,913	2,960,388	47.0	6,299,669	12,466.64	2,338.45
4	1,111	44	1,784	2,943	1	0	1	167,450	32,815	200,265	45.7	438,027	8,433.33	1,870.78
40	2,903	164	5,229	8,336	59	2	70	422,831	103,075	525,906	46.3	1,136,917	8,351.03	1,701.61
32	1,320	73	2,444	3,869	51	1	61	199,404	44,770	244,175	45.6	535,526	9,170.13	2,016.11
533	11,419	297	23,008	35,257	450	2	452	1,975,163	583,435	2,558,598	42.1	6,080,745	12,959.43	2,579.27
90	1,909	78	3,816	5,893	50	15	65	341,045	77,949	418,993	47.9	874,337	8,334.88	1,682.60
41	206	12	532	791	0	0	0	59,840	14,868	74,708	53.4	139,972	8,374.54	1,939.29
53	605	61	1,492	2,211	24	3	27	153,879	39,667	193,547	46.4	417,150	7,892.50	1,698.84
107	1,997	73	4,208	6,385	91	15	215	319,399	51,589	370,989	38.5	962,575	7,966.10	1,809.22
97	1,167	41	2,904	4,209	21	2	27	247,072	57,505	304,576	49.1	620,602	7,681.76	1,714.33
18	818	40	1,309	2,185	31	0	31	118,812	26,082	144,894	42.7	339,288	8,905.20	1,736.54
59	609	20	1,319	2,007	4	1	5	122,563	25,600	148,164	53.7	275,906	7,769.36	1,604.71
110	1,416	101	3,210	4,837	66	1	67	263,261	63,659	326,920	51.2	639,058	8,553.27	1,778.92
586	13,222	585	24,981	39,374	597	50	665	2,466,433	588,684	3,055,117	46.9	6,516,771	10,144.26	1,982.58
93	4,710	156	8,828	13,787	103	6	127	944,629	223,969	1,168,600	47.2	2,475,709	8,461.88	1,815.06
1,894	37,332	2,674	86,677	128,577	1,293	100	1,671	7,311,925	1,901,316	9,213,242	47.2	19,519,696	10,348.92	1,604.68
478	5,684	903	15,641	22,706	65	8	107	1,116,078	310,634	1,426,712	51.6	2,767,386	7,858.16	897.11
1,416	31,648	1,771	71,036	105,871	1,228	92	1,564	6,195,847	1,590,682	7,786,530	46.5	16,752,310	10,920.74	1,845.07
0	824	78	2,342	3,244	21	0	21	190,947	76,064	267,011	45.0	592,967	11,577.32	2,106.99
25	964	34	2,513	3,536	7	1	8	210,070	59,243	269,314	49.7	542,062	9,776.04	2,255.24
776	17,920	848	38,605	58,149	570	71	822	3,401,174	827,523	4,228,697	44.8	9,440,138	11,340.19	1,968.43
103	2,587	172	5,419	8,281	92	4	110	518,486	116,357	634,844	47.1	1,348,031	12,300.12	2,188.76
74	344	25	1,066	1,509	0	0	0	123,228	33,235	156,463	55.5	281,806	10,768.28	956.64
30	241	24	676	971	7	1	17	51,385	16,632	68,017	54.5	124,769	9,070.15	930.47
152	1,451	86	3,385	5,074	50	2	61	282,466	70,468	352,933	48.4	729,382	9,760.63	1,625.50
0	400	39	797	1,236	0	0	0	91,888	25,280	117,167	50.1	234,081	10,855.68	2,830.42
112	786	26	1,850	2,774	130	9	161	204,578	57,551	262,129	48.0	546,558	10,487.74	1,375.82
6	56	14	185	261	0	0	0	16,505	4,411	20,917	54.4	38,481	5,307.06	1,420.92
24	1,716	95	3,649	5,484	127	0	127	343,274	104,643	447,916	50.3	889,645	11,485.07	2,082.36
67	835	98	2,287	3,287	39	1	49	205,143	53,645	258,788	51.0	507,481	10,000.01	1,910.44
30	2,095	72	4,904	7,101	169	0	169	349,214	72,964	422,178	46.1	915,808	10,009.05	1,344.09
13	844	76	1,913	2,846	0	1	1	114,250	46,486	160,735	48.5	331,706	9,775.60	1,508.86
4	585	84	1,445	2,118	16	2	18	93,240	26,181	119,421	52.1	229,395	6,361.67	1,369.01

Table continues

MSAs

TABLE 8

U.S. CENSUS DIVISION 3, SOUTH ATLANTIC CONTINUED

U.S. Community Hospitals
(Nonfederal, short-term general and other special hospitals)

2013 Utilization, Personnel and Finances

CLASSIFICATION	Hospitals	Beds	Admissions	Inpatient Days	Adjusted Inpatient Days	Average Daily Census	Adjusted Average Daily Census	Average Stay (days)	Surgical Operations	NEWBORNS Bassinets	Births	OUTPATIENT VISITS Emergency	Total
Maryland............	50	12,392	628,485	3,165,089	5,738,963	8,731	15,511	5.0	537,763	966	66,699	2,542,407	9,421,781
Nonmetropolitan............	6	425	26,859	99,542	240,796	273	660	3.7	33,053	35	2,541	204,242	655,840
Metropolitan.............	44	11,967	601,626	3,065,547	5,498,167	8,458	14,851	5.1	504,710	931	64,158	2,338,165	8,765,941
Baltimore-Towson.........	24	7,758	385,574	2,062,733	3,656,599	5,650	10,018	5.3	348,681	486	34,607	1,410,576	5,498,509
Bethesda-Gaithersburg-Frederick .	7	1,763	106,566	472,131	826,240	1,293	1,952	4.4	65,800	224	18,446	306,082	1,039,558
Cumberland	1	355	13,139	84,539	162,935	232	446	6.4	8,415	20	1,004	54,139	515,201
Hagerstown-Martinsburg.........	1	257	15,827	66,981	126,389	184	346	4.2	7,851	41	1,974	77,611	192,147
Salisbury	3	500	22,471	120,894	256,221	331	702	5.4	19,372	28	1,945	95,583	591,452
Washington-Arlington-Alexandria. .	7	1,215	52,301	236,843	416,892	709	1,242	4.5	48,294	120	5,498	350,767	772,631
Wilmington	1	119	5,748	21,426	52,891	59	145	3.7	6,297	12	684	43,407	156,443
North Carolina.............	117	22,617	1,011,304	5,730,722	12,210,155	15,703	33,086	5.7	833,475	1,706	112,844	4,689,431	19,659,380
Nonmetropolitan............	57	6,042	234,437	1,309,868	3,236,061	3,589	8,643	5.6	200,616	589	23,453	1,554,833	5,067,554
Metropolitan.............	60	16,575	776,867	4,420,854	8,974,094	12,114	24,443	5.7	632,859	1,117	89,391	3,134,598	14,591,826
Asheville............	6	1,257	59,655	300,634	623,707	825	1,708	5.0	58,603	58	5,173	181,593	1,411,057
Burlington............	1	218	11,285	48,171	134,289	132	368	4.3	9,739	21	1,304	55,837	178,815
Charlotte-Gastonia-Concord.....	13	3,670	176,388	922,506	1,936,004	2,528	5,304	5.2	133,582	297	23,809	794,192	3,000,999
Durham	6	2,003	93,004	599,235	1,219,673	1,642	3,341	6.4	83,110	62	8,665	241,920	2,180,539
Fayetteville	1	660	33,681	215,424	354,509	590	971	6.4	14,259	48	4,552	135,616	551,723
Goldsboro	1	274	10,742	49,929	128,016	137	351	4.6	12,720	30	1,425	61,872	181,034
Greensboro-High Point........	6	1,810	75,135	434,362	948,840	1,190	2,598	5.8	44,789	111	9,079	347,995	1,261,504
Greenville............	1	909	41,167	260,111	366,700	713	1,005	6.3	22,133	42	3,569	121,389	397,312
Hickory-Lenoir-Morganton......	4	777	33,118	160,079	370,092	439	918	4.8	29,667	62	3,567	178,735	577,165
Jacksonville	1	152	8,362	32,370	86,255	89	236	3.9	5,708	23	2,170	64,262	136,414
Raleigh-Cary..........	6	1,868	88,614	503,506	1,131,764	1,379	3,100	5.7	93,522	156	13,977	430,149	2,598,797
Rocky Mount........	3	403	17,285	98,153	197,042	269	540	5.7	11,343	34	1,606	86,846	247,540
Wilmington	4	884	44,679	242,947	513,801	665	1,408	5.4	37,810	48	4,355	182,018	559,729
Winston-Salem	7	1,690	83,752	553,427	963,402	1,516	2,595	6.6	75,874	125	6,140	252,174	1,309,198
South Carolina.............	69	12,758	498,344	2,864,513	5,328,684	7,851	14,300	5.7	512,152	842	52,388	1,575,728	6,710,476
Nonmetropolitan............	24	2,966	90,795	551,665	1,248,466	1,513	3,303	6.1	98,806	239	9,536	349,786	1,254,833
Metropolitan.............	45	9,792	407,549	2,312,848	4,080,218	6,338	10,997	5.7	413,346	603	42,852	1,225,942	5,455,643
Anderson	2	469	21,028	117,032	199,464	321	546	5.6	16,108	28	1,900	115,105	704,093
Augusta-Richmond County . .	2	296	12,277	63,800	107,607	175	295	5.2	10,407	18	1,098	52,144	146,482
Charleston-North Charleston	7	1,839	85,860	447,128	788,577	1,224	2,160	5.2	81,658	111	9,421	252,644	1,547,518
Charlotte-Gastonia-Concord.....	2	330	15,089	77,717	121,258	213	332	5.2	15,464	37	1,740	69,643	167,772
Columbia	7	2,170	92,566	547,700	951,562	1,501	2,607	5.9	74,719	115	9,927	149,612	823,103
Florence	6	1,245	42,642	247,701	405,416	679	1,111	5.8	56,558	58	2,645	56,683	204,274
Greenville............	11	1,527	69,344	371,312	675,586	1,018	1,850	5.4	77,700	107	8,541	246,987	962,302
Myrtle Beach-Conway-North Myrtle Beach . .	3	801	28,677	181,569	371,326	498	905	6.3	27,554	54	3,002	67,591	248,842
Spartanburg	4	845	33,923	192,035	326,435	526	827	5.7	42,739	51	3,549	155,280	512,072
Sumter............	1	270	6,143	66,854	132,987	183	364	10.9	10,439	24	1,029	60,253	139,185
Virginia.............	93	17,975	780,153	4,436,963	9,118,577	12,175	24,386	5.7	714,878	1,333	93,002	3,626,500	15,814,044
Nonmetropolitan	29	2,530	78,218	543,234	1,359,483	1,486	3,647	6.9	82,238	157	5,920	536,410	2,218,296
Metropolitan.............	64	15,445	701,935	3,893,729	7,759,094	10,689	20,739	5.5	632,640	1,176	87,082	3,090,090	13,595,748
Blacksburg-Christiansburg-Radford	4	254	15,380	61,137	151,328	167	414	4.0	18,572	24	1,954	91,818	245,432
Charlottesville	3	759	40,437	211,144	427,990	578	1,173	5.2	78,062	42	3,355	113,265	2,246,065
Danville............	1	151	8,110	36,919	77,112	101	211	4.6	5,502	20	865	22,885	111,267
Harrisonburg	1	244	12,763	47,010	146,903	129	402	3.7	17,508	22	1,695	71,350	383,385
Kingsport-Bristol-Bristol	2	141	7,856	30,058	79,383	82	218	3.8	9,214	16	744	42,434	130,867
Lynchburg	2	1,188	31,358	317,807	597,937	871	1,638	10.1	17,110	39	2,559	105,086	512,471
Richmond	14	3,603	147,376	835,162	1,507,473	2,312	3,612	5.7	119,913	211	14,426	562,947	1,780,969
Roanoke	3	1,182	60,764	342,765	585,613	939	1,605	5.6	42,548	67	4,660	263,849	667,614
Virginia Beach-Norfolk-Newport News . .	16	3,581	159,386	944,849	2,041,554	2,588	5,593	5.9	140,479	282	18,101	880,193	4,760,402
Washington-Arlington-Alexandria. .	17	3,867	195,095	952,844	1,932,036	2,610	5,293	4.9	172,748	437	36,422	868,196	2,478,444
Winchester............	1	475	23,410	114,034	211,765	312	580	4.9	10,984	16	2,301	68,067	278,832
West Virginia.............	55	7,054	265,292	1,549,653	3,540,329	4,248	9,664	5.8	311,945	425	20,974	1,164,759	6,897,290
Nonmetropolitan	29	2,756	80,705	520,032	1,507,469	1,424	4,094	6.4	86,369	164	6,681	517,168	2,532,518
Metropolitan.............	26	4,298	184,587	1,029,621	2,032,860	2,824	5,570	5.6	225,576	261	14,293	647,591	4,364,772
Charleston	7	1,265	50,931	283,208	551,819	777	1,512	5.6	93,029	69	3,846	154,853	981,427
Cumberland	1	25	793	3,245	14,896	9	41	4.1	1,235	0	0	12,132	51,173
Hagerstown-Martinsburg.........	2	211	8,396	44,952	121,608	124	333	5.4	9,809	26	955	60,101	265,053
Huntington-Ashland.........	3	748	45,418	208,702	366,808	572	1,005	4.6	31,144	55	3,177	116,347	734,597
Morgantown	4	810	36,775	217,594	345,761	597	947	5.9	36,893	10	2,480	85,246	895,221
Parkersburg-Marietta-Vienna	2	295	15,019	71,407	126,063	196	345	4.8	17,122	25	1,562	59,032	325,207
Washington-Arlington-Alexandria. .	1	25	1,410	4,082	18,902	11	52	2.9	2,696	10	258	24,857	80,312
Weirton-Steubenville	1	168	6,151	35,620	98,494	98	270	5.8	6,222	21	383	37,552	213,819
Wheeling	4	707	19,246	147,013	315,477	402	865	7.6	26,999	45	1,632	88,304	774,506
Winchester............	1	44	448	13,798	73,032	38	200	30.8	427	0	0	9,167	43,457

MSAs

TABLE 8

U.S. Community Hospitals
(Nonfederal, short-term general and other special hospitals)

2013 Utilization, Personnel and Finances

FULL-TIME EQUIVALENT PERSONNEL					FULL-TIME EQUIV. TRAINEES			EXPENSES						
								LABOR				TOTAL		
Physicians and Dentists	Registered Nurses	Licensed Practical Nurses	Other Salaried Personnel	Total Personnel	Medical and Dental Residents	Other Trainees	Total Trainees	Payroll (in thousands)	Employee Benefits (in thousands)	Total (in thousands)	Percent of Total	Amount (in thousands)	Adjusted per Admission	Adjusted per Inpatient Day
2,845	24,156	541	59,417	86,959	1,620	107	1,777	5,497,095	1,347,931	6,845,027	49.5	13,836,111	11,741.34	2,410.91
43	920	21	2,311	3,295	3	8	11	221,954	54,257	276,211	53.7	514,570	7,935.38	2,136.95
2,802	23,236	520	57,106	83,664	1,617	99	1,766	5,275,141	1,293,673	6,568,816	49.3	13,321,541	11,962.97	2,422.91
2,460	16,102	290	40,209	59,061	1,507	90	1,601	3,735,811	907,026	4,642,836	48.6	9,560,352	13,262.52	2,614.55
143	3,039	91	6,995	10,268	68	7	116	681,391	163,877	845,269	49.8	1,696,758	9,249.71	2,053.59
32	486	23	1,242	1,783	0	0	0	104,097	39,745	143,843	49.5	290,612	11,476.20	1,783.61
6	574	20	1,249	1,849	0	0	0	108,219	30,695	138,914	48.6	285,886	9,572.94	2,261.96
54	788	36	1,944	2,822	1	0	6	180,575	47,862	228,438	50.5	452,458	9,734.46	1,765.89
72	2,029	53	4,792	6,946	41	1	42	401,826	92,443	494,270	55.3	894,340	9,573.83	2,145.26
35	218	7	675	935	0	1	1	63,221	12,025	75,246	53.3	141,135	9,946.80	2,668.42
2,043	46,754	1,718	103,924	154,439	3,299	109	3,421	8,444,550	2,215,684	10,660,235	47.5	22,436,225	10,256.29	1,837.51
422	9,474	604	24,063	34,563	37	9	59	1,666,198	420,331	2,086,531	49.7	4,202,128	7,052.12	1,298.53
1,621	37,280	1,114	79,861	119,876	3,262	100	3,362	6,778,352	1,795,353	8,573,704	47.0	18,234,096	11,455.81	2,031.86
147	2,547	50	6,108	8,852	0	0	0	463,931	125,836	589,768	44.2	1,335,552	10,283.45	2,141.31
24	446	2	1,457	1,929	0	0	0	84,224	22,623	106,847	44.3	241,079	7,663.02	1,795.22
393	7,909	255	15,634	24,191	314	14	328	1,334,176	358,323	1,692,499	42.1	4,022,257	10,883.08	2,077.61
59	6,362	94	13,206	19,721	1,690	14	1,704	1,119,032	296,687	1,415,719	46.0	3,075,751	16,468.91	2,521.78
120	1,242	129	3,310	4,801	0	0	0	308,514	70,040	378,554	58.7	645,112	11,638.95	1,819.73
0	492	13	1,097	1,602	0	0	0	80,062	29,155	109,217	55.1	198,089	7,192.25	1,547.38
364	3,226	156	8,003	11,749	57	0	57	566,694	173,064	739,758	47.0	1,575,302	9,550.52	1,660.24
0	2,359	11	3,677	6,047	388	23	411	365,045	112,904	477,949	47.9	998,376	17,202.40	2,722.60
119	1,171	24	3,284	4,598	30	0	30	277,254	68,659	345,914	48.3	715,464	9,144.24	1,933.21
0	293	14	770	1,077	0	0	0	52,349	15,087	67,435	49.8	135,423	6,077.66	1,570.03
381	4,798	80	9,443	14,702	5	20	25	982,979	214,835	1,197,815	55.1	2,172,439	10,794.84	1,919.52
2	799	34	1,362	2,197	0	0	0	127,087	38,303	165,390	52.5	315,193	8,507.47	1,599.63
6	1,558	43	3,691	5,298	64	0	64	303,011	81,321	384,331	48.1	799,472	9,427.29	1,556.00
6	4,078	209	8,819	13,112	714	29	743	713,993	188,516	902,508	45.0	2,004,589	13,879.12	2,080.74
1,542	21,015	810	42,290	65,657	1,318	5	1,332	3,578,923	966,350	4,545,270	45.3	10,033,331	10,631.21	1,882.89
249	3,474	270	8,381	12,374	51	3	54	643,519	174,117	817,635	47.6	1,717,391	8,184.99	1,375.60
1,293	17,541	540	33,909	53,283	1,267	2	1,278	2,935,404	792,233	3,727,635	44.8	8,315,940	11,330.55	2,038.11
108	895	56	2,612	3,671	46	0	46	181,065	55,806	236,871	50.4	470,312	12,668.33	2,357.88
9	379	15	620	1,023	0	0	0	58,308	13,333	71,641	46.6	153,586	7,413.17	1,427.29
19	4,006	101	7,372	11,498	678	0	678	698,439	189,856	888,296	43.6	2,036,115	13,082.71	2,582.01
1	498	8	1,012	1,519	0	0	0	72,688	17,166	89,853	42.3	212,402	8,636.31	1,751.65
97	3,770	121	7,715	11,703	245	1	255	693,242	188,122	881,364	49.5	1,779,091	11,001.94	1,869.65
52	1,824	110	3,292	5,278	24	0	24	280,323	66,741	347,064	44.4	781,816	10,512.23	1,928.43
680	3,203	40	5,827	9,750	203	0	203	471,999	129,763	601,760	39.8	1,510,630	11,374.88	2,236.03
4	862	37	1,534	2,437	0	0	0	149,561	40,254	189,815	46.8	405,819	7,406.12	1,092.89
323	1,624	41	2,877	4,865	71	1	72	257,327	72,068	329,395	42.0	784,599	13,082.98	2,403.54
0	480	11	1,048	1,539	0	0	0	72,452	19,124	91,576	50.4	181,572	14,858.57	1,365.33
1,657	31,435	2,200	62,830	98,122	2,025	131	2,188	6,394,275	1,582,291	7,976,569	46.9	17,002,869	10,388.94	1,864.64
177	3,066	473	7,330	11,046	60	4	64	604,066	148,881	752,946	49.4	1,524,157	7,337.98	1,121.13
1,480	28,369	1,727	55,500	87,076	1,965	127	2,124	5,790,209	1,433,410	7,223,623	46.7	15,478,712	10,832.43	1,994.91
9	563	43	1,148	1,763	2	0	2	109,869	24,482	134,352	46.7	287,631	7,538.28	1,900.71
72	2,282	135	4,877	7,366	760	3	763	510,923	129,411	640,334	46.5	1,377,124	15,842.67	3,217.66
22	288	19	728	1,057	7	1	8	55,593	15,381	70,974	49.3	144,057	8,504.48	1,868.16
78	585	79	1,535	2,277	0	0	0	139,700	35,068	174,768	52.4	333,811	8,369.77	2,272.33
16	261	24	461	762	0	0	0	37,876	8,303	46,180	54.1	85,358	4,016.28	1,075.27
116	881	172	3,389	4,558	18	7	25	284,028	80,764	364,791	57.7	632,117	10,921.35	1,057.16
161	6,501	485	11,514	18,661	801	83	907	1,240,051	347,508	1,587,560	46.9	3,382,719	12,666.18	2,243.97
489	2,589	143	4,593	7,814	272	4	285	586,378	125,688	712,066	51.0	1,397,495	13,174.72	2,386.38
140	6,598	450	13,210	20,398	4	20	24	1,292,886	329,849	1,622,736	44.9	3,614,108	10,078.89	1,770.27
362	6,892	149	12,134	19,537	101	9	110	1,383,119	292,396	1,675,515	44.6	3,753,220	9,557.67	1,942.62
15	929	28	1,911	2,883	0	0	0	149,788	44,560	194,347	41.3	471,071	10,835.94	2,224.50
687	10,961	1,259	27,190	40,097	666	26	692	1,979,363	591,427	2,570,791	47.9	5,371,863	8,881.90	1,517.33
328	2,870	643	8,193	12,034	56	8	64	577,412	161,792	739,207	50.7	1,457,460	6,451.54	966.83
359	8,091	616	18,997	28,063	610	18	628	1,401,950	429,635	1,831,584	46.8	3,914,403	10,330.94	1,925.56
124	2,433	212	5,153	7,922	171	0	171	400,702	126,718	527,419	44.3	1,191,254	11,598.12	2,158.78
0	39	11	140	190	0	0	0	7,127	2,546	9,674	46.9	20,620	5,664.95	1,384.29
2	397	19	868	1,286	0	0	0	64,670	17,044	81,714	48.4	168,705	8,247.21	1,387.28
37	1,446	126	2,938	4,547	0	0	0	261,468	110,834	372,301	48.9	760,758	9,316.97	2,074.00
48	1,772	104	4,458	6,382	340	18	358	338,417	93,938	432,354	46.4	931,180	14,911.52	2,693.13
19	460	18	1,470	1,967	18	0	18	81,429	19,190	100,619	39.8	252,514	9,046.16	2,003.08
0	87	8	210	305	0	0	0	17,756	4,967	22,723	49.0	46,400	7,106.82	2,454.79
24	283	0	688	995	0	0	0	44,188	12,649	56,838	55.4	102,552	6,029.66	1,041.20
102	1,146	109	2,949	4,306	81	0	81	178,055	39,715	217,769	52.2	417,440	7,705.83	1,323.20
3	28	9	123	163	0	0	0	8,138	2,035	10,173	44.3	22,978	9,691.23	314.63

MSAs

TABLE 8   U.S. CENSUS DIVISION 4, EAST NORTH CENTRAL

U.S. Community Hospitals
(Nonfederal, short-term general and other special hospitals)

2013 Utilization, Personnel and Finances

CLASSIFICATION	Hospitals	Beds	Admissions	Inpatient Days	Adjusted Inpatient Days	Average Daily Census	Adjusted Average Daily Census	Average Stay (days)	Surgical Operations	NEWBORNS Bassinets	NEWBORNS Births	OUTPATIENT VISITS Emergency	OUTPATIENT VISITS Total
UNITED STATES	4,974	795,603	33,609,083	182,370,189	362,566,276	500,222	962,267	5.4	26,566,037	56,342	3,699,411	133,611,670	677,951,120
Nonmetropolitan	1,971	130,332	3,839,423	24,309,871	69,408,427	66,633	181,025	6.3	3,948,240	10,447	436,830	23,881,030	127,477,109
Metropolitan	3,003	665,271	29,769,660	158,060,318	293,157,849	433,589	781,242	5.3	22,617,797	45,895	3,262,581	109,730,640	550,474,011
CENSUS DIVISION 4, EAST NORTH CENTRAL	775	120,050	5,309,578	26,367,306	57,933,558	72,249	156,976	5.0	4,531,828	9,593	520,879	21,840,082	137,536,213
Nonmetropolitan	273	17,109	602,916	3,065,362	10,775,275	8,403	29,385	5.1	694,415	1,738	64,606	4,027,220	25,237,082
Metropolitan	502	102,941	4,706,662	23,301,944	47,158,283	63,846	127,591	5.0	3,837,413	7,855	456,273	17,812,862	112,299,131
Illinois	189	31,745	1,426,848	6,865,573	14,400,426	18,814	38,989	4.8	1,112,115	2,646	146,392	5,252,340	32,808,526
Nonmetropolitan	64	3,739	135,980	603,711	2,012,716	1,652	5,515	4.4	143,734	306	12,245	826,373	5,543,117
Metropolitan	125	28,006	1,290,868	6,261,862	12,387,710	17,162	33,474	4.9	968,381	2,340	134,147	4,425,967	27,265,409
Bloomington-Normal	2	348	16,343	63,070	122,588	173	336	3.9	11,265	52	2,461	61,393	492,810
Champaign-Urbana	4	622	28,425	147,721	330,983	405	906	5.2	22,251	66	3,647	111,669	1,101,978
Chicago-Naperville-Joliet	76	19,606	926,411	4,533,053	8,692,769	12,426	23,354	4.9	656,067	1,570	95,686	2,978,788	18,317,636
Danville	2	140	6,572	21,604	59,516	59	163	3.3	3,680	26	747	45,055	202,909
Davenport-Moline-Rock Island	5	552	21,517	104,682	270,084	287	741	4.9	17,625	70	2,206	107,172	499,998
Decatur	2	420	19,179	85,010	227,250	233	623	4.4	15,577	36	1,628	85,070	459,158
Kankakee-Bradley	2	480	16,162	75,138	185,044	206	506	4.6	16,597	34	1,459	70,281	577,540
Lake County-Kenosha County	5	898	49,555	187,140	388,195	513	1,064	3.8	40,101	117	6,430	201,724	773,251
Peoria	7	1,265	59,208	300,567	572,966	824	1,568	5.1	63,082	79	5,347	197,522	1,856,452
Rockford	4	907	40,727	201,215	363,846	550	997	4.9	36,680	80	4,457	161,279	946,371
Springfield	3	953	45,472	232,926	405,885	638	1,111	5.1	34,936	54	3,424	119,634	732,430
St. Louis	13	1,815	61,297	309,736	768,584	848	2,105	5.1	50,520	156	6,655	285,670	1,304,876
Indiana	123	17,264	701,743	3,653,922	8,112,012	10,011	21,686	5.2	607,620	1,457	71,984	3,129,456	18,399,556
Nonmetropolitan	40	2,198	80,764	386,268	1,389,029	1,057	3,767	4.8	105,624	271	10,989	670,733	3,903,997
Metropolitan	83	15,066	620,979	3,267,654	6,722,983	8,954	17,919	5.3	501,996	1,186	60,995	2,458,723	14,495,559
Anderson	2	210	7,543	38,246	123,344	105	338	5.1	14,119	12	557	55,535	278,634
Bloomington	3	349	14,923	62,591	147,833	172	405	4.2	12,659	19	2,096	61,107	301,576
Cincinnati-Middletown	1	78	4,141	16,068	42,607	44	117	3.9	6,267	11	436	18,211	136,787
Columbus	1	198	8,949	34,180	81,452	94	223	3.8	11,548	20	1,161	39,414	222,317
Elkhart-Goshen	2	382	17,273	68,317	155,878	187	427	4.0	11,579	66	2,717	98,571	620,435
Evansville	7	1,244	47,528	270,402	568,542	741	1,558	5.7	38,148	62	4,742	184,930	1,003,641
Fort Wayne	9	1,629	68,969	366,437	703,640	1,004	1,781	5.3	82,594	121	7,078	215,869	1,072,072
Gary	11	2,528	106,564	593,101	1,095,099	1,625	3,000	5.6	63,172	215	6,239	428,094	1,909,947
Indianapolis	24	4,908	198,920	1,058,377	2,178,936	2,901	5,760	5.3	136,493	401	21,857	819,867	6,091,021
Kokomo	4	360	12,123	53,061	152,577	145	418	4.4	13,660	37	1,255	58,969	475,966
Lafayette	2	266	12,155	54,558	161,305	149	371	4.5	14,476	14	1,312	43,145	118,827
Louisville	6	858	33,851	228,300	492,749	625	1,278	6.7	29,636	38	2,805	112,262	775,089
Michigan City-La Porte	2	375	13,459	69,071	151,664	189	415	5.1	11,097	35	1,089	56,040	272,664
Muncie	1	344	16,096	81,248	139,876	223	383	5.0	6,025	20	1,637	58,298	311,050
South Bend-Mishawaka	3	744	34,366	163,621	259,339	448	710	4.8	23,114	59	3,663	103,589	337,003
Terre Haute	5	593	24,119	110,076	268,142	302	735	4.6	27,409	56	2,351	104,822	568,530
Michigan	151	25,059	1,158,802	5,912,166	13,075,908	16,199	35,817	5.1	989,842	1,673	107,429	4,875,899	32,568,496
Nonmetropolitan	58	4,096	139,082	797,296	2,889,623	2,187	7,916	5.7	173,606	349	13,160	890,028	6,134,827
Metropolitan	93	20,963	1,019,720	5,114,870	10,186,285	14,012	27,901	5.0	816,236	1,324	94,269	3,985,871	26,433,669
Ann Arbor	5	1,632	84,309	462,002	919,643	1,266	2,508	5.5	82,357	61	7,630	207,061	3,301,334
Battle Creek	3	302	14,134	57,949	159,281	158	436	4.1	10,803	26	1,617	74,272	404,054
Bay City	2	364	15,568	80,491	140,621	220	385	5.2	9,908	14	866	43,142	354,101
Detroit-Livonia-Dearborn	20	5,122	250,612	1,295,702	2,565,715	3,549	7,028	5.2	170,471	304	21,684	1,048,801	5,575,572
Flint	4	1,190	59,676	305,778	552,761	838	1,515	5.1	38,524	89	5,268	228,589	1,414,237
Grand Rapids-Wyoming	8	1,889	93,569	461,783	897,279	1,265	2,460	4.9	88,530	144	12,179	387,007	3,500,534
Holland-Grand Haven	3	237	10,905	39,130	103,247	107	284	3.6	10,983	49	1,321	122,748	603,613
Jackson	2	347	18,456	87,132	203,691	239	558	4.7	11,156	11	1,701	81,611	477,125
Kalamazoo-Portage	5	934	43,463	208,797	404,196	573	1,108	4.8	36,756	73	5,196	203,002	1,320,140
Lansing-East Lansing	6	1,107	50,986	237,021	512,351	649	1,404	4.6	43,111	41	5,438	202,769	1,112,371
Monroe	1	179	9,388	38,681	91,489	106	251	4.1	6,567	13	801	46,759	169,410
Muskegon-Norton Shores	4	452	18,236	82,141	213,785	225	586	4.5	20,804	26	2,059	107,854	923,477
Niles-Benton Harbor	3	471	17,672	122,164	197,310	335	541	6.9	9,329	35	477	79,616	376,667
Saginaw-Saginaw Township North	3	800	37,906	193,044	360,508	528	988	5.1	21,030	31	3,049	133,556	670,782
South Bend-Mishawaka	1	25	692	1,965	14,391	5	39	2.8	558	0	0	10,579	95,841
Warren-Farmington Hills-Troy	23	5,912	294,148	1,441,090	2,850,017	3,949	7,810	4.9	255,349	407	24,983	1,008,505	6,134,411

TABLE **8**

U.S. CENSUS DIVISION 4, EAST NORTH CENTRAL

U.S. Community Hospitals
(Nonfederal, short-term general and other special hospitals)

2013 Utilization, Personnel and Finances

FULL-TIME EQUIVALENT PERSONNEL					FULL-TIME EQUIV. TRAINEES			EXPENSES						
								LABOR				TOTAL		
Physicians and Dentists	Registered Nurses	Licensed Practical Nurses	Other Salaried Personnel	Total Personnel	Medical and Dental Residents	Other Trainees	Total Trainees	Payroll (in thousands)	Employee Benefits (in thousands)	Total (in thousands)	Percent of Total	Amount (in thousands)	Adjusted per Admission	Adjusted per Inpatient Day
122,119	1,366,402	78,164	3,219,402	4,786,087	107,029	9,592	120,142	$303,635,275	$83,520,086	$387,155,349	49.5	$782,035,350	$11,650.90	$2,156.94
16,394	163,074	23,407	470,243	673,118	1,951	433	2,686	36,502,464	9,848,281	46,350,747	52.0	89,112,057	8,086.11	1,283.88
105,725	1,203,328	54,757	2,749,159	4,112,969	105,078	9,159	117,456	267,132,811	73,671,804	340,804,602	49.2	692,923,293	12,351.15	2,363.65
23,593	226,474	9,999	551,826	811,892	21,092	2,229	23,659	50,649,022	13,584,444	64,233,458	49.3	130,380,820	11,148.36	2,250.52
3,123	27,524	3,062	82,477	116,186	209	160	406	6,718,686	1,946,746	8,665,437	52.8	16,412,609	8,084.24	1,523.17
20,470	198,950	6,937	469,349	695,706	20,883	2,069	23,253	43,930,336	11,637,698	55,568,021	48.8	113,968,211	11,792.00	2,416.72
5,702	57,065	1,989	133,451	198,207	5,578	591	6,232	12,394,329	3,419,076	15,813,391	48.3	32,752,852	10,790.12	2,274.44
560	6,098	778	17,351	24,787	46	3	49	1,345,287	432,894	1,778,177	52.6	3,378,220	7,600.56	1,678.44
5,142	50,967	1,211	116,100	173,420	5,532	588	6,183	11,049,042	2,986,182	14,035,214	47.8	29,374,632	11,337.28	2,371.27
108	536	10	1,270	1,924	17	0	17	109,774	31,281	141,055	43.7	322,570	10,151.07	2,631.34
20	1,426	58	2,699	4,203	30	0	30	194,165	52,429	246,592	39.3	627,267	10,524.79	1,895.16
4,093	36,738	757	81,980	123,568	4,912	525	5,500	8,304,026	2,197,889	10,501,911	48.6	21,593,788	11,955.82	2,484.11
7	224	19	563	813	0	0	0	43,450	11,122	54,571	41.7	130,773	7,257.49	2,197.27
44	996	22	2,069	3,131	0	3	3	138,990	33,621	172,612	41.7	413,649	7,653.65	1,531.56
72	541	81	2,198	2,892	15	0	15	151,710	41,740	193,449	47.3	409,121	7,686.35	1,800.31
49	776	21	1,565	2,411	18	0	18	132,078	32,753	164,831	45.8	360,127	9,071.90	1,946.17
41	1,647	29	3,652	5,369	2	0	2	345,928	89,481	435,408	44.0	989,667	9,684.48	2,549.41
401	2,602	47	6,304	9,354	260	7	267	559,139	145,167	704,306	47.3	1,487,457	12,992.14	2,596.06
257	1,635	16	3,936	5,844	0	36	36	352,758	113,347	466,104	49.2	946,982	12,440.49	2,602.70
1	1,618	68	4,434	6,121	278	2	280	320,973	112,752	433,725	43.2	1,002,977	12,450.99	2,471.09
49	2,228	83	5,430	7,790	0	15	15	396,051	124,600	520,650	47.8	1,090,253	7,028.18	1,418.52
2,539	30,526	1,820	75,739	110,624	1,151	281	1,549	6,574,698	1,783,757	8,358,457	46.7	17,893,508	11,118.63	2,205.80
574	3,914	575	11,942	17,005	3	55	58	971,282	267,023	1,238,306	51.3	2,411,817	7,994.33	1,736.33
1,965	26,612	1,245	63,797	93,619	1,148	226	1,491	5,603,417	1,516,735	7,120,151	46.0	15,481,692	11,839.46	2,302.80
14	326	25	721	1,086	0	0	0	74,571	21,988	96,559	43.8	220,291	8,862.35	1,785.99
21	738	37	1,773	2,569	0	0	0	149,010	50,356	199,365	50.6	394,092	11,022.31	2,665.79
5	125	17	489	636	0	0	0	31,144	11,690	42,835	56.6	75,637	6,888.59	1,775.22
0	313	22	1,151	1,486	0	0	0	67,723	19,288	87,010	42.3	205,909	9,655.29	2,527.98
95	882	41	1,944	2,962	3	0	3	156,910	52,635	209,545	45.9	456,447	11,305.19	2,928.23
158	1,969	58	5,263	7,448	24	61	85	393,370	112,614	505,983	47.4	1,067,451	10,863.75	1,877.52
62	2,763	126	5,512	8,463	33	2	53	420,309	118,059	538,368	41.7	1,291,688	10,052.68	1,835.72
183	3,780	142	8,614	12,719	108	24	217	762,519	199,414	961,933	47.3	2,034,794	10,256.74	1,858.09
942	10,320	470	24,592	36,324	837	123	965	2,361,652	624,088	2,985,740	45.2	6,606,364	15,346.29	3,031.92
60	453	22	1,392	1,927	0	3	3	122,915	30,245	153,160	51.3	298,715	8,279.94	1,957.80
180	651	58	1,748	2,637	2	4	11	182,216	43,838	226,054	53.4	423,584	11,789.15	2,625.98
87	1,057	89	3,275	4,508	0	0	0	234,096	53,772	287,868	54.1	532,121	7,264.05	1,079.90
79	437	21	1,630	2,167	4	3	11	133,663	40,426	174,089	50.8	342,417	11,698.97	2,257.74
5	510	7	1,150	1,672	52	2	54	103,481	36,434	139,915	44.6	313,513	11,313.68	2,241.37
8	1,248	22	2,617	3,895	64	4	68	214,204	58,494	272,698	41.1	663,318	11,992.94	2,557.72
66	1,040	88	1,926	3,120	21	0	21	195,633	43,396	239,029	43.0	555,351	9,078.66	2,071.11
4,956	48,163	1,738	119,370	174,227	6,166	128	6,357	10,913,920	2,699,006	13,612,928	49.9	27,272,389	10,767.74	2,085.70
787	6,021	747	19,529	27,084	71	17	101	1,561,073	433,393	1,994,467	51.6	3,867,512	8,470.09	1,338.41
4,169	42,142	991	99,841	147,143	6,095	111	6,256	9,352,847	2,265,613	11,618,461	49.6	23,404,877	11,273.06	2,297.69
158	5,975	114	13,235	19,482	1,508	0	1,508	1,234,666	361,835	1,596,501	49.5	3,224,653	18,923.24	3,506.42
64	579	19	1,562	2,224	0	0	0	151,490	33,845	185,335	56.8	326,117	8,077.81	2,047.43
40	470	45	1,337	1,892	11	2	13	121,400	26,409	147,809	54.9	269,064	9,451.80	1,913.40
1,507	9,834	142	22,084	33,567	2,321	42	2,390	2,436,733	527,084	2,963,816	51.1	5,800,629	11,650.31	2,260.82
89	2,514	45	5,158	7,806	296	22	318	516,472	152,222	668,695	55.7	1,201,069	11,056.61	2,172.85
269	3,559	170	9,302	13,300	101	0	101	772,193	221,066	993,260	39.7	2,502,042	13,233.21	2,788.48
38	534	40	1,528	2,140	9	1	10	101,440	28,761	130,201	48.1	270,517	8,961.09	2,620.10
69	613	63	3,080	3,825	0	0	0	196,040	43,752	239,791	53.3	450,116	9,778.97	2,209.80
258	1,883	42	4,414	6,597	0	2	2	476,251	101,084	577,335	54.2	1,065,007	12,274.61	2,634.88
254	2,151	24	5,000	7,429	255	2	257	521,933	135,792	657,726	56.2	1,170,711	9,957.99	2,284.98
14	254	6	946	1,220	6	0	6	69,541	19,122	88,663	54.3	163,275	7,353.06	1,784.64
113	685	17	3,111	3,926	24	3	27	201,453	51,601	253,055	52.2	484,492	9,753.82	2,266.26
65	855	58	2,080	3,058	27	2	43	147,471	39,407	186,878	50.4	370,619	10,936.58	1,878.36
167	1,377	52	4,501	6,097	1	0	1	316,841	77,751	394,593	52.5	752,237	10,523.15	2,086.60
13	49	0	158	220	0	0	0	13,325	3,728	17,053	65.1	26,183	5,166.34	1,819.40
1,051	10,810	154	22,345	34,360	1,536	35	1,580	2,075,599	442,152	2,517,750	47.3	5,328,146	9,210.74	1,869.51

Table continues

MSAs

MSAs

CLASSIFICATION	Hospitals	Beds	Admissions	Inpatient Days	Adjusted Inpatient Days	Average Daily Census	Adjusted Average Daily Census	Average Stay (days)	Surgical Operations	NEWBORNS Bassinets	Births	OUTPATIENT VISITS Emergency	Total
Ohio	183	33,222	1,455,817	7,126,702	14,877,553	19,527	40,024	4.9	1,195,093	2,596	130,476	6,484,063	37,260,719
Nonmetropolitan	55	4,301	154,345	642,760	1,924,402	1,764	5,174	4.2	167,263	528	17,157	1,135,908	5,749,289
Metropolitan	128	28,921	1,301,472	6,483,942	12,953,151	17,763	34,850	5.0	1,027,830	2,068	113,319	5,348,155	31,511,430
Akron	8	1,768	85,961	414,248	886,495	1,135	2,430	4.8	56,820	104	7,052	410,774	2,194,841
Canton-Massillon	5	1,187	47,456	271,903	576,441	745	1,580	5.7	41,840	111	4,528	218,331	1,331,505
Cincinnati-Middletown	19	4,107	199,221	981,318	1,759,980	2,688	4,678	4.9	153,124	313	20,252	726,750	3,616,481
Cleveland-Elyria-Mentor	29	7,618	334,953	1,796,308	3,800,298	4,921	10,409	5.4	312,171	383	24,495	1,158,223	10,378,236
Columbus	19	5,176	250,713	1,169,625	2,257,127	3,204	6,186	4.7	196,311	419	28,044	1,036,773	5,920,810
Dayton	11	2,823	116,622	521,532	1,005,373	1,429	2,754	4.5	85,015	260	10,689	523,882	2,073,963
Lima	5	675	25,853	117,938	243,461	323	668	4.6	20,726	63	2,501	107,293	745,889
Mansfield	2	271	12,083	51,606	95,098	142	142	4.3	5,036	24	979	49,189	268,662
Parkersburg-Marietta-Vienna	2	177	8,436	37,651	87,032	103	239	4.5	7,607	16	239	50,796	249,042
Sandusky	1	236	8,666	43,082	111,765	118	306	5.0	13,647	15	713	45,291	286,886
Springfield	1	254	16,148	69,293	122,625	190	336	4.3	4,055	38	1,246	75,166	301,603
Toledo	13	2,529	105,705	531,721	1,100,754	1,456	2,638	5.0	87,704	166	8,417	428,972	2,424,950
Weirton-Steubenville	2	373	11,845	85,356	187,648	234	513	7.2	4,728	18	545	47,796	272,669
Wheeling	3	230	6,028	39,998	104,633	109	287	6.6	7,475	19	281	41,469	233,011
Youngstown-Warren-Boardman	8	1,497	71,782	352,363	614,421	966	1,684	4.9	31,571	119	3,338	427,450	1,212,882
Wisconsin	129	12,760	566,368	2,808,943	7,467,659	7,698	20,460	5.0	627,158	1,221	64,598	2,098,324	16,498,916
Nonmetropolitan	56	2,775	92,745	635,327	2,559,505	1,743	7,013	6.9	104,188	284	11,055	504,178	3,905,852
Metropolitan	73	9,985	473,623	2,173,616	4,908,154	5,955	13,447	4.6	522,970	937	53,543	1,594,146	12,593,064
Appleton	4	400	17,535	71,518	186,982	195	512	4.1	38,001	45	2,489	74,159	343,832
Duluth	1	25	467	3,115	46,028	9	126	6.7	3,796	0	0	14,306	48,444
Eau Claire	5	573	24,092	120,721	276,073	331	757	5.0	19,484	33	2,311	55,060	460,974
Fond du Lac	3	210	8,363	33,454	127,990	91	350	4.0	15,317	23	1,009	42,791	783,925
Green Bay	5	682	32,779	128,322	331,078	351	907	3.9	43,009	95	4,531	128,040	1,239,070
Janesville	4	295	13,917	61,272	183,681	168	504	4.4	15,299	29	1,732	79,596	1,442,051
La Crosse	2	413	20,733	83,489	236,075	229	647	4.0	25,235	42	2,387	36,951	677,260
Lake County-Kenosha County	3	523	22,878	92,021	232,156	252	636	4.0	21,270	56	2,992	165,108	914,144
Madison	8	1,519	70,958	386,719	883,002	1,058	2,418	5.4	140,431	89	7,582	166,791	1,553,265
Milwaukee-Waukesha-West Allis	24	3,912	196,044	912,985	1,745,875	2,502	4,783	4.7	134,289	343	20,094	606,936	3,931,293
Minneapolis-St. Paul-Bloomington	4	74	3,754	11,864	54,106	32	148	3.2	5,974	20	1,021	26,866	141,687
Oshkosh-Neenah	4	376	17,781	68,496	156,362	188	429	3.9	26,428	60	2,488	54,797	289,291
Racine	2	460	18,203	103,418	244,135	284	669	5.7	12,699	47	1,822	70,716	482,028
Sheboygan	2	189	8,598	29,273	81,316	81	223	3.4	8,361	29	1,192	29,092	162,821
Wausau	2	334	17,521	66,949	123,295	184	338	3.8	13,377	26	1,893	42,937	122,979

TABLE 8

U.S. CENSUS DIVISION 4, EAST NORTH CENTRAL CONTINUED

U.S. Community Hospitals
(Nonfederal, short-term general and other special hospitals)

2013 Utilization, Personnel and Finances

FULL-TIME EQUIVALENT PERSONNEL					FULL-TIME EQUIV. TRAINEES			EXPENSES						
								LABOR				TOTAL		
Physicians and Dentists	Registered Nurses	Licensed Practical Nurses	Other Salaried Personnel	Total Personnel	Medical and Dental Residents	Other Trainees	Total Trainees	Payroll (in thousands)	Employee Benefits (in thousands)	Total (in thousands)	Percent of Total	Amount (in thousands)	Adjusted per Admission	Adjusted per Inpatient Day
9,131	67,183	3,494	161,322	241,130	7,391	445	7,918	14,963,791	4,026,931	18,990,725	51.3	37,050,071	11,853.16	2,490.33
701	7,421	697	20,131	28,950	89	9	122	1,525,978	450,410	1,976,390	51.6	3,827,741	7,845.90	1,989.05
8,430	59,762	2,797	141,191	212,180	7,302	436	7,796	13,437,813	3,576,521	17,014,335	51.2	33,222,330	12,594.28	2,564.81
669	3,937	301	9,785	14,692	517	64	585	870,948	225,372	1,096,319	50.3	2,177,500	11,717.76	2,456.30
170	1,922	176	5,263	7,531	75	9	84	371,308	101,163	472,471	52.1	906,856	9,115.87	1,573.20
1,953	9,034	275	24,837	36,099	1,369	124	1,512	2,205,033	624,311	2,829,344	51.9	5,447,738	14,671.99	3,095.34
3,067	16,901	1,076	42,486	63,530	2,781	220	3,001	4,507,534	1,127,312	5,634,845	57.0	9,884,540	13,853.77	2,600.99
2,248	11,569	176	24,627	38,620	1,356	11	1,367	2,290,530	606,207	2,896,737	46.8	6,193,334	12,211.84	2,743.90
59	5,194	105	11,223	16,581	402	4	414	1,056,528	346,983	1,403,510	50.4	2,786,507	12,295.46	2,771.61
7	1,037	52	2,560	3,656	153	0	153	181,601	56,588	238,190	46.4	512,973	9,212.54	2,107.00
2	506	58	1,644	2,210	0	0	0	126,698	34,076	160,774	49.6	324,133	14,593.99	3,408.41
28	338	26	873	1,265	7	1	13	95,528	26,385	121,913	49.5	246,269	12,389.65	2,829.64
5	396	62	1,227	1,690	20	0	20	80,172	22,228	102,400	51.2	200,174	8,903.73	1,791.02
0	417	30	679	1,126	0	0	0	70,559	19,947	90,506	40.9	221,350	7,746.01	1,805.10
82	4,882	207	9,129	14,300	474	1	479	989,097	235,896	1,224,994	45.9	2,666,951	12,558.22	2,422.84
32	503	39	1,203	1,777	0	0	0	89,465	29,788	119,254	51.6	231,136	7,941.46	1,231.75
25	262	39	630	956	1	0	1	44,590	11,791	56,382	48.9	115,338	7,146.51	1,102.31
83	2,864	175	5,025	8,147	147	2	167	458,222	108,473	566,696	43.3	1,307,534	10,250.18	2,128.08
1,265	23,537	958	61,945	87,705	806	784	1,603	5,802,284	1,655,674	7,457,957	48.4	15,412,001	11,073.78	2,063.83
501	4,070	265	13,524	18,360	0	76	76	1,315,067	363,027	1,678,097	57.3	2,927,320	8,620.82	1,143.71
764	19,467	693	48,421	69,345	806	708	1,527	4,487,217	1,292,647	5,779,860	46.3	12,484,680	11,865.40	2,543.66
31	543	52	1,649	2,275	0	3	3	169,085	49,032	218,117	54.0	404,018	8,831.38	2,160.73
7	38	8	147	200	0	0	0	15,676	4,246	19,922	68.2	29,227	4,235.18	634.98
43	952	18	2,382	3,395	0	0	0	221,810	75,672	297,480	56.4	527,882	10,821.25	1,912.11
54	492	162	1,327	2,035	0	0	0	129,439	31,457	160,897	46.9	342,795	10,685.97	2,678.30
107	1,265	105	3,660	5,137	0	87	87	356,012	92,741	448,753	48.5	925,904	10,841.97	2,796.64
330	857	34	2,769	3,990	18	0	18	222,228	71,195	293,422	46.8	627,321	15,367.61	3,415.28
25	961	56	2,728	3,770	0	0	0	267,409	88,605	356,014	56.4	631,316	10,888.51	2,674.22
35	1,048	39	2,665	3,787	15	47	75	237,086	71,726	308,812	53.9	572,563	9,806.34	2,466.28
116	3,217	52	8,902	12,287	568	148	716	847,969	283,708	1,131,677	52.5	2,155,426	15,555.34	2,441.02
0	7,661	73	15,705	23,439	190	376	566	1,473,011	363,288	1,836,299	38.3	4,789,838	12,586.12	2,743.52
8	202	12	763	985	0	0	0	59,508	13,867	73,375	49.8	147,222	8,773.66	2,720.99
7	582	21	1,333	1,943	0	29	29	139,357	42,699	182,055	51.3	354,889	8,621.57	2,269.67
0	709	43	2,107	2,859	0	17	17	152,199	46,363	198,562	50.8	390,835	8,982.45	1,600.90
0	264	4	598	866	0	1	1	52,754	18,410	71,164	41.4	171,979	7,228.14	2,114.95
1	676	14	1,686	2,377	15	0	15	143,673	39,638	183,311	44.3	413,464	13,036.05	3,353.46

MSAs

TABLE 8

U.S. CENSUS DIVISION 5, EAST SOUTH CENTRAL

U.S. Community Hospitals
(Nonfederal, short-term general and other special hospitals)

2013 Utilization, Personnel and Finances

CLASSIFICATION	Hospitals	Beds	Admissions	Inpatient Days	Adjusted Inpatient Days	Average Daily Census	Adjusted Average Daily Census	Average Stay (days)	Surgical Operations	NEWBORNS Bassinets	NEWBORNS Births	OUTPATIENT VISITS Emergency	OUTPATIENT VISITS Total
UNITED STATES	4,974	795,603	33,609,083	182,370,189	362,566,276	500,222	962,267	5.4	26,566,037	56,342	3,699,411	133,611,670	677,951,120
Nonmetropolitan	1,971	130,332	3,839,423	24,309,871	69,408,427	66,633	181,025	6.3	3,948,240	10,447	436,830	23,881,030	127,477,109
Metropolitan	3,003	665,271	29,769,660	158,060,318	293,157,849	433,589	781,242	5.3	22,617,797	45,895	3,262,581	109,730,640	550,474,011
CENSUS DIVISION 5, EAST SOUTH CENTRAL	432	62,235	2,419,265	13,421,013	27,193,939	36,769	69,027	5.5	2,027,198	4,234	215,234	9,732,264	35,701,320
Nonmetropolitan	232	20,665	600,247	3,754,409	9,250,114	10,283	21,999	6.3	552,092	1,373	56,215	3,368,273	11,166,812
Metropolitan	200	41,570	1,819,018	9,666,604	17,943,825	26,486	47,028	5.3	1,475,106	2,861	159,019	6,363,991	24,534,508
Alabama	97	15,129	641,249	3,369,852	6,527,979	9,236	17,040	5.3	566,280	1,326	57,811	2,279,572	8,312,122
Nonmetropolitan	44	3,176	104,774	517,025	1,345,322	1,416	3,351	4.9	96,817	249	9,666	599,269	1,913,966
Metropolitan	53	11,953	536,475	2,852,827	5,182,657	7,820	13,689	5.3	469,463	1,077	48,145	1,680,303	6,398,156
Anniston-Oxford	3	420	17,472	78,217	170,025	214	432	4.5	12,058	38	1,683	81,395	201,836
Auburn-Opelika	1	371	13,626	96,045	234,473	263	642	7.0	13,587	38	1,543	38,874	125,426
Birmingham-Hoover	15	4,405	204,460	1,074,229	1,825,500	2,945	4,593	5.3	178,174	382	16,441	532,110	2,482,002
Columbus	1	48	1,122	15,661	35,575	43	43	14.0	0	0	0	0	4,039
Decatur	2	190	8,821	37,499	87,267	102	239	4.3	9,405	23	797	50,320	176,021
Dothan	4	765	32,293	195,921	396,373	537	1,086	6.1	34,011	57	2,676	108,915	271,351
Florence-Muscle Shoals	3	574	23,786	110,826	234,885	304	643	4.7	14,698	46	1,093	45,700	219,152
Gadsden	3	580	20,364	121,829	212,503	334	582	6.0	21,849	32	1,316	50,227	140,328
Huntsville	4	1,197	57,790	285,094	576,533	782	1,579	4.9	69,605	92	6,332	223,601	974,414
Mobile	5	1,381	68,211	375,642	573,619	1,030	1,572	5.5	51,952	187	6,116	173,832	636,042
Montgomery	8	1,102	48,109	248,663	467,686	682	1,282	5.2	40,761	115	5,495	187,066	609,413
Tuscaloosa	4	920	40,421	213,201	368,218	584	996	5.3	23,363	67	4,653	188,263	558,132
Kentucky	106	14,021	578,841	3,026,582	6,483,053	8,290	17,166	5.2	528,599	905	54,263	2,279,740	10,521,363
Nonmetropolitan	63	5,728	206,568	1,040,177	2,582,308	2,847	6,663	5.0	184,572	413	19,104	1,006,962	4,053,686
Metropolitan	43	8,293	372,273	1,986,405	3,900,745	5,443	10,503	5.3	344,027	492	35,159	1,272,778	6,467,677
Bowling Green	3	564	23,371	122,351	226,171	335	441	5.2	19,110	19	2,299	77,443	174,882
Cincinnati-Middletown	5	895	45,201	222,542	435,641	609	1,194	4.9	28,787	38	4,291	198,903	1,128,471
Clarksville	2	164	6,765	32,594	78,563	89	216	4.8	3,793	18	704	33,258	149,607
Elizabethtown	2	308	13,393	64,368	185,563	176	509	4.8	11,812	26	1,548	56,655	355,109
Evansville	1	158	5,082	24,359	70,381	67	193	4.8	3,623	12	668	28,606	288,380
Huntington-Ashland	2	616	29,005	161,785	461,323	444	1,264	5.6	54,906	25	1,380	90,582	566,976
Lexington-Fayette	13	2,139	90,423	494,266	875,834	1,355	2,393	5.5	74,748	154	8,894	270,282	1,810,940
Louisville	14	3,102	141,614	783,017	1,397,241	2,146	3,827	5.5	130,118	170	13,574	453,378	1,437,859
Owensboro	1	347	17,419	81,123	170,028	222	466	4.7	17,130	30	1,801	63,671	555,453
Mississippi	99	12,826	380,059	2,499,123	5,189,987	6,843	10,991	6.6	274,750	742	36,911	1,794,793	4,955,576
Nonmetropolitan	71	7,541	170,600	1,427,467	3,261,633	3,909	6,527	8.4	137,373	423	17,709	964,398	2,574,897
Metropolitan	28	5,285	209,459	1,071,656	1,928,354	2,934	4,464	5.1	137,377	319	19,202	830,395	2,380,679
Gulfport-Biloxi	6	945	29,794	141,978	262,249	388	591	4.8	26,472	61	2,808	168,691	664,687
Hattiesburg	3	756	34,366	170,935	269,292	468	673	5.0	18,137	27	3,580	115,780	224,340
Jackson	14	2,812	108,338	587,094	1,060,954	1,608	2,343	5.4	76,356	168	9,303	342,771	885,074
Memphis	3	343	17,396	83,859	150,233	229	387	4.8	5,633	24	1,880	76,002	122,560
Pascagoula	2	429	19,565	87,790	185,626	241	470	4.5	10,779	39	1,631	127,151	484,018
Tennessee	130	20,259	819,116	4,525,456	8,992,920	12,400	23,830	5.5	657,569	1,261	66,249	3,378,159	11,912,259
Nonmetropolitan	54	4,220	118,305	769,740	2,060,851	2,111	5,458	6.5	133,330	288	9,736	797,644	2,624,263
Metropolitan	76	16,039	700,811	3,755,716	6,932,069	10,289	18,372	5.4	524,239	973	56,513	2,580,515	9,287,996
Chattanooga	6	1,567	70,448	387,733	648,033	1,062	1,775	5.5	62,348	95	6,934	280,371	985,636
Clarksville	1	247	12,359	49,646	78,404	136	215	4.0	8,117	30	173	68,516	165,057
Cleveland	2	211	9,077	39,111	95,703	108	234	4.3	7,932	19	1,119	56,707	122,008
Jackson	2	767	33,442	177,113	352,007	485	914	5.3	28,773	46	3,291	105,157	218,546
Johnson City	4	836	37,386	214,817	376,304	589	1,030	5.7	22,268	40	2,488	109,659	398,191
Kingsport-Bristol-Bristol	6	990	44,175	210,496	431,473	576	1,182	4.8	26,201	70	1,902	148,879	520,409
Knoxville	11	2,356	105,245	577,360	1,094,943	1,582	3,000	5.5	94,185	124	10,026	401,800	1,544,788
Memphis	14	3,591	138,265	828,502	1,487,949	2,272	3,939	6.0	81,057	241	16,555	552,092	1,252,957
Morristown	3	348	12,600	53,219	108,244	145	297	4.2	12,945	25	919	72,768	181,180
Nashville-Davidson--Murfreesboro	27	5,126	237,814	1,217,719	2,259,009	3,334	5,786	5.1	180,413	283	13,106	784,566	3,899,224

TABLE 8

U.S. CENSUS DIVISION 5, EAST SOUTH CENTRAL

U.S. Community Hospitals
(Nonfederal, short-term general and other special hospitals)

2013 Utilization, Personnel and Finances

FULL-TIME EQUIVALENT PERSONNEL					FULL-TIME EQUIV. TRAINEES			EXPENSES						
								LABOR				TOTAL		
Physicians and Dentists	Registered Nurses	Licensed Practical Nurses	Other Salaried Personnel	Total Personnel	Medical and Dental Residents	Other Trainees	Total Trainees	Payroll (in thousands)	Employee Benefits (in thousands)	Total (in thousands)	Percent of Total	Amount (in thousands)	Adjusted per Admission	Adjusted per Inpatient Day
122,119	1,366,402	78,164	3,219,402	4,786,087	107,029	9,592	120,142	$303,635,275	$83,520,086	$387,155,349	49.5	$782,035,350	11,650.90	2,156.94
16,394	163,074	23,407	470,243	673,118	1,951	433	2,686	36,502,464	9,848,281	46,350,747	52.0	89,112,057	8,086.11	1,283.88
105,725	1,203,328	54,757	2,749,159	4,112,969	105,078	9,159	117,456	267,132,811	73,671,804	340,804,602	49.2	692,923,293	12,351.15	2,363.65
6,343	90,062	6,785	194,527	297,717	5,338	301	5,894	15,785,672	4,092,148	19,877,827	46.6	42,687,366	8,626.86	1,569.74
1,582	21,230	3,112	56,639	82,563	231	63	335	3,957,156	1,038,270	4,995,433	49.8	10,031,563	6,663.87	1,084.48
4,761	68,832	3,673	137,889	215,155	5,107	238	5,559	11,828,515	3,053,878	14,882,394	45.6	32,655,803	9,485.17	1,819.89
1,193	23,517	1,393	48,308	74,411	1,627	53	1,828	3,592,860	912,902	4,505,767	46.5	9,699,338	7,659.44	1,485.81
210	3,622	399	8,969	13,200	46	6	61	535,085	139,411	674,499	49.0	1,375,436	4,998.95	1,022.38
983	19,895	994	39,339	61,211	1,581	47	1,767	3,057,775	773,491	3,831,268	46.0	8,323,902	8,397.98	1,606.11
46	477	47	1,223	1,793	18	1	28	81,064	18,367	99,431	46.7	212,891	5,648.33	1,252.12
37	680	52	1,603	2,372	128	0	182	90,379	34,186	124,565	53.3	233,852	7,029.96	997.35
271	7,543	207	13,647	21,668	886	2	897	1,272,550	300,399	1,572,949	44.1	3,570,391	10,144.08	1,955.84
2	42	6	106	156	0	0	0	4,663	1,086	5,749	42.6	13,484	5,289.75	379.02
35	279	34	807	1,155	7	1	12	49,919	15,737	65,656	54.5	120,487	5,888.05	1,380.67
61	1,182	97	2,549	3,889	110	4	141	185,790	47,726	233,514	48.9	477,281	7,206.64	1,204.12
72	555	52	1,534	2,213	24	2	35	95,765	30,146	125,912	52.6	239,208	4,760.36	1,018.41
22	609	39	1,192	1,862	16	0	16	80,832	18,473	99,306	31.0	320,841	8,753.47	1,509.82
169	2,881	137	5,032	8,219	15	4	19	374,338	123,804	498,143	52.0	957,210	7,888.98	1,660.29
188	2,283	40	5,006	7,517	371	9	398	357,514	91,516	449,030	48.1	932,605	8,886.27	1,625.83
32	1,803	69	3,355	5,259	1	1	2	235,441	42,477	277,919	37.9	732,367	7,701.99	1,565.94
48	1,561	214	3,285	5,108	5	23	37	229,520	49,574	279,094	54.4	513,286	7,255.96	1,393.97
1,255	21,868	1,375	47,103	71,601	760	24	798	3,832,176	1,102,327	4,934,504	45.3	10,884,059	8,496.02	1,678.85
682	6,880	835	18,037	26,434	94	12	120	1,325,976	381,632	1,707,609	49.3	3,462,977	6,638.23	1,341.04
573	14,988	540	29,066	45,167	666	12	678	2,506,200	720,695	3,226,895	43.5	7,421,082	9,772.22	1,902.48
2	784	18	1,524	2,328	0	0	0	119,769	33,173	152,942	47.1	325,054	7,541.68	1,437.20
11	1,393	65	3,272	4,741	24	0	24	312,890	108,622	421,513	51.6	817,347	8,990.92	1,876.19
19	242	23	697	981	6	0	6	46,575	12,515	59,090	50.0	118,236	7,455.00	1,504.99
36	458	12	1,357	1,863	0	0	0	104,968	24,825	129,793	54.2	239,448	6,118.68	1,290.39
25	281	26	732	1,064	10	5	15	39,252	16,262	55,513	53.9	102,913	7,008.50	1,462.22
196	1,314	93	2,532	4,135	10	0	10	276,894	70,503	347,396	51.6	672,790	8,023.16	1,458.39
49	3,932	129	7,784	11,894	616	0	616	547,254	177,282	724,536	35.4	2,046,926	12,036.78	2,337.12
234	5,786	125	8,900	15,045	0	7	7	934,203	234,545	1,168,748	43.0	2,719,650	10,251.30	1,946.44
1	798	49	2,268	3,116	0	0	0	124,395	42,969	167,364	44.2	378,717	10,373.26	2,227.38
821	14,332	1,619	35,243	52,015	611	38	649	2,802,520	692,336	3,494,853	49.2	7,101,440	9,188.92	1,368.30
456	6,383	1,186	18,283	26,308	51	38	89	1,310,074	321,522	1,631,596	50.2	3,250,611	8,337.36	996.62
365	7,949	433	16,960	25,707	560	0	560	1,492,446	370,814	1,863,257	48.4	3,850,829	10,055.93	1,996.95
156	1,343	98	2,760	4,357	0	0	0	268,106	58,406	326,512	51.4	635,416	11,116.84	2,422.95
36	1,020	85	2,676	3,817	0	0	0	195,468	47,417	242,885	47.0	517,048	9,403.79	1,920.03
74	4,023	184	8,754	13,035	560	0	560	770,610	197,393	968,001	48.6	2,015,427	10,190.56	1,899.64
1	630	36	1,160	1,827	0	0	0	97,328	25,687	123,015	43.2	284,808	9,155.46	1,895.78
98	933	30	1,610	2,671	0	0	0	160,935	41,910	202,844	50.9	398,129	9,497.80	2,144.79
3,074	30,345	2,398	63,874	99,691	2,340	186	2,619	5,558,116	1,384,583	6,942,703	46.3	15,002,529	9,215.51	1,668.26
234	4,345	692	11,350	16,621	40	7	65	786,021	195,705	981,729	50.5	1,942,539	6,095.90	942.59
2,840	26,000	1,706	52,524	83,070	2,300	179	2,554	4,772,094	1,188,878	5,960,974	45.6	13,059,990	9,974.77	1,884.00
199	2,789	149	5,173	8,310	217	49	279	521,756	132,773	654,528	50.7	1,290,898	10,712.93	1,992.02
10	394	20	629	1,053	15	0	15	54,112	12,240	66,352	45.5	145,918	7,476.08	1,861.11
4	380	31	646	1,061	0	1	1	46,558	10,841	57,399	43.1	133,092	5,985.42	1,390.68
0	1,160	152	3,114	4,426	0	0	0	219,208	56,136	275,344	48.6	566,535	8,551.73	1,609.44
0	1,231	74	1,865	3,170	0	0	0	183,553	40,262	223,816	55.6	402,487	6,145.12	1,069.58
45	1,227	56	3,208	4,536	29	3	36	251,979	76,027	328,007	45.6	719,296	7,386.64	1,667.07
169	4,007	292	8,178	12,646	13	8	21	697,898	169,250	867,149	43.7	1,982,412	9,908.29	1,810.52
47	5,727	207	10,501	16,482	871	25	905	957,886	242,131	1,200,017	42.3	2,839,435	10,957.19	1,908.29
6	390	27	680	1,103	3	0	3	57,742	11,391	69,133	43.9	157,480	6,123.36	1,454.87
2,360	8,695	698	18,530	30,283	1,152	93	1,294	1,781,403	437,826	2,219,229	46.0	4,822,437	11,137.45	2,134.76

MSAs

TABLE 8

U.S. CENSUS DIVISION 6, WEST NORTH CENTRAL

U.S. Community Hospitals
(Nonfederal, short-term general and other special hospitals)

2013 Utilization, Personnel and Finances

CLASSIFICATION	Hospitals	Beds	Admissions	Inpatient Days	Adjusted Inpatient Days	Average Daily Census	Adjusted Average Daily Census	Average Stay (days)	Surgical Operations	NEWBORNS Bassinets	NEWBORNS Births	OUTPATIENT VISITS Emergency	OUTPATIENT VISITS Total
UNITED STATES	4,974	795,603	33,609,083	182,370,189	362,566,276	500,222	962,267	5.4	26,566,037	56,342	3,699,411	133,611,670	677,951,120
Nonmetropolitan	1,971	130,332	3,839,423	24,309,871	69,408,427	66,633	181,025	6.3	3,948,240	10,447	436,830	23,881,030	127,477,109
Metropolitan	3,003	665,271	29,769,660	158,060,318	293,157,849	433,589	781,242	5.3	22,617,797	45,895	3,262,581	109,730,640	550,474,011
CENSUS DIVISION 6, WEST NORTH CENTRAL	683	67,386	2,355,948	14,286,092	33,737,288	39,248	90,980	6.1	2,005,584	4,848	267,407	8,653,473	60,567,733
Nonmetropolitan	459	24,701	526,498	4,703,843	14,412,647	12,900	38,122	8.9	573,054	1,848	67,299	2,802,917	23,154,739
Metropolitan	224	42,685	1,829,450	9,582,249	19,324,641	26,348	52,858	5.2	1,432,530	3,000	200,108	5,850,556	37,412,994
Iowa	118	9,839	326,593	2,001,590	5,581,268	5,482	15,291	6.1	328,013	714	38,344	1,292,810	10,608,846
Nonmetropolitan	84	4,212	90,906	775,699	2,853,683	2,124	7,816	8.5	124,411	304	10,458	517,046	4,999,167
Metropolitan	34	5,627	235,687	1,225,891	2,727,585	3,358	7,475	5.2	203,602	410	27,886	775,764	5,609,679
Ames	2	269	9,213	61,005	143,819	167	395	6.6	10,038	17	1,086	28,887	192,290
Cedar Rapids	4	748	28,796	166,577	480,535	457	1,317	5.8	26,364	54	3,209	112,887	999,346
Davenport-Moline-Rock Island	3	464	20,632	90,866	167,274	249	459	4.4	11,806	33	2,771	98,283	230,323
Des Moines	8	1,485	68,612	347,664	679,740	953	1,863	5.1	45,949	126	9,996	205,370	927,031
Dubuque	3	406	13,756	71,804	141,835	197	388	5.2	13,281	34	1,527	46,210	131,644
Iowa City	3	981	40,092	243,342	498,911	666	1,367	6.1	34,422	54	3,307	89,036	1,512,981
Omaha-Council Bluffs	3	293	13,253	53,797	119,273	147	327	4.1	12,905	22	985	54,099	206,398
Sioux City	2	389	19,434	84,616	146,509	231	401	4.4	10,963	31	2,286	58,624	324,973
Waterloo-Cedar Falls	6	592	21,899	106,220	349,689	291	958	4.9	37,874	39	2,719	82,368	1,084,693
Kansas	130	9,998	289,696	1,899,716	4,785,933	5,247	13,063	6.6	227,244	710	37,311	1,127,551	7,090,344
Nonmetropolitan	96	4,685	85,892	846,961	2,823,027	2,336	7,739	9.9	88,804	334	10,560	384,453	3,336,572
Metropolitan	34	5,313	203,804	1,052,755	1,962,906	2,911	5,324	5.2	138,440	376	26,751	743,098	3,753,772
Kansas City	15	2,449	97,819	502,707	958,293	1,403	2,570	5.1	75,897	188	13,009	322,079	2,040,358
Lawrence	1	152	6,669	23,241	86,689	64	238	3.5	4,586	13	1,132	37,678	160,733
Topeka	6	847	30,144	165,585	338,877	454	930	5.5	17,108	42	2,872	97,926	693,925
Wichita	12	1,865	69,172	361,222	579,047	990	1,586	5.2	40,849	133	9,738	285,415	858,756
Minnesota	131	14,781	562,035	3,395,406	7,696,912	9,376	21,048	6.0	504,653	1,278	67,898	1,933,651	11,666,124
Nonmetropolitan	82	4,929	101,495	1,058,941	3,176,161	2,903	8,580	10.4	127,561	378	15,127	590,767	4,624,521
Metropolitan	49	9,852	460,540	2,336,465	4,520,751	6,473	12,468	5.1	377,092	900	52,771	1,342,884	7,041,603
Duluth	10	1,233	40,151	289,404	753,851	792	2,066	7.2	40,815	104	3,282	130,611	603,302
Grand Forks	2	124	1,491	29,223	96,079	81	263	19.6	3,478	11	186	9,776	84,323
Minneapolis-St. Paul-Bloomington	29	6,302	331,647	1,493,409	2,595,434	4,163	7,323	4.5	255,315	647	43,046	1,022,652	5,189,991
Rochester	3	1,447	58,756	342,720	613,130	939	1,680	5.8	61,810	101	3,274	96,081	632,463
St. Cloud	5	746	28,495	181,709	462,257	498	1,136	6.4	15,674	37	2,983	83,764	531,524
Missouri	123	18,899	781,070	4,060,151	8,864,334	11,121	24,286	5.2	585,384	1,252	74,688	2,987,268	21,844,257
Nonmetropolitan	53	3,575	120,894	579,279	1,736,045	1,584	4,754	4.8	103,157	342	13,961	708,183	5,609,094
Metropolitan	70	15,324	660,176	3,480,872	7,128,289	9,537	19,532	5.3	482,227	910	60,727	2,279,085	16,235,163
Columbia	3	892	40,177	199,064	324,981	545	891	5.0	36,589	41	4,053	84,723	969,419
Jefferson City	3	290	13,970	55,863	151,350	153	415	4.0	10,638	24	1,507	73,139	644,596
Joplin	4	661	30,807	155,514	333,921	426	915	5.0	18,396	65	3,117	147,981	1,026,175
Kansas City	23	3,772	152,570	835,290	1,810,919	2,288	4,962	5.5	107,739	216	15,257	652,601	3,738,128
Springfield	5	1,456	73,286	364,313	849,673	998	2,328	5.0	64,979	85	6,771	259,819	2,487,941
St. Joseph	1	352	16,792	72,057	168,641	197	462	4.3	11,257	20	1,604	54,028	974,217
St. Louis	31	7,901	332,574	1,798,771	3,488,804	4,930	9,559	5.4	232,629	459	28,418	1,006,794	6,394,687
Nebraska	87	6,784	199,933	1,335,733	2,971,472	3,660	7,447	6.7	180,163	512	25,323	692,717	4,759,460
Nonmetropolitan	69	3,364	70,986	598,226	1,624,315	1,640	3,852	8.4	70,241	274	8,170	303,753	2,524,677
Metropolitan	18	3,420	128,947	737,507	1,347,157	2,020	3,595	5.7	109,922	238	17,153	388,964	2,234,783
Lincoln	5	996	38,640	238,350	374,519	652	1,026	6.2	23,787	64	5,015	110,097	410,303
Omaha-Council Bluffs	13	2,424	90,307	499,157	972,638	1,368	2,569	5.5	86,135	174	12,138	278,867	1,824,480
North Dakota	40	2,924	94,743	658,748	1,642,954	1,804	4,098	7.0	101,002	171	11,061	328,299	2,335,490
Nonmetropolitan	32	1,441	24,279	311,040	759,392	851	1,677	12.8	28,485	68	3,703	142,038	764,767
Metropolitan	8	1,483	70,464	347,708	883,562	953	2,421	4.9	72,517	103	7,358	186,261	1,570,723
Bismarck	3	520	23,450	108,015	246,889	296	677	4.6	17,194	27	2,336	56,332	375,816
Fargo	3	617	33,482	157,049	379,678	431	1,040	4.7	43,145	53	3,374	61,164	441,100
Grand Forks	2	346	13,532	82,644	256,995	226	704	6.1	12,178	23	1,648	68,765	753,807
South Dakota	54	4,161	101,878	934,748	2,194,415	2,558	5,747	9.2	79,125	211	12,782	291,177	2,263,212
Nonmetropolitan	43	2,495	32,046	533,697	1,440,024	1,462	3,704	16.7	30,395	148	5,320	156,677	1,295,941
Metropolitan	11	1,666	69,832	401,051	754,391	1,096	2,043	5.7	48,730	63	7,462	134,500	967,271
Rapid City	3	543	20,065	139,574	229,275	382	629	7.0	8,629	24	2,365	58,507	205,123
Sioux Falls	8	1,123	49,767	261,477	525,116	714	1,414	5.3	40,101	39	5,097	75,993	762,148

TABLE 8

U.S. CENSUS DIVISION 6, WEST NORTH CENTRAL

U.S. Community Hospitals
(Nonfederal, short-term general and other special hospitals)

2013 Utilization, Personnel and Finances

FULL-TIME EQUIVALENT PERSONNEL					FULL-TIME EQUIV. TRAINEES			EXPENSES						
								LABOR				TOTAL		
Physicians and Dentists	Registered Nurses	Licensed Practical Nurses	Other Salaried Personnel	Total Personnel	Medical and Dental Residents	Other Trainees	Total Trainees	Payroll (in thousands)	Employee Benefits (in thousands)	Total (in thousands)	Percent of Total	Amount (in thousands)	Adjusted per Admission	Adjusted per Inpatient Day
122,119	1,366,402	78,164	3,219,402	4,786,087	107,029	9,592	120,142	$303,635,275	$83,520,086	$387,155,349	49.5	$782,035,350	$11,650.90	$2,156.94
16,394	163,074	23,407	470,243	673,118	1,951	433	2,686	36,502,464	9,848,281	46,350,747	52.0	89,112,057	8,086.11	1,283.88
105,725	1,203,328	54,757	2,749,159	4,112,969	105,078	9,159	117,456	267,132,811	73,671,804	340,804,602	49.2	692,923,293	12,351.15	2,363.65
13,416	108,368	9,122	281,123	412,029	4,521	1,556	6,150	23,755,636	6,262,294	30,017,933	50.4	59,579,627	11,138.60	1,765.99
3,097	27,414	4,665	81,594	116,770	188	50	292	6,171,716	1,621,298	7,793,017	52.8	14,763,243	8,756.56	1,024.33
10,319	80,954	4,457	199,529	295,259	4,333	1,506	5,858	17,583,920	4,640,996	22,224,916	49.6	44,816,384	12,235.00	2,319.13
1,197	15,014	950	38,828	55,989	771	28	799	3,095,750	846,192	3,941,941	50.3	7,832,928	9,281.70	1,403.43
490	5,402	614	15,260	21,766	24	0	24	1,109,597	293,724	1,403,321	52.5	2,671,894	7,956.68	936.30
707	9,612	336	23,568	34,223	747	28	775	1,986,153	552,468	2,538,620	49.2	5,161,034	10,157.40	1,892.16
4	343	15	953	1,315	0	0	0	70,696	21,791	92,488	51.2	180,534	9,453.03	1,255.29
73	1,192	40	3,246	4,551	0	3	3	240,069	64,451	304,520	48.7	625,522	8,499.64	1,301.72
2	724	5	1,341	2,072	15	0	15	111,529	24,179	135,708	36.1	376,377	9,333.13	2,250.06
279	2,538	44	6,437	9,298	192	3	195	564,064	135,646	699,710	50.3	1,391,071	10,394.70	2,046.47
9	598	16	1,160	1,783	0	0	0	86,050	21,642	107,692	44.8	240,506	8,717.46	1,695.67
134	2,272	23	5,517	7,946	535	16	551	474,745	179,992	654,737	51.9	1,261,659	15,831.49	2,528.83
17	407	16	853	1,293	0	4	4	75,906	21,284	97,190	51.4	189,096	6,409.58	1,585.40
61	643	14	1,493	2,211	2	0	2	133,811	31,825	165,636	49.9	332,188	9,859.27	2,267.36
128	895	163	2,568	3,754	3	2	5	229,283	51,656	280,939	49.8	564,081	7,968.94	1,613.09
1,019	14,583	1,235	31,238	48,075	12	165	177	2,727,760	650,064	3,377,826	51.1	6,616,602	9,507.36	1,382.51
407	4,512	706	12,989	18,614	0	0	0	919,138	217,714	1,136,853	54.9	2,072,301	7,189.70	734.07
612	10,071	529	18,249	29,461	12	165	177	1,808,622	432,350	2,240,973	49.3	4,544,301	11,145.83	2,315.09
204	5,249	96	8,917	14,466	0	157	157	887,026	220,524	1,107,551	45.6	2,430,440	12,027.77	2,536.22
46	304	21	829	1,200	0	0	0	72,127	17,116	89,242	51.2	174,211	7,003.46	2,009.61
287	1,447	341	3,464	5,539	7	1	8	381,847	82,862	464,709	59.3	783,150	11,717.66	2,311.02
75	3,071	71	5,039	8,256	5	7	12	467,622	111,850	579,471	50.1	1,156,500	10,150.62	1,997.25
5,870	23,227	2,400	80,501	111,998	1,751	1,193	2,995	6,811,309	1,868,400	8,679,708	54.6	15,886,276	13,597.34	2,063.98
790	5,206	1,312	17,622	24,930	20	7	64	1,455,279	386,878	1,842,156	53.4	3,450,166	10,400.31	1,086.27
5,080	18,021	1,088	62,879	87,068	1,731	1,186	2,931	5,356,030	1,481,522	6,837,552	55.0	12,436,110	14,865.06	2,750.89
495	1,811	226	5,871	8,403	8	0	8	641,837	171,916	813,753	63.4	1,282,558	13,913.18	1,701.34
21	102	71	458	652	0	0	0	36,780	8,042	44,823	59.9	74,844	15,638.02	778.98
1,875	12,363	453	30,930	45,621	489	77	580	3,669,975	1,013,521	4,683,495	54.4	8,606,852	14,901.63	3,316.15
2,660	2,474	141	21,969	27,244	1,219	1,109	2,328	702,890	193,434	896,325	50.9	1,762,663	16,360.79	2,874.86
29	1,271	197	3,651	5,148	15	0	15	304,548	94,608	399,156	56.3	709,193	13,056.80	1,534.20
3,274	34,548	2,653	78,488	118,963	1,836	149	1,985	6,837,072	1,841,638	8,678,710	46.3	18,734,465	10,922.12	2,113.47
757	5,350	1,078	15,747	22,932	53	30	83	1,185,907	322,980	1,508,887	50.3	2,998,476	8,256.56	1,727.19
2,517	29,198	1,575	62,741	96,031	1,783	119	1,902	5,651,165	1,518,658	7,169,823	45.6	15,735,989	11,638.06	2,207.54
31	1,551	219	3,904	5,705	349	7	356	304,431	104,338	408,769	42.0	972,829	14,479.42	2,993.49
93	554	117	1,373	2,137	10	0	10	120,781	32,483	153,264	50.6	302,818	8,278.90	2,000.78
153	1,267	68	3,119	4,607	23	0	23	286,820	58,298	345,119	47.9	720,039	10,830.42	2,156.32
458	7,366	227	14,858	22,909	206	107	313	1,450,638	345,447	1,796,085	46.7	3,842,264	12,702.83	2,121.72
846	3,347	506	11,266	15,965	25	0	25	648,685	175,818	824,503	43.2	1,909,597	10,964.92	2,247.45
151	718	155	2,000	3,024	0	0	0	231,915	57,290	289,205	55.3	523,153	13,311.78	3,102.17
785	14,395	283	26,221	41,684	1,170	5	1,175	2,607,894	744,984	3,352,878	44.9	7,465,291	11,210.17	2,139.79
554	10,267	765	23,316	34,902	50	9	63	1,886,034	512,396	2,398,436	49.2	4,870,430	10,962.87	1,639.06
300	3,606	545	10,140	14,591	42	7	53	731,007	204,378	935,389	50.1	1,866,613	9,535.99	1,149.17
254	6,661	220	13,176	20,311	8	2	10	1,155,028	308,018	1,463,047	48.7	3,003,817	12,086.72	2,229.74
17	1,569	112	3,559	5,257	1	1	2	292,531	82,225	374,756	48.9	766,103	11,246.70	2,045.56
237	5,092	108	9,617	15,054	7	1	8	862,496	225,794	1,088,291	48.6	2,237,714	12,403.90	2,300.66
651	4,993	716	15,098	21,458	81	8	107	1,226,178	274,974	1,501,149	50.6	2,966,838	11,512.36	1,805.79
158	1,661	237	4,726	6,782	48	5	66	377,508	95,862	473,368	57.5	823,228	10,644.14	1,084.06
493	3,332	479	10,372	14,676	33	3	41	848,670	179,112	1,027,781	47.9	2,143,610	11,884.65	2,426.10
236	1,160	173	3,952	5,521	3	0	3	321,608	50,230	371,838	56.6	656,766	12,004.72	2,660.17
32	1,639	266	3,744	5,681	4	1	10	280,704	74,646	355,350	35.1	1,011,185	12,286.12	2,663.27
225	533	40	2,676	3,474	26	2	28	246,358	54,235	300,593	63.2	475,658	10,971.00	1,850.85
851	5,736	403	13,654	20,644	20	4	24	1,171,533	268,630	1,440,163	53.9	2,672,088	11,956.40	1,217.68
195	1,677	173	5,110	7,155	1	1	2	393,281	99,762	493,043	56.0	880,564	9,373.49	611.49
656	4,059	230	8,544	13,489	19	3	22	778,252	168,868	947,120	52.9	1,791,524	13,829.46	2,374.79
70	869	55	2,042	3,036	19	3	22	182,719	21,550	204,268	48.8	418,171	12,508.87	1,823.89
586	3,190	175	6,502	10,453	0	0	0	595,533	147,318	742,852	54.1	1,373,352	14,288.78	2,615.33

MSAs

TABLE 8

U.S. CENSUS DIVISION 7, WEST SOUTH CENTRAL

U.S. Community Hospitals
(Nonfederal, short-term general and other special hospitals)

2013 Utilization, Personnel and Finances

CLASSIFICATION	Hospitals	Beds	Admissions	Inpatient Days	Adjusted Inpatient Days	Average Daily Census	Adjusted Average Daily Census	Average Stay (days)	Surgical Operations	NEWBORNS Bassinets	NEWBORNS Births	OUTPATIENT VISITS Emergency	OUTPATIENT VISITS Total
UNITED STATES	4,974	795,603	33,609,083	182,370,189	362,566,276	500,222	962,267	5.4	26,566,037	56,342	3,699,411	133,611,670	677,951,120
Nonmetropolitan	1,971	130,332	3,839,423	24,309,871	69,408,427	66,633	181,025	6.3	3,948,240	10,447	436,830	23,881,030	127,477,109
Metropolitan	3,003	665,271	29,769,660	158,060,318	293,157,849	433,589	781,242	5.3	22,617,797	45,895	3,262,581	109,730,640	550,474,011
CENSUS DIVISION 7, WEST SOUTH CENTRAL.	746	97,967	3,852,821	20,284,467	38,194,414	55,669	103,120	5.3	2,774,266	7,492	530,165	16,301,738	61,529,047
Nonmetropolitan	308	16,180	487,272	2,199,302	6,137,044	6,030	16,269	4.5	397,724	1,356	62,246	3,152,235	12,548,970
Metropolitan	438	81,787	3,365,549	18,085,165	32,057,370	49,639	86,851	5.4	2,376,542	6,136	467,919	13,149,503	48,980,077
Arkansas	84	9,452	352,362	1,817,099	3,596,584	4,975	9,773	5.2	270,815	680	36,313	1,438,617	5,113,519
Nonmetropolitan	48	3,184	93,537	490,600	1,208,120	1,342	3,229	5.2	67,587	234	9,717	525,034	1,822,042
Metropolitan	36	6,268	258,825	1,326,499	2,388,464	3,633	6,544	5.1	203,228	446	26,596	913,583	3,291,477
Fayetteville-Springdale-Rogers . . .	6	927	43,479	178,698	318,782	490	873	4.1	44,579	80	6,788	184,725	541,326
Fort Smith	7	924	33,603	187,060	337,020	512	924	5.6	31,792	50	2,904	135,646	373,063
Hot Springs	3	501	18,863	98,530	173,760	271	476	5.2	16,355	24	1,484	64,010	219,641
Jonesboro	3	547	25,115	112,454	240,621	308	659	4.5	15,736	38	2,130	81,572	287,826
Little Rock-North Little Rock	15	2,941	125,521	683,926	1,179,692	1,872	3,233	5.4	87,050	206	11,634	369,589	1,628,630
Memphis	1	95	3,028	12,545	26,764	34	73	4.1	3,215	12	633	23,785	37,938
Pine Bluff	1	333	9,216	53,286	111,825	146	306	5.8	4,501	36	1,023	54,256	203,053
Louisiana	122	15,550	565,779	3,073,041	6,152,897	8,517	16,101	5.4	401,870	998	64,083	2,587,672	9,664,268
Nonmetropolitan	48	3,091	92,818	441,771	1,118,567	1,214	3,001	4.8	85,969	219	11,180	560,101	1,994,412
Metropolitan	74	12,459	472,961	2,631,270	5,034,330	7,303	13,100	5.6	315,901	779	52,903	2,027,571	7,669,856
Alexandria	5	737	28,294	170,243	271,644	466	743	6.0	15,409	55	3,088	115,217	318,732
Baton Rouge	12	2,449	79,998	535,472	1,127,014	1,466	3,087	6.7	60,704	150	11,048	346,853	1,276,941
Houma-Bayou Cane-Thibodaux . .	5	518	24,918	112,819	237,349	308	651	4.5	18,556	44	3,126	148,283	566,226
Lafayette	8	1,125	44,727	233,652	410,953	657	1,038	5.2	19,002	55	2,602	165,593	576,526
Lake Charles	8	755	26,809	145,105	315,440	398	791	5.4	25,871	54	3,214	122,337	493,570
Monroe	9	818	36,269	200,390	360,791	549	832	5.5	17,590	68	3,452	137,692	528,429
New Orleans-Metairie-Kenner . . .	18	3,977	148,727	817,750	1,581,988	2,320	4,361	5.5	107,778	225	18,448	660,302	2,767,552
Shreveport-Bossier City	9	2,080	83,219	415,839	729,151	1,139	1,597	5.0	50,991	128	7,925	331,294	1,141,880
Oklahoma	116	11,365	412,225	2,221,235	4,680,849	6,084	12,231	5.4	323,791	810	52,910	1,871,330	6,613,137
Nonmetropolitan	65	3,688	109,965	502,258	1,485,238	1,375	3,671	4.6	97,438	325	15,080	682,407	2,405,717
Metropolitan	51	7,677	302,260	1,718,977	3,195,611	4,709	8,560	5.7	226,353	485	37,830	1,188,923	4,207,420
Fort Smith	2	110	2,448	10,917	25,713	30	57	4.5	1,778	11	588	18,344	47,564
Lawton	2	552	14,674	122,006	269,097	334	737	8.3	10,091	43	1,653	70,528	221,672
Oklahoma City	23	3,959	152,471	921,420	1,658,697	2,525	4,506	6.0	126,058	264	20,301	697,323	2,255,272
Tulsa	24	3,056	132,667	664,634	1,242,104	1,820	3,260	5.0	88,426	167	15,288	402,728	1,682,912
Texas	424	61,600	2,522,455	13,173,092	23,764,084	36,093	65,015	5.2	1,777,790	5,004	376,859	10,404,119	40,138,123
Nonmetropolitan	147	6,217	190,952	764,673	2,325,119	2,099	6,368	4.0	146,730	578	26,269	1,384,693	6,326,799
Metropolitan	277	55,383	2,331,503	12,408,419	21,438,965	33,994	58,647	5.3	1,631,060	4,426	350,590	9,019,426	33,811,324
Abilene	5	660	23,466	119,999	224,133	330	614	5.1	19,927	46	2,791	97,516	394,266
Amarillo	5	889	39,410	212,834	337,287	583	924	5.4	20,839	54	4,731	113,894	363,072
Austin-Round Rock	23	3,097	140,227	697,473	1,198,612	1,912	3,256	5.0	104,261	307	24,165	657,461	2,026,776
Beaumont-Port Arthur	7	1,176	47,874	230,886	417,608	631	1,144	4.8	31,985	99	5,160	231,493	618,220
Brownsville-Harlingen	3	870	36,548	182,098	282,745	499	775	5.0	25,035	92	7,399	129,928	245,969
College Station-Bryan	4	373	23,072	97,377	190,027	267	521	4.2	18,592	58	3,494	106,149	392,095
Corpus Christi	6	1,513	59,744	338,711	526,391	929	1,442	5.7	36,977	92	6,943	250,315	576,099
Dallas-Plano-Irving	51	9,126	394,886	2,121,628	3,564,837	5,812	9,737	5.4	237,508	781	58,072	1,611,680	5,360,162
El Paso	6	1,711	77,011	367,816	600,526	1,007	1,646	4.8	47,972	172	14,039	252,553	1,281,987
Fort Worth-Arlington	26	4,752	212,844	1,103,948	1,826,444	3,025	5,006	5.2	144,307	399	32,862	1,019,902	2,752,098
Houston-Sugar Land-Baytown . . .	67	14,608	596,236	3,401,666	6,083,940	9,318	16,633	5.7	427,463	1,227	95,407	2,037,226	9,232,671
Killeen-Temple-Fort Hood	6	983	43,559	214,731	522,967	589	1,433	4.9	33,541	70	4,845	201,016	1,613,993
Laredo	2	509	23,818	115,898	194,832	317	534	4.9	21,875	63	6,106	81,767	268,401
Longview	5	696	28,307	135,497	252,772	371	693	4.8	25,619	70	3,739	150,610	342,818
Lubbock	6	1,207	54,675	255,866	438,328	701	1,200	4.7	35,710	93	5,632	176,406	724,043
McAllen-Edinburg-Mission	7	2,153	87,695	416,928	689,744	1,143	1,889	4.8	85,785	193	17,316	236,063	557,739
Midland	2	294	12,561	68,243	123,840	187	340	5.4	9,694	26	2,325	60,022	143,799
Odessa	2	568	19,762	100,938	168,122	276	460	5.1	11,202	39	4,126	79,819	344,827
San Angelo	2	420	16,803	77,106	165,877	211	455	4.6	20,366	36	1,982	75,949	194,574
San Antonio	17	5,434	234,076	1,224,289	1,990,660	3,354	5,454	5.2	153,683	321	33,013	763,360	3,989,617
Sherman-Denison	2	523	18,040	91,932	160,707	252	441	5.1	9,735	35	1,447	77,719	140,986
Texarkana TX-Texarkana AR. . . .	5	714	24,865	138,027	220,340	378	603	5.6	12,002	31	2,821	111,503	272,305
Tyler	7	1,183	51,549	281,889	474,350	772	1,298	5.5	40,658	38	3,387	148,395	974,247
Victoria	4	589	17,812	92,408	176,621	253	484	5.2	23,517	24	2,559	83,146	232,007
Waco	2	883	29,702	238,140	467,628	652	1,282	8.0	17,298	40	4,125	135,448	569,562
Wichita Falls	5	452	16,961	82,091	139,627	225	383	4.8	15,509	20	2,104	90,486	199,011

TABLE 8

U.S. CENSUS DIVISION 7, WEST SOUTH CENTRAL

U.S. Community Hospitals
(Nonfederal, short-term general and other special hospitals)

2013 Utilization, Personnel and Finances

FULL-TIME EQUIVALENT PERSONNEL					FULL-TIME EQUIV. TRAINEES			EXPENSES						
								LABOR				TOTAL		
Physicians and Dentists	Registered Nurses	Licensed Practical Nurses	Other Salaried Personnel	Total Personnel	Medical and Dental Residents	Other Trainees	Total Trainees	Payroll (in thousands)	Employee Benefits (in thousands)	Total (in thousands)	Percent of Total	Amount (in thousands)	Adjusted per Admission	Adjusted per Inpatient Day
122,119	1,366,402	78,164	3,219,402	4,786,087	107,029	9,592	120,142	$303,635,275	$83,520,086	$387,155,349	49.5	$782,035,350	$11,650.90	$2,156.94
16,394	163,074	23,407	470,243	673,118	1,951	433	2,686	36,502,464	9,848,281	46,350,747	52.0	89,112,057	8,086.11	1,283.88
105,725	1,203,328	54,757	2,749,159	4,112,969	105,078	9,159	117,456	267,132,811	73,671,804	340,804,602	49.2	692,923,293	12,351.15	2,363.65
6,239	149,961	14,713	322,274	493,187	4,851	1,083	5,993	28,990,500	6,936,668	35,927,157	46.3	77,562,496	10,296.88	2,030.73
1,034	17,107	4,863	49,199	72,203	62	20	82	3,448,375	840,944	4,289,315	49.2	8,719,661	6,389.80	1,420.82
5,205	132,854	9,850	273,076	420,985	4,789	1,063	5,911	25,542,126	6,095,724	31,637,842	46.0	68,842,835	11,161.30	2,147.49
627	13,594	1,772	27,766	43,759	51	14	65	2,200,590	578,003	2,778,593	47.0	5,917,263	8,080.56	1,645.25
206	3,328	874	8,345	12,753	11	0	11	594,729	139,048	733,777	50.3	1,458,476	5,915.51	1,207.23
421	10,266	898	19,421	31,006	40	14	54	1,605,862	438,955	2,044,816	45.9	4,458,788	9,179.50	1,866.80
172	1,559	107	2,871	4,709	21	0	21	218,998	44,762	263,761	43.5	605,958	7,234.03	1,900.86
84	1,070	220	2,303	3,677	0	0	0	159,603	109,167	268,769	52.7	510,127	7,887.79	1,513.64
30	602	68	1,170	1,870	0	0	0	92,858	23,641	116,499	46.0	253,485	7,482.28	1,458.82
20	993	109	1,677	2,799	0	0	0	124,885	31,315	156,200	43.2	361,714	6,684.43	1,503.25
85	5,457	285	10,262	16,089	19	10	29	905,765	208,922	1,114,686	44.8	2,488,330	11,133.32	2,109.30
12	154	39	261	466	0	0	0	25,393	5,903	31,297	52.8	59,245	9,171.04	2,213.60
18	431	70	877	1,396	0	4	4	78,359	15,245	93,604	52.0	179,928	9,302.94	1,609.01
2,225	22,310	3,117	56,305	83,957	646	27	691	4,041,930	923,984	4,965,915	46.5	10,689,977	9,148.62	1,737.39
267	3,379	690	10,331	14,667	14	6	20	686,057	159,472	845,528	51.8	1,631,147	6,695.13	1,458.25
1,958	18,931	2,427	45,975	69,291	632	21	671	3,355,873	764,513	4,120,387	45.5	9,058,830	9,794.94	1,799.41
3	1,003	109	2,429	3,544	0	0	0	152,760	37,977	190,737	45.3	421,271	9,224.45	1,550.82
243	3,613	334	9,115	13,305	85	0	85	668,571	134,562	803,132	46.2	1,738,334	10,109.59	1,542.42
53	801	103	2,569	3,526	3	9	12	185,038	42,386	227,425	47.1	482,857	9,074.72	2,034.38
79	1,515	178	3,211	4,983	13	0	13	287,097	68,914	356,012	42.4	839,287	10,535.86	2,042.29
90	1,163	198	2,961	4,412	1	2	3	173,929	46,897	220,826	44.9	491,635	7,989.91	1,558.57
42	967	206	2,996	4,211	0	0	0	206,269	49,623	255,891	47.7	536,992	7,989.41	1,488.38
1,122	7,178	901	15,203	24,404	345	4	358	1,248,440	265,543	1,513,983	44.1	3,435,708	11,737.99	2,171.77
326	2,691	398	7,491	10,906	185	6	200	433,769	118,612	552,381	49.6	1,112,745	7,276.84	1,526.08
768	14,777	1,830	34,596	51,971	150	85	235	2,775,435	680,660	3,456,090	45.0	7,684,078	8,643.87	1,641.60
355	3,693	883	10,396	15,327	37	11	48	748,143	184,938	933,080	48.6	1,921,706	6,346.72	1,293.87
413	11,084	947	24,200	36,644	113	74	187	2,027,292	495,722	2,523,010	43.8	5,762,373	9,830.45	1,803.21
4	89	41	326	460	0	0	0	15,306	3,814	19,119	56.0	34,154	5,682.91	1,328.29
90	355	156	1,355	1,956	0	4	4	113,830	21,890	135,720	47.0	288,784	8,997.51	1,073.16
258	6,381	434	12,608	19,681	103	69	172	1,117,964	284,141	1,402,103	43.1	3,251,068	11,234.29	1,960.01
61	4,259	316	9,911	14,547	10	1	11	780,191	185,877	966,068	44.1	2,188,367	8,459.68	1,761.82
2,619	99,280	7,994	203,607	313,500	4,004	957	5,002	19,972,545	4,754,020	24,726,559	46.4	53,271,177	11,231.79	2,241.67
206	6,707	2,416	20,127	29,456	0	3	3	1,419,442	357,487	1,776,930	47.9	3,708,333	6,487.06	1,594.90
2,413	92,573	5,578	183,480	284,044	4,004	954	4,999	18,553,100	4,396,534	22,949,629	46.3	49,562,845	11,882.04	2,311.81
2	837	184	1,774	2,797	0	26	26	145,649	31,100	176,749	44.5	397,271	9,088.38	1,772.48
45	1,530	111	2,704	4,390	0	0	0	212,102	45,278	257,381	42.6	604,184	9,137.69	1,791.31
119	6,149	184	9,884	16,336	308	9	317	1,050,853	228,304	1,279,159	44.0	2,906,809	11,721.52	2,425.15
3	1,436	136	2,326	3,901	0	0	0	251,443	56,922	308,364	43.2	714,084	7,924.93	1,709.94
30	928	104	1,669	2,731	27	8	35	242,468	34,508	276,976	57.6	480,496	8,463.75	1,699.40
39	719	72	1,482	2,312	0	0	0	150,130	36,863	186,992	46.6	401,046	8,887.64	2,110.47
2	1,940	119	4,219	6,280	162	5	167	364,469	92,814	457,283	44.3	1,031,929	10,912.96	1,960.39
244	17,259	497	32,480	50,480	1,225	0	1,225	3,561,866	794,482	4,356,349	48.2	9,046,284	13,046.12	2,537.64
27	2,444	87	4,734	7,292	0	0	0	419,026	91,335	510,360	38.1	1,340,122	10,472.08	2,231.58
13	8,799	548	16,136	25,496	266	0	266	1,636,625	410,477	2,047,102	46.8	4,371,536	11,915.31	2,393.47
957	27,070	1,123	57,364	86,514	974	890	1,864	6,257,468	1,570,007	7,827,474	47.5	16,487,069	14,783.77	2,709.93
601	1,800	377	5,383	8,161	469	0	469	399,943	90,063	490,006	48.5	1,009,592	9,217.07	1,930.51
0	616	44	1,259	1,919	0	0	0	90,677	21,245	111,921	32.2	347,971	8,645.45	1,786.00
0	954	31	1,494	2,479	0	0	0	159,690	33,126	192,815	43.5	442,841	8,004.93	1,751.94
0	2,197	157	3,945	6,299	0	0	0	346,487	94,118	440,605	42.3	1,041,428	10,951.45	2,375.91
21	2,664	152	4,804	7,641	0	4	4	419,393	91,009	510,403	54.8	930,961	6,273.83	1,349.72
0	491	30	1,217	1,738	0	0	0	99,152	24,266	123,417	52.3	235,954	9,590.46	1,905.31
0	882	71	1,602	2,555	0	1	1	125,112	35,531	160,643	47.6	337,482	10,255.63	2,007.36
0	596	103	1,291	1,990	0	0	0	105,603	53,427	159,029	50.6	314,502	8,686.23	1,896.00
181	7,957	643	14,572	23,353	508	10	559	1,484,265	313,240	1,797,505	43.3	4,155,794	10,657.17	2,087.65
0	595	38	1,209	1,842	0	0	0	94,033	22,903	116,936	33.2	352,238	11,203.50	2,191.80
0	787	142	1,735	2,664	0	0	0	124,937	30,339	155,276	44.5	348,773	8,197.55	1,582.89
61	1,816	272	4,778	6,927	64	0	64	380,784	100,829	481,612	42.4	1,135,136	12,157.13	2,393.03
23	701	117	1,366	2,207	0	0	0	112,985	24,711	137,697	48.4	284,573	8,034.92	1,611.21
45	776	148	2,424	3,393	1	1	2	181,469	40,166	221,635	42.8	517,994	8,952.54	1,107.71
0	630	88	1,629	2,347	0	0	0	136,470	29,471	165,940	50.8	326,775	10,718.14	2,340.34

MSAs

CLASSIFICATION	Hospitals	Beds	Admissions	Inpatient Days	Adjusted Inpatient Days	Average Daily Census	Adjusted Average Daily Census	Average Stay (days)	Surgical Operations	NEWBORNS Bassinets	NEWBORNS Births	OUTPATIENT VISITS Emergency	OUTPATIENT VISITS Total
UNITED STATES	4,974	795,603	33,609,083	182,370,189	362,566,276	500,222	962,267	5.4	26,566,037	56,342	3,699,411	133,611,670	677,951,120
Nonmetropolitan	1,971	130,332	3,839,423	24,309,871	69,408,427	66,633	181,025	6.3	3,948,240	10,447	436,830	23,881,030	127,477,109
Metropolitan	3,003	665,271	29,769,660	158,060,318	293,157,849	433,589	781,242	5.3	22,617,797	45,895	3,262,581	109,730,640	550,474,011
CENSUS DIVISION 8, MOUNTAIN . . .	390	47,322	1,962,391	9,977,101	20,449,262	27,333	53,306	5.1	1,584,361	4,056	266,237	7,787,157	40,616,281
Nonmetropolitan	197	9,233	224,737	1,598,155	5,063,685	4,377	13,199	7.1	268,110	891	42,240	1,574,830	8,794,595
Metropolitan	193	38,089	1,737,654	8,378,946	15,385,577	22,956	40,107	4.8	1,316,251	3,165	223,997	6,212,327	31,821,686
Arizona	72	13,347	639,279	2,890,733	5,200,284	7,921	13,523	4.5	467,300	992	75,166	2,066,382	8,739,592
Nonmetropolitan	14	503	21,059	73,949	258,536	201	595	3.5	20,750	66	3,415	130,843	594,758
Metropolitan	58	12,844	618,220	2,816,784	4,941,748	7,720	12,928	4.6	446,550	926	71,751	1,935,539	8,144,834
Flagstaff	3	365	16,694	73,128	154,282	201	422	4.4	12,838	43	1,939	80,304	879,272
Lake Havasu City-Kingman	4	523	25,994	112,539	223,274	308	611	4.3	18,226	33	2,281	131,367	600,724
Phoenix-Mesa-Scottsdale	36	8,609	427,839	1,948,856	3,344,878	5,340	8,700	4.6	309,937	658	49,726	1,133,685	4,764,441
Prescott	3	316	15,670	55,076	115,740	151	318	3.5	8,818	27	1,636	89,727	217,882
Tucson	10	2,584	114,633	551,714	953,066	1,513	2,465	4.8	86,438	146	12,820	430,834	1,506,159
Yuma	2	447	17,390	75,471	150,508	207	412	4.3	10,293	19	3,349	69,622	176,356
Colorado	82	10,301	407,432	2,147,937	4,414,509	5,884	11,110	5.3	360,236	926	56,439	1,875,842	8,780,394
Nonmetropolitan	38	1,569	35,246	253,776	885,978	696	2,172	7.2	46,490	154	6,506	275,612	1,580,380
Metropolitan	44	8,732	372,186	1,894,161	3,528,531	5,188	8,938	5.1	313,746	772	49,933	1,600,230	7,200,014
Boulder	4	630	32,899	133,978	262,396	367	719	4.1	24,758	94	6,643	118,442	701,742
Colorado Springs	5	920	38,562	169,174	344,562	464	912	4.4	32,822	86	5,960	199,357	574,907
Denver-Aurora	24	5,292	225,584	1,205,302	2,130,065	3,300	5,268	5.3	192,387	435	27,055	842,750	3,814,342
Fort Collins-Loveland	4	565	27,208	112,801	236,866	309	558	4.1	21,245	53	4,179	122,094	842,052
Grand Junction	3	524	14,523	105,396	228,663	289	588	7.3	10,119	32	2,191	96,069	470,054
Greeley	2	278	13,559	58,689	99,733	161	273	4.3	10,618	38	1,902	102,113	504,797
Pueblo	2	523	19,851	108,821	226,246	298	620	5.5	21,797	34	2,003	119,405	292,120
Idaho	40	3,355	126,164	609,999	1,479,949	1,673	3,874	4.8	113,077	280	19,285	590,382	4,778,157
Nonmetropolitan	26	1,065	30,856	175,803	558,471	482	1,455	5.7	37,300	113	6,669	175,383	1,476,589
Metropolitan	14	2,290	95,308	434,196	921,478	1,191	2,419	4.6	75,777	167	12,616	414,999	3,301,568
Boise City-Nampa	8	1,358	56,147	237,308	520,027	651	1,426	4.2	48,669	107	7,861	215,242	2,386,762
Coeur d'Alene	1	254	12,899	58,226	123,290	160	338	4.5	6,519	18	1,615	47,254	363,718
Idaho Falls	1	309	12,029	67,146	106,041	184	184	5.6	6,760	10	626	82,774	199,405
Lewiston	1	119	5,040	21,223	44,997	58	123	4.2	4,131	12	793	31,796	117,421
Logan	1	65	476	12,771	40,567	35	111	26.8	982	5	259	1,138	6,026
Pocatello	2	185	8,717	37,522	86,556	103	237	4.3	8,716	15	1,462	36,795	228,236
Montana	50	3,722	95,321	820,251	2,115,221	2,246	5,765	8.6	80,903	206	10,245	376,845	3,763,541
Nonmetropolitan	44	2,316	41,113	484,008	1,323,443	1,326	3,596	11.8	35,515	127	4,501	221,641	1,531,838
Metropolitan	6	1,406	54,208	336,243	791,778	920	2,169	6.2	45,388	79	5,744	155,204	2,231,703
Billings	3	646	27,015	161,636	416,703	443	1,142	6.0	20,741	30	2,704	73,755	1,512,871
Great Falls	1	434	13,139	107,844	240,318	295	658	8.2	7,727	24	1,540	35,234	355,950
Missoula	2	326	14,054	66,763	134,757	182	369	4.8	16,920	25	1,500	46,215	362,882
Nevada	38	5,655	253,822	1,384,938	2,304,550	3,795	6,113	5.5	150,416	286	28,592	928,562	2,626,034
Nonmetropolitan	11	393	9,865	60,682	182,661	168	461	6.2	15,034	32	1,363	107,735	486,084
Metropolitan	27	5,262	243,957	1,324,256	2,121,889	3,627	5,652	5.4	135,382	254	27,229	820,827	2,139,950
Carson City	1	190	10,362	45,578	80,735	125	221	4.4	5,808	12	900	32,646	211,746
Las Vegas-Paradise	19	3,837	182,501	1,021,189	1,607,754	2,797	4,244	5.6	92,125	171	20,384	613,423	1,339,469
Reno-Sparks	7	1,235	51,094	257,489	433,400	705	1,187	5.0	37,449	71	5,945	174,758	588,735
New Mexico	37	3,806	166,307	771,150	1,751,973	2,112	4,524	4.6	132,538	517	22,252	826,885	4,483,912
Nonmetropolitan	23	1,264	46,866	166,622	495,562	456	1,288	3.6	50,698	171	8,997	397,496	1,511,067
Metropolitan	14	2,542	119,441	604,528	1,256,411	1,656	3,236	5.1	81,840	346	13,255	429,389	2,972,845
Albuquerque	9	1,668	78,708	431,927	920,253	1,183	2,435	5.5	53,777	254	8,609	275,832	2,378,061
Farmington	1	200	10,788	45,076	88,531	123	243	4.2	5,814	22	1,337	49,351	157,366
Las Cruces	3	406	18,199	78,295	154,580	215	423	4.3	14,257	46	2,220	69,005	265,544
Santa Fe	1	268	11,746	49,230	93,047	135	135	4.2	7,992	24	1,089	35,201	171,874

TABLE 8

U.S. CENSUS DIVISION 8, MOUNTAIN

U.S. Community Hospitals
(Nonfederal, short-term general and other special hospitals)

2013 Utilization, Personnel and Finances

FULL-TIME EQUIVALENT PERSONNEL					FULL-TIME EQUIV. TRAINEES			EXPENSES						
								LABOR				TOTAL		
Physicians and Dentists	Registered Nurses	Licensed Practical Nurses	Other Salaried Personnel	Total Personnel	Medical and Dental Residents	Other Trainees	Total Trainees	Payroll (in thousands)	Employee Benefits (in thousands)	Total (in thousands)	Percent of Total	Amount (in thousands)	Adjusted per Admission	Adjusted per Inpatient Day
122,119	1,366,402	78,164	3,219,402	4,786,087	107,029	9,592	120,142	$303,635,275	$83,520,086	$387,155,349	49.5	$782,035,350	$11,650.90	$2,156.94
16,394	163,074	23,407	470,243	673,118	1,951	433	2,686	36,502,464	9,848,281	46,350,747	52.0	89,112,057	8,086.11	1,283.88
105,725	1,203,328	54,757	2,749,159	4,112,969	105,078	9,159	117,456	267,132,811	73,671,804	340,804,602	49.2	692,923,293	12,351.15	2,363.65
6,486	83,195	3,595	190,082	283,358	2,722	332	3,204	17,382,162	4,354,579	21,736,744	48.2	45,094,874	11,526.90	2,205.21
1,517	11,344	1,295	35,589	49,745	34	22	61	2,763,898	673,996	3,437,893	51.9	6,627,540	9,415.88	1,308.84
4,969	71,851	2,300	154,493	233,613	2,688	310	3,143	14,618,264	3,680,583	18,298,851	47.6	38,467,335	11,990.04	2,500.22
1,617	24,943	634	46,967	74,161	1,311	78	1,475	4,772,302	1,175,380	5,947,683	48.1	12,377,785	10,652.72	2,380.21
82	862	78	2,756	3,778	7	6	13	220,199	54,480	274,679	51.2	536,210	7,545.03	2,074.03
1,535	24,081	556	44,211	70,383	1,304	72	1,462	4,552,103	1,120,900	5,673,004	47.9	11,841,574	10,855.18	2,396.23
116	820	5	1,764	2,705	3	2	5	196,836	48,906	245,741	51.8	474,379	12,835.96	3,074.75
74	954	56	2,376	3,460	16	2	18	195,446	49,110	244,557	50.3	486,144	9,460.82	2,177.34
1,218	16,490	350	29,151	47,209	1,195	45	1,326	3,126,425	796,830	3,923,255	48.1	8,156,171	11,053.31	2,438.41
58	655	0	1,328	2,041	0	4	4	137,460	41,538	178,998	51.4	347,918	10,529.26	3,006.03
59	4,592	133	8,392	13,176	84	2	86	768,557	152,180	920,737	45.1	2,039,867	10,340.17	2,140.32
10	570	12	1,200	1,792	6	17	23	127,378	32,337	159,716	47.4	337,095	9,823.85	2,239.72
1,449	18,819	570	46,766	67,604	337	150	524	4,316,992	1,035,989	5,352,979	46.7	11,468,752	14,116.48	2,597.97
313	2,175	193	7,362	10,043	6	1	12	588,101	152,665	740,763	51.5	1,437,057	12,757.85	1,622.00
1,136	16,644	377	39,404	57,561	331	149	512	3,728,892	883,324	4,612,216	46.0	10,031,695	14,335.17	2,843.02
90	1,249	31	3,122	4,492	4	0	4	307,640	71,947	379,587	47.5	799,108	12,403.31	3,045.43
130	1,590	38	3,884	5,642	31	4	58	317,626	80,036	397,663	45.7	869,740	10,902.82	2,524.19
741	10,958	230	24,532	36,461	220	142	371	2,397,719	554,204	2,951,924	46.4	6,363,196	15,660.25	2,987.33
14	751	30	2,644	3,439	21	1	22	279,304	80,404	359,708	43.3	830,706	15,320.18	3,507.07
115	687	25	1,915	2,742	1	2	3	162,183	36,384	198,567	46.7	425,500	14,939.25	1,860.82
12	588	10	1,259	1,869	33	0	33	103,389	24,686	128,074	37.4	342,360	13,865.79	3,432.77
34	821	13	2,048	2,916	21	0	21	161,030	35,663	196,693	49.0	401,085	9,578.61	1,772.78
900	6,221	546	19,153	26,820	34	21	64	1,435,034	324,821	1,759,852	49.6	3,549,203	11,987.63	2,398.19
194	1,667	287	5,696	7,844	3	3	6	358,850	89,271	448,120	50.9	880,504	9,281.75	1,576.63
706	4,554	259	13,457	18,976	31	18	58	1,076,184	235,549	1,311,732	49.2	2,668,699	13,263.38	2,896.11
540	3,001	151	9,881	13,573	13	4	17	726,236	157,250	883,485	49.0	1,801,228	14,494.82	3,463.72
76	428	12	1,394	1,910	0	13	13	140,965	33,972	174,936	55.8	313,781	11,488.34	2,545.06
10	465	23	744	1,242	18	1	28	71,913	16,267	88,180	45.5	193,922	10,208.03	1,828.74
30	256	8	488	782	0	0	0	52,762	11,788	64,550	48.9	132,066	12,358.79	2,935.00
5	59	10	184	258	0	0	0	7,125	2,025	9,150	54.2	16,893	11,172.77	416.43
45	345	55	766	1,211	0	0	0	77,184	14,247	91,431	43.4	210,809	11,436.52	2,435.53
930	4,334	611	14,101	19,976	2	3	5	1,226,585	282,054	1,508,641	52.5	2,874,247	11,762.59	1,358.84
392	2,128	267	7,285	10,072	1	1	2	570,790	132,232	703,024	54.9	1,281,197	10,721.22	968.08
538	2,206	344	6,816	9,904	1	2	3	655,795	149,821	805,617	50.6	1,593,050	12,759.30	2,011.99
353	1,067	183	3,620	5,223	1	2	3	387,056	83,737	470,793	53.8	875,305	13,041.08	2,100.55
67	534	72	1,539	2,212	0	0	0	139,657	30,349	170,006	49.9	340,741	11,637.72	1,417.87
118	605	89	1,657	2,469	0	0	0	129,082	35,736	164,818	43.7	377,004	13,248.68	2,797.66
175	8,744	346	16,362	25,627	67	5	72	1,722,129	458,935	2,181,069	49.5	4,407,998	10,264.05	1,912.74
46	463	60	1,341	1,910	2	0	2	109,588	26,521	136,111	51.1	266,555	8,905.34	1,459.29
129	8,281	286	15,021	23,717	65	5	70	1,612,541	432,414	2,044,958	49.4	4,141,444	10,365.84	1,951.77
0	336	6	646	988	0	0	0	67,420	16,322	83,742	42.8	195,786	10,666.61	2,425.04
125	5,923	252	10,641	16,941	62	5	67	1,223,405	355,044	1,578,452	51.8	3,046,070	10,444.66	1,894.61
4	2,022	28	3,734	5,788	3	0	3	321,716	61,048	382,764	42.5	899,588	10,047.44	2,075.65
897	7,442	386	16,427	25,152	72	37	118	1,558,608	338,102	1,896,710	49.7	3,818,357	9,982.50	2,179.46
244	1,870	170	4,846	7,130	13	5	18	406,576	87,644	494,220	48.0	1,030,309	7,377.32	2,079.07
653	5,572	216	11,581	18,022	59	32	100	1,152,032	250,458	1,402,490	50.3	2,788,047	11,480.72	2,219.06
535	4,079	167	8,116	12,897	16	29	45	840,965	167,264	1,008,230	49.9	2,022,327	12,353.78	2,197.58
64	459	2	1,104	1,629	0	0	0	115,987	36,688	152,674	61.5	248,130	11,710.86	2,802.74
15	550	24	1,219	1,808	25	1	26	99,910	20,314	120,224	44.0	273,365	7,645.09	1,768.44
39	484	23	1,142	1,688	18	2	29	95,171	26,192	121,362	49.7	244,225	11,001.14	2,624.75

Table continues

TABLE 8

U.S. CENSUS DIVISION 8, MOUNTAIN CONTINUED

U.S. Community Hospitals
(Nonfederal, short-term general and other special hospitals)

2013 Utilization, Personnel and Finances

CLASSIFICATION	Hospitals	Beds	Admissions	Inpatient Days	Adjusted Inpatient Days	Average Daily Census	Adjusted Average Daily Census	Average Stay (days)	Surgical Operations	NEWBORNS Bassinets	NEWBORNS Births	OUTPATIENT VISITS Emergency	OUTPATIENT VISITS Total
Utah	47	5,216	229,492	979,856	2,128,670	2,684	5,528	4.3	242,240	688	47,854	888,611	6,181,131
Nonmetropolitan	19	632	14,921	94,227	450,294	257	1,161	6.3	34,946	107	6,719	110,047	644,631
Metropolitan	28	4,584	214,571	885,629	1,678,376	2,427	4,367	4.1	207,294	581	41,135	778,564	5,536,500
Logan	2	157	7,424	20,845	53,240	57	137	2.8	9,514	34	2,554	34,764	361,322
Ogden-Clearfield	4	780	36,068	135,886	245,704	373	600	3.8	29,193	103	7,065	135,656	511,992
Provo-Orem	6	727	36,094	138,305	256,326	379	704	3.8	29,749	133	10,215	143,505	655,255
Salt Lake City	15	2,659	120,654	540,806	1,025,402	1,482	2,658	4.5	126,670	295	19,060	421,317	3,534,834
St. George	1	261	14,331	49,787	97,704	136	268	3.5	12,168	16	2,241	43,322	473,097
Wyoming	24	1,920	44,574	372,237	1,054,106	1,018	2,869	8.4	37,651	161	6,404	233,648	1,263,520
Nonmetropolitan	22	1,491	24,811	289,088	908,740	791	2,471	11.7	27,377	121	4,070	156,073	969,248
Metropolitan	2	429	19,763	83,149	145,366	227	398	4.2	10,274	40	2,334	77,575	294,272
Casper	1	191	9,080	34,460	52,965	94	145	3.8	5,083	24	1,138	38,185	80,027
Cheyenne	1	238	10,683	48,689	92,401	133	253	4.6	5,191	16	1,196	39,390	214,245

TABLE 8

U.S. CENSUS DIVISION 8, MOUNTAIN
CONTINUED

U.S. Community Hospitals
(Nonfederal, short-term general and other special hospitals)

2013 Utilization, Personnel and Finances

FULL-TIME EQUIVALENT PERSONNEL					FULL-TIME EQUIV. TRAINEES			EXPENSES						
								LABOR				TOTAL		
Physicians and Dentists	Registered Nurses	Licensed Practical Nurses	Other Salaried Personnel	Total Personnel	Medical and Dental Residents	Other Trainees	Total Trainees	Payroll (in thousands)	Employee Benefits (in thousands)	Total (in thousands)	Percent of Total	Amount (in thousands)	Adjusted per Admission	Adjusted per Inpatient Day
243	10,524	380	23,965	35,112	898	35	942	1,822,425	599,513	2,421,939	45.1	5,364,835	11,255.79	2,520.28
59	719	134	2,203	3,115	1	4	5	149,188	40,749	189,937	49.0	387,703	6,285.01	861.00
184	9,805	246	21,762	31,997	897	31	937	1,673,237	558,765	2,232,002	44.8	4,977,132	11,994.76	2,965.44
3	320	16	813	1,152	0	0	0	53,190	18,811	72,002	46.2	155,876	8,212.66	2,927.81
16	1,308	58	2,531	3,913	25	1	26	225,023	66,160	291,183	44.6	653,158	10,027.14	2,658.31
19	1,438	45	3,189	4,691	50	9	59	226,361	77,361	303,723	45.5	668,220	9,609.84	2,606.92
143	6,276	127	13,887	20,433	822	21	852	1,075,388	361,628	1,437,015	45.6	3,153,953	13,526.76	3,075.82
3	463	0	1,342	1,808	0	0	0	93,274	34,805	128,079	37.0	345,924	12,299.96	3,540.53
275	2,168	122	6,341	8,906	1	3	4	528,085	139,785	667,871	54.1	1,233,698	11,344.77	1,170.37
187	1,460	106	4,100	5,853	1	2	3	360,605	90,433	451,039	55.8	808,005	10,843.37	889.15
88	708	16	2,241	3,053	0	1	1	167,480	49,351	216,832	50.9	425,694	12,436.28	2,928.43
15	299	5	732	1,051	0	1	1	63,144	22,604	85,748	47.6	180,164	12,909.45	3,401.57
73	409	11	1,509	2,002	0	0	0	104,336	26,748	131,084	53.4	245,529	12,110.56	2,657.22

MSAs

MSAs

CLASSIFICATION	Hospitals	Beds	Admissions	Inpatient Days	Adjusted Inpatient Days	Average Daily Census	Adjusted Average Daily Census	Average Stay (days)	Surgical Operations	NEWBORNS Bassinets	NEWBORNS Births	OUTPATIENT VISITS Emergency	OUTPATIENT VISITS Total
UNITED STATES	4,974	795,603	33,609,083	182,370,189	362,566,276	500,222	962,267	5.4	26,566,037	56,342	3,699,411	133,611,670	677,951,120
Nonmetropolitan	1,971	130,332	3,839,423	24,309,871	69,408,427	66,633	181,025	6.3	3,948,240	10,447	436,830	23,881,030	127,477,109
Metropolitan	3,003	665,271	29,769,660	158,060,318	293,157,849	433,589	781,242	5.3	22,617,797	45,895	3,262,581	109,730,640	550,474,011
CENSUS DIVISION 9, PACIFIC	543	93,661	4,361,054	21,838,216	38,788,242	59,841	97,878	5.0	3,023,782	7,007	603,650	16,484,071	80,178,491
Nonmetropolitan	123	5,453	185,515	1,062,794	3,197,658	2,915	7,976	5.7	217,765	553	31,274	1,322,187	7,650,433
Metropolitan	420	88,208	4,175,539	20,775,422	35,590,584	56,926	89,902	5.0	2,806,017	6,454	572,376	15,161,884	72,528,058
Alaska	22	1,560	57,621	376,393	867,328	1,033	2,239	6.5	52,217	166	7,372	257,285	1,367,310
Nonmetropolitan	16	583	13,729	126,714	386,086	348	920	9.2	18,512	51	2,843	88,908	466,412
Metropolitan	6	977	43,892	249,679	481,242	685	1,319	5.7	33,705	115	4,529	168,377	900,898
Anchorage	5	760	38,755	203,109	369,396	557	1,013	5.2	28,630	99	3,365	135,251	586,653
Fairbanks	1	217	5,137	46,570	111,846	128	306	9.1	5,075	16	1,164	33,126	314,245
California	347	70,326	3,255,312	16,482,984	27,723,644	45,162	69,680	5.1	2,111,789	5,009	465,752	12,088,159	53,813,141
Nonmetropolitan	31	1,306	50,617	244,438	656,014	671	1,751	4.8	60,565	128	9,078	459,857	2,244,655
Metropolitan	316	69,020	3,204,695	16,238,546	27,067,630	44,491	67,929	5.1	2,051,224	4,881	456,674	11,628,302	51,568,486
Bakersfield	10	1,289	68,566	323,779	589,866	888	1,563	4.7	37,176	95	10,291	216,401	857,492
Chico	4	495	29,882	135,700	266,108	371	729	4.5	16,217	43	3,129	122,193	736,564
El Centro	2	268	11,809	40,780	98,251	112	269	3.5	9,822	32	2,880	94,484	285,962
Fresno	8	1,772	84,304	438,849	708,597	1,202	1,940	5.2	42,369	101	13,556	314,243	1,390,342
Hanford-Corcoran	2	248	12,003	45,710	121,886	125	334	3.8	8,710	30	2,746	108,026	624,864
Los Angeles-Long Beach-Glendale	89	20,882	964,810	4,884,848	7,733,309	13,381	19,563	5.1	546,762	1,387	125,844	2,741,127	12,530,883
Madera	2	446	17,420	96,702	148,886	265	408	5.6	16,194	10	1,568	132,561	384,510
Merced	2	232	11,529	45,022	87,043	124	238	3.9	7,214	28	1,526	91,441	264,926
Modesto	4	1,382	52,539	328,299	515,804	900	1,413	6.2	33,820	73	8,202	234,311	392,191
Napa	2	290	12,540	55,287	103,478	151	186	4.4	11,972	12	1,021	37,511	276,193
Oakland-Fremont-Hayward	19	4,158	200,318	956,689	1,581,999	2,622	3,878	4.8	110,171	334	29,032	969,419	4,306,123
Oxnard-Thousand Oaks-Ventura. .	6	1,200	61,917	272,774	516,329	747	1,013	4.4	34,623	108	10,168	230,113	1,153,613
Redding	3	491	20,549	114,456	192,708	314	528	5.6	12,728	14	2,059	75,243	211,154
Riverside-San Bernardino-Ontario .	34	6,902	335,574	1,622,505	2,621,438	4,444	6,783	4.8	198,925	501	47,213	1,346,041	4,045,512
Sacramento--Arden-Arcade--Roseville	17	3,967	198,520	974,201	1,578,930	2,669	3,884	4.9	149,897	259	22,784	732,769	3,186,067
Salinas	4	693	32,153	147,551	219,489	404	602	4.6	17,906	79	6,416	147,759	580,940
San Diego-Carlsbad-San Marcos .	21	5,436	288,454	1,468,231	2,552,817	4,025	6,765	5.1	204,112	314	41,394	945,263	3,019,991
San Francisco-San Mateo-Redwood City	19	5,103	161,141	1,220,816	2,150,848	3,345	4,617	7.6	131,652	212	18,827	624,624	5,308,918
San Jose-Sunnyvale-Santa Clara .	11	3,059	157,747	799,889	1,382,560	2,190	3,443	5.1	121,570	315	29,121	476,315	4,662,748
San Luis Obispo-Paso Robles . . .	4	465	17,056	67,246	105,175	185	289	3.9	11,714	38	2,571	88,690	223,207
Santa Ana-Anaheim-Irvine	24	5,550	253,606	1,189,289	1,990,011	3,258	5,027	4.7	178,705	410	38,577	778,059	3,196,679
Santa Barbara-Santa Maria	5	898	33,021	213,645	353,086	585	968	6.5	25,238	52	5,652	159,338	451,037
Santa Cruz-Watsonville	3	411	18,332	81,847	127,523	224	309	4.5	17,360	50	3,087	70,627	274,221
Santa Rosa-Petaluma	6	626	31,997	137,043	266,284	376	645	4.3	25,919	44	5,429	142,364	454,282
Stockton	7	1,184	55,565	231,819	430,077	636	1,025	4.2	36,858	213	10,069	344,315	1,286,993
Vallejo-Fairfield	4	660	26,974	109,516	205,466	301	421	4.1	18,928	65	4,374	144,886	415,504
Visalia-Porterville	3	680	33,913	184,950	338,349	507	866	5.5	15,835	48	7,097	225,646	891,983
Yuba City	1	233	12,456	51,103	81,313	140	223	4.1	8,827	14	2,041	34,533	155,587
Hawaii	25	2,817	110,374	760,960	1,520,126	2,086	3,890	6.9	73,553	201	10,229	401,191	2,153,887
Nonmetropolitan	13	952	29,818	233,722	590,663	641	1,491	7.8	19,645	71	4,041	107,243	391,886
Metropolitan	12	1,865	80,556	527,238	929,463	1,445	2,399	6.5	53,908	130	6,188	293,948	1,762,001
Honolulu	12	1,865	80,556	527,238	929,463	1,445	2,399	6.5	53,908	130	6,188	293,948	1,762,001
Oregon.	59	6,778	337,228	1,454,053	3,012,838	3,983	8,087	4.3	316,429	643	42,393	1,399,434	10,385,755
Nonmetropolitan	29	1,323	52,981	223,180	727,947	610	1,994	4.2	54,857	169	7,986	368,258	2,886,798
Metropolitan	30	5,455	284,247	1,230,873	2,284,891	3,373	6,093	4.3	261,572	474	34,407	1,031,176	7,498,957
Bend.	2	308	17,310	67,625	112,120	185	307	3.9	18,653	33	2,021	53,127	233,572
Corvallis.	1	165	9,257	40,594	72,378	111	198	4.4	9,640	20	974	22,679	366,420
Eugene-Springfield	5	631	33,416	142,387	241,201	390	662	4.3	20,657	52	3,623	133,709	393,955
Medford	3	470	22,839	100,256	172,146	275	471	4.4	20,846	40	2,349	78,763	729,703
Portland-Vancouver-Beaverton . . .	15	3,370	175,476	771,319	1,456,555	2,114	3,824	4.4	173,836	297	20,683	603,137	5,154,167
Salem	4	511	25,949	108,692	230,491	298	631	4.2	17,940	32	4,757	139,761	621,140

TABLE 8

U.S. CENSUS DIVISION 9, PACIFIC

U.S. Community Hospitals
(Nonfederal, short-term general and other special hospitals)

2013 Utilization, Personnel and Finances

FULL-TIME EQUIVALENT PERSONNEL					FULL-TIME EQUIV. TRAINEES			EXPENSES						
								LABOR				TOTAL		
Physicians and Dentists	Registered Nurses	Licensed Practical Nurses	Other Salaried Personnel	Total Personnel	Medical and Dental Residents	Other Trainees	Total Trainees	Payroll (in thousands)	Employee Benefits (in thousands)	Total (in thousands)	Percent of Total	Amount (in thousands)	Adjusted per Admission	Adjusted per Inpatient Day
122,119	1,366,402	78,164	3,219,402	4,786,087	107,029	9,592	120,142	$303,635,275	$83,520,086	$387,155,349	49.5	$782,035,350	$11,650.90	$2,156.94
16,394	163,074	23,407	470,243	673,118	1,951	433	2,686	36,502,464	9,848,281	46,350,747	52.0	89,112,057	8,086.11	1,283.88
105,725	1,203,328	54,757	2,749,159	4,112,969	105,078	9,159	117,456	267,132,811	73,671,804	340,804,602	49.2	692,923,293	12,351.15	2,363.65
10,770	177,779	8,707	395,875	593,131	12,149	917	14,159	45,141,437	14,866,399	60,007,830	50.6	118,675,376	15,266.86	3,059.57
951	8,984	820	26,451	37,206	31	17	58	2,536,033	803,148	3,339,176	54.4	6,137,011	11,576.97	1,919.22
9,819	168,795	7,887	369,424	555,925	12,118	900	14,101	42,605,404	14,063,252	56,668,654	50.4	112,538,365	15,536.90	3,162.03
221	2,507	173	7,082	9,983	53	10	81	727,937	223,978	951,914	52.2	1,824,097	14,270.93	2,103.12
118	817	85	2,729	3,749	2	4	6	273,639	93,579	367,218	57.0	643,858	15,038.84	1,667.65
103	1,690	88	4,353	6,234	51	6	75	454,298	130,398	584,696	49.5	1,180,239	13,884.18	2,452.49
97	1,473	86	3,581	5,237	51	6	75	372,988	105,510	478,498	49.3	970,889	13,360.42	2,628.31
6	217	2	772	997	0	0	0	81,309	24,888	106,198	50.7	209,350	16,969.30	1,871.77
5,832	130,864	7,011	282,602	426,309	9,176	790	10,801	32,480,489	11,166,348	43,646,834	50.3	86,710,653	15,690.39	3,127.68
75	2,405	239	6,171	8,890	5	3	13	629,388	226,081	855,470	51.0	1,678,879	12,565.14	2,559.21
5,757	128,459	6,772	276,431	417,419	9,171	787	10,788	31,851,101	10,940,267	42,791,364	50.3	85,031,774	15,767.83	3,141.46
146	2,382	169	6,024	8,721	45	4	63	554,127	162,644	716,771	50.1	1,429,828	11,690.67	2,423.99
61	972	85	2,581	3,699	21	4	38	303,401	88,193	391,595	51.5	759,935	13,293.25	2,855.74
0	380	22	1,122	1,524	0	0	0	85,784	20,486	106,270	48.1	221,082	7,737.18	2,250.18
63	3,063	117	6,007	9,250	16	2	32	582,931	151,791	734,723	44.8	1,641,054	11,600.92	2,315.92
0	468	14.	1,884	2,366	12	0	12	112,919	37,505	150,423	49.8	302,011	9,149.64	2,477.82
2,476	39,011	2,359	83,546	127,392	3,908	297	4,457	8,971,136	2,922,037	11,893,171	48.7	24,409,997	15,767.65	3,156.48
1	739	50	1,965	2,755	0	11	11	204,794	85,560	290,354	55.9	519,059	18,990.90	3,486.29
1	379	26	914	1,320	24	0	24	105,054	37,296	142,351	49.3	288,858	12,425.62	3,318.57
17	2,344	53	3,116	5,530	4	1	14	442,288	159,685	601,972	51.9	1,159,570	14,672.16	2,248.08
21	502	25	1,356	1,904	6	1	11	144,552	65,873	210,425	48.7	432,473	18,528.46	4,179.37
392	7,797	482	17,484	26,155	328	22	413	2,289,871	965,212	3,255,084	52.7	6,182,237	18,516.34	3,907.86
123	1,972	121	4,298	6,514	57	4	92	588,743	164,241	752,985	51.1	1,472,216	12,445.08	2,851.31
14	834	43	1,381	2,272	31	1	32	190,275	72,122	262,397	51.5	509,371	15,998.34	2,643.23
824	12,749	897	24,155	38,625	929	56	1,011	2,503,648	737,873	3,241,523	49.5	6,543,192	12,043.98	2,496.03
342	8,655	291	17,691	26,979	904	11	960	2,378,064	836,069	3,214,134	52.1	6,163,613	18,840.61	3,903.66
47	1,239	37	2,755	4,078	29	0	29	369,692	204,899	574,591	59.2	971,284	20,324.42	4,425.20
541	12,050	367	23,148	36,106	743	293	1,045	2,566,477	698,461	3,264,938	49.1	6,649,183	12,946.56	2,604.65
179	7,509	330	18,447	26,465	283	30	385	2,733,913	1,016,001	3,749,913	53.0	7,075,042	24,950.07	3,289.42
80	6,599	268	16,313	23,260	1,401	9	1,540	2,473,814	1,109,252	3,583,066	53.3	6,724,484	24,770.54	4,863.79
0	797	2	917	1,716	0	0	0	139,554	40,823	180,377	51.2	352,314	13,168.63	3,349.78
269	10,008	339	21,507	32,123	262	25	395	2,094,857	711,504	2,806,360	47.3	5,936,587	13,673.70	2,983.19
8	1,380	61	2,640	4,089	55	0	55	334,365	110,380	444,744	47.0	946,376	18,419.88	2,680.30
8	673	20	1,317	2,018	6	1	7	237,464	81,032	318,496	60.5	526,137	17,539.06	4,125.82
13	1,099	72	2,932	4,116	34	0	34	286,890	128,276	415,166	48.1	862,717	14,553.26	3,239.84
131	2,115	364	5,618	8,228	52	6	98	488,195	139,772	627,966	51.1	1,228,740	11,849.33	2,857.02
0	1,205	58	3,239	4,502	9	6	15	313,159	88,249	401,409	51.3	782,719	15,458.68	3,809.48
0	1,137	99	3,279	4,515	12	3	15	270,800	73,375	344,175	52.7	653,658	10,442.49	1,931.91
0	401	1	795	1,197	0	0	0	84,332	31,653	115,985	40.3	288,036	14,532.57	3,542.31
401	4,526	237	10,667	15,831	37	22	59	1,219,079	333,479	1,552,558	53.2	2,917,345	13,881.74	1,919.15
95	1,036	110	3,022	4,263	18	1	19	298,833	94,771	393,603	55.4	710,571	10,498.99	1,203.01
306	3,490	127	7,645	11,568	19	21	40	920,247	238,708	1,158,955	52.5	2,206,774	15,488.63	2,374.25
306	3,490	127	7,645	11,568	19	21	40	920,247	238,708	1,158,955	52.5	2,206,774	15,488.63	2,374.25
1,628	14,577	184	31,577	47,966	1,166	22	1,188	3,596,150	1,170,725	4,766,875	50.9	9,358,602	13,403.42	3,106.24
433	2,499	72	7,528	10,532	0	6	6	732,120	221,777	953,895	56.1	1,701,126	10,610.16	2,336.88
1,195	12,078	112	24,049	37,434	1,166	16	1,182	2,864,030	948,949	3,812,980	49.8	7,657,476	14,236.00	3,351.35
71	695	0	1,828	2,594	0	0	0	208,908	67,667	276,574	55.4	499,356	17,067.34	4,453.77
94	327	12	991	1,424	81	3	84	132,560	42,042	174,602	53.2	328,151	19,881.91	4,533.85
94	1,116	16	2,242	3,468	0	0	0	270,615	85,904	356,520	44.1	808,841	14,336.32	3,353.39
42	880	14	1,801	2,737	0	3	3	189,683	76,807	266,490	46.5	573,673	14,410.63	3,332.48
793	7,798	62	14,361	23,014	1,085	10	1,095	1,756,417	592,883	2,349,301	49.4	4,759,888	14,070.19	3,267.91
101	1,262	8	2,826	4,197	0	0	0	305,848	83,646	389,493	56.6	687,567	11,935.27	2,983.05

Table continues

MSAs

TABLE 8 — U.S. CENSUS DIVISION 9, PACIFIC CONTINUED

TABLE 8

U.S. CENSUS DIVISION 9, PACIFIC CONTINUED

U.S. Community Hospitals
(Nonfederal, short-term general and other special hospitals)

2013 Utilization, Personnel and Finances

CLASSIFICATION	Hospitals	Beds	Admissions	Inpatient Days	Adjusted Inpatient Days	Average Daily Census	Adjusted Average Daily Census	Average Stay (days)	Surgical Operations	NEWBORNS Bassinets	NEWBORNS Births	OUTPATIENT VISITS Emergency	OUTPATIENT VISITS Total
Washington	90	12,180	600,519	2,763,826	5,664,306	7,577	13,982	4.6	469,794	988	77,904	2,338,002	12,458,398
Nonmetropolitan	34	1,289	38,370	234,740	836,948	645	1,820	6.1	64,186	134	7,326	297,921	1,660,682
Metropolitan	56	10,891	562,149	2,529,086	4,827,358	6,932	12,162	4.5	405,608	854	70,578	2,040,081	10,797,716
Bellingham	1	253	15,138	59,353	112,180	163	163	3.9	7,028	24	1,818	18,272	89,217
Bremerton-Silverdale	1	262	13,466	55,645	105,171	152	152	4.1	9,814	24	1,882	48,758	238,068
Kennewick-Richland-Pasco	4	440	22,675	89,122	202,641	244	528	3.9	17,967	37	4,750	171,292	746,827
Lewiston	1	25	1,294	4,468	17,673	12	12	3.5	2,268	0	0	24,651	128,655
Longview	1	200	8,558	33,982	90,048	93	247	4.0	5,018	14	981	50,076	182,081
Mount Vernon-Anacortes	3	205	11,202	40,620	125,096	111	343	3.6	14,701	27	1,535	54,505	783,401
Olympia	2	481	25,221	109,435	160,910	300	441	4.3	18,266	46	2,573	82,786	337,139
Portland-Vancouver-Beaverton	2	648	35,528	138,171	246,013	379	457	3.9	12,826	60	5,255	76,159	360,204
Seattle-Bellevue-Everett	22	4,899	259,633	1,221,273	2,351,168	3,348	5,957	4.7	196,103	381	32,080	837,401	5,542,732
Spokane	6	1,444	60,158	317,240	519,226	870	1,423	5.3	44,509	70	5,726	206,297	683,703
Tacoma	6	1,274	75,078	324,851	610,849	891	1,674	4.3	49,508	87	8,873	283,529	862,745
Wenatchee	3	232	10,877	44,537	81,358	122	212	4.1	8,651	25	1,424	41,274	220,142
Yakima	4	528	23,321	90,389	205,025	247	553	3.9	18,949	59	3,681	145,081	622,802

MSAs

TABLE 8

U.S. CENSUS DIVISION 9, PACIFIC
CONTINUED

U.S. Community Hospitals
(Nonfederal, short-term general and other special hospitals)

2013 Utilization, Personnel and Finances

FULL-TIME EQUIVALENT PERSONNEL					FULL-TIME EQUIV. TRAINEES			EXPENSES						
								LABOR				TOTAL		
Physicians and Dentists	Registered Nurses	Licensed Practical Nurses	Other Salaried Personnel	Total Personnel	Medical and Dental Residents	Other Trainees	Total Trainees	Payroll (in thousands)	Employee Benefits (in thousands)	Total (in thousands)	Percent of Total	Amount (in thousands)	Adjusted per Admission	Adjusted per Inpatient Day
2,688	25,305	1,102	63,947	93,042	1,717	73	2,030	7,117,782	1,971,869	9,089,649	50.9	17,864,679	14,753.88	3,153.30
230	2,227	314	7,001	9,772	6	3	14	602,053	166,939	768,990	54.8	1,402,577	11,160.97	1,675.82
2,458	23,078	788	56,946	83,270	1,711	70	2,016	6,515,729	1,804,930	8,320,659	50.5	16,462,103	15,169.96	3,410.17
62	740	35	1,762	2,599	30	1	40	159,444	54,847	214,290	50.5	424,082	14,822.34	3,780.37
42	532	25	1,216	1,815	18	2	33	140,582	38,239	178,822	48.1	371,826	14,609.49	3,535.44
48	1,038	51	2,397	3,534	9	1	19	284,704	65,045	349,750	54.9	636,605	12,232.05	3,141.54
13	93	12	282	400	1	2	3	22,746	4,452	27,198	46.4	58,615	11,452.79	3,316.66
62	360	4	944	1,370	0	0	0	99,422	33,105	132,527	54.8	241,666	10,656.39	2,683.74
96	618	22	1,949	2,685	14	1	15	156,954	37,170	194,125	50.0	388,362	11,031.76	3,104.51
8	663	26	1,315	2,012	9	1	10	175,343	49,699	225,042	48.7	461,826	12,292.74	2,870.09
129	1,289	37	2,884	4,339	66	4	88	311,706	96,419	408,125	50.5	808,344	12,791.66	3,285.78
1,508	11,767	321	30,691	44,287	1,439	49	1,642	3,579,969	1,009,418	4,589,386	50.9	9,023,024	18,055.91	3,837.68
80	2,175	45	4,314	6,614	34	4	61	556,776	158,657	715,433	47.7	1,498,291	14,877.73	2,885.62
352	2,252	138	6,013	8,755	77	4	81	733,749	199,298	933,046	52.2	1,786,141	12,584.31	2,924.03
10	475	12	867	1,364	0	0	0	94,560	24,363	118,923	45.7	259,979	13,878.88	3,195.50
48	1,076	60	2,312	3,496	14	1	24	199,775	34,218	233,992	46.5	503,342	9,285.03	2,455.03

MSAs

Statistics for Health Care Systems and their Hospitals

The following tables describing health care systems refers to information in section B of the 2015 *AHA Guide*. Table 1 shows the number of health care systems by type of control. Table 2 provides a breakdown of the number of systems that own, lease, sponsor or contract manage hospitals within each control category. Table 3 gives the number of hospitals and beds in each control category as well as total hospitals and beds. Finally, shows the percentage of hospitals and beds in each control category.

For more information on health care systems, please write to the Section for Health Care Systems, 155 N. Wacker Drive, Chicago, Illinois 60606 or call 312/422–3000.

Table 1. Multihospital Health Care Systems, by Type of Organizaton Control

Type of Control	Code	Number of Systems
Catholic (Roman) church–related	CC	34
Other church–related	CO	7
Subtotal, church–related		41
Other not–for–profit	NP	307
Subtotal, not–for–profit		348
Investor Owned	IO	83
Federal Government	FG	5
Total		436

Table 2. Multihospital Health Care Systems, by Type of Ownership and Control

Type of Ownership	Catholic Church–Related (CC)	Other Church–Related (CO)	Total Church–Related (CC + CO)	Other Not–for–Profit (NP)	Total Not–for–Profit (CC, CO, + NP)	Investor–Owned (IO)	Federal Government (FG)	All Systems
Systems that only own, lease or sponsor	25	5	30	274	304	74	5	383
Systems that only contract–manage	0	0	0	2	2	3	0	5
Systems that manage, own, lease, or sponsor	9	2	11	31	42	6	0	48
Total	34	7	41	307	348	83	5	436

Table 3. Hospitals and Beds in Multihospital Health Care Systems, by Type of Ownership and Control

Type of Ownership	Catholic Church–Related (CC)		Other Church–Related (CO)		Total Church–Related (CC + CO)		Other Not–for–Profit (NP)		Total Not–for–Profit (CC, CO, + NP)		Investor–Owned (IO)		Federal Government (FG)		All Systems	
	H	B	H	B	H	B	H	B	H	B	H	B	H	B	H	B
Owned, leased or sponsored	567	103,514	75	16,260	642	119,774	1,507	326,740	2,149	446,514	1,362	160,389	212	39,658	3,723	646,561
Contract–managed	40	1,918	4	585	44	2,503	94	7,939	138	10,442	111	6,525	0	0	249	16,967
Total	607	105,432	79	16,845	686	122,277	1,601	334,679	2,287	456,956	1,473	166,914	212	39,658	3,972	663,528

H = hospitals; **B** = beds.

Table 4. Hospitals and Beds in Multihospital Health Care Systems, by Type of Ownership and Control as a Percentage of All Systems

Type of Ownership	Catholic Church–Related (CC)		Other Church–Related (CO)		Total Church–Related (CC + CO)		Other Not–for–Profit (NP)		Total Not–for–Profit (CC, CO, + NP)		Investor–Owned (IO)		Federal Government (FG)		All Systems	
	H	B	H	B	H	B	H	B	H	B	H	B	H	B	H	B
Owned, leased or sponsored	15.2	16.0	2.0	2.5	17.2	18.5	40.5	50.5	57.7	69.1	36.6	24.8	5.7	6.1	100.0	100.0
Contract–managed	16.1	11.3	1.6	3.4	17.7	14.8	37.8	46.8	55.4	61.5	44.6	38.5	0.0	0.0	100.0	100.0
Total	15.3	15.9	2.0	2.5	17.3	18.4	40.3	50.4	57.6	68.9	37.1	25.2	5.3	6.0	100.0	100.0

H = hospitals; **B** = beds.
*Please note that figures may not always equal the provided subtotal or total percentages due to rounding.

Glossary

This glossary explains specific terms as they are used in the tables and text of AHA Hospital Statistics

Ablation of Barrett's esophagus: Premalignant condition that can lead to adenocarcinoma of the esophagus. The non surgical ablation of the premalignant tissue in Barrett's esophagus by the application of thermal energy or light through an endoscope passed from the mouth into the esophagus.

Acute long term care: Providers specialized acute hospital care to medically complex patients who are critically ill, have multisystem complications and/or failure, and require hospitalization averaging 25 days, in a facility offering specialized treatment programs and therapeutic intervention on a 24 hour/7day a week basis.

Adjusted admission: An aggregate measure of workload reflecting the sum of admissions and equivalent admissions attributed to outpatient services. The number of equivalent admissions attributed to outpatient services is derived by multiplying admissions by the ratio of outpatient revenue to inpatient revenue.

$$\text{Adjusted admissions} = \text{admissions} + \left[\text{admissions} * \left(\frac{\text{outpatient revenue}}{\text{inpatient revenue}}\right)\right]$$

Adjusted average daily census: An estimate of the average number of patients (both inpatients and outpatients) receiving care each day during the reporting period, which is usually 12 months. The figure is derived by dividing the number of inpatient day equivalents (also called adjusted inpatient days) by the number of days in the reporting period.

Adjusted inpatient days: An aggregate measure of workload reflecting the sum of inpatient days and equivalent patient days attributed to outpatient services. The number of equivalent patient days attributed to outpatient services is derived by multiplying inpatient days by the ratio of outpatient revenue to inpatient revenue.

$$\text{Adjusted inpatient days} = \text{inpatient days} + \left[\text{inpatient days} * \left(\frac{\text{outpatient revenue}}{\text{inpatient revenue}}\right)\right]$$

Admissions: The number of patients, excluding newborns, accepted for inpatient service during the reporting period; the number includes patients who visit the emergency room and are later admitted for inpatient service.

Adult Cardiac Surgery: Includes minimally invasive procedures that include surgery done with only a small incision or no incision at all, such as through a laparoscope or an endoscope and more invasive major surgical procedures that include open chest and open heart surgery.

Adult Cardiology Services: An organized clinical service offering diagnostic and interventional procedures to manage the full range of adult heart conditions.

Adult day care program: Program providing supervision, medical and psychological care, and social activities for older adults who live at home or in another family setting, but cannot be alone or prefer to be with others during the day. May include intake assessment, health monitoring, occupational therapy, personal care, noon meal, and transportation services.

Adult Diagnostic/invasive catheterization: (also called coronary angiography or coronary arteriography) is used to assist in diagnosing complex heart conditions. Cardiac angiography involves the insertion of a tiny catheter into the artery in the groin then carefully threading the catheter up into the aorta where the coronary arteries originate. Once the catheter is in place, a dye is injected which allows the cardiologist to see the size, shape, and distribution of the coronary arteries. These images are used to diagnose heart disease and to determine, among other things, whether or not surgery is indicated.

Adult Interventional cardiac catheterization: Non surgical procedure that utilizes the same basic principles as diagnostic catheterization and then uses advanced techniques to improve the heart's function. It can be a less-invasive alternative to heart surgery.

Airborne infection isolation room: A single-occupancy room for patient care where environmental factors are controlled in an effort to minimize the transmission of those infectious agents, usually spread person to person by droplet nuclei associated with coughing and inhalation. Such rooms typically have specific ventilation requirements for controlled ventilation, air pressure and filtration.

Alcoholism-drug abuse or dependency inpatient care: Provides diagnosis and therapeutic services to patients with alcoholism or other drug dependencies. Includes care for inpatient/residential treatment for patients whose course of treatment involves more intensive care than provided in an outpatient setting or where patient requires supervised withdrawal.

Alcoholism-drug abuse or dependency outpatient services: Organized hospital services that provide medical care and/or rehabilitative treatment services to outpatients for whom the primary diagnosis is alcoholism or other chemical dependency.

Alzheimer Center: Facility that offers care to persons with Alzheimer's disease and their families through an integrated program of clinical services, research, and education.

Ambulance services: Provision of ambulance services to the ill and injured who require medical attention on a scheduled or unscheduled basis.

Ambulatory Surgery Center: Facility that provides care to patients requiring surgery who are admitted and discharged on the same day. Ambulatory surgery centers are distinct from same day surgical units within the hospital outpatient departments for purposes of Medicare payments.

Arthritis treatment center: Specifically equipped and staffed center for the diagnosis and treatment of arthritis and other joint disorders.

Assisted living: A special combination of housing, supportive services, personalized assistance and health care designed to respond to the individual needs of those who need help in activities of daily living and instrumental activities of daily living. Supportive services are available, 24 hours a day, to meet scheduled and unscheduled needs, in a way that promotes maximum independence and dignity for each resident and encourages the involvement of a resident's family, neighbor and friends.

Assistive Technology Center: A program providing access to specialized hardware and software with adaptations allowing individuals greater independence with mobility, dexterity, or increased communication options.

Auxiliary: A volunteer community organization formed to assist the hospital in carrying out its purpose and to serve as a link between the institution and the community.

Average daily census: The average number of people served on an inpatient basis on a single day during the reporting period; the figure is calculated by dividing the number of inpatient days by the number of days in the reporting period.

Bariatric/weight control services: Bariatrics is the medical practice of weight reduction.

Beds: Number of beds regularly maintained (set up and staffed for use) for inpatients as of the close of the reporting period. Excludes newborn bassinets.

Bed-size category: Hospitals are categorized by the number of beds set up and staffed for use at the end of the reporting period. The eight categories in Hospital Statistics are: 6 to 24 beds; 25 to 49; 50 to 99; 100 to 199; 200 to 299; 300 to 399; 400 to 499; and 500 or more.

Birthing room-LDR room-LDRP room: A single-room type of maternity care with a more homelike setting for families than the traditional three-room unit (labor/delivery/recovery) with a separate postpartum area. A birthing room combines labor and delivery in one room. An LDR room accommodates three stages in the birthing process—labor, delivery, and recovery. An LDRP room accommodates all four stages of the birth process—labor, delivery, recovery, and postpartum.

Births: Total number of infants born in the hospital during the reporting period. Births do not include infants transferred from other institutions, and are excluded from admission and discharge figures.

Blood Donor Center: A facility that performs, or is responsible for the collection, processing, testing or distribution of blood and components.

Bone marrow transplant: See definition for Transplant service on page 212.

Breast cancer screening/mammograms: Mammography screening – The use of breast x-ray to detect unsuspected breast cancer in asymptomatic women. Diagnostic mammography – The x-ray imaging of breast tissue in symptomatic women who are considered to have a substantial likelihood of having breast cancer already.

Burn care: Provides care to severely burned patients. Severely burned patients are those with any of the following: (1) second-degree burns of more than 25% total body surface area for adults or 20% total body surface area for children: (2) third-degree burns of more than 10% total body surface area; (3) any severe burns of the hands, face, eyes, ears, or feet; or (4) all inhalation injuries, electrical burns, complicated burn injuries involving fractures and other major traumas, and all other poor risk factors.

Cardiac electrophysiology: Evaluation and management of patients with complex rhythm or conduction abnormalities, including diagnostic testing, treatment of arrhythmias by catheter ablation or drug therapy, and pacemaker/defibrillator implantation and follow-up.

Cardiac intensive care: Provides patient care of a more specialized nature than the usual medical and surgical care, on the basis of physicians' orders and approved nursing care plans. The unit is staffed with specially trained nursing personnel and contains monitoring and specialized support or treatment equipment for patients who, because of heart seizure, open-heart surgery, or other life-threatening conditions, require intensified, comprehensive observation and care. May include myocardial infarction, pulmonary care, and heart transplant units.

Cardiac Rehabilitation: A medically supervised program to help heart patients recover quickly and improve their overall physical and mental functioning. The goal is to reduce risk of another cardiac event or to keep an already present heart condition from getting worse. Cardiac rehabilitation programs include: counseling to patients, an exercise program, helping patients modify risk factors such as smoking and high blood pressure, providing vocational guidance to enable the patient to return to work, supplying information on physical limitations and lending emotional support.

Case management: A system of assessment, treatment planning, referral and follow-up that ensures the provision of comprehensive and continuous services and the coordination of payment and reimbursement for care.

Chaplaincy/pastoral care services: A service ministering religious activities and providing pastoral counseling to patients, their families, and staff of a health care organization.

Chemotherapy: An organized program for the treatment of cancer by the use of drugs or chemicals.

Children's wellness program: A program that encourages improved health status and a healthful lifestyle of children through health education, exercise, nutrition and health promotion.

Chiropractic services: An organized clinical service including spinal manipulation or adjustment and related diagnostic and therapeutic services.

Closed physician-hospital organization (Closed PHO): A joint venture between the hospital and physicians who have been selected on the basis of cost-effectiveness and/or high quality. The PHO can act as a unified agent in managed care contracting, own a managed care plan, own and operate ambulatory care centers or ancillary services projects, or provide administrative services to physician members.

Community health education: Education that provides health information to individuals and populations, as well as support for personal, family and community health decisions with the objective of improving health status.

Community hospitals: All nonfederal, short-term general, and special hospitals whose facilities and services are available to the public. (Special hospitals include obstetrics and gynecology; eye, ear, nose, and throat; rehabilitation; orthopedic; and other individually described specialty services.) Short-term general and special childrens hospitals are also considered to be community hospitals.

A hospital may include a nursing-home-type unit and still be classified as short-term, provided that the majority of its patients are admitted to units where the average length of stay is less than 30 days. Therefore, statistics for community hospitals often include some data about such nursing-home-type units. An example is furnished by Montana, where in 1995 63.6 percent of all hospitals classified as community hospitals include nursing-home-type units. Expense, revenue, utilization, and personnel data for these hospitals include data about their nursing-home-type units. Thus, total admissions to Montana community hospitals in 1995 were 96,154; total inpatient days, 997,759; total expenses, $791,806,393; and total payroll expenses, $352,583,331. If nursing-home-type unit data were excluded, these same items would be 94,034; 457,340; 752,567,865; and $328,911841, respectively.

Note that before 1972, hospital units of institutions such as prison and college infirmaries were included in the category of community hospitals. Including these units made this category equivalent to the short-term general and other special hospitals category. Although these hospital units are few in number and small in size, this change in definition should be taken into consideration when comparing data.

Community outreach: A program that systematically interacts with the community to identify those in need of services, alerting persons and their families to the availability of services, locating needed services, and enabling persons to enter the service delivery system.

Complementary and alternative medicine services: Organized hospital services or formal arrangements to providers that provide care or treatment not based solely on traditional western allopathic medical teachings as instructed in most U.S. medical schools. Includes any of the following: acupuncture, chiropractic, homeopathy, osteopathy, diet and lifestyle changes, herbal medicine, message therapy, etc.

Computer assisted orthopedic surgery (CAOS): Orthopedic surgery using computer technology, enabling three-dimensional graphic models to visualize a patient's anatomy.

Control: The type of organization responsible for establishing policy concerning the overall operation of hospitals. The three major categories are government (including federal, state, and local); nongovernment (nonprofit); and investor-owned (for-profit).

Crisis prevention: Services provided in order to promote physical and mental well being and the early identification of disease and ill health prior to the onset and recognition of symptoms so as to permit early treatment.

CT scanner: Computed tomographic scanner for head or whole body scans.

Deduction from revenue: The difference between revenue at full established rates (gross) and the payment actually received from payers (net).

Dental Services: An organized dental service or dentists on staff, not necessarily involving special facilities, providing dental or oral services to inpatients or outpatients.

Diagnostic radioisotope facility: The use of radioactive isotopes (Radiopharmaceuticals) as tracers or indicators to detect an abnormal condition or disease.

Electrodiagnostic Services: Diagnostic testing services for nerve and muscle function including services such as nerve conduction studies and needle electromyography.

Electron beam computed tomography (EBCT): A high tech computed tomography scan used to detect coronary artery disease by measuring coronary calcifications. This imaging procedure uses electron beams which are magnetically steered to produce a visual of the coronary artery and the images are produced faster than conventional CT scans.

Emergency department: Hospital facilities for the provision of unscheduled outpatient services to patients whose conditions require immediate care.

Emergency room visits: The number of visits to the emergency unit. When emergency outpatients are admitted to the inpatient areas of the hospital, they are counted as emergency room visits and subsequently, as inpatient admissions.

Emergency services: Health services that are provided after the onset of a medical condition that manifests itself by symptoms of sufficient severity, including severe pain, that the absence of immediate medical attention could reasonably be expected by a prudent layperson, who possesses an average knowledge of health and medicine, to result in placing the patient's health in serious jeopardy.

Enabling services: A program that is designed to help the patient access health care services by offering any of the following: transportation services and/or referrals to local social services agencies.

End of Life: Services offered to patients suffering from chronic, severe, and life-threatening diseases including comprehensive services that give patients and caregivers the resources and the confidence to manage symptoms, avoid emergency room admissions and frequent hospitalization, and remain in familiar and comfortable settings.

Endoscopic retrograde cholangiopancreatography (ERCP): A procedure in which a catheter is introduced through an endoscope into the bile ducts and pancreatic ducts. Injection of contrast materials permits detailed x-ray of these structures. The procedure is used diagnostically as well as therapeutically to relieve obstruction or remove stones.

Endoscopic ultrasound: Specially designed endoscope that incorporates an ultrasound transducer used to obtain detailed images of organs in the chest and abdomen. The endoscope can be passed through the mouth or the anus. When combined with needle biopsy the procedure can assist in diagnosis and staging of cancer.

Enrollment (insurance) assistance services: A program that provides enrollment assistance for patients who are potentially eligible for public health insurance programs such as Medicaid, State Children's Health Insurance, or local/state indigent care programs. The specific services offered could include explanation of benefits, assist applicants in completing the application and locating all relevant documents, conduct eligibility interviews, and/or forward applications and documentation to state/local social service or health agency.

Equity model: An arrangement that allows established practitioners to become shareholders in a professional corporation in exchange for tangible and intangible assets of their existing practices.

Esophageal impedance study: A test in which a catheter is placed through the nose into the esophagus to measure whether gas or liquids are passing from the stomach into the esophagus and causing symptoms.

Expenses: Includes all expenses for the reporting period including payroll, non-payroll, and all operating expenses. *Payroll expenses* include all salaries and wages. *Non-payroll expenses* are all professional fees and those salary expenditures excluded from payroll. *Labor related expenses* are defined as payroll expenses plus employee benefits. *Non-labor related expenses* are all other non-payroll expenses. Bad debt has been reclassified from an expense to a deduction from revenue in accordance with the revised AICPA Audit Guide. Note: Financial data may not add due to rounding.

Expenses per adjusted admission stay: Total expenses divided by adjusted admissions (see *adjusted admission*).

Expenses per adjusted inpatient days: Expenses divided by adjusted inpatient days (see *adjusted inpatient days*).

Extracorporeal shock wave lithotripter (ESWL): A medical device used for treating stones in the kidney or urethra. The device disintegrates kidney stones noninvasively through the transmission of acoustic shock waves directed at the stones.

Fertility Clinic: A specialized program set in an infertility center that provides counseling and education as well as advanced reproductive techniques such as: injectable therapy, reproductive surgeries, treatment for endometriosis, male factor infertility, tubal reversals, in vitro fertilization (IVF), donor eggs, and other such services to help patients achieve successful pregnancies.

Fitness center: Provides exercise, testing, or evaluation programs and fitness activities to the community and hospital employees.

Foundation: A corporation, organized as a hospital affiliate or subsidiary, that purchases both tangible and intangible assets of one or more medical group practices. Physicians remain in a separate corporate entity but sign a professional services agreement with the foundation.

Freestanding outpatient care center: A facility owned and operated by the hospital, that is physically separate from the hospital and provides various medical treatments and diagnostic services on an outpatient basis only. Laboratory and radiology services are usually available.

Full-field digital mammography (FFDM): Combines the x-ray generators and tubes used in analog screen-film mammography (SFM) with a detector plate that converts the x-rays into a digital signal.

Full time equivalent employees (FTE): Full time personnel on payroll plus one half of the part time personnel on payroll. For purposes of *AHA Hospital Statistics*, full time and part time medical and dental residents/interns and other trainees are excluded from the calculation.

General medical-surgical care: Provides acute care to patients in medical and surgical units on the basis of physicians' orders and approved nursing care plans.

Genetic testing/counseling: A service equipped with adequate laboratory facilities and directed by a qualified physician to advise parents and prospective parents on potential problems in cases of genetic defects. A genetic test is the analysis of human DNA, RNA, chromosomes, proteins, and certain metabolites in order to detect heritable disease-related genotypes, mutations, phenotypes, or karyotypes for clinical purposes. Genetic tests can have diverse purposes, including the diagnosis of genetic diseases in newborns, children, and adults; the identification of future health risks; the prediction of drug responses; and the assessment of risks to future children.

Geriatric services: The branch of medicine dealing with the physiology of aging and the diagnosis and treatment of disease affecting the aged. Services could include: Adult day care; Alzheimer's diagnostic-assessment services; Comprehensive geriatric assessment; Emergency response system; Geriatric acute care unit; and/or Geriatric clinics.

Government, nonfederal, state, local: Controlled by an agency of state, county, or city government.

Gross inpatient revenue: Revenue from services rendered to inpatients at full established rates (also known as "charges").

Gross outpatient revenue: Revenue from services rendered to outpatients at full established rates.

Group practice without walls: In this organization, the hospital sponsors the formation of a physician group or provides capital to physicians to establish one. The group shares administrative expenses, although the physicians remain independent practitioners.

Group Purchasing Organization: An organization whose primary function is to negotiate contracts for the purpose of purchasing for members of the group or has a central supply site for its members.

Health fair: Community health education events that focus on the prevention of disease and promotion of health through such activities as audiovisual exhibits and free diagnostic services.

Health maintenance organization (HMO): A health care organization that acts as both insurer and provider of comprehensive but specified medical services in return for prospective per capita (capitation) payments.

Health Research: Organized hospital research program in any of the following areas: basic research, clinical research, community health research, and/or research on innovative health care delivery.

Health screening: A preliminary procedure such as a test or examination to detect the most characteristic sign or signs of a disorder that may require further investigation.

Heart transplant: See definition for Transplant services on page 212.

Hemodialysis: Provision of equipment and personnel for the treatment of renal insufficiency on an inpatient or outpatient basis.

HIV-AIDS services: (could include). *HIV-AIDS unit* – Special unit or team designated and equipped specifically for diagnosis, treatment, continuing care planning, and counseling services for HIV-AIDS patients and their families. *General inpatient care for HIV-AIDS* – Inpatient diagnosis and treatment for human immunodeficiency virus and acquired immunodeficiency syndrome patients, but dedicated unit is not available. *Specialized outpatient program for HIV-AIDS* – Special outpatient program providing diagnostic, treatment, continuing care planning, and counseling for HIV-AIDS patients and their families.

Home health services: Service providing nursing, therapy, and health-related homemaker or social services in the patient's home.

Hospice: A program providing palliative care, chiefly medical relief of pain and supportive services, addressing the emotional, social, financial, and legal needs of terminally ill patients and their families. Care can be provided in a variety of settings, both inpatient and at home.

Hospital unit: The hospital operation, excluding activity pertaining to nursing-home-type unit (as described below), for the following items: Admissions, Beds, FTEs (full-time, part-time, and total), Inpatient Days, Length of Stay, Net Revenue, and Total Expense.

Hospital unit of institutions: A hospital unit that is not open to the public and is contained within a nonhospital unit. An example is an infirmary that is contained within a college.

Hospitals in a network: Hospitals participating in a group that may include other hospitals, physicians, other providers, insurers, and/or community agencies that work together to coordinate and deliver a broad spectrum of services to the community.

Hospitals in a system: Hospitals belonging to a corporate body that owns and/or manages health provider facilities or health-related subsidiaries; the system may also own non-health-related facilities.

Image-guided radiation therapy (IGRT): Automated system for image-guided radiation therapy that enables clinicians to obtain high-resolution x-ray images to pinpoint tumor sites, adjust patient positioning when necessary, and complete a treatment, all within the standard treatment time slot, allowing for more effective cancer treatments.

Immunization program: Program that plans, coordinates and conducts immunization services in the community.

Indemnity fee for service: The traditional type of health insurance, in which the insured is reimbursed for covered expenses without regard to choice of provider. Payment up to a stated limit may be made either to the individual incurring and claiming the expense, or directly to providers.

Independent practice association (IPA): An IPA is a legal entity that holds managed care contracts and contracts with physicians, usually in solo practice, to provide care either on a fee-for-services or capitated basis. The purpose of an IPA is to assist solo physicians in obtaining managed care contracts.

Indigent care clinic: Health care services for uninsured and underinsured persons where care is free of charge or charged on a sliding scale. This would include "free clinics" staffed by volunteer practitioners, but could also be staffed by employees with sponsoring health care organizations subsidizing the cost of service.

Inpatient days: The number of adult and pediatric days of care, excluding newborn days of care, rendered during the entire reporting period.

Inpatient palliative care unit: An inpatient palliative care ward is a physically discreet, inpatient nursing unit where the focus is palliative care. The patient care focus is on symptom relief for complex patients who may be continuing to undergo primary treatment. Care is delivered by palliative medicine specialists.

Inpatient surgeries: Surgical services provided to patients who remain in the hospital overnight.

Insurance product: In tables 3 through 6, insurance product refers to a hospital-owned insurance product.

Integrated salary model: In this arrangement, physicians are salaried by the hospital or other entity of a health system to provide medical services for primary care and specialty care.

Intensity-Modulated Radiation Therapy (IMRT): A type of three-dimensional radiation therapy, which improves the targeting of treatment delivery in a way that is likely to decrease damage to normal tissues and allows varying intensities.

Intermediate nursing care: Provides health-related services (skilled nursing care and social services) to residents with a variety of physical conditions or functional disabilities. These residents do not require the care provided by a hospital or skilled nursing facility, but do need supervision and support services.

Intraoperative magnetic resonance imaging: An integrated surgery system which provides an MRI system in an operating room. The system allows for immediate evaluation of the degree to tumor resection while the patient is undergoing a surgical resection. Intraoperative MRI exists when a MRI (low-field or high-field) is placed in the operating theater and is used during surgical resection without moving the patient from the operating room to the diagnostic imaging suite.

Investor-owned, for-profit: Investor-owned, for-profit hospitals are those controlled on a for-profit basis by an individual, partnership, or profit-making corporation.

Kidney transplant: See definition for Transplant sevices on page 212.

Labor-related expenses: Payroll expenses plus employee benefits. *Non-labor-related expenses refers to all other nonpayroll expenses, such as interest depreciation, supplies, purchased services, professional fees, and others.*

Length of stay (LOS): LOS refers to the average number of days a patient stays at the facility. Short-term hospitals are those where the average LOS is less than 30 days. Long-term hospitals are those where the average LOS is 30 days or more. The figure is derived by dividing the number of inpatient days by the number of admissions.

Note that this publication carries two LOS variables: *total facility length of stay and hospital unit length of stay. Total facility* includes admissions and inpatient days from nursing-home-type units under control of the hospital. In *hospital unit length of stay,* nursing home utilization is subtracted.

Licensed practical nurse (LPN): A nurse who has graduated from an approved school of practical (vocational) nursing and works under the supervision of registered nurses and/or physicians.

Linguistic/Translation services: Services provided by the hospital designed to make health care more accessible to non-English speaking patients and their physicians.

Liver transplant: See definition for Transplant on page 212.

Long-term: Hospitals are classified either short-term or long-term according to the average length of stay (LOS). A long-term hospital is one in which the average LOS is 30 days or more.

Lung transplant: See definition for Transplant services on page 212.

Magnetic resonance imaging (MRI): The use of a uniform magnetic field and radio frequencies to study tissue and structure of the body. This procedure enables the visualization of biochemical activity of the cell in vivo without the use of ionizing radiation, radio-isotopic substances, or high-frequency sound.

Magnetoencephalography: a noninvasive neurophysiological measurement tool used to study magnetic fields generated by neuronal activity of the brain. The primary uses of MEG include assisting surgeons in localizing the source of epilepsy, sensory mapping, and the study of brain function. When it is combined with structural imaging, it is known as magnetic source imaging (MSI).

Managed care: A term covering a broad spectrum of arrangements for health care delivery and financing, including managed indemnity plans (MIP), health maintenance organizations (HMO), preferred provider organizations (PPO), point-of-service plans (POS), and direct contracting arrangements between employers and providers.

Managed care contract: A contract between the hospital and a managed care organization.

Management services organization (MSO): A corporation owned by the hospital or a physician/hospital joint venture that provides management services to one or more medical group practices. As part of a full-service management agreement, the MSO purchases the tangible assets of the practices and leases them back, employs all non-physician staff, and provides all supplies/administrative systems for a fee.

Meals on wheels: A hospital sponsored program which delivers meals to people, usually the elderly, who are unable to prepare their own meals. Low cost, nutritional meals are delivered to individuals' homes on a regular basis.

Medical surgical intensive care: Provides patient care of a more intensive nature than the usual medical and surgical care, on the basis of physicians' orders and approved nursing care plans. These units are staffed with specially trained nursing personnel and contain monitoring and specialized support equipment for patients who, because of shock, trauma, or other life-threatening conditions, require

intensified, comprehensive observation and care. Includes mixed intensive care units.

Mobile health services: Vans and other vehicles used to deliver primary care services.

Multi-slice spiral computed tomography (<64 slice CT): A specialized computed tomography procedure that provides three-dimensional processing and allows narrower and multiple slices with increased spatial resolution and faster scanning times as compared to a regular computed tomography scan.

Multi-slice spiral computed tomography (64+ slice CT): Involves the acquisition of volumetric tomographic x-ray absorption data expressed in Hounsfield units using multiple rows of detectors. 64+ systems reconstruct the equivalent of 64 or greater slices to cover the imaged volume.

Neonatal intensive care: A unit that must be separate from the newborn nursery providing intensive care to all sick infants including those with the very lowest birth weights (less than 1500 grams). NICU has potential for providing mechanical ventilation, neonatal surgery, and special care for the sickest infants born in the hospital or transferred from another institution. A full-time neonatologist serves as director of the NICU.

Neonatal intermediate care: A unit that must be separate from the normal newborn nursery and that provides intermediate and/or recovery care and some specialized services, including immediate resuscitation, intravenous therapy, and capacity for prolonged oxygen therapy and monitoring.

Net patient revenue: The estimated net realizable amounts from patients, third-party payers, and others for services rendered. The number includes estimated retroactive adjustments called for by agreements with third-party payers; retroactive adjustments are accrued on an estimated basis in the period the related services are rendered and then adjusted later as final settlements are determined.

Net total revenue: Net patient revenue plus all other revenue, including contributions, endowment revenue, governmental grants, and all other payments not made on behalf of individual patients.

Neurological services: Services provided by the hospital dealing with the operative and nonoperative management of disorders of the central, peripheral, and autonomic nervous system.

Nongovernment, nonprofit: Hospitals that are nongovernment, nonprofit are controlled by not-for-profit organizations, including religious organizations (Catholic hospitals, for example), fraternal societies, and others.

Nursing-home-type unit/facility: A unit/facility that primarily offers the following type of services to a majority of all admissions:

- *Skilled nursing:* The provision of medical and nursing care services, health-related services, and social services under the supervision of a registered nurse on a 24-hour basis.

- *Intermediate care:* The provision, on a regular basis, of health-related care and services to individuals who do not require the degree of care or treatment that a skilled nursing unit is designed to provide.

- *Personal care:* The provision of general supervision and direct personal care services for residents who require assistance in activities of daily living but who do not need nursing services or inpatient care. Medical and nursing services are available as needed.

- *Sheltered/residential care:* The provision of general supervision and protective services for residents who do not need nursing services or continuous personal care services in the conduct of daily life. Medical and nursing services are available as needed.

Nutrition programs: Those services within a health care facility which are designed to provide inexpensive, nutritionally sound meals to patients.

Obstetrics: Levels should be designated: (1) unit provides services for uncomplicated maternity and newborn cases; (2) unit provides services for uncomplicated cases, the majority of complicated problems, and special neonatal services; and (3) unit provides services for all serious illnesses and abnormalities and is supervised by a full-time maternal/fetal specialist.

Occupational health services: Includes services designed to protect the safety of employees from hazards in the work environment.

Oncology services: Inpatient and outpatient services for patients with cancer, including comprehensive care, support and guidance in addition to patient education and prevention, chemotherapy, counseling and other treatment methods.

Open physician hospital organization (Open PHO): A joint venture between the hospital and all members of the medical staff who wish to participate. The open PHO can act as a unified agent in managed care contracting, own a managed care plan, own and operate ambulatory care centers or ancillary services projects, or provide administrative services to physician members.

Optical colonoscopy: An examination of the interior of the colon using a long, flexible, lighted tube with a small built-in camera.

Orthopedic services: Services provided for the prevention or correction of injuries or disorders of the skeletal system and associated muscles, joints and ligaments.

Osteopathic hospitals: Osteopathic medicine is a medical practice based on a theory that diseases are due chiefly to a loss of structural integrity, which can be restored by manipulation of the neuro-muscular and skeletal systems, supplemented by therapeutic measures (such as medicine or surgery).

Other Intensive Care: A specially staffed, specialty equipped, separate section of a hospital dedicated to the observation, care, and treatment of patients with life threatening illnesses, injuries, or complications from which recovery is possible. It provides special expertise and facilities for the support of vital function and utilizes the skill of medical nursing and other staff experienced in the management of these problems.

Other long-term care: Provision of long-term care other than skilled nursing care or intermediate care for those who do not require daily medical or nursing services, but may require some assistance in the activities of daily living. This can include residential care, elderly care, or sheltered care facilities for developmentally disabled.

Other special care: Provides care to patients requiring care more intensive than that provided in the acute area, yet not sufficiently intensive to require admission to an intensive care unit. Patients admitted to this area are usually transferred here from an intensive care unit once their condition has improved. These units are sometimes referred to as definitive observation, step-down, or progressive care units.

Other transplant: See definition for Transplant services on page 212.

Outpatient care: Treatment provided to patients who do not remain in the hospital for overnight care. Hospitals may deliver outpatient care on site or through a facility owned and operated by the hospital, but physically separate from the hospital. In addition to treating minor illnesses or injuries, a free-standing center will stabilize seriously ill or injured patients before transporting them to a hospital. Laboratory and radiology services are usually available.

Outpatient care center (Freestanding): A facility owned and operated by the hospital, but physically separate from the hospital, that provides various medical treatments on an outpatient basis only. In addition to treating minor illnesses or injuries, the center will stabilize seriously ill or injured patients before transporting them to a hospital. Laboratory and radiology services are usually available.

Outpatient care center-services (Hospital-based): Organized hospital health care services offered by appointment on an ambulatory basis. Services may include outpatient surgery, examination, diagnosis, and treatment of a variety of medical conditions on a nonemergency basis, and laboratory and other diagnostic testing as ordered by staff or outside physician referral.

Outpatient surgery: Scheduled surgical services provided to patients who do not remain in the hospital overnight. The surgery may be performed in operating suites also used for inpatient surgery, specially designated surgical suites for outpatient surgery, or procedure rooms within an outpatient care facility.

Outpatient visit: A visit by a patient who is not lodged in the hospital while receiving medical, dental, or other services. Each visit an outpatient makes to a discrete unit constitutes one visit regardless of the number of diagnostic and/or therapeutic treatments that the patient receives. Total outpatient visits should include all clinic visits, referred visits, observation services, outpatient surgeries, and emergency room visits.

Pain Management Program: A recognized clinical service or program providing specialized medical care, drugs or therapies for the management of acute or chronic pain or other distressing symptom, administered by specially trained physicians and other clinicians, to patients suffering from acute illness of diverse causes.

Palliative Care Inpatient Unit: An inpatient palliative care ward is a physically discreet, inpatient nursing unit where the focus is palliative care. The patient care focus is on symptom relief for complex patients who may be continuing to undergo primary treatment. Care is delivered by palliative medicine specialists.

Palliative care program: An organized program providing specialized medical care, drugs or therapies for the management of acute or chronic pain and/or the control of symptoms administered by specially trained physicians and other clinicians; and supportive care services, such as counseling on advanced directives, spiritual care, and social services, to patients with advanced disease and their families.

Patient Controlled Analgesia (PCA). Patient-controlled Analgesia (PCA) is intravenously administered pain medicine under the patient's control. The patient has a button on the end of a cord than can be pushed at will, whenever more pain medicine is desired. This button will only deliver more pain medicine at pre-determined intervals, as programmed by the doctor's order.

Patient education center: Written goals and objectives for the patient and/or family related to therapeutic regimens, medical procedures, and self care.

Patient representative services: Organized hospital services providing personnel through whom patients and staff can seek solutions to institutional problems affecting the delivery of high-quality care and services.

Payroll expenses: Includes all salaries and wages. All professional fees and salary expenditures excluded from payroll, such as employee benefits, are defined as nonpayroll expenses and are included in total expenses.

Pediatric Cardiac Surgery: Includes minimally invasive procedures that include surgery done with only a small incision or no incision at all, such as through a laparoscope or an endoscope and more invasive major surgical procedures that include open chest and open heart surgery.

Pediatric Cardiology Services: An organized clinical service offering diagnostic and interventional procedures to manage the full range of pediatric heart conditions.

Pediatric Diagnostic/invasive catheterization: (also called coronary angiography or coronary arteriography) is used to assist in diagnosing complex heart conditions. Cardiac angiography involves the insertion of a tiny catheter into the artery in the groin then carefully threading the catheter up into the aorta where the coronary arteries originate. Once the catheter is in place, a dye is injected which allows the cardiologist to see the size, shape, and distribution of the coronary arteries. These images are used to diagnose heart disease and to determine, among other things, whether or not surgery is indicated.

Pediatric intensive care: Provides care to pediatric patients that is of a more intensive nature than that usually provided to pediatric patients. The unit is staffed with specially trained personnel and contains monitoring and specialized support equipment for treatment of patients who, because of shock, trauma, or other life-threatening conditions, require intensified, comprehensive observation and care.

Pediatric Interventional cardiac catheterization: Non surgical procedure that utilizes the same basic principles as diagnostic catheterization and then uses advanced techniques to improve the heart's function. It can be a less-invasive alternative to heart surgery.

Pediatric medical-surgical care: Provides acute care to pediatric patients on the basis of physicians' orders and approved nursing care plans.

Personnel: Number of persons on the hospital payroll at the end of the reporting period. Personnel are recorded in *Hospital Statistics* as full-time equivalents (FTEs), which are calculated by adding the number of full-time personnel to one-half the number of part-time personnel, excluding medical and dental residents, interns, and other trainees. *Per 100 adjusted census* indicates the ratio of personnel to adjusted average daily census, calculated on a per-100 basis.

Physical rehabilitation inpatient care: Provides care encompassing a comprehensive array of restoration services for the disabled and all support services necessary to help patients attain their maximum functional capacity.

Physical rehabilitation outpatient services: Outpatient program providing medical, health-related, therapy, social, and/or vocational services to help disabled persons attain or retain their maximum functional capacity.

Population: Population refers to the residential population of the United States. This includes both civilian and military personnel. Note that population is being used to calculate the values *for community health indicators per 1000 population*.

Positron emission tomography/CT (PET/CT): Provides metabolic functional information for the monitoring of chemotherapy, radiotherapy and surgical planning.

Positron emission tomography scanner (PET): A nuclear medicine imaging technology which uses radioactive (positron emitting) isotopes created in a cyclotron or generator and computers to produce composite pictures of the brain and heart at work. PET scanning produces sectional images depicting metabolic activity or blood flow rather than anatomy.

Preferred provider organization (PPO): A pre-set arrangement in which purchasers and providers agree to furnish specified health services to a group of employees/patients.

Primary care department: A unit or clinic within the hospital that provides primary care services (e.g. general pediatric care, general internal medicine, family practice, gynecology) through hospital-salaried medical and/or nursing staff, focusing on evaluating and diagnosing medical problems and providing medical treatment on an outpatient basis.

Prosthetic and Orthotic Services: Services providing comprehensive prosthetic and orthotic evaluation, fitting, and training.

Proton beam therapy: A form of radiation therapy which administers proton beams. While producing the same biologic effects as x-ray beams, the energy distribution of protons differs from conventional x-ray beams in that they can be more precisely focused in tissue volumes in a three-dimensional pattern resulting in less surrounding tissue damage than conventional radiation therapy permitting administration of higher doses.

Psychiatric child-adolescent services: Provides care to emotionally disturbed children and adolescents, including those admitted for diagnosis and those admitted for treatment.

Psychiatric consultation-liaison services: Provides organized psychiatric consultation/liaison services to nonpsychiatric hospital staff and/or departments on psychological aspects of medical care that may be generic or specific to individual patients.

Psychiatric education services: Provides psychiatric educational services to community agencies and workers such as schools, police, courts, public health nurses, welfare agencies, clergy, and so forth. The purpose is to expand the mental health knowledge and competence of personnel not working in the mental health field and to promote good mental health through improved understanding, attitudes, and behavioral patterns.

Psychiatric emergency services: Services of facilities available on a 24-hour basis to provide immediate unscheduled out-patient care, diagnosis, evaluation, crisis intervention, and assistance to persons suffering acute emotional or mental distress.

Psychiatric geriatric services: Provides care to emotionally disturbed elderly patients, including those admitted for diagnosis and those admitted for treatment.

Psychiatric inpatient care: Provides acute or long-term care to emotionally disturbed patients, including patients admitted for diagnosis and those admitted for treatment of psychiatric problems, on the basis of physicians' orders and approved nursing care plans. Long-term care may include intensive supervision to the chronically mentally ill, mentally disordered, or other mentally incompetent persons.

Psychiatric outpatient services: Provides medical care, including diagnosis and treatment, of psychiatric outpatients.

Psychiatric partial hospitalization program: Organized hospital services of intensive day/evening outpatient services of three hours of more duration, distinguished from other outpatient visits of one hour.

Psychiatric residential treatment: Overnight psychiatric care in conjunction with an intensive treatment program in a setting other than a hospital.

Radiology, diagnostic: The branch of radiology that deals with the utilization of all modalities of radiant energy in medical diagnoses and therapeutic procedures using radiologic guidance. This includes, but is not restricted to, imaging techniques and methodologies utilizing radiation emitted by x-ray tubes, radionnuclides, and ultrasonographic devices and the radiofrequency electromagnetic radiation emitted by atoms.

Radiology, therapeutic: The branch of medicine concerned with radioactive substances and using various techniques of visualization, with the diagnosis and treatment of disease using any of the various sources of radiant energy. Services could include: megavoltage radiation therapy; radioactive implants; stereotactic radiosurgery; therapeutic radioisotope facility; X-ray radiation therapy.

Registered nurse (RN): A nurse who has graduated from an approved school of nursing and who is currently registered by the state. RNs are responsible for the nature and quality of all nursing care that patients receive. In these tables, the number of RNs does not include those registered nurses more appropriately reported in other occupational categories, such as facility administrators, which are listed under *all other personnel* (Tables 1 and 2).

Rehabilitation services: A wide array of restoration services for disabled and recuperating patients, including all support services necessary to help them attain their maximum functional capacity.

Retirement housing: A facility which provides social activities to senior citizens, usually retired persons, who do not require health care but some short-term skilled nursing care may be provided. A retirement center may furnish housing and may also have acute hospital and long-term care facilities, or it may arrange for acute and long term care through affiliated institutions.

Robot-assisted walking therapy: A form of physical therapy that uses a robotic device to assist patients who are relearning how to walk.

Robotic surgery: The use of mechanical guidance devices to remotely manipulate surgical instrumentation.

Rural: A rural hospital is located outside a Metropolitan Statistical Area (MSA), as designated by the U.S. Office of Management and Budget (OMB) effective June 6, 2003. An urban area is a geographically defined, integrated social and economic unit with a large population nucleus. Micropolitan areas, which are new to the OMB June 6, 2003 definitions, continue to be classified as rural for purposes of this publication.

Rural Health Clinic: A clinic located in a rural, medically under-served area in the United States that has a separate reimbursement structure from the standard medical office under the Medicare and Medicaid programs.

Satellite Emergency Department: A facility owned and operated by the hospital but physically separate from the hospital for the provision of unscheduled outpatient services to patients whose conditions require immediate care. A freestanding ED is not physically connected to a hospital, but has all necessary emergency staffing and equipment on-site.

Shaped beam radiation system: A precise, non-invasive treatment that involves targeting beams of radiation that mirrors the exact size and shape of a tumor at a specific area of a tumor to shrink or destroy cancerous cells. This procedure delivers a therapeutic dose of radiation that conforms precisely to the shape of the tumor, thus minimizing the risk to nearby tissues.

Simulated rehabilitation environment: Rehabilitation focused on retraining functional skills in a contextually appropriate environment (simulated home and community settings) or in a traditional setting (gymnasium) using motor learning principles.

Single photon emission computerized tomography (SPECT): A nuclear medicine imaging technology that combines existing technology of gamma camera imaging with computed tomographic imaging technology to provide a more precise and clear image.

Skilled nursing care: Provides non-acute medical and skilled nursing care services, therapy, and social services under the supervision of a licensed registered nurse on a 24-hour basis.

Sleep Center: Specially equipped and staffed center for the diagnosis and treatment of sleep disorders.

Social work services (could include): Organized services that are properly directed and sufficiently staffed by qualified individuals who provide assistance and counseling to patients and their families in dealing with social, emotional, and environmental problems associated with illness or disability, often in the context of financial or discharge planning coordination.

Sports medicine: Provision of diagnostic screening and assessment and clinical and rehabilitation services for the prevention and treatment of sports-related injuries.

Stereotactic radiosurgery: Stereotactic radiosurgery (SRS) is a radiotherapy modality that delivers a high dosage of radiation to a discrete treatment area in as few as one treatment session. Includes gamma knife, cyberknife, etc.

Support groups: A hospital sponsored program that allows a group of individuals with the same or similar problems who meet periodically to share experiences, problems, and solutions in order to support each other.

Surgical operations: Those surgical operations, whether major or minor, performed in the operating room(s). A surgical operation involving more than one surgical procedure is still considered only one surgical operation.

Swing bed services: A hospital bed that can be used to provide either acute or long-term care depending on community or patient needs. To be eligible a hospital must have a Medicare provider agreement in place, have fewer than 100 beds, be located in a rural area, do not have a 24 hour nursing service waiver in effect, have not been terminated from the program in the prior two years, and meet various service conditions.

Teen outreach services: A program focusing on the teenager which encourages an improved health status and a healthful lifestyle including physical, emotional, mental, social, spiritual and economic health through education, exercise, nutrition and health promotion.

Tissue transplant: See definition for Transplant sevices on page 212.

Tobacco treatment/cessation program: Organized hospital services with the purpose of ending tobacco-use habits of patients addicted to tobacco/nicotine.

Transplant services: The branch of medicine that transfers an organ or tissue from one person to another or from one body part to another to replace a diseased structure or to restore function or to change appearance. Services could include: bone marrow transplant program; heart, lung, kidney, intestine, or tissue transplant. The other transplant services include transplant services other than bone marrow, heart, kidney, liver, lung, tissue and heart/lung or other multi-transplant surgeries.

Transportation to health facilities: A long-term care support service designed to assist the mobility of the elderly. Some programs offer improved financial access by offering reduced rates and barrier-free buses or vans with ramps and lifts to assist the elderly or handicapped; others offer subsidies for public transport systems or operate mini-bus services exclusively for use by senior citizens.

Trauma center (certified): A facility to provide emergency and specialized intensive care to critically ill and injured patients. **Level 1:** A regional resource trauma center, which is capable of providing total care for every aspect of injury and plays a leadership role in trauma research and education. **Level 2:** A community trauma center, which is capable of providing trauma care to all but the most severely injured patients who require highly specialized care. **Level 3:** A rural trauma hospital, which is capable of providing care to a large number of injury victims and can resuscitate and stabilize more severely injured patients so that they can be transported to Level 1 or 2 facilities.

Ultrasound: The use of acoustic waves above the range of 20,000 cycles per second to visualize internal body structures.

Urban: An urban hospital is located inside a Metropolitan Statistical Area (MSA), designated by the U.S. Office of Management and Budget effective June 6, 2003. An urban areas is a geographically defined, integrated social and economic unit with a large population base. Micropolitan areas, which are new to the OMB June 6, 2003 definitions, are not considered to be urban for purposes of this publication.

Urgent care center: A facility that provides care and treatment for problems that are not life-threatening but require attention over the short term.

Virtual colonoscopy: Noninvasive screening procedure used to visualize, analyze and detect cancerous or potentially cancerous polyps in the colon.

Volunteer services department: An organized hospital department responsible for coordinating the services of volunteers working within the institution.

Women's health center/services: An area set aside for coordinated education and treatment services specifically for and promoted to women as provided by this special unit. Services may or may not include obstetrics but include a range of services other than OB.

Wound Management Services: Services for patients with chronic wounds and nonhealing wounds often resulting from diabetes, poor circulation, improper seating and immunocompromising conditions. The goals are to progress chronic wounds through stages of healing, reduce and eliminate infections, increase physical function to minimize complications from current wounds and prevent future chronic wounds. Wound management services are provided on an inpatient or outpatient basis, depending on the intensity of service needed.

2013 AHA Annual Survey
Health Forum, L.L.C.

Please return to:
AHA Annual Survey
155 N Wacker Dr
Suite 400
Chicago IL 60606

A. REPORTING PERIOD (please refer to the instructions and definitions at the end of this questionnaire)

Report data for a full 12-month period, preferably your last completed fiscal year (365 days). Be consistent in using the same reporting period for responses throughout various sections of this survey.

1. Reporting Period used (beginning and ending date) ...... __ __ / __ __ / __ __ __ __ to __ __ / __ __ / __ __ __ __
   Month   Day   Year   Month   Day   Year

2. a. Were you in operation 12 full months
   at the end of your reporting period .... YES ☐   NO ☐

   b. Number of days open
   during reporting period .... _____

3. Indicate the beginning of your current fiscal year .... __ __ / __ __ / __ __ __ __
   Month   Day   Year

B. ORGANIZATIONAL STRUCTURE

1. CONTROL

Indicate the type of organization that is responsible for establishing policy for overall operation of your hospital. CHECK ONLY ONE:

Government, nonfederal
- ☐ 12 State
- ☐ 13 County
- ☐ 14 City
- ☐ 15 City-County
- ☐ 16 Hospital district or authority

Nongovernment, not-for profit (NFP)
- ☐ 21 Church-operated
- ☐ 23 Other not-for-profit (including NFP Corporation)

Investor-owned, for-profit
- ☐ 31 Individual
- ☐ 32 Partnership
- ☐ 33 Corporation

Government, federal
- ☐ 41 Air Force
- ☐ 42 Army
- ☐ 43 Navy
- ☐ 44 Public Health Service
- ☐ 45 Veterans' Affairs
- ☐ 46 Federal other than 41-45 or 47-48
- ☐ 47 PHS Indian Service
- ☐ 48 Department of Justice

2. SERVICE

Indicate the ONE category that BEST describes your hospital or the type of service it provides to the MAJORITY of patients:

- ☐ 10 General medical and surgical
- ☐ 11 Hospital unit of an institution (prison hospital, college infirmary)
- ☐ 12 Hospital unit within a facility for persons with intellectual disabilities
- ☐ 13 Surgical
- ☐ 22 Psychiatric
- ☐ 33 Tuberculosis and other respiratory diseases
- ☐ 41 Cancer
- ☐ 42 Heart
- ☐ 44 Obstetrics and gynecology
- ☐ 45 Eye, ear, nose, and throat

- ☐ 46 Rehabilitation
- ☐ 47 Orthopedic
- ☐ 48 Chronic disease

- ☐ 62 Intellectual disabilities
- ☐ 80 Acute long-term care hospital
- ☐ 82 Alcoholism and other chemical dependency
- ☐ 49 Other-specify treatment area: _____

B. ORGANIZATIONAL STRUCTURE (continued)

3. OTHER

a. Does your hospital restrict admissions primarily to children? .... YES ☐ NO ☐

b. Does the hospital itself operate subsidiary corporations? .... YES ☐ NO ☐

c. Is the hospital contract managed? If yes, please provide the name, city, and state of the organization.... YES ☐ NO ☐

   Name: _____ City: _____ State: _____

d. Is the hospital a participant in a network? ....YES ☐ NO ☐
   If yes, please provide the name, city and state and telephone number of the network. If the hospital participates in more than one network, please provide the name, city, and state and telephone number of the network on page 13, under supplemental information.

   Name: _____ City: _____ State: _____ Telephone_____

e. Is your hospital owned in whole or in part by physicians or a physician group?.. YES ☐ NO ☐

f. If you checked 80 Acute long-term care hospital (LTCH) in the Section B2 (Service), please indicate if you are a freestanding LTCH or a LTCH arranged within a general acute care hospital.
   ☐ Free standing LTCH   ☐ LTCH arranged in a general acute care hospital

   If you are arranged in a general acute care hospital, what is your host hospital's name?

   Name_____ City_____ State_____

C. FACILITIES AND SERVICES

For each service or facility listed below, please check all the categories that describe how each item is provided **as of the last day of the reporting period**. Check all categories that apply for an item. If you check column (1) C1-19, please include the number of **staffed beds**.
**The sum of the beds reported in 1-19 should equal Section D(1b), beds set up and staffed on page 9.**

	(1) Owned or provided by my hospital or its subsidiary	(2) Provided by my Health System (in my local community)	(3) Provided through a formal contractual arrangement or joint venture with another provider that is not in my system (in my local community)	(4) Do Not Provide
1. General medical-surgical care ....(#Beds____)	☐	☐	☐	☐
2. Pediatric medical-surgical care ....(#Beds____)	☐	☐	☐	☐
3. Obstetrics [Level of unit (1-3): (___)].............(#Beds____)	☐	☐	☐	☐
4. Medical-surgical intensive care ....(#Beds____)	☐	☐	☐	☐
5. Cardiac intensive care ....(#Beds____)	☐	☐	☐	☐
6. Neonatal intensive care ....(#Beds____)	☐	☐	☐	☐
7. Neonatal intermediate care ....(#Beds____)	☐	☐	☐	☐
8. Pediatric intensive care ....(#Beds____)	☐	☐	☐	☐
9. Burn care...(#Beds____)	☐	☐	☐	☐
10. Other special care _____.........(#Beds____)	☐	☐	☐	☐
11. Other intensive care_____.........(#Beds____)	☐	☐	☐	☐
12. Physical rehabilitation ....(#Beds____)	☐	☐	☐	☐
13. Alcoholism-drug abuse or dependency care ....(#Beds____)	☐	☐	☐	☐
14. Psychiatric care ....(#Beds____)	☐	☐	☐	☐
15. Skilled nursing care ....(#Beds____)	☐	☐	☐	☐
16. Intermediate nursing care ....(#Beds____)	☐	☐	☐	☐
17. Acute long-term care..................................(#Beds____)	☐	☐	☐	☐
18. Other long-term care...................................(#Beds____)	☐	☐	☐	☐
19. Other care (specify):_____.......(#Beds____)	☐	☐	☐	☐
20. Adult day care program.................................	☐	☐	☐	☐
21. Airborne infection isolation room (# rooms _____)	☐	☐	☐	☐
22. Alcoholism-drug abuse or dependency outpatient services...........	☐	☐	☐	☐
23. Alzheimer Center..	☐	☐	☐	☐
24. Ambulance services....................................	☐	☐	☐	☐
25. Ambulatory surgery center...........................	☐	☐	☐	☐
26. Arthritis treatment center.............................	☐	☐	☐	☐
27. Assisted living...	☐	☐	☐	☐
28. Auxiliary...	☐	☐	☐	☐
29. Bariatric/weight control services....................	☐	☐	☐	☐
30. Birthing room/LDR room/LDRP room	☐	☐	☐	☐
31. Blood Donor Center....................................	☐	☐	☐	☐
32. Breast cancer screening/mammograms	☐	☐	☐	☐

C. FACILITIES AND SERVICES (continued)

	(1) Owned or provided by my hospital or its subsidiary	(2) Provided by my Health System (in my local community)	(3) Provided through a formal contractual arrangement or joint venture with another provider that is not in my system (in my local community)	(4) Do Not Provide
33. Cardiology and cardiac surgery services				
a. Adult cardiology services	☐	☐	☐	☐
b. Pediatric cardiology services	☐	☐	☐	☐
c. Adult diagnostic catheterization	☐	☐	☐	☐
d. Pediatric diagnostic catheterization	☐	☐	☐	☐
e. Adult interventional cardiac catheterization	☐	☐	☐	☐
f. Pediatric interventional cardiac catheterization	☐	☐	☐	☐
g. Adult cardiac surgery	☐	☐	☐	☐
h. Pediatric cardiac surgery	☐	☐	☐	☐
i. Adult cardiac electrophysiology	☐	☐	☐	☐
j. Pediatric cardiac electrophysiology	☐	☐	☐	☐
k. Cardiac rehabilitation	☐	☐	☐	☐
34. Case management	☐	☐	☐	☐
35. Chaplaincy/pastoral care services	☐	☐	☐	☐
36. Chemotherapy	☐	☐	☐	☐
37. Children's wellness program	☐	☐	☐	☐
38. Chiropractic services	☐	☐	☐	☐
39. Community outreach	☐	☐	☐	☐
40. Complementary and alternative medicine services	☐	☐	☐	☐
41. Computer assisted orthopedic surgery (CAOS)	☐	☐	☐	☐
42. Crisis prevention	☐	☐	☐	☐
43. Dental services	☐	☐	☐	☐
44. Emergency services				
a. Emergency department	☐	☐	☐	☐
b. Pediatric emergency department	☐	☐	☐	☐
c. Satellite emergency department	☐	☐		☐
d. If you checked column 1 for Satellite ED (44c), is the department open 24 hours a day, 7 days a week?			Yes ☐	No ☐
e. Trauma center (certified) [Level of unit (1-3) _____]	☐	☐	☐	☐
45. Enabling services	☐	☐	☐	☐
46. Endoscopic services				
a. Optical colonoscopy	☐	☐	☐	☐
b. Endoscopic ultrasound	☐	☐	☐	☐
c. Ablation of Barrett's esophagus	☐	☐	☐	☐
d. Esophageal impedance study	☐	☐	☐	☐
e. Endoscopic retrograde cholangiopancreatography (ERCP)	☐	☐	☐	☐
47. Enrollment (insurance) assistance services	☐	☐	☐	☐
48. Extracorporeal shock wave lithotripter (ESWL)	☐	☐	☐	☐
49. Fertility clinic	☐	☐	☐	☐
50. Fitness center	☐	☐	☐	☐
51. Freestanding outpatient care center	☐	☐	☐	☐
52. Geriatric services	☐	☐	☐	☐
53. Health fair	☐	☐	☐	☐

C. FACILITIES AND SERVICES (continued)

	(1) Owned or provided by my hospital or its subsidiary	(2) Provided by my Health System (in my local community)	(3) Provided through a formal contractual arrangement or joint venture with another provider that is not in my system (in my local community)	(4) Do Not Provide
54. Community health education	☐	☐	☐	☐
55. Genetic testing/counseling	☐	☐	☐	☐
56. Health screenings	☐	☐	☐	☐
57. Health research	☐	☐	☐	☐
58. Hemodialysis	☐	☐	☐	☐
59. HIV/AIDS services	☐	☐	☐	☐
60. Home health services	☐	☐	☐	☐
61. Hospice program	☐	☐	☐	☐
62. Hospital-based outpatient care center services	☐	☐	☐	☐
63. Immunization program	☐	☐	☐	☐
64. Indigent care clinic	☐	☐	☐	☐
65. Linguistic/translation services	☐	☐	☐	☐
66. Meal on wheels	☐	☐	☐	☐
67. Mobile health services	☐	☐	☐	☐
68. Neurological services	☐	☐	☐	☐
69. Nutrition program	☐	☐	☐	☐
70. Occupational health services	☐	☐	☐	☐
71. Oncology services	☐	☐	☐	☐
72. Orthopedic services	☐	☐	☐	☐
73. Outpatient surgery	☐	☐	☐	☐
74. Pain management program	☐	☐	☐	☐
75. Palliative care program	☐	☐	☐	☐
76. Palliative care inpatient unit	☐	☐	☐	☐
77. Patient controlled analgesia (PCA)	☐	☐	☐	☐
78. Patient education center	☐	☐	☐	☐
79. Patient representative services	☐	☐	☐	☐
80. Physical rehabilitation services				
a. Assistive technology center	☐	☐	☐	☐
b. Electrodiagnostic services	☐	☐	☐	☐
c. Physical rehabilitation outpatient services	☐	☐	☐	☐
d. Prosthetic and orthotic services	☐	☐	☐	☐
e. Robot-assisted walking therapy	☐	☐	☐	☐
f. Simulated rehabilitation environment	☐	☐	☐	☐
81. Primary care department	☐	☐	☐	☐
82. Psychiatric services				
a. Psychiatric child-adolescent services	☐	☐	☐	☐
b. Psychiatric consultation-liaison services	☐	☐	☐	☐
c. Psychiatric education services	☐	☐	☐	☐
d. Psychiatric emergency services	☐	☐	☐	☐
e. Psychiatric geriatric services	☐	☐	☐	☐
f. Psychiatric outpatient services	☐	☐	☐	☐
g. Psychiatric partial hospitalization services	☐	☐	☐	☐
h. Psychiatric residential treatment	☐	☐	☐	☐

C. FACILITIES AND SERVICES (continued)

	(1) Owned or provided by my hospital or its subsidiary	(2) Provided by my Health System (in my local community)	(3) Provided through a formal contractual arrangement or joint venture with another provider that is not in my system (in my local community)	(4) Do Not Provide
83. Radiology, diagnostic				
a. CT Scanner	☐	☐	☐	☐
b. Diagnostic radioisotope facility	☐	☐	☐	☐
c. Electron beam computed tomography (EBCT)	☐	☐	☐	☐
d. Full-field digital mammography (FFDM)	☐	☐	☐	☐
e. Magnetic resonance imaging (MRI)	☐	☐	☐	☐
f. Intraoperative magnetic resonance imaging	☐	☐	☐	☐
g. Magnetoencephalography (MEG)	☐	☐	☐	☐
h. Multi-slice spiral computed tomography (<64+ slice CT)	☐	☐	☐	☐
i. Multi-slice spiral computed tomography (64+ slice CT)	☐	☐	☐	☐
j. Positron emission tomography (PET)	☐	☐	☐	☐
k. Positron emission tomography/CT (PET/CT)	☐	☐	☐	☐
l. Single photon emission computerized tomography (SPECT)	☐	☐	☐	☐
m. Ultrasound	☐	☐	☐	☐
84. Radiology, therapeutic				
a. Image-guided radiation therapy (IGRT)	☐	☐	☐	☐
b. Intensity-modulated radiation therapy (IMRT)	☐	☐	☐	☐
c. Proton beam therapy	☐	☐	☐	☐
d. Shaped beam radiation system	☐	☐	☐	☐
e. Stereotactic radiosurgery	☐	☐	☐	☐
85. Retirement housing	☐	☐	☐	☐
86. Robotic surgery	☐	☐	☐	☐
87. Rural health clinic	☐	☐	☐	☐
88. Sleep center	☐	☐	☐	☐
89. Social work services	☐	☐	☐	☐
90. Sports medicine	☐	☐	☐	☐
91. Support groups	☐	☐	☐	☐
92. Swing bed services	☐	☐	☐	☐
93. Teen outreach services	☐	☐	☐	☐
94. Tobacco treatment/cessation program	☐	☐	☐	☐
95. Transplant services				
a. Bone marrow	☐	☐	☐	☐
b. Heart	☐	☐	☐	☐
c. Kidney	☐	☐	☐	☐
d. Liver	☐	☐	☐	☐
e. Lung	☐	☐	☐	☐

	(1)	(2)	(3)	(4)
f. Tissue..	☐	☐	☐	☐
g. Other..	☐	☐	☐	☐
96. Transportation to health services...........................	☐	☐	☐	☐
97. Urgent care center...	☐	☐	☐	☐
98. Virtual colonoscopy	☐	☐	☐	☐
99. Volunteer services department	☐	☐	☐	☐
100. Women's health center/services	☐	☐	☐	☐
101. Wound management services.............................	☐	☐	☐	☐

C. FACILITIES AND SERVICES (continued)

102a. In which of the following physician arrangements does your hospital or system/network participate? Column 3 refers to the networks that were identified in section B, question 3d. For hospital level physician arrangements that are reported in column 1, please report the number of physicians involved.

		(1) My Hospital	(2) My Health System	(3) My Health Network	(4) Do Not Provide
a. Independent Practice Association (IPA)	(# of physicians _____)	☐	☐	☐	☐
b. Group practice without walls	(# of physicians _____)	☐	☐	☐	☐
c. Open Physician-Hospital Organization (PHO)	(# of physicians _____)	☐	☐	☐	☐
d. Closed Physician-Hospital Organization (PHO)..............	(# of physicians _____)	☐	☐	☐	☐
e. Management Service Organization (MSO)	(# of physicians _____)	☐	☐	☐	☐
f. Integrated Salary Model	(# of physicians _____)	☐	☐	☐	☐
g. Equity Model	(# of physicians _____)	☐	☐	☐	☐
h. Foundation..	(# of physicians _____)	☐	☐	☐	☐
i. Other, please specify _____	(# of physicians _____)	☐	☐	☐	☐

102b. Looking across all the relationships identified in question 102a, what is the total number of physicians (count each physician only once) that are engaged in an arrangement with your hospital that allows for joint contracting with payers or shared responsibility for financial risk or clinical performance between the hospital and physician? (arrangement may be at the hospital, system or network level)   # of physicians _____

103a. Does your hospital participate in any joint venture arrangements with physicians or physician groups?   YES ☐   NO ☐

103b. If your hospital participates in any joint ventures with physicians or physician groups, please indicate which types of services are involved in those joint ventures (Check all that apply)

- **a.** ☐ Limited service hospital
- **b.** ☐ Ambulatory surgical centers
- **c.** ☐ Imaging centers
- **d.** ☐ Other _____

103c. If you selected 'a. Limited Service Hospital', please tell us what type(s) of services are provided. (Check all that apply.)

- **a.** ☐ Cardiac
- **b.** ☐ Orthopedic
- **c.** ☐ Surgical
- **d.** ☐ Other _____

103d. Does your hospital participate in joint venture arrangements with organizations other than physician groups?   YES ☐   NO ☐

104a. Has your hospital or health care system established an accountable care organization (ACO)?   YES ☐   NO ☐

104b. If yes, please indicate the patient population that participates in the ACO. (Check all that apply):

- **a.** ☐ Medicaid
- **b.** ☐ Medicare
- **c.** ☐ Privately insured
- **d.** ☐ Other, please specify_____

105. Does your hospital have an established medical home program?   YES ☐   NO ☐

106. Does your hospital participate in a bundled payment program involving inpatient, physician, and/or post acute care services where the hospital receives a single payment from a payer for a package of services and then distributes payments to participating providers of care (such as a single fee for hospital and physician services for a specific procedure, e.g. hip replacement, CABG)?   YES ☐   NO ☐

C. FACILITIES AND SERVICES (continued)

107. Does your hospital, health system or health network have an equity interest in any of the following insurance products? (Check all that apply) Contractual relationships with HMOs and PPOs should not be reported here but in Question 108. Column 3 refers to the networks that were identified in section B, question 3d.

	(1) My Hospital	(2) My Health System	(3) My Health Network	(4) Joint Venture with Insurer	(5) Do Not Provide
a. Health Maintenance Organization	☐	☐	☐	☐	☐
b. Preferred Provider Organization.................	☐	☐	☐	☐	☐
c. Indemnity Fee for Service Plan	☐	☐	☐	☐	☐

108. Does your hospital have a formal written contract that specifies the obligations of each party with:

    a. Health maintenance organization (HMO) .... YES ☐   NO ☐   **b.** If YES, how many contracts?   _____

    c. Preferred provider organization (PPO) .... YES ☐   NO ☐   **d.** If YES, how many contracts?   _____

109. What percentage of the hospital's net patient revenue is paid on a capitated basis?
If the hospital does not participate in capitated arrangements, please enter "0"   _____ %

110. What percentage of the hospital's net patient revenue is paid on a shared risk basis?   _____ %

111. Does your hospital contract directly with employers or a coalition of employers to provide

    care on a capitated, predetermined, or shared risk basis? ....YES ☐   NO ☐

112. If your hospital has arrangements to care for a specific group of enrollees in exchange for a capitated payment,
how many lives are covered?   _____

113. Does your hospital have contracts with commercial payers where payment is tied to performance on quality/safety metrics? YES ☐   NO ☐

D. TOTAL FACILITY BEDS, UTILIZATION, FINANCES, AND STAFFING

Please report beds, utilization, financial, and staffing data for the 12-month period that is consistent with the period reported on page 1. Report financial data for reporting period only. Include within your operations all activities that are wholly owned by the hospital, including subsidiary corporations regardless of where the activity is physically located. Please do not include within your operations distinct and separate divisions that may be owned by your hospital's parent corporation. If final figures are not available, please estimate. Round to the nearest dollar. Report all personnel who were on the payroll and whose payroll expenses are reported in D3f. (Please refer to specific definitions on pages 21-23.)

Fill out column (2) if hospital owns and operates a nursing home type unit/facility. Column (1) should be the combined total of hospital plus nursing home unit/facility.	(1) Total Facility	(2) Nursing Home Unit/Facility

1. BEDS AND UTILIZATION

a. Total licensed beds... _____ _____

b. Beds set up and staffed for use at the end of the reporting period .... _____ _____

c. Bassinets set up and staffed for use at the end of the reporting period .... _____

d. Births (exclude fetal deaths) .... _____

e. Admissions (exclude newborns, include neonatal & swing admissions) .... _____ _____

f. Inpatient days (exclude newborns, include neonatal & swing days) .... _____ _____

g. Emergency department visits.. _____

i. Total outpatient visits (include emergency department visits & outpatient surgeries).... _____

j. Inpatient surgical operations .... _____

k. Number of operating rooms .... _____

l. Outpatient surgical operations.. _____

2. MEDICARE/MEDICAID UTILIZATION (exclude newborns, include neonatal & swing days and deaths)

a1. Total Medicare (Title XVIII) inpatient discharges (including Medicare Managed Care) .... _____ _____

a2. How many Medicare inpatient discharges were Medicare Managed Care .... _____ _____

b1. Total Medicare (Title XVIII) inpatient days (including Medicare Managed Care) .... _____ _____

b2. How many Medicare inpatient days were Medicare Managed Care .... _____ _____

c1. Total Medicaid (Title XIX) inpatient discharges (including Medicaid Managed Care) .... _____ _____

c2. How many Medicaid inpatient discharges were Medicaid Managed Care .... _____ _____

d1. Total Medicaid (Title XIX) inpatient days (including Medicaid Managed Care) .... _____ _____

d2. How many Medicaid inpatient days were Medicaid Managed Care .... _____ _____

3. FINANCIAL

*a. Net patient revenue (treat bad debt as a deduction from revenue).................. _____.00 _____.00

*b. Tax appropriations .... _____.00

*c. Other operating revenue .... _____.00

*d. Nonoperating revenue .... _____.00

*e. TOTAL REVENUE (add 3a thru 3d) .... _____.00 _____.00

f. Payroll expenses (only) .... _____.00 _____.00

g. Employee benefits .... _____.00 _____.00

h. Depreciation expense (for reporting period only) .... _____.00

i. Interest expense .... _____.00

j. Supply expense.. _____.00

k. All other expenses.. _____.00

l. TOTAL EXPENSES (add 3f thru 3k. Exclude bad debt) .... _____.00 _____.00

4. REVENUE BY TYPE

*a. Total gross inpatient revenue... _____.00

*b. Total gross outpatient revenue.. _____.00

*c. Total gross patient revenue .... _____.00

D. TOTAL FACILITY BEDS, UTILIZATION, FINANCES, AND STAFFING (continued)

*5. UNCOMPENSATED CARE & PROVIDER TAXES

a. Bad debt **(Revenue forgone at full established rates. Include in gross revenue)** .... _____.00

b. Financial Assistance (includes Charity Care) (Revenue forgone at full-established rates. Include in gross revenue.)........ _____.00

c. Is your bad debt reported here (5a) reported on the basis of full charges?　　YES ☐　　NO ☐

d. Does your state have a provider Medicaid tax/assessment program?　　YES ☐　　NO ☐

e. If yes, please report the total gross amount paid into the program.. _____.00

f. Due to differing accounting standards please indicate whether the provider tax/assessment amount is included in:
1. Total expense　　YES ☐　　NO ☐
2. Deductions from net patient revenue　　YES ☐　　NO ☐

*6. REVENUE BY PAYOR (report total facility gross and net figures)

		(1) Gross	(2) Net
*a. GOVERNMENT　(1) Medicare:			
a) Fee for service patient revenue		_____.00	_____.00
b) Managed care revenue ……………………,............		_____.00	_____.00
c) Total (a + b) …………………………...............		_____**.00**	_____**.00**
(2) Medicaid:			
a) Fee for service patient revenue.................................		_____.00	_____.00
b) Managed care revenue ……...............................……		_____.00	_____.00
c) Medicaid Disproportionate Share Hospital Payments (DSH)			_____.00
d) Medicaid supplemental payments: not including Medicaid Disproportionate Share Hospital Payments (DSH)			_____.00
e) Total (a + b + c + d) ………………………………		_____**.00**	_____**.00**
(3) Other government: …………………………….........……		_____.00	_____.00
*b. NONGOVERNMENT　　(1) Self-pay………………………….......		_____.00	_____.00
(2) Third-party payors:			
a)　Managed care (includes HMO and PPO) ……		_____.00	_____.00
b)　Other third-party payors …………………………		_____.00	_____.00
c)　Total third-party payors (a + b) ……………		_____**.00**	_____**.00**
(3) All Other nongovernment: ……………………………		_____.00	_____.00
*c. TOTAL ……………………………………………………………		_____**.00**	_____**.00**

(Total gross should equal 4c on page 9. Total net should equal 3a on page 9.)

Are the financial data on pages 9 and 10 from your audited financial statement? .... YES ☐　　NO ☐

---

7. FIXED ASSETS
a. Property, plant and equipment at <u>cost</u> .... _____.00
b. Accumulated <u>depreciation</u> .... _____.00
c. Net property, plant and equipment (a-b) .... _____.00
d. Total gross square feet of your physical plant used for or in support of your healthcare activities .... _____

8. TOTAL CAPITAL EXPENSES
Include all expenses used to acquire assets, including buildings, remodeling projects, equipment, or property.　_____.00

D. TOTAL FACILITY BEDS, UTILIZATION, FINANCES, AND STAFFING (continued)

9. INFORMATION TECHNOLOGY

*a. IT operating expense..._____.00

*b. IT capital expense.._____.00

*c. Number of employed IT staff (in FTEs) ...._____

*d. Number of outsourced IT staff (in FTEs).._____

e. Does your hospital have an electronic health record (see definition)?
    ☐ Yes, fully implemented   ☐ Yes, partially implemented   ☐ No

10. STAFFING

Report full-time (35 hours or more) and part-time (less than 35 hours) personnel who were on the hospital/facility **payroll at the end of your reporting period.** Include members of religious orders for whom dollar equivalents were reported. Exclude private-duty nurses, volunteers, and all personnel whose salary is financed entirely by outside research grants. Exclude physicians and dentists who are paid on a fee basis. FTE is the total number of hours worked by all employees over the full (12 month) reporting period divided by the normal number of hours worked by a full-time employee for that same time period. For example, if your hospital considers a normal workweek for a full-time employee to be 40 hours, a total of 2,080 would be worked over a full year (52 weeks). If the total number of hours worked by all employees on the payroll is 208,000, then the number of Full-Time Equivalents (FTE) is 100 (employees). The FTE calculation for a specific occupational category such as registered nurses is exactly the same. The calculation for each occupational category should be based on the number of hours worked by staff employed in that specific category.

For each occupational category, please report the number of staff vacancies as of the last day of your reporting period. A vacancy is defined as a budgeted staff position which is unfilled as of the last day of the reporting period and for which the hospital is actively seeking either a full-time or part-time permanent replacement. Personnel who work in more than one area should be included only in the category of their primary responsibility and should be counted only once.

	(1) Full-Time (35 hr/wk or more) On Payroll	(2) Part-Time (Less than 35hr/wk) On Payroll	(3) FTE	(4) Vacancies
a. Physicians	_____	_____	_____	_____
b. Dentists	_____	_____	_____	_____
c. Medical and dental residents/interns	_____	_____	_____	_____
d. Other trainees	_____	_____	_____	_____
e. Registered nurses	_____	_____	_____	_____
f. Licensed practical (vocational) nurses	_____	_____	_____	_____
g. Nursing assistive personnel	_____	_____	_____	_____
h. Radiology technicians	_____	_____	_____	_____
i. Laboratory technicians	_____	_____	_____	_____
j. Pharmacists, licensed	_____	_____	_____	_____
k. Pharmacy technicians	_____	_____	_____	_____
l. Respiratory therapists	_____	_____	_____	_____
m. All other personnel	_____	_____	_____	_____
n. Total facility personnel (add 11a through 11m)	_____	_____	_____	_____

(Total facility personnel should include hospital plus nursing home type unit/facility personnel reported separately in 11o and 11p.)

o. Nursing home type unit/facility registered nurses	_____	_____	_____	_____
p. Total nursing home type unit/facility personnel	_____	_____	_____	_____

q. For your employed RNs reported above (D.10.e), please report the number of full time equivalents who are involved in direct patient care.

_____ Number of direct patient care FTEs

*These data will be treated as confidential and not released without written permission. AHA will however, share these data with your respective state hospital association and, if requested, with your appropriate metropolitan/regional association.

For members of the Catholic Health Association of the United States (CHA), AHA will also share these data with CHA unless there are objections expressed by checking this box☐. The state/metropolitan/regional association and CHA may not release these data without written permission from the hospital.

D. TOTAL FACILITY BEDS, UTILIZATION, FINANCES, AND STAFFING (continued)

11. PRIVILEGED PHYSICIANS

Report the total number of physicians with privileges at your hospital by type of relationship with the hospital. <u>The sum of the physicians reported in 11a-11f should equal the total number of privileged physicians (11g) in the hospital.</u>

	(1) Total Employed	(2) Total Individual Contract	(3) Total Group Contract	(4) Not Employed or Under Contract	(5) Total Privileged (add columns 1-4)
a. Primary care (general practitioner, general internal medicine, family practice, general pediatrics, obstetrics/gynecology, geriatrics)	_____	_____	_____	_____	_____
b. Emergency medicine	_____	_____	_____	_____	_____
c. Hospitalist	_____	_____	_____	_____	_____
d. Intensivist	_____	_____	_____	_____	_____
e. Radiologist/pathologist/anesthesiologist	_____	_____	_____	_____	_____
f. Other specialist	_____	_____	_____	_____	_____
g. Total (add 11a-11f)	_____	_____	_____	_____	_____

12. HOSPITALISTS

a. Do hospitalists provide care for patients in your hospital?(if no, please skip to 13)............. YES ☐　　NO ☐ **(if yes, please report in D.11c.)**

b. If yes, please report the total number of full-time equivalents (FTE) hospitalists.....................FTE _____

13. INTENSIVISTS

a. Do intensivists provide care for patients in your hospital? (If no, please skip to 14.) YES ☐　　NO ☐ **(if yes, please report in D.11d.)**

b. If yes, please report the total number of FTE intensivists and assign them to the following areas. Please indicate whether the intensive care area is closed to intensivists. (Meaning that only intensivists are authorized to care for ICU patients.)

		FTE	Closed to Intensivists
1.	Medical-surgical intensive care	_____	☐
2.	Cardiac intensive care	_____	☐
3.	Neonatal intensive care	_____	☐
4.	Pediatric intensive care	_____	☐
5.	Other intensive care	_____	☐
6.	**Total**	_____	

14. ADVANCED PRACTICE REGISTERED NURSES

a. Do advanced practice nurses provide care for patients in your hospital? .... YES ☐　　NO ☐　(if no, please skip to 15.)

b. If yes, please report the number of full time, part time and FTE advanced practice nurses who provide care for patients in your hospital.

_____ Full-time　_____ Part-time　_____ FTE

c. If yes, please indicate the type of service the nurses provide (check all that apply).

☐ Primary care　　☐ Anesthesia services (Certified registered nurse anesthetist)　　☐ Emergency department care

☐ Other specialty care　☐ Patient education　☐ Case management　☐ Other

15. FOREIGN EDUCATED NURSES

a. Did your facility hire more foreign-educated nurses (including contract or agency nurses) to help fill RN vacancies in 2013 vs. 2012?

More ☐　　Less ☐　　Same ☐　　Did not hire foreign nurses ☐

b. If yes, from which countries/continents are you recruiting foreign-educated nurses? (check all that apply)

Africa ☐　South Korea ☐　Canada ☐　Philippines ☐　China ☐　India ☐　Other ☐

E. SUPPLEMENTAL INFORMATION

1. Does your hospital provide services through one or more satellite facilities?   YES ☐   NO ☐

2. . Does the hospital participate in a group purchasing arrangement?   YES ☐   NO ☐

If yes, please provide the name, city, and state of the group purchasing organization(s)

Name: _____   City: _____   State: _____

3. Does the hospital purchase medical/surgical supplies directly through a distributor?   YES ☐   NO ☐
If yes, please provide the name of the distributor(s).

Name: _____

4. If your hospital hired RNs during the reporting period, how many were new graduates from nursing schools? _____

5. Use this space to describe your community benefit activities as well as any partners you are currently working with on such activities. Also use this space or additional sheets if more space is required for comments or to elaborate on any information supplied on this survey. Refer to the response by page, section and item name.

_____
_____
_____
_____
_____
_____
_____
_____
_____
_____
_____
_____
_____
_____
_____
_____
_____
_____
_____
_____
_____
_____
_____
_____
_____
_____
_____

As declared previously, hospital specific revenue data are treated as confidential. AHA's policy is not to release these data without written permission from your institution. The AHA will however, share these data with your respective state hospital association and if requested with your appropriate metropolitan/regional association.

On occasion, the AHA is asked to provide these data to external organizations, both public and private, for their use in analyzing crucial health care policy or research issues. The AHA is requesting your permission to allow us to release your confidential data to those requests that we consider legitimate and worthwhile. In every instance of disclosure, the receiving organization will be prohibited from releasing hospital specific information.

Please indicate below whether or not you agree to these types of disclosure:

[   ] I hereby grant AHA permission to release my hospital's revenue data to external users that the AHA determines have a legitimate and worthwhile need to gain access to these data subject to the user's agreement with the AHA not to release hospital specific information.

_____

Chief Executive Officer   Date

[   ] I do not grant AHA permission to release my confidential data.

_____

Chief Executive Officer   Date

Does your hospital or health system have an Internet or Homepage address?   Yes ☐ No ☐

If yes, please provide the address: http:// _____

Thank you for your cooperation in completing this survey. If there are any questions about your responses to this survey, who should be contacted?

_____   _____   (___) _____
Name (please print)   Title   (Area Code) Telephone Number

____/____/____   _____   (___) _____
Date of Completion   Chief Executive Officer   Hospital's Main Fax Number

Contact Email address: _____

NOTE: PLEASE PHOTOCOPY THE INFORMATION FOR YOUR HOSPITAL FILE BEFORE RETURNING THE ORIGINAL FORM TO THE AMERICAN HOSPITAL ASSOCIATION. ALSO, PLEASE FORWARD A PHOTOCOPY OF THE COMPLETED QUESTIONNAIRE TO YOUR STATE HOSPITAL ASSOCIATION.

THANK YOU

INSTRUCTIONS AND DEFINITIONS FOR THE 2013 ANNUAL SURVEY OF HOSPITALS.
For purposes of this survey, a hospital is defined as the organization or corporate entity licensed or registered as a hospital by a state to provide diagnostic and therapeutic patient services for a variety of medical conditions, both surgical and nonsurgical.

1. Reporting period used (beginning and ending date): Record the beginning and ending dates of the reporting period in an eight-digit number: for example, January 1, 2013 should be shown as 01/01/2013. Number of days should equal the time span between the two dates that the hospital was open. If you are reporting for less than 365 days, utilization and finances should be presented for days reported only.
2. Were you in operation 12 full months at the end of your reporting period? If you are reporting for less than 365 days, utilization and finances should be presented for days reported only.
3. Number of days open during reporting period: Number of days should equal the time span between the two dates that the hospital was open.

SECTION B
ORGANIZATIONAL STRUCTURE
Instructions and Definitions

1. **CONTROL**
   Check the box to the left of the type of organization that is responsible for establishing policy for overall operation of the hospital.
   Government, nonfederal.
      State. Controlled by an agency of state government.
      County. Controlled by an agency of county government.
      City. Controlled by an agency of municipal government.
      City-County. Controlled jointly by agencies of municipal and county governments.
      Hospital district or authority. Controlled by a political subdivision of a state, county, or city created solely for the purpose of establishing and maintaining medical care or health-related care institutions.
   Nongovernment, not for profit. Controlled by not-for-profit organizations, including religious organizations (Catholic hospitals, for example), community hospitals, cooperative hospitals, hospitals operated by fraternal societies, and so forth.
   Investor owned, for profit. Controlled on a for profit basis by an individual, partnership, or a profit making corporation.
   Government, federal. Controlled by an agency or department of the federal government.
2. **SERVICE**
   Indicate the ONE category that best describes the type of service that your hospital provides to the majority of patients.
   General medical and surgical. Provides diagnostic and therapeutic services to patients for a variety of medical conditions, both surgical and nonsurgical.
   Hospital unit of an institution. Provides diagnostic and therapeutic services to patients in an institution.
   Hospital unit within a facility for persons with intellectual disabilities (formerly hospital unit within an institution for the mentally retarded). Provides diagnostic and therapeutic services to persons with intellectual disabilities.
   Surgical. An acute care specialty hospital where 2/3 or more of its inpatient claims are for surgical/diagnosis related groups.
   Psychiatric. Provides diagnostic and therapeutic services to patients with mental or emotional disorders.
   Tuberculosis and other respiratory diseases. Provides medical care and rehabilitative services to patients for whom the primary diagnosis is tuberculosis or other respiratory diseases.
   Cancer. Provides medical care to patients for whom the primary diagnosis is cancer.
   Heart. Provides diagnosis and treatment of heart disease.
   Obstetrics and gynecology. Provides medical and surgical treatment to pregnant women and to mothers following delivery. Also provides diagnostic and therapeutic services to women with diseases or disorders of the reproductive organs.
   Eye, ear, nose, and throat. Provides diagnosis and treatment of diseases and injuries of the eyes, ears, nose, and throat.
   Rehabilitation. Provides a comprehensive array of restoration services for the disabled and all support services necessary to help them attain their maximum functional capacity.
   Orthopedic. Provides corrective treatment of deformities, diseases, and ailments of the locomotive apparatus, especially affecting the limbs, bones, muscles, and joints.
   Chronic disease. Provides medical and skilled nursing services to patients with long-term illnesses who are not in an acute phase, but who require an intensity of services not available in nursing homes.
   Intellectual Disabilities (Formerly Institution for the mentally retarded). Provides health-related care on a regular basis to patients with developmental or intellectual disabilities who cannot be treated in a skilled nursing unit.
   Acute long term care hospital. Provides high acuity interdisciplinary services to medically complex patients that require more intensive recuperation and care than can be provided in a typical nursing facility.
   Alcoholism and other chemical dependency. Provides diagnostic and therapeutic services to patients with alcoholism or other drug dependencies.
3. **OTHER**
   a. **Children admissions.** A hospital whose primary focus is the health and treatment of children and adolescents.
   b. **Subsidiary.** A company that is wholly controlled by another or one that is more than 50% owned by another organization.
   c. **Contract managed.** General day-to-day management of an entire organization by another organization under a formal contract. Managing organization reports directly to the board of trustees or owners of the managed organization; managed organization retains total legal responsibility and ownership of the facility's assets and liabilities.
   d. **Network.** A group of hospitals, physicians, other providers, insurers and/or community agencies that voluntarily work together to coordinate and deliver health services

Owned/provided by the hospital or its subsidiary. All patient revenues, expenses and utilization related to the provision of the service are reflected in the hospital's statistics reported elsewhere in this survey.

Provided by my Health System (in my local community). Another health care provider in the same system as your hospital provides the service and patient revenue, expenses, and utilization related to the provision of the service are recorded at the point where the service was provided and would not be reflected in your hospital's statistics reported elsewhere in this survey. (A system is a corporate body that owns, leases, religiously sponsors and/or manages health providers)

Provided through a formal contractual arrangement or joint venture with another provider that is not in my system or network. All patient revenues and utilization related to the provision of the service are recorded at the site where the service was provided and would not be reflected in your hospital statistics reported elsewhere in this survey. (A joint venture is a contractual arrangement between two or more parties forming an unincorporated business. The participants in the arrangement remain independent and separate outside of the venture's purpose.)

1. **General medical-surgical care.** Provides acute care to patients in medical and surgical units on the basis of physicians' orders and approved nursing care plans.
2. **Pediatric medical-surgical care.** Provides acute care to pediatric patients on the basis of physicians' orders and approved nursing care plans.
3. **Obstetrics.** Level should be designated: (1) unit provides services for uncomplicated maternity and newborn cases; (2) unit provides services for uncomplicated cases, the majority of complicated problems, and special neonatal services; and (3) unit provides services for all serious illnesses and abnormalities and is supervised by a full-time maternal/fetal specialist.
4. **Medical surgical intensive care.** Provides patient care of a more intensive nature than the usual medical and surgical care, on the basis of physicians' orders and approved nursing care plans. These units are staffed with specially trained nursing personnel and contain monitoring and specialized support equipment for patients who because of shock, trauma or other life-threatening conditions require intensified comprehensive observation and care. Includes mixed intensive care units.
5. **Cardiac intensive care.** Provides patient care of a more specialized nature than the usual medical and surgical care, on the basis of physicians' orders and approved nursing care plans. The unit is staffed with specially trained nursing personnel and contains monitoring and specialized support or treatment equipment for patients who, because of heart seizure, open-heart surgery, or other life-threatening conditions, require intensified, comprehensive observation and care. May include myocardial infarction, pulmonary care, and heart transplant units.
6. **Neonatal intensive care.** A unit that must be separate from the newborn nursery providing intensive care to all sick infants including those with the very lowest birth weights (less than 1500 grams). NICU has potential for providing mechanical ventilation, neonatal surgery, and special care for the sickest infants born in the hospital or transferred from another institution. A full-time neonatologist serves as director of the NICU.
7. **Neonatal intermediate care.** A unit that must be separate from the normal newborn nursery and that provides intermediate and/or recovery care and some specialized services, including immediate resuscitation, intravenous therapy, and capacity for prolonged oxygen therapy and monitoring.
8. **Pediatric intensive care.** Provides care to pediatric patients that is of a more intensive nature than that usually provided to pediatric patients. The unit is staffed with specially trained personnel and contains monitoring and specialized support equipment for treatment of patients who, because of shock, trauma, or other life-threatening conditions, require intensified, comprehensive observation and care.
9. **Burn care.** Provides care to severely burned patients. Severely burned patients are those with any of the following: (1) second-degree burns of more than 25% total body surface area for adults or 20% total body surface area for children; (2) third-degree burns of more than 10% total body surface area; (3) any severe burns of the hands, face, eyes, ears, or feet; or (4) all inhalation injuries, electrical burns, complicated burn injuries involving fractures and other major traumas, and all other poor risk factors.
10. **Other special care.** Provides care to patients requiring care more intensive than that provided in the acute area, yet not sufficiently intensive to require admission to an intensive care unit. Patients admitted to this area are usually transferred here from an intensive care unit once their condition has improved. These units are sometimes referred to as definitive observation, step-down or progressive care units.
11. **Other intensive care.** A specially staffed, specialty equipped, separate section of a hospital dedicated to the observation, care, and treatment of patients with life threatening illnesses, injuries, or complications from which recovery is possible. It provides special expertise and facilities for the support of vital function and utilizes the skill of medical nursing and other staff experienced in the management of these problems.
12. **Physical rehabilitation.** Provides care encompassing a comprehensive array of restoration services for the disabled and all support services necessary to help patients attain their maximum functional capacity.
13. **Alcoholism-drug abuse or dependency care.** Provides diagnosis and therapeutic services to patients with alcoholism or other drug dependencies. Includes care for inpatient/residential treatment for patients whose course of treatment involves more intensive care than provided in an outpatient setting or where patient requires supervised withdrawal.
14. **Psychiatric care.** Provides acute or long-term care to emotionally disturbed patients, including patients admitted for diagnosis and those admitted for treatment of psychiatric problems, on the basis of physicians' orders and approved nursing care plans. Long-term care may include intensive supervision to the chronically mentally ill, mentally disordered, or other mentally incompetent persons.
15. **Skilled nursing care.** Provides non-acute medical and skilled nursing care services, therapy, and social services under the supervision of a licensed registered nurse on a 24-hour basis.
16. **Intermediate nursing care.** Provides health-related services (skilled nursing care and social services) to residents with a variety of physical conditions or functional disabilities. These residents do not require the care provided by a hospital or skilled nursing facility, but do need supervision and support services.
17. **Acute long-term care.** Provides specialized acute hospital care to medically complex patients who are critically ill, have multisystem complications and/or failure, and require hospitalization averaging 25 days, in a facility offering specialized treatment programs and therapeutic intervention on a 24-hour/7 day a week basis.
18. **Other long-term care.** Provision of long-term care other than skilled nursing care or intermediate care for those who do not require daily medical or nursing services, but may requires some assistance in the activities of daily living. This can include residential care, elderly care, or sheltered care facilities for developmentally disabled.
19. **Other care.** (specify) Any type of care other than those listed above.
    The sum of the beds reported in Section C 1-19 should equal what you have reported in Section D(1b) for beds set up and staffed.
20. **Adult day care program.** Program providing supervision, medical and psychological care, and social activities for older adults who live at home or in another family setting, but cannot be alone or prefer to be with others during the day. May include intake assessment, health monitoring, occupational therapy, personal care, noon meal, and transportation services.
21. **Airborne infection isolation room.** A single-occupancy room for patient care where environmental factors are controlled in an effort to minimize the transmission of those infectious agents, usually spread person to person by droplet nuclei associated with coughing and inhalation. Such rooms typically have specific ventilation requirements for controlled ventilation, air pressure and filtration.
22. **Alcoholism-drug abuse or dependency outpatient services.** Organized hospital services that provide medical care and/or rehabilitative treatment services to outpatients for whom the primary diagnosis is alcoholism or other chemical dependency.

23. **Alzheimer center.** Facility that offers care to persons with Alzheimer's disease and their families through an integrated program of clinical services, research, and education.
24. **Ambulance services.** Provision of ambulance service to the ill and injured who require medical attention on a scheduled and unscheduled basis.
25. **Ambulatory surgery center.** Facility that provides care to patients requiring surgery that are admitted and discharged on the same day. Ambulatory surgery centers are distinct from same day surgical units within the hospital outpatient departments for purposes of Medicare payment.
26. **Arthritis treatment center.** Specifically equipped and staffed center for the diagnosis and treatment of arthritis and other joint disorders.
27. **Assisted living.** A special combination of housing, supportive services, personalized assistance and health care designed to respond to the individual needs of those who need help in activities of daily living and instrumental activities of daily living. Supportive services are available, 24 hours a day, to meet scheduled and unscheduled needs, in a way that promotes maximum independence and dignity for each resident and encourages the involvement of a resident's family, neighbor and friends.
28. **Auxiliary.** A volunteer community organization formed to assist the hospital in carrying out its purpose and to serve as a link between the institution and the community.
29. **Bariatric/weight control services.** The medical practice of weight reduction.
30. **Birthing room/LDR room/LDRP room.** A single-room type of maternity care with a more homelike setting for families than the traditional three-room unit (labor/delivery/recovery) with a separate postpartum area. A birthing room combines labor and delivery in one room. An LDR room accommodates three stages in the birthing process--labor, delivery, and recovery. An LDRP room accommodates all four stages of the birth process--labor, delivery, recovery, and postpartum.
31. **Blood donor center.** A facility that performs, or is responsible for the collection, processing, testing or distribution of blood and components.
32. **Breast cancer screening/mammograms.** Mammography screening - The use of breast x-ray to detect unsuspected breast cancer in asymptomatic women. Diagnostic mammography - The x-ray imaging of breast tissue in symptomatic women who are considered to have a substantial likelihood of having breast cancer already.
33. **Cardiology and cardiac surgery services.** Services which include the diagnosis and treatment of diseases and disorders involving the heart and circulatory system.
   a-b. Cardiology services. An organized clinical service offering diagnostic and interventional procedures to manage the full range of heart conditions.
   c-d. Diagnostic catheterization. (also called coronary angiography or coronary arteriography) is used to assist in diagnosing complex heart conditions. Cardiac angiography involves the insertion of a tiny catheter into the artery in the groin then carefully threading the catheter up into the aorta where the coronary arteries originate. Once the catheter is in place, a dye is injected which allows the cardiologist to see the size, shape, and distribution of the coronary arteries. These images are used to diagnose heart disease and to determine, among other things, whether or not surgery is indicated.
   e-f. Interventional cardiac catheterization. Nonsurgical procedure that utilizes the same basic principles as diagnostic catheterization and then uses advanced techniques to improve the heart's function. It can be a less-invasive alternative to heart surgery.
   g-h. Cardiac surgery. Includes minimally invasive procedures that include surgery done with only a small incision or no incision at all, such as through a laparoscope or an endoscope and more invasive major surgical procedures that include open chest and open heart surgery.
   i-j. Cardiac electrophysiology. Evaluation and management of patients with complex rhythm or conduction abnormalities, including diagnostic testing, treatment of arrhythmias by catheter ablation or drug therapy, and pacemaker/defibrillator implantation and follow-up.
   k. Cardiac rehabilitation. A medically supervised program to help heart patients recover quickly and improve their overall physical and mental functioning. The goal is to reduce risk of another cardiac event or to keep an already present heart condition from getting worse. Cardiac rehabilitation programs include: counseling to patients, an exercise program, helping patients modify risk factors such as smoking and high blood pressure, providing vocational guidance to enable the patient to return to work, supplying information on physical limitations and lending emotional support.
34. **Case management.** A system of assessment, treatment planning, referral and follow-up that ensures the provision of comprehensive and continuous services and the coordination of payment and reimbursement for care.
35. **Chaplaincy/pastoral care services.** A service ministering religious activities and providing pastoral counseling to patients, their families, and staff of a health care organization.
36. **Chemotherapy.** An organized program for the treatment of cancer by the use of drugs or chemicals.
37. **Children's wellness program.** A program that encourages improved health status and a healthful lifestyle of children through health education, exercise, nutrition and health promotion.
38. **Chiropractic services.** An organized clinical service including spinal manipulation or adjustment and related diagnostic and therapeutic services.
39. **Community outreach.** A program that systematically interacts with the community to identify those in need of services, alerting persons and their families to the availability of services, locating needed services, and enabling persons to enter the service delivery system.
40. **Complementary and alternative medicine services.** Organized hospital services or formal arrangements to providers that provide care or treatment not based solely on traditional western allopathic medical teachings as instructed in most U.S. medical schools. Includes any of the following: acupuncture, chiropractic, homeopathy, osteopathy, diet and lifestyle changes, herbal medicine, massage therapy, etc.
41. **Computer assisted orthopedic surgery (CAOS).** Orthopedic surgery using computer technology, enabling three-dimensional graphic models to visualize a patient's anatomy.
42. **Crisis prevention.** Services provided in order to promote physical and mental wellbeing and the early identification of disease and ill health prior to the onset and recognition of symptoms so as to permit early treatment.
43. **Dental Services.** An organized dental service or dentists on staff, not necessarily involving special facilities, providing dental or oral services to inpatients or outpatients.
44. **Emergency services.** Health services that are provided after the onset of a medical condition that manifests itself by symptoms of sufficient severity, including severe pain, that the absence of immediate medical attention could reasonably be expected by a prudent layperson, who possesses an average knowledge of health and medicine, to result in placing the patient's health in serious jeopardy.
   a-b. Emergency department. Hospital facilities for the provision of unscheduled outpatient services to patients whose conditions require immediate care.
   c. Satellite Emergency Department. A facility owned and operated by the hospital but physically separate from the hospital for the provision of unscheduled outpatient services to patients whose conditions require immediate care. A freestanding ED is not physically connected to a hospital, but has all necessary emergency staffing and equipment on-site.
   e. Trauma center (certified). A facility to provide emergency and specialized intensive care to critically ill and injured patients. Level 1: A regional resource trauma center, which is capable of providing total care for every aspect of injury and plays a leadership role in trauma research and education. Level 2: A community trauma center, which is capable of providing trauma care to all but the most severely injured patients who require highly specialized care. Level 3: A rural trauma hospital, which is capable of providing care to a large number of injury victims and can resuscitate and stabilize more severely injured patients so that they can be transported to level 1 or 2 facilities. Please provide explanation on page 15 if necessary.

45. **Enabling services.** A program that is designed to help the patient access health care services by offering any of the following: transportation services and/or referrals to local social services agencies.
46. **Endoscopic services.**
  a. **Optical colonoscopy.** An examination of the interior of the colon using a long, flexible, lighted tube with a small built-in camera.
  b. **Endoscopic ultrasound.** Specially designed endoscope that incorporates an ultrasound transducer used to obtain detailed images of organs in the chest and abdomen. The endoscope can be passed through the mouth or the anus. When combined with needle biopsy the procedure can assist in diagnosis of disease and staging of cancer.
  c. **Ablation of Barrett's esophagus.** Premalignant condition that can lead to adenocarcinoma of the esophagus. The nonsurgical ablation of premalignant tissue in Barrett's esophagus by the application of thermal energy or light through an endoscope passed from the mouth into the esophagus.
  d. **Esophageal impedance study.** A test in which a catheter is placed through the nose into the esophagus to measure whether gas or liquids are passing from the stomach into the esophagus and causing symptoms.
  e. **Endoscopic retrograde cholangiopancreatography (ERCP).** A procedure in which a catheter is introduced through an endoscope into the bile ducts and pancreatic ducts. Injection of contrast material permits detailed x-ray of these structures. The procedure is used diagnostically as well as therapeutically to relieve obstruction or remove stones.
47. **Enrollment (insurance) assistance services.** A program that provides enrollment assistance for patients who are potentially eligible for public health insurance programs such as Medicaid, State Children's Health Insurance, or local/state indigent care programs. The specific services offered This could include explanation of benefits, assist applicants in completing the application and locating all relevant documents, conduct eligibility interviews, and/or forward applications and documentation to state/local social service or health agency.
48. **Extracorporeal shock wave lithotripter (ESWL).** A medical device used for treating stones in the kidney or urethra. The device disintegrates kidney stones noninvasively through the transmission of acoustic shock waves directed at the stones.
49. **Fertility clinic.** A specialized program set in an infertility center that provides counseling and education as well as advanced reproductive techniques such as: injectable therapy, reproductive surgeries, treatment for endometriosis, male factor infertility, tubal reversals, in vitro fertilization (IVF), donor eggs, and other such services to help patients achieve successful pregnancies.
50. **Fitness center.** Provides exercise, testing, or evaluation programs and fitness activities to the community and hospital employees.
51. **Freestanding outpatient care center.** A facility owned and operated by the hospital, that is physically separate from the hospital and provides various medical treatments and diagnostic services on an outpatient basis only. Laboratory and radiology services are usually available.
52. **Geriatric services.** The branch of medicine dealing with the physiology of aging and the diagnosis and treatment of disease affecting the aged. Services could include: Adult day care; Alzheimer's diagnostic-assessment services; Comprehensive geriatric assessment; Emergency response system; Geriatric acute care unit; and/or Geriatric clinics.
53. **Health fair.** Community health education events that focus on the prevention of disease and promotion of health through such activities as audiovisual exhibits and free diagnostic services.
54. **Community health education.** Education that provides health information to individuals and populations as well as support for personal, family and community health decisions with the objective of improving health status.
55. **Genetic testing/counseling.** A service equipped with adequate laboratory facilities and directed by a qualified physician to advise parents and prospective parents on potential problems in cases of genetic defects. A genetic test is the analysis of human DNA, RNA, chromosomes, proteins, and certain metabolites in order to detect heritable disease-related genotypes, mutations, phenotypes, or karyotypes for clinical purposes. Genetic tests can have diverse purposes, including the diagnosis of genetic diseases in newborns, children, and adults; the identification of future health risks; the prediction of drug responses; and the assessment of risks to future children.
56. **Health screening.** A preliminary procedure such as a test or examination to detect the most characteristic sign or signs of a disorder that may require further investigation.
57. **Health research.** Organized hospital research program in any of the following areas: basic research, clinical research, community health research, and/or research on innovative health care delivery.
58. **Hemodialysis.** Provision of equipment and personnel for the treatment of renal insufficiency on an inpatient or outpatient basis.
59. **HIV-AIDS services.** Could include: HIV-AIDS unit-Special unit or team designated and equipped specifically for diagnosis, treatment, continuing care planning, and counseling services for HIV-AIDS patients and their families. General inpatient care for HIV-AIDS-Inpatient diagnosis and treatment for human immunodeficiency virus and acquired immunodeficiency syndrome patients, but dedicated unit is not available. Specialized outpatient program for HIV-AIDS-Special outpatient program providing diagnostic, treatment, continuing care planning, and counseling for HIV-AIDS patients and their families.
60. **Home health services.** Service providing nursing, therapy, and health-related homemaker or social services in the patient's home.
61. **Hospice.** A program providing palliative care, chiefly medical relief of pain and supportive services, addressing the emotional, social, financial, and legal needs of terminally ill patients and their families. Care can be provided in a variety of settings, both inpatient and at home.
62. **Hospital-based outpatient care center-services.** Organized hospital health care services offered by appointment on an ambulatory basis. Services may include outpatient surgery, examination, diagnosis, and treatment of a variety of medical conditions on a nonemergency basis, and laboratory and other diagnostic testing as ordered by staff or outside physician referral.
63. **Immunization program.** Program that plans, coordinates and conducts immunization services in the community.
64. **Indigent care clinic.** Health care services for uninsured and underinsured persons where care is free of charge or charged on a sliding scale. This would include "free clinics" staffed by volunteer practitioners, but could also be staffed by employees with the sponsoring health care organization subsidizing the cost of service.
65. **Linguistic/translation services.** Services provided by the hospital designed to make health care more accessible to non-English speaking patients and their physicians.
66. **Meals on wheels.** A hospital sponsored program which delivers meals to people, usually the elderly, who are unable to prepare their own meals. Low cost, nutritional meals are delivered to individuals' homes on a regular basis.
67. **Mobile health services.** Vans and other vehicles used for delivery to primary care services.
68. **Neurological services.** Services provided by the hospital dealing with the operative and nonoperative management of disorders of the central, peripheral, and autonomic nervous systems.
69. **Nutrition programs.** Services within a health care facility which are designed to provide inexpensive, nutritionally sound meals to patients.
70. **Occupational health services.** Includes services designed to protect the safety of employees from hazards in the work environment.
71. **Oncology services.** Inpatient and outpatient services for patients with cancer, including comprehensive care, support and guidance in addition to patient education and prevention, chemotherapy, counseling and other treatment methods.
72. **Orthopedic services.** Services provided for the prevention or correction of injuries or disorders of the skeletal system and associated muscles, joints and ligaments.
73. **Outpatient surgery.** Scheduled surgical services provided to patients who do not remain in the hospital overnight. The surgery may be performed in operating suites also used for inpatient surgery, specially designated surgical suites for outpatient surgery, or procedure rooms within an outpatient care facility.

74. **Pain management program.** A recognized clinical service or program providing specialized medical care, drugs or therapies for the management of acute or chronic pain and other distressing symptoms, administered by specially trained physicians and other clinicians, to patients suffering from an acute illness of diverse causes.

75. **Palliative care program.** An organized program providing specialized medical care, drugs or therapies for the management of acute or chronic pain and/or the control of symptoms administered by specially trained physicians and other clinicians; and supportive care services, such as counseling on advanced directives, spiritual care, and social services, to patients with advanced disease and their families.

76. **Palliative care inpatient unit.** An inpatient palliative care ward is a physically discreet, inpatient nursing unit where the focus is palliative care. The patient care focus is on symptom relief for complex patients who may be continuing to undergo primary treatment. Care is delivered by palliative medicine specialists.

77. **Patient controlled analgesia (PCA).** Intravenously administered pain medicine under the patient's control. The patient has a button on the end of a cord than can be pushed at will, whenever more pain medicine is desired. This button will only deliver more pain medicine at pre-determined intervals, as programmed by the doctor's order.

78. **Patient education center.** Written goals and objectives for the patient and/or family related to therapeutic regimens, medical procedures, and self-care.

79. **Patient representative services.** Organized hospital services providing personnel through whom patients and staff can seek solutions to institutional problems affecting the delivery of high quality care and services.

80. **Physical rehabilitation services.** Program providing medical, health-related, therapy, social, and/or vocational services to help disabled persons attain or retain their maximum functional capacity.
    a. **Assistive technology center.** A program providing access to specialized hardware and software with adaptations allowing individuals greater independence with mobility, dexterity, or increased communication options.
    b. **Electrodiagnostic services.** Diagnostic testing services for nerve and muscle function including services such as nerve conduction studies and needle electromyography.
    c. **Physical rehabilitation outpatient services.** Outpatient program providing medical, health-related, therapy, social, and/or vocational services to help disabled persons attain or retain their maximum functional capacity.
    d. **Prosthetic and orthotic services.** Services providing comprehensive prosthetic and orthotic evaluation, fitting, and training.
    e. **Robot-assisted walking therapy.** A form of physical therapy that uses a robotic device to assist patients who are relearning how to walk.
    f. **Simulated rehabilitation environment.** Rehabilitation focused on retraining functional skills in a contextually appropriate environment (simulated home and community settings) or in a traditional setting (gymnasium) using motor learning principles.

81. **Primary care department.** A unit or clinic within the hospital that provides primary care services (e.g. general pediatric care, general internal medicine, family practice, gynecology) through hospital-salaried medical and/or nursing staff, focusing on evaluating and diagnosing medical problems and providing medical treatment on an outpatient basis.

82. **Psychiatric services.** Services provided by the hospital that offer immediate initial evaluation and treatment to patients with mental or emotional disorders.
    a. **Psychiatric child-adolescent services.** Provides care to emotionally disturbed children and adolescents, including those admitted for diagnosis and those admitted for treatment.
    b. **Psychiatric consultation-liaison services.** Provides organized psychiatric consultation/liaison services to nonpsychiatric hospital staff and/or departments on psychological aspects of medical care that may be generic or specific to individual patients.
    c. **Psychiatric education services.** Provides psychiatric educational services to community agencies and workers such as schools, police, courts, public health nurses, welfare agencies, clergy, and so forth. The purpose is to expand the mental health knowledge and competence of personnel not working in the mental health field and to promote good mental health through improved understanding, attitudes, and behavioral patterns.
    d. **Psychiatric emergency services.** Services of facilities available on a 24-hour basis to provide immediate unscheduled out-patient care, diagnosis, evaluation, crisis intervention, and assistance to persons suffering acute emotional or mental distress.
    e. **Psychiatric geriatric services.** Provides care to emotionally disturbed elderly patients, including those admitted for diagnosis and those admitted for treatment.
    f. **Psychiatric outpatient services.** Provides medical care, including diagnosis and treatment, of psychiatric outpatients.
    g. **Psychiatric partial hospitalization program.** Organized hospital services of intensive day/evening outpatient services of three hours or more duration, distinguished from other outpatient visits of one hour.
    h. **Psychiatric residential treatment.** Overnight psychiatric care in conjunction with an intensive treatment program in a setting other than a hospital.

83. **Radiology, diagnostic.** The branch of radiology that deals with the utilization of all modalities of radiant energy in medical diagnoses and therapeutic procedures using radiologic guidance. This includes, but is not restricted to, imaging techniques and methodologies utilizing radiation emitted by x-ray tubes, radionuclides, and ultrasonographic devices and the radiofrequency electromagnetic radiation emitted by atoms.
    a. **CT Scanner.** Computed tomographic scanner for head or whole body scans.
    b. **Diagnostic radioisotope facility.** The use of radioactive isotopes (Radiopharmaceuticals) as tracers or indicators to detect an abnormal condition or disease.
    c. **Electron beam computed tomography (EBCT).** A high tech computed tomography scan used to detect coronary artery disease by measuring coronary calcifications. This imaging procedure uses electron beams which are magnetically steered to produce a visual of the coronary artery and the images are produced faster than conventional CT scans.
    d. **Full-field digital mammography (FFDM).** Combines the x-ray generators and tubes used in analog screen-film mammography (SFM) with a detector plate that converts the x-rays into a digital signal.
    e. **Magnetic resonance imaging (MRI).** The use of a uniform magnetic field and radio frequencies to study tissue and structure of the body. This procedure enables the visualization of biochemical activity of the cell in vivo without the use of ionizing radiation, radioisotopic substances or high-frequency sound.
    f. **Intraoperative magnetic resonance imaging.** An integrated surgery system which provides an MRI system in an operating room. The system allows for immediate evaluation of the degree to tumor resection while the patient is undergoing a surgical resection. Intraoperative MRI exists when a MRI (low-field or high-field) is placed in the operating theater and is used during surgical resection without moving the patient from the operating room to the diagnostic imaging suite.
    g. **Magnetoencephalography (MEG).** A noninvasive neurophysiological measurement tool used to study magnetic fields generated by neuronal activity of the brain. MEG provides direct information about the dynamics of evoked and spontaneous neural activity and the location of their sources in the brain. The primary uses of MEG include assisting surgeons in localizing the source of epilepsy, sensory mapping, and the study of brain function. When it is combined with structural imaging, it is known as *magnetic source imaging* (MSI).
    h. **Multi-slice spiral computed tomography (<64+slice CT).** A specialized computed tomography procedure that provides three-dimensional processing and allows narrower and multiple slices with increased spatial resolution and faster scanning times as compared to a regular computed tomography scan.
    i. **Multi-slice spiral computed tomography (64+ slice CT).** Involves the acquisition of volumetric tomographic x-ray absorption data expressed in Hounsfield units using multiple rows of detectors. 64+ systems reconstruct the equivalent of 64 or greater slices to cover the imaged volume.

j. **Positron emission tomography (PET).** A nuclear medicine imaging technology which uses radioactive (positron emitting) isotopes created in a cyclotron or generator and computers to produce composite pictures of the brain and heart at work. PET scanning produces sectional images depicting metabolic activity or blood flow rather than anatomy.

k. **Positron emission tomography/CT (PET/CT).** Provides metabolic functional information for the monitoring of chemotherapy, radiotherapy and surgical planning.

l. **Single photon emission computerized tomography (SPECT).** A nuclear medicine imaging technology that combines existing technology of gamma camera imaging with computed tomographic imaging technology to provide a more precise and clear image.

m. **Ultrasound.** The use of acoustic waves above the range of 20,000 cycles per second to visualize internal body structures.

84. **Radiology, therapeutic.** The branch of medicine concerned with radioactive substances and using various techniques of visualization, with the diagnosis and treatment of disease using any of the various sources of radiant energy. Services could include: megavoltage radiation therapy; radioactive implants; stereotactic radiosurgery; therapeutic radioisotope facility; X-ray radiation therapy.

a. **Image-guided radiation therapy (IGRT).** Automated system for image-guided radiation therapy that enables clinicians to obtain high-resolution x-ray images to pinpoint tumor sites, adjust patient positioning when necessary, and complete a treatment, all within the standard treatment time slot, allowing for more effective cancer treatments.

b. **Intensity-Modulated Radiation Therapy (IMRT).** A type of three-dimensional radiation therapy, which improves the targeting of treatment delivery in a way that is likely to decrease damage to normal tissues and allows varying intensities.

c. **Proton beam therapy.** A form of radiation therapy which administers proton beams. While producing the same biologic effects as x-ray beams, the energy distribution of protons differs from conventional x-ray beams in that they can be more precisely focused in tissue volumes in a three-dimensional pattern resulting in less surrounding tissue damage than conventional radiation therapy permitting administration of higher doses.

d. **Shaped beam radiation system.** A precise, non-invasive treatment that involves targeting beams of radiation that mirrors the exact size and shape of a tumor at a specific area of a tumor to shrink or destroy cancerous cells. This procedure delivers a therapeutic dose of radiation that conforms precisely to the shape of the tumor, thus minimizing the risk to nearby tissues.

e. **Stereotactic radiosurgery.** A radiotherapy modality that delivers a high dosage of radiation to a discrete treatment area in as few as one treatment session. Includes gamma knife, cyberknife, etc.

85. **Retirement housing.** A facility that provides social activities to senior citizens, usually retired persons, who do not require health care but some short-term skilled nursing care may be provided. A retirement center may furnish housing and may also have acute hospital and long-term care facilities, or it may arrange for acute and long-term care through affiliated institutions.

86. **Robotic surgery.** The use of mechanical guidance devices to remotely manipulate surgical instrumentation.

87. **Rural health clinic.** A clinic located in a rural, medically under-served area in the United States that has a separate reimbursement structure from the standard medical office under the Medicare and Medicaid programs.

88. **Sleep center.** Specially equipped and staffed center for the diagnosis and treatment of sleep disorders.

89. **Social work services.** Could include: organized services that are properly directed and sufficiently staffed by qualified individuals who provide assistance and counseling to patients and their families in dealing with social, emotional, and environmental problems associated with illness or disability, often in the context of financial or discharge planning coordination.

90. **Sports medicine.** Provision of diagnostic screening and assessment and clinical and rehabilitation services for the prevention and treatment of sports-related injuries.

91. **Support groups.** A hospital sponsored program that allows a group of individuals with the same or similar problems who meet periodically to share experiences, problems, and solutions in order to support each other.

92. **Swing bed services.** A hospital bed that can be used to provide either acute or long-term care depending on community or patient needs. To be eligible a hospital must have a Medicare provider agreement in place, have fewer than 100 beds, be located in a rural area, do not have a 24 hour nursing service waiver in effect, have not been terminated from the program in the prior two years, and meet various service conditions.

93. **Teen outreach services.** A program focusing on the teenager which encourages an improved health status and a healthful lifestyle including physical, emotional, mental, social, spiritual and economic health through education, exercise, nutrition and health promotion.

94. **Tobacco treatment/cessation program.** Organized hospital services with the purpose of ending tobacco-use habits of patients addicted to tobacco/nicotine.

95. **Transplant services.** The branch of medicine that transfers an organ or tissue from one person to another or from one body part to another to replace a diseased structure or to restore function or to change appearance. Services could include: Bone marrow transplant program; heart, lung, kidney, intestine, or tissue transplant. Please include heart/lung or other multi-transplant surgeries in 'other'.

96. **Transportation to health facilities.** A long-term care support service designed to assist the mobility of the elderly. Some programs offer improved financial access by offering reduced rates and barrier-free buses or vans with ramps and lifts to assist the elderly or handicapped; others offer subsidies for public transport systems or operate mini-bus services exclusively for use by senior citizens.

97. **Urgent care center.** A facility that provides care and treatment for problems that are not life threatening but require attention over the short term.

98. **Virtual colonoscopy.** Noninvasive screening procedure used to visualize, analyze and detect cancerous or potentially cancerous polyps in the colon.

99. **Volunteer services department.** An organized hospital department responsible for coordinating the services of volunteers working within the institution.

100. **Women's health center/services.** An area set aside for coordinated education and treatment services specifically for and promoted to women as provided by this special unit. Services may or may not include obstetrics but include a range of services other than OB.

101. **Wound management services.** Services for patients with chronic wounds and nonhealing wounds often resulting from diabetes, poor circulation, improper seating and immunocompromising conditions. The goals are to progress chronic wounds through stages of healing, reduce and eliminate infections, increase physical function to minimize complications from current wounds and prevent future chronic wounds. Wound management services are provided on an inpatient or outpatient basis, depending on the intensity of service needed.

102a. **Physician arrangements.** An integrated healthcare delivery program implementing physician compensation and incentive systems for managed care services.

a. **Independent practice association (IPA).** A legal entity that holds managed care contracts. The IPA then contracts with physicians, usually in solo practice, to provide care either on a fee-for-services or capitated basis. The purpose of an IPA is to assist solo physicians in obtaining managed care contracts.

b. **Group practice without walls.** Hospital sponsors the formation of, or provides capital to physicians to establish, a "quasi" group to share administrative expenses while remaining independent practitioners.

c. **Open physician-hospital organization (PHO).** A joint venture between the hospital and all members of the medical staff who wish to participate. The PHO can act as a unified agent in managed care contracting, own a managed care plan, own and operate ambulatory care centers or ancillary services projects, or provide administrative services to physician members.

d. **Closed physician-hospital organization (PHO).** A PHO that restricts physician membership to those practitioners who meet criteria for cost effectiveness and/or high quality.

e. **Management services organization (MSO).** A corporation, owned by the hospital or a physician/hospital joint venture, that provides management services to one or more medical group practices. The MSO purchases the tangible assets of the practices and leases them back as part of a full-service management agreement, under which the MSO employs all non-physician staff and provides all supplies/administrative systems for a fee.

    f.   **Integrated salary model.** Physicians are salaried by the hospital or another entity of a health system to provide medical services for primary care and specialty care.

    g.   **Equity model.** Allows established practitioners to become shareholders in a professional corporation in exchange for tangible and intangible assets of their existing practices.

    h.   **Foundation.** A corporation, organized either as a hospital affiliate or subsidiary, which purchases both the tangible and intangible assets of one or more medical group practices. Physicians remain in a separate corporate entity but sign a professional services agreement with the foundation.

102b. Of all physician arrangements listed in question 102a (a-i), indicate the total number of physicians (count each physician only once) that are engaged in an arrangement with your hospital that allows for joint contracting with payers or shared responsibility for financial risk or clinical performance between the hospital and physician (arrangement may be at the hospital, system or network level). *Joint contracting* does not include contracting between physicians participating in an independent practice.

103. Joint venture. A contractual arrangement between two or more parties forming an unincorporated business. The participants in the arrangement remain independent and separate outside of the ventures purpose.

104a. Accountable Care Organization (ACO) Contract. An ACO contract as having two essential elements: (1) accountability for the total costs of care for the population of patients attributed to the primary care physicians in the organization; (2) financial incentives that link the magnitude of bonus payments to performance on quality measures (which could include technical quality, patient experience and/or health outcome measures). This will generally involve a contract where the payer establishes a target budget for one or more years for the total costs of care for the agreed-upon patient population, the payer tracks actual spending and performance on quality; and the provider receives bonus payments that could include a share of savings that are (or are not) contingent on meeting quality targets, with (or without) additional bonuses related to performance on those quality measures.

105. Patient-Centered Medical Home. The medical home concept refers to the provision of comprehensive primary care services that facilitates communication and shared decision-making between the patient, his/her primary care providers, other providers, and the patient's family.

106. Bundling. Bundling is a payment mechanism whereby a provider entity receives a single payment for services provided across one or more parts of the care continuum. For example, an entity might receive a single payment for the hospital and physician services provided as part of an inpatient stay or might receive a single payment for the post-acute care services involved in a single episode of care. The entity then has responsibility for compensating each of the individual providers involved in the episode of care.

109. Capitation. An at-risk payment arrangement in which an organization receives a fixed prearranged payment and in turn guarantees to deliver or arrange all medically necessary care required by enrollers in the capitated plan. The fixed amount is specified within contractual agreements between the payor and the involved organization. The fixed payment amount is based on an actuarial assessment of the services required by enrollees and the costs of providing these services, recognizing enrollees' adjustment factors such as age, sex, and family size.

110. Shared risk payments. A payment arrangement in which a hospital and a managed care organization share the risk of adverse claims experience. Methods for sharing risk could include: capitation with partial refunds or supplements if billed hospital charges or costs differ from capitated payments, and service or discharge-based payments with withholds and bonus payouts that depend on expenditure targets.

SECTION D
TOTAL FACILITY BEDS, UTILIZATION, FINANCES, AND STAFFING
Instructions and Definitions

For the purposes of this survey, nursing home type unit/facility provides **long-term care for the elderly or other patients requiring chronic care** in a non-acute setting in any of the following categories: *Skilled nursing care *Intermediate care *Other Long-term Care (*see page 16 definitions)The nursing home type units/facilities are to be owned and operated by the hospital. Only one legal entity may be vested with title to the physical property or operate under the authority of a duly executed lease of the physical property.

1   a.   **Total licensed beds** are the total number of beds authorized by the state licensing (certifying agency).

    b.   Report the number of **beds** regularly available (those **set up and staffed for use**) at the end of the reporting period. Report only operating beds, not constructed bed capacity. Include all bed facilities that are set up and staffed for use by inpatients that have no other bed facilities, such as pediatric bassinets, isolation units, quiet rooms, and reception and observation units assigned to or reserved for them. Exclude newborn bassinets and bed facilities for patients receiving special procedures for a portion of their stay and who have other bed facilities assigned to or reserved for them. Exclude, for example, labor room, post anesthesia, or postoperative recovery room beds, psychiatric holding beds, and beds that are used only as holding facilities for patients prior to their transfer to another hospital.

    c.   Report the number of normal newborn **bassinets**. Do not include neonatal intensive care or intermediate care bassinets. These should be reported on page 3, C6 and C7.

    d.   Total **births** should exclude fetal deaths.

    e.   Include the number of adult and pediatric **admissions** only (exclude births). This figure should include all patients admitted during the reporting period, including neonatal and swing admissions.

    f.   Report the number of adult and pediatric **days of care** rendered during the entire reporting period. Do not include days of care rendered for normal infants born in the hospital, but do include those for their mothers. Include days of care for infants born in the hospital and transferred into a neonatal care unit. Also include swing bed inpatient days. **Inpatient day** of care (also commonly referred to as a __patient day__ or a __census day__, or by some federal hospitals as an **occupied bed day**) is a period of service between the census-taking hours on two successive calendar days, the day of discharge being counted only when the patient was admitted the same day.

    g.   **Emergency department visits** should reflect the number of visits to the emergency unit. Emergency outpatients can be admitted to the inpatient areas of the hospital, but they are still counted as emergency visits and subsequently as inpatient admissions.

    h.   An **Outpatient visit** is a visit by a patient who is not lodged in the hospital while receiving medical, dental, or other services. Each appearance of an outpatient in each unit constitutes one visit regardless of the number of diagnostic and/or therapeutic treatments that the patient receives. Total outpatient visits should include all clinic visits, referred visits, observation services, outpatient surgeries (also reported on line D1k), home health service visits, and emergency department visits (also reported on line D1g).

        Clinic visits should reflect total number of visits to each specialized medical unit that is responsible for the diagnosis and treatment of patients on an outpatient, nonemergency basis (i.e., alcoholism, dental, gynecology, etc.). Visits to the satellite clinics and primary group practices should be included if revenue is received by the hospital.

        Referred visits should reflect total number of outpatient ancillary visits to each specialty unit of the hospital established for providing technical aid used in the diagnosis and treatment of patients. Examples of such units are diagnostic radiology, EKG, pharmacy, etc.

        Observation services are those services furnished on a hospital's premises, including use of a bed and periodic monitoring by a hospital's nursing or other staff, which are reasonable and necessary to evaluate an outpatient's condition or determine the need for a possible admission to the hospital as an inpatient. Observation services usually do not exceed 24 hours. However, there is no hourly limit on the extent to which they may be used.

Home health service visits are visits by home health personnel to a patient's residence.

i. **Inpatient surgical operation.** Count each patient undergoing surgery as one surgical operation regardless of the number of surgical procedures that were performed while the patient was in the operating or procedure room.

j. **Operating room.** A unit/room of a hospital or other health care facility in which surgical procedures requiring anesthesia are performed.

k. **Outpatient surgical operation.** For outpatient surgical operations, please record operations performed on patients who do not remain in the hospital overnight. Include all operations whether performed in the inpatient operating rooms or in procedure rooms located in an outpatient facility. Include an endoscopy only when used as an operative tool and not when used for diagnosis alone. Count each patient undergoing surgery as one surgical operation regardless of the number of surgical procedures that were performed while the patient was in the operating or procedure room.

2a2. Managed Care Medicare Discharges. A discharge day where a Medicare Managed Care Plan is the source of payment.

2b2. Managed Care Medicare Inpatient Days. An inpatient day where a Medicare Managed Care Plan is the source of payment.

2c2. Managed Care Medicaid Discharges. A discharge day where a Medicaid Managed Care Plan is the source of payment.

2d2. Managed Care Medicaid Inpatient Days. An inpatient day where a Medicaid Managed Care Plan is the source of payment.

3a. Net patient revenue. Reported at the estimated net realizable amounts from patients, third-party payors, and others for services rendered, including estimated retroactive adjustments under reimbursement agreements with third-party payors. Retroactive adjustments are accrued on an estimated basis in the period the related services are rendered and adjusted in future periods, as final settlements are determined.

3b. Tax appropriations. A predetermined amount set aside by the government from its taxing authority to support the operation of the hospital.

3c. Other operating revenue. Revenue from services other than health care provided to patients, as well as sales and services to nonpatients. Revenue that arises from the normal day-to-day operations from services other than health care provided to patients. Includes sales and services to nonpatients, and revenue from miscellaneous sources (rental of hospital space, sale of cafeteria meals, gift shop sales). Also include operating gains in this category.

3d. Nonoperating revenue. Includes investment income, extraordinary gains and other nonoperating gains.

3e. Total revenue. Add net patient revenue, tax appropriations, other operating revenue and nonoperating revenue.

3f. Payroll expenses. Include payroll for all personnel including medical and dental residents/interns and trainees.

3g. Employee benefits. Includes social security, group insurance, retirement benefits, workman's compensation, unemployment insurance, etc.

3h. Depreciation expense (for reporting period only) report only the depreciation expense applicable to the reporting period. The amount also Should be included in accumulated depreciation (D7b).

3i. Interest expense. Report interest expense for the reporting period only.

3j. Supply expense. The net cost of all tangible items that are expensed including freight, standard distribution cost, and sales and use tax minus rebates. This would exclude labor, labor-related expenses and services as well as some tangible items that are frequently provided as part of labor costs.

3k. All other expenses. Any total facility expenses not included in 3f-3j.

3l. Total expenses. Includes all payroll and non-payroll expenses as well as any nonoperating losses (including extraordinary losses). **Treat bad debt as a deduction from gross patient revenue and not as an expense.**

4a. Total gross inpatient revenue. The hospitals full-established rates(charges) for all services rendered to inpatients.

4b. Total gross outpatient revenue. The hospitals full-established rates(charges) for all services rendered to outpatients.

4c. Total gross patient revenue. Total gross patient revenue (add total gross inpatient revenue and total gross outpatient revenue).

5. Uncompensated care. Care for which no payment is expected or no charge is made. It is the sum of bad debt and charity care absorbed by a hospital or other health care organization in providing medical care for patients who are uninsured or are unable to pay.

5a. Bad debt. The provision for actual or expected uncollectibles resulting from the extension of credit. Report as a deduction from revenue. **For Question 6 (Revenue by payor), if you cannot break out your bad debt by payor, deduct the amount from self-pay.**

5b. Financial Assistance (Includes **Charity care).** Financial assistance and charity care refer to health services provided free of charge or at reduced rates to individuals who meet certain financial criteria . For purposes of this survey, charity care is measured on the basis of revenue forgone, at full-established rates.

5d. Medicaid Provider Tax, Fee or Assessment. Dollars paid as a result of a state law that authorizes collecting revenue from specified categories of providers. Federal matching funds may be received for the revenue collected from providers and some or all of the revenues may be returned directly or indirectly back to providers in the form of a Medicaid payment.

6. REVENUE BY PAYOR

6a1 Medicare. Should agree with the Medicare utilization reported in questions D2a1-D2b2.

6a1a Fee for service patient revenue. Include traditional Medicare fee-for-service.

6a1c. Total. Medicare revenue (add Medicare fee for service patient revenue and Medicare managed care revenue).

6a2. Medicaid. Should agree with Medicaid utilization reported in questions D2c1-D2d2.

6a2a. Fee for service patient revenue. Do not include Medicaid disproportionate payments(DSH) or Medicaid supplemental payments that are non-Medicaid disproportionate payments (DSH).

6a2c. Medicaid disproportionate share payments. DSH minus associated provider taxes or assessments. Report in 'Net' column only.

6a2d. Medicaid supplemental payments. Not including Medicaid DSH payments (these are supplemental payments the Medicaid program pays the hospital that are NOT Medicaid DSH) and minus associated provider taxes or assessments. Report in 'Net' column only.

7 a-c. Fixed Assets. Represent land and physical properties that are consumed or used in the creation of economic activity by the health care entity. The historical or acquisition costs are used in recording fixed assets. Net plant, property, and equipment represent the original costs of these items less accumulated depreciation and amortization.

7d. Gross Square Footage. Include all inpatient, outpatient, office, and support space used for or in support of your health care activities. Exclude exterior, roof, and garage space in the figure.

8. Capital Expenses. Expenses used to acquire assets, including buildings, remodeling projects, equipment, or property.

9. Information Technology.

a. **IT Operating expense.** Exclude department depreciation and operating dollars paid against capital leases.

b. **IT Capital expense.** Include IT capital expense for the current year only. Any capital expense that is carried forward from the previous year should be excluded from this figure. Include IT related capital included in the budget of other departments. (i.e. lab, radiology, etc., if known or can be reasonably estimated.) Include the total value of capital leases to be signed in the current year.

c. **Number of Employed IT staff (in FTEs).** Number of full-time equivalent (FTE) staff employed in the IT department/organization and on the hospital payroll.

d. **Total number of outsourced IT staff (in FTEs).** i.e. contracted staff.

e. **Electronic Health Record.** An electronic health record (EHR) integrates electronically originated and maintained patient-level clinical health information, derived from multiple sources, into one point of access. An EHR replaces the paper medical record as the primary source of patient information.

10. Full-Time Equivalent (FTE) is the total number of hours worked by all employees over the full (12 month) reporting period divided by the normal number of hours worked by a full-time employee for that same time period. For example, if your hospital considers a normal workweek for a full-time employee to be 40 hours, a total of 2,080 would be worked over a full year (52 weeks). If the total number of hours worked by all employees on the payroll is 208,000, then the number of Full-Time Equivalents (FTE) is 100 (employees). The FTE calculation for a specific occupational category such as registered nurses is exactly the same. The calculation for each occupational category should be based on the number of hours worked by staff employed in that specific category.

   a-b. Physicians and dentists. Include only those physicians and dentists engaged in clinical practice and on the payroll. Those who hold administrative positions should be reported in "All other personnel."

   d. Other trainees. A trainee is a person who has not completed the necessary requirements for certification or met the qualifications required for full salary under a related occupational category. Exclude medical and dental residents/interns who should be reported on line 10c.

   e. Registered nurses. Nurses who have graduated from approved schools of nursing and who are currently registered by the state. They are responsible for the nature and quality of all nursing care that patients receive. Do not include any registered nurses more appropriately reported in other occupational categories, such as facility administrators, and therefore listed under "All other personnel."

   f. Licensed practical (vocational) nurses. Nurses who have graduated from an approved school of practical (vocational) nursing who work under the supervision of registered nurses and/or physicians.

   g. Nursing assistive personnel. Certified nursing assistant or equivalent unlicensed staff assigned to patient care units and reporting to nursing.

   h. Radiology Technicians. Technical positions in imaging fields, including, but not limited to, radiology, sonography, nuclear medicine, radiation therapy, CT, MRI.

   i. Laboratory professional/technical. Professional and technical positions in all areas of the laboratory, including, but not limited to, histology, phlebotomy, microbiology, pathology, chemistry, etc.

   j. Pharmacists, licensed. Persons licensed within the state who are concerned with the preparation and distribution of medicinal products.

   k. Pharmacy technicians. Persons who assist the pharmacist with selected activities, including medication profile reviews for drug incompatibilities, typing labels and prescription packaging, handling of purchase records and inventory control.

   l. Respiratory Therapists. An allied health professional who specializes in scientific knowledge and theory of clinical problems of respiratory care. Duties include the collection and evaluation of patient data to determine an appropriate care plan, selection and assembly of equipment, conduction of therapeutic procedures, and modification of prescribed plans to achieve one or more specific objectives.

   m. All other personnel. This should include all other personnel not already accounted for in other categories.

   n. Total facility personnel. This line is to include the total facility personnel - hospital plus nursing home type unit/facility personnel (for those hospitals that own and operate a nursing home type unit/facility).

   o-p. Nursing home type unit/facility personnel. These lines should be filled out only by hospitals that own and operate a nursing home type unit/facility, where only one legal entity is vested with title to the physical property or operates under the authority of a duly executed lease of the physical property. If nursing home type unit/facility personnel are reported on the total facility personnel line, but cannot be broken out, please write "cannot break out" on this line.

   q. Direct patient care RN. Registered nurses providing care directly to patients Direct patient care responsibilities are patient-centered nursing activities carried out in the presence of the patient (such as admission, transfer/discharge, patient teaching, patient communication, treatments, counseling, and administration of medication.

11. Privileged Physicians. Report the total number of physicians (by type) on the medical staff with privileges except those with courtesy, honorary and provisional privileges. Do not include residents or interns.

   Employed by your hospital. Physicians that are either direct hospital employees or employees of a hospital subsidiary corporation. Physicians that are employed for non-clinical services (administrative services, medical director services, etc.) should be excluded.

   Individual contract. An independent physician under a formal contract to provide services at your hospital including at outpatient facilities, clinics and offices. Physicians that are contracted only for non-clinical services (administrative services, medical director services, etc.) should be excluded.

   Group contract. A physician that is part of a group (group practice, faculty practice plan or medical foundation) under a formal contract to provide services at your hospital including at inpatient and outpatient facilities, clinics and offices. Physicians that are contracted only for non-clinical services (administrative services, medical director services, etc.) should be excluded.

   Not employed or under contract. Other physicians with privileges that have no employment or contractual relationship with the hospital to provide services.

   __The sum of the physicians reported in 12a-12f should equal the total number of privileged physicians in the hospital.__

   a. Primary care. A physician that provides primary care services including general practice, general internal medicine, family practice, general pediatrics, obstetrics/gynecology and geriatrics.

   b. Emergency medicine. Physicians who provide care in the emergency department.

   c. Hospitalist. Physician whose primary professional focus is the care of hospitalized medical patients (through clinical, education, administrative and research activity).

   d. Intensivist. A physician with special training to work with critically ill patients. Intensivists generally provided medical-surgical, cardiac, neonatal, pediatric and other types of intensive care.

   e. Radiologist/pathologist/anesthesiologist. Radiologist. A physician who has specialized training in imaging, including but not limited to radiology, sonography, nuclear medicine, radiation therapy, CT, MRI. **Pathologist.** A physician who examines samples of body tissues for diagnostic purposes. **Anesthesiologist.** A physician who specializes in administering medications or other agents that prevent or relieve pain, especially during surgery.

   f. Other specialist. Other physicians not included in the above categories that specialize in a specific type of medical care.

14. Advanced Practice Registered Nurses. Registered nurses with advanced didactic and clinical education, knowledge, skills, and scope of practice. Includes: **Physician assistant.** A healthcare professional licensed to practice medicine with supervision of a licensed physician. **Nurse practitioner.** A registered nurse with at least a master's degree in nursing and advanced education in primary care, capable of independent practice in a variety of settings. **Clinical nurse specialist (CNS).** A registered nurse who, through a formal graduate degree (masters or doctorate) CNS education program, is prepared as CNS with expertise in a specialty area of nursing practice. CNSs are clinical experts in the diagnosis and treatment of illness, and the delivery of evidence-based nursing interventions.

14c. Primary care. Medical services including general practice, general internal medicine, family practice, general pediatrics, obstetrics/gynecology. **Emergency department care.** The provision of unscheduled outpatient services to patients whose conditions require immediate care in the emergency department setting. **Other specialty care.** A clinic that provides specialized medical care beyond the scope of primary care. **Patient education.** Goals and objectives for the patient and/or family related to therapeutic regimens, medical procedures and self-care.

Case management. A system of assessment, treatment planning, referral and follow-up that ensures the provision of comprehensive and continuous services and the coordination of payment and reimbursement for care.

Other. Any type of care other than those listed above.

15. **Foreign-educated nurses.** Individuals who are foreign born and received basic nursing education in a foreign country. In general many of these nurses come to the US on employment-based visas which allow them to obtain a green card.

SECTION E. SUPPLEMENTAL INFORMATION
DEFINITIONS

3a. **Satellite facility(ies).** Services are available at a facility geographically remote from the hospital campus.

3b. **Group Purchasing Organization.** An organization whose primary function is to negotiate contracts for the purpose of purchasing for members of the group or has a central supply site for its members.

3c. **Distributor.** An entity that typically does not manufacture most of its own products but purchases and re-sells these products. Such a business usually maintains an inventory of products for sales to hospitals and physician offices and others.